TEXAS GRASSES

CLASSIFICATION AND DESCRIPTION
OF GRASSES

Descriptive Systematic Agrostology

BY

W. A. SILVEUS, B. A., LL. B.

Waynesburg College, Waynesburg, Pennsylvania
University of Texas, Austin, Texas

———

PLANTS ILLUSTRATED BY PHOTOGRAPHS AND DRAWINGS
ILLUSTRATED KEYS OF SUBFAMILIES AND TRIBES
TECHNICAL TERMS DEFINED AND ILLUSTRATED

———

Drawings by
OLIVE VANDRUFF

———

Published by the Author
1933

Printed by
THE CLEGG COMPANY
San Antonio, Texas

NATURE IS GOD'S HANDIWORK

Study the Grasses

And Learn God's Ways:

Efficiency means Life and Perpetuation;

Inefficiency means Death and Elimination.

From the Humble Blade of Grass

to the Human in his Pride,

From the Genera of the Poaceae

to the Nations of the Earth,

This Universal Law of God holds Good.

"He that Heareth, Let Him Hear."

PREFACE

The author wishes to make grateful acknowledgement to the following persons:

To Dr. A. S. Hitchcock, Systematic Agrostologist, and Mrs. Agnes Chase, Associate Agrostologist, of the United States Department of Agriculture, for verification in the identity of species, and for valuable suggestions and criticisms as to drawings, descriptions and photographs. Their spirit of coöperation and helpfulness is greatly appreciated.

To Dr. Samuel Peterson, of San Antonio, Texas, for painstaking assistance with reference to literary expression, diacritical marks, and proof-reading.

To Dr. B. C. Tharp, of the University of Texas, for useful suggestions and loan of specimens.

To Ellen D. Schulz (Mrs. Roy W. Quillin), of San Antonio, Texas, author of *Wild Flowers* and co-author of *Texas Cacti*, for encouraging an interest in plant life and helpful hints.

To Benjamin J. Studer, of Studer Photo Company, of San Antonio, Texas, for expert advice as to equipment and photography.

San Antonio, Texas,
November 1, 1933.

W. A. SILVEUS

CONTENTS

INTRODUCTION . . . . .IX-XVII

    EXPLANATIONS XI

    DRAWINGS ILLUSTRATING

        BOTANICAL EQUIPMENT XIV

        SPIKELET OF RESCUE-GRASS AND ITS PARTS XV

        BOTANICAL TERMS XVI

GLOSSARY OF SPECIAL TERMS XIX

POACEAE, THE GRASS FAMILY XXXI

HOW TO IDENTIFY THE GRASSES XXXII

DESCRIPTIONS OF THE SUBFAMILIES AND KEY TO
    THE TRIBES XXXIV

DESCRIPTIONS OF THE TRIBES AND KEYS TO THE
    GENERA XXXVII

DESCRIPTIONS OF THE GENERA AND THEIR SPECIES

    1. BAMBUSEAE, THE BAMBOO TRIBE 1

    2. FESTUCEAE, THE FESCUE TRIBE 5

    3. HORDEAE, THE BARLEY TRIBE 157

    4. AVENEAE, THE OAT TRIBE 191

    5. AGROSTIDEAE, THE TIMOTHY TRIBE 206

    6. ZOYSIEAE, THE CURLY MESQUITE TRIBE 357

    7. CHLORIDEAE, THE GRAMA TRIBE 367

    8. PHALARIDEAE, THE CANARY-GRASS TRIBE 452

    9. ORYZEAE, THE RICE TRIBE 461

   10. ZIZANIEAE, THE INDIAN-RICE TRIBE 471

   11. PANICEAE, THE MILLET TRIBE 476

   12. ANDROPOGONEAE, THE SORGHUM TRIBE 697

   13. TRIPSACEAE, THE CORN TRIBE 763

BIBLIOGRAPHY 772

INDEX 773

INTRODUCTION

Poales, one of the many orders of flowering plants, is composed of two families — *Cyperaceae*, including the grasslike plants, the *Sedges*, and *Poaceae (Gramineae)*, including all the *Grasses*.

The *Poaceae* family is divided into two subfamilies — *Poatae*, with laterally compressed spikelets, and *Panicatae*, with dorsally compressed spikelets. These subfamilies are divided into *Tribes*, which in turn are divided into many *Genera*, each genus including one or more *Species*.

Agrostology is that branch of botany which treats of grasses, and one who makes a study of grasses is called an *Agrostologist*. The subject is usually divided into *Economic Agrostology* and *Systematic Agrostology*. It is further divided as are other branches of botany.

While *Economic Agrostology* treats primarily of the uses of grasses, *Systematic Agrostology* deals with their botanical rather than with their practical aspect. This work treats chiefly of their classification, description, and arrangement in groups, and may properly be denominated *Descriptive Systematic Agrostology.*

The grass family is naturally distinctive, and the plants will not ordinarily be confused with those of any other family except the closely related sedges (*Cyperaceae*), or the rushes (*Juncaceae*). The sedges are chiefly distinguished from the grasses by their three-sided, solid or pithy, not jointed culms, their 3-ranked-leaves, always closed sheaths, and the fact that there is no palea between the flower and the rachilla. The rushes are distinguished by having small green flowers with a 6-parted perianth much like those of the lilies.

The grass family does not include many other plants used as forage, such as clovers, alfalfa, vetches, peas, beans and other leguminous species.

One important as well as interesting characteristic of the grasses, distinguishing them from all other leaf-bearing plants, is that a blade losing its upper portion will continue or resume its growth until it has reached its natural or former size. Such growth is due to the presence at the base of the blade of a transverse intercalary growth zone. Such a zone is also found on the culm above each node.

Of all the families of the plant kingdom the grasses are the most important. Their spreading roots and culms prevent the soil from becoming as shifting sand before the rain and wind, rendering it possible for other plants to grow and thrive. Without them the earth's surface would be bare rock or unstable soil, making the world a desolate place in which to live.

Besides directly and indirectly (indirectly because animals live mostly on grasses) supplying most of our food, they furnish food for beasts and birds, materials for the manufacture of rope, baskets, paper, thatching of roofs, and even, as in the case of the giant bamboos growing to a height of 100 feet and a foot in diameter, for the building of houses, as well as for many other uses. Grasses are indispensable in the beautification of our lawns and public grounds, and without their green pastures, meadows and grain fields our landscapes would lose their chief charm.

Texas with its great variation in climate naturally has a corresponding diversity of genera and species. In altitude it ranges from sea level to 10,000 feet; in latitude and longitude it extends from the valleys of the Sabine and the lower Rio Grande westward and northward upwards of a thousand miles to the regions of El Paso and the Llano Estacado. Texas has about 550 species of grasses, representing 13 of the 14 tribes, and nearly all the genera of the United States. There are from 1100 to 1200 species in the United States, being about one-fifth of the total number known. It is estimated that Texas has at least three-fourths of the species to be found in any state east of the Rocky Mountains.

Buffalo, curly mesquite, bermuda and Johnson grass are the best known of our wild species, while timothy and Kentucky bluegrass are the best known in other parts of the country.

Our cultivated species and their varieties are numerous, including such as rice, oats, barley, rye, sugar-cane, corn, wheat, sudan-grass, broom-corn, kafir-corn, milo-maize and the sweet sorghums.

Nature has been bountiful, not only in her supply of the grasses, but also in their variations as to size, texture, fitness for use, and adaptation. Through countless ages nature slowly but surely eliminated the inefficient and perpetuated the efficient, but her efforts in the direction of making plants useful to man were always limited by the absolute necessity that their chief quality should be an ability to fight their own battles in the never-ceasing struggle for existence. Their highest development had to wait until man should reach the agricultural stage and by cultivation of selected species help nature raise them to a higher stage of development. Thus it was only by man taking hold of the primitive corn and relieving it of the necessity of devoting its energies chiefly to the struggle for existence that nature was enabled to make it the king of the grasses.

To increase the efficiency of our grasses, wild or cultivated, would probably add more to the productive capacity of our country, besides being less costly, than the building of expensive dams and canals for irrigation.

Anyone who should succeed in improving the yield of any of our wild or cultivated grasses—as by converting our curly mesquite into a more hardy plant or adding a few inches to its height—would deserve the unstinted praise and gratitude of our state and Nation.

In the past those born with an irresistible urge to benefit their fellow-men have directed their energies chiefly along the lines of discoveries and de-velopments in the fields of exploration, invention, industrial organization and physical and chemical research. It remained for Luther Burbank to reveal the wonderful possibilities lying in the field of experimental botany, and it is to be most earnestly hoped that others following in his footsteps will consecrate their lives to accomplish with grasses such remarkable results as he accomplished with other flowering plants. Exceptional opportunities for unlimited service and undying fame lie ready at hand in this virgin field.

If this book should only be the inspiration to some one to devote his life to the development of Economic Agrostology, elevating it to the plane reached by Systematic Agrostology by reason of the notable labors and leadership of Dr. A. S. Hitchcock, assisted by Agnes Chase, the author would feel himself most abundantly compensated for all the time, labor and expense that this work has entailed.

In this book the same sequence of arrangement has been followed as to subfamilies, tribes and genera, as in the U. S. Department of Agriculture Bulletin No. 772, the *Genera of Grasses of the United States,* by A. S. Hitchcock. The descriptions of the family, sub-families, tribes, and genera, as well as keys, so far as applicable, have been adopted from the above bulletin.

The author has drawn liberally upon the following Bulletins:

Contributions from the United States National Herbarium.
Mexican Grasses in the United States National Herbarium, by A. S. Hitchcock.
The North American Species of Aristida, by A. S. Hitchcock.
The North American Species of Stipa, by A. S. Hitchcock.
The North American Species of Panicum and Tropical North American Species of Panicum, by A. S. Hitchcock and Agnes Chase.
The North American Species of Paspalum, by Agnes Chase.
The Grama Grasses, by David Griffiths.
The Flora of New Mexico, by E. O. Wooton and Paul C. Standley.

EXPLANATIONS

The primary object of this work is to remove most of the difficulties confronting the student entering upon a study of the grasses—to make it as easy as possible for those with but little knowledge of botany as well as for the botanist to identify them—with the hope that such an interest may be created that the student will ultimately penetrate deeper into their mysteries.

The classification of numerous grasses is a necessary prerequisite for the further study of this subject; with this foundation the student is then ready to enter into the various fields of experimentation.

Plants are classified, not with reference to any one characteristic, but according to a combination of distinctive features. Since descriptions of species are based on average specimens they should not be taken too literally; allowance must be made for departures. Nature never exactly repeats herself and plants of the same species are never precisely alike—as would please the botanist—of uniform height, the blades and sheaths of equal length and alike as to pubescence or roughness, with spikelets of uniform size and the same number of hairs at the same place. The younger plants are often more hairy than the older ones, and on the same plant some sheaths may be glabrous (especially the upper) while others are hairy (especially the lower). Also, spikelets that are usually glabrous may occasionally be hairy, and vice versa.

GLABROUS AND SMOOTH. When culms, blades, sheaths or spikelets are not described as hairy or rough they are to be taken as glabrous or smooth.

EQUIPMENT. To make any progress in the study of grasses a few inexpensive tools are necessary, such as a millimeter measure, tweezers, dissecting needle, and a good magnifier or dissecting microscope. A magnifier similar to the one illustrated is preferable as it has a ring to which a reel can be attached and the reel then fastened to some convenient portion of one's clothing. It thus has the advantage over the pocket magnifier or over the dissecting microscope in that it is always ready for immediate use. Any such instrument should magnify at least 14x (times), better 20x. A magnifier is much cheaper than a dissecting microscope. The price of a good magnifier varies from $2.00 or $3.00 to $7.50. If a local dealer does not have a desired instrument in stock it can be ordered from Bausch & Lomb Optical Company, Rochester, New York, or Spencer Lens Company, Buffalo, New York.

ABBREVIATIONS AND SYMBOLS. While it is customary to use many symbols and abbreviations, these have been purposely reduced to a minimum. Most authors use the metric system, or the metric and English systems combined. In this work "feet" is written out, the sign ' is used for inches, and mm. (millimeters) for all measurements less than an inch, and sometimes for those more than an inch, as the use of fractions is objectionable. (See drawings of equipment for table of measurements.) In describing a species figures in parentheses are occasionally inserted following those given as the length of the culm, blade, spikelet, etc.; e. g. "Spikelets 4-6 mm. (4-10) long". The figures in parentheses represent measurements given by others and differing from those of the author.

NOMENCLATURE. The botanical names of plants consist of two parts, the first, the generic, indicating the genus to which the species belongs, the second, the specific, designating the species of that genus. These names consist of Latin or Latinized words. No two genera may bear the same name but the same specific name may be used in different genera. A lack of knowledge of any one botanist or group of botanists of all the grasses of the world has resulted in much confusion as to names, giving rise to many synonyms and homonyms. The reader may wonder why so many names of species and even genera in this work have been replaced by others. Dr. Hitchcock, after examination of much material in herbaria in America and Europe, found many names incorrectly applied. He has made the necessary corrections, and has kindly supplied the author with corrected names.

PRONUNCIATION OF LATIN NAMES. The use of unpronounceable Latin or Latinized names forms one of the beginner's major difficulties, there being no dictionary or other authority to aid him. Some uniform system of pronunciation is very important, not only to facilitate the memorizing of names, but also to enable the student to discuss the subject intelligently and without embarrassment. Botanical names, chiefly because of their Latinized form, do not always readily yield to easy or consistent pronunciation. Botanists are themselves divided as to the correct pronunciation, some using the old Latin system, some the English system, and many changing the sounds of particular letters to accommodate their sense of euphony. The author has endeavored to follow the prevailing usage among botanists in ordinary speech, fully realizing that in marking these terms diacritically he is inviting criticism from many botanists. However, in this matter of pronunciation it is the amateur botanists rather than the professional who require the service offered by these diacritical marks.

In determining the proper pronunciation of botanical names and marking them diacritically the author considers himself fortunate in having the invaluable assistance of Samuel Peterson, Ph. D., D. C. L., whose knowledge of Greek and Latin as well as his acquaintance with a number of modern languages, coupled with a lifelong interest in etymological studies, makes him exceptionally well qualified to exercise sound judgment in these respects.

KEYS AND DISTINCTIVE WORDS. The use of letters and figures tend to push the key too far to the right, and are somewhat difficult for the inexperienced to follow. In order to distinctify the divisions and sub-divisions so that the eye may more readily follow the arrangement, certain words are set out in bold-face type or in italics. Full line (or nearly so) black caps are used for the first or main divisions; two words in black caps, for the second; one word in black caps, for the third. For further sub-divisions, if necessary, repeat first in black Roman; then in italic caps; then in lower-case italics. Only one or two words in black caps are used when the key is short. In descriptions of genera as well as in descriptions of species, and also elsewhere, words are frequently put in black type or italics for emphasis or easy comparison.

PHOTOGRAPHS AND DRAWINGS. The photographs and drawings, except in *Panicum,* are placed immediately following the description of a genus. The photographs as well as most of the drawings and descriptions were made from green plants. During the last three years the author traveled more than 60,000 miles collecting some 450 plants, and taking about 325 photographs. A few specimens are described and illustrated from government bulletins. About 80 species have been kindly loaned by A. S. Hitchcock from the National Herbarium, Washington, D. C., and B. C. Tharp, of the University of Texas.

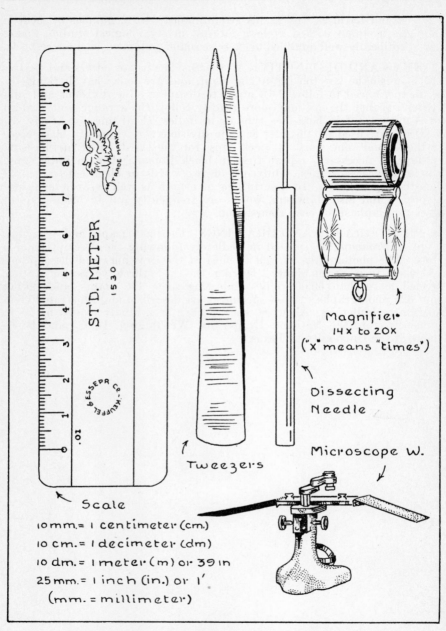

DRAWINGS OF BOTANICAL EQUIPMENT

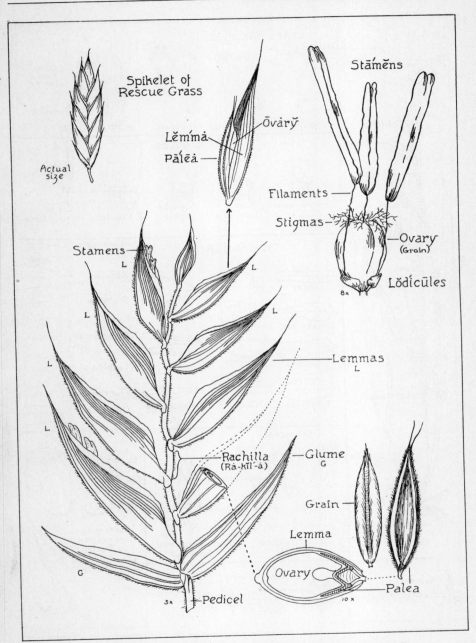

Spikelet of
Rescue Grass

Actual
size

Lĕmmá
Pā´lēá

Ōvárў

Stā´mĕns

Filaments

Stigmas

Ovary
(Grain)

Lŏdícūles

8x

Stamens

L

L

L

L

L

L

L

Lemmas
L

Rachilla
(Rà-kĭl´-á)

Glume
G

Grain

Lemma

Ovary

Palea

G

3x

Pedicel

10 x

SPIKELET OF RESCUE-GRASS AND ITS PARTS

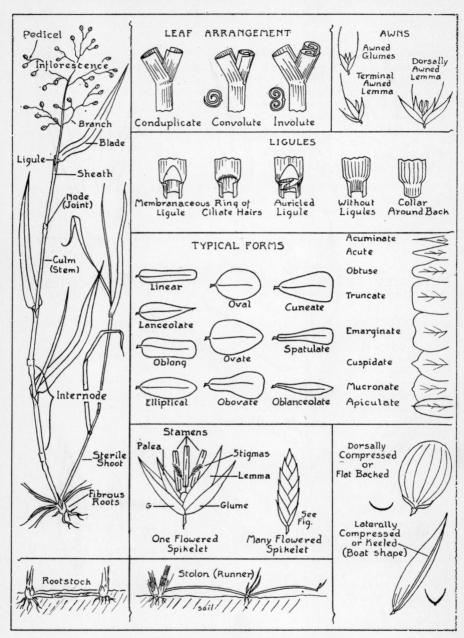

BOTANICAL TERMS ILLUSTRATED

PANICLE *(păn'-ĭ-kl)* A loose compound inflorescence of a racemose type, usually irregular and commonly with pediceled spikelets.

AXIS *(ăks'ĭs)* Commonly applied to the main axis of a compound inflorescence

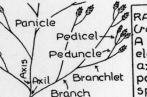

Panicle
Pedicel
Peduncle
Axis
Axil — Branchlet
Branch

RACEME *(ră-sēm')* A simple elongated axis with pediceled spikelets.

SPIKE *(spīk)* A simple elongated axis with sessile or nearly sessile spikelets.

RACHIS *(rā'-kĭs)* The backbone or axis of a spike or spike-like raceme.

SECUND *(sē'-kund)* Borne along one side of a rachis or axis.

TYPES OF PUBESCENCE

PUBESCENT *(pū-bĕs'-ent)* In a general sense, hairy — In a restricted sense covered with soft, fine hairs, downy, not long

VILLOUS *(vĭl'-lus)* Covered with long, close, soft, and fine hairs.

PUBESCENT Covered with fine hairs, downy, not long.

PUBERULENT *(pū-bĕr'-u-lent)* Minutely or finely pubescent.

HISPID *(hĭs'-pĭd)* Rough with hairs, bristles or minute spines.

HISPIDULOUS *(hĭs-pĭd'-u-lus)* Minutely hispid.

PILOSE *(pī-lose)* Covered with soft hairs, distinctive, not close.

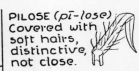

PAPILLOSE *(păp'-ĭl-lose)* Bearing or resembling papillae, minute, nipple-shaped projections usually at the base of hairs—

HIRSUTE *(hŭr'-sūt)* Covered with rather long coarse hairs, shaggy.

LANATE *(lā'-nāt)* Covered with long wool-like tangled hairs.

SERICEOUS *(sē-rĭsh'-us)* Covered with long, very soft, silky hairs closely appressed to the surface; satiny pubescence

SCABROUS *(scā'-brus)* Roughened with minute points or scurfy

CILIATE *(sĭl'-ĭ-āt)* Margins fringed with hairs.

BOTANICAL TERMS ILLUSTRATED

GLOSSARY OF SPECIAL TERMS

Abortive (à-bôr'tĭv). Imperfectly developed; rudimentary, hence sterile.

Abrupt (ăb-rŭpt'). Terminating suddenly.

Acuminate (à-kū'mĭ-nāt). Tapering into a long point.

Acute (à-kūt'). Terminating with a sharp angle.

Agronomist (ăg-rŏn'ō-mĭst). One skilled in agronomy.

Agronomy (ăg-rŏn'ō-mĭ). That branch of agriculture dealing with the theory and practice of crop production; the scientific management of land.

Agrostology (ăg-rŏs-tŏl'ō-jĭ). That branch of botany treating of grasses.

Agrostologist (ăg-rŏs-tŏl'ō-jĭst). One who makes a study of grasses.

Alternate (ăl-tẽr'nāt). Singly, not opposite or in pairs; first one and then another, as leaves or branches.

Annual (ăn'ū-al). Enduring for not more than one year.

Anterior (ăn-tē'rĭ-ẽr). External side toward the bract.

Anther (ăn'thẽr). Polleniferous part of a stamen.

Anthesis (ăn-thē'sĭs). Flowering; time or action when the floral envelope opens.

Apex (ā'pĕks). Tip of a thing.

Apiculate (à-pĭk'ū-lāt). Ending in a short, sharp, abrupt, rather soft tip.

Appressed (ă-prĕst'). Lying close to or against another organ or part.

Approximate (ă-prŏks'ĭ-māt). Next to or near; close together.

Aquatic (à-kwăt'ĭk). Growing in water.

Arachnoid (à-răk'noid). Cobwebby.

Arborescent (är-bō-rĕs'ĕnt). Treelike in form, size and texture.

Arcuate (är'kū-āt). Bowlike or bow-shaped.

Aristate (à-rĭs'tāt). Tipped by an awn or bristle.

Articulate (är-tĭk'ū-lāt). Jointed, having a node or joint.

Ascending (ă-sĕnd'ing). Curved or arising obliquely upward.

Asexual (ā-sĕks'ū-al). Without sex.

Attenuate (ă-tĕn'ū-āt). Tapering into a long slender point.

Auricled (ô'rĭ-kld). Having auricles, or earlike appendages.

Awl-shaped (ôl'shăpt). Narrow and attenuate from a broader base to a slender rigid point.

Awn (ôn). A bristle-like appendage, especially on the floral bracts of grasses, or beards of wheat or rye, etc.

Awned (ônd). Provided with awns; bearded.

Axil (ăks'ĭl). The upper angle formed between a culm and leaf blade or between the axis and branches of an inflorescence. (See Ill.)

Axillary (ăks'ĭ-lā-rĭ). Occurring in or borne at the axil.

Axis (ăks'ĭs). That part of the culm supporting the branches of a compound inflorescence.

Barbed (bärbd). Furnished with rigid points or short bristles, usually reflexed like the barb of a fish-hook.

Barbellate (bär'bĕl-āt). Minutely barbed.

Basal (bā'săl). At or pertaining to the base.

Beak (bēk). A narrow, usually rather elongated, neck-line appendage.

Biennial (bī-ĕn'ĭ-ăl). Enduring for two years.

Bifurcate (bī-fûr'kāt). To divide into two branches.

Blade (blād). The expanded part of a leaf; in grasses, flat, folded, or with folded margins, sometimes terete.

Bract (brăkt). A leaf-like or scale-like organ subtending a flower or aggregation of flowers; sometimes called scales. In grasses, the two lower, usually empty, are called glumes, and the upper, usually subtending a flower, are called lemmas.

Bristle (brĭs'l). A stiff hair or any similar outgrowth.

Bulb (bŭlb). A bud with fleshy scales, usually underground.

Bulbous (bŭlb'ŭs). Bulb-like in shape or structure.

Bullate (bōōl'āt). Appearing as if blistered.

Caespitose (see cespitose).

Calcareous (kăl-kā'rē-ŭs). Growing upon limestone or a soil impregnated with lime.

Callus (kăl'ŭs). A hard protuberance or callosity; especially the hard sharp-pointed base of certain grass fruits as in the genus *Stipa*.

Capillary (kăp'ĭ-lā-rĭ). Hair-like.

Capitate (kăp'ĭ-tāt). Borne in a head or cluster, usually dense.

Carinate (kăr'ĭ-nāt). Keel-like; keeled like the keel of a ship.

Carpel (kär'pĕl). A pistil or one number of a compound pistil.

Cartilaginous (kär-tĭ-lăj'ĭ-nŭs). Gristly.

Caryopsis (kär-ĭ-ŏp'sĭs). A grain, the fruit of a grass. The seed and fruit are united, the seed adhering to the thin pericarp, or the outer covering of the fruit throughout. (In *Sporobolus* the pericarp loosely encloses the seed.)

Caudex (kô'dĕks). The woody base of a perennial plant.

Centimeter (sĕn'tĭ-mē-tēr). Ten millimeters equals one centimeter.

Cespitose (sĕs'pĭ-tōs). Tufted; having the stems in a tuft, as in a bunch of grass.

Chartaceous (kär-tā'shŭs). Papery or paper-like in texture.

Ciliate (sĭl'ĭ-āt). Fringed with hairs, such as margins.

Clavate (klā'vāt). Club-shaped; gradually enlarged upward.

Cleft (klĕft). Cut about half way to the midvein or base, especially when the incision is sharp.

Cleistogamous (klīs-tŏg'ă-mŭs). Spikelets self-fertilized without opening of the flower. Usually found hidden in the sheaths, sometimes on underground branches.

Coma (kō'mȧ). A dense tuft of hairs, often at the apex of a seed.

Compound (kŏm'pound). Composed of two or more separate but similar parts joined together. Applied to an inflorescence when branched once or repeatedly.

Conduplicate (kŏn-dū'plĭ-kāt). Folded together lengthwise.

Continuous (kŏn-tĭn'ū-ŭs). Not jointed.

Convolute (kŏn'vō-lūt). Rolled up lengthwise; one margin rolled in and the other around it. (See Ill.)

Cordate (kôr'dāt). Heart-shaped.

Coriaceous (kō-rĭ-ā'shŭs). Leathery in texture.

Corm (kôrm). The enlarged fleshy base of a stem, bulb-like but solid.

Correlate (kŏr'ē-lāt). To put in relation with each other.

Cucullate (kū'kŭl-āt). Hooded or resembling a hood.

Culm (kŭlm). The jointed stalk or stem, usually hollow save at the nodes, and mostly herbaceous, of a plant belonging to the grass family. The term is also applied to the usually solid stalks of grass-like plants of the sedges and rushes.

Cuneate (kū'nē-āt). Wedge-shaped.

Cusp (kŭsp). A sharp, stiff point.

Cuspidate (kŭs'pĭ-dāt). To make pointed or sharp.

Cytology (sī-tŏl'ō-jĭ). Treating of the cell.

Deciduous (dē-sĭd'ū-ŭs). Soon falling, especially at the close of the growing period.

Decimeter (dĕs'ĭ-mē-tẽr). A metric measure in length equal to 3.937 (nearly 4) inches.

Decompound (dē-kŏm-pound'). More than once compound or divided.

Decumbent (dē-kŭm'bĕnt). Stems or branches in an inclined position, but the end ascending.

Decurrent (dē-kŭr'ĕnt). Applied to the prolongation of an organ, or a part of an organ running along the sides of another.

Deflexed (dē-flĕkst'). Bent abruptly downward.

Deltoid (dĕl'toid). Like the Greek letter delta. Broadly triangular.

Dentate (dĕn'tāt). Equal-sided teeth projecting forward or at a right angle, and usually acutish.

Denticulate (dĕn-tĭk'ū-lāt). Minutely dentate.

Depauperate (dē-pô'pẽr-āt). Dwarfed, undeveloped, small.

Depressed (dē-prĕst'). Vertically flattened; i. e., as if pressed downward from above.

Dextrorse (dĕks-trôrs'). Turned to the right.

Dichotomous (dī-kŏt'ō-mŭs). Regularly dividing in pairs.

Diffuse (dĭ-fūz'). Loosely, widely and irregularly spreading, the branches usually numerous.

Digitate (dĭj'ĭ-tāt). Finger-like; similar parts radiating from a common point, as the digitate leaflets of the lupine.

Dimorphous (dī-môr'fŭs). Two forms.

Dioecious (dī-ē'shŭs). One-sexed. The male (staminate) borne on one plant and the female (pistillate) borne on another plant. (See the flowers of buffalo grass.)

Distichous (dĭs'tĭk-ŭs). Arranged in two ranks. Thus, the leaves and floral bracts of the true grasses are distichous.

Divaricate (dī-văr'ĭ-kāt). Widely spreading, as branches.

Divergent (dĭ-vẽr'jĕnt). Inclining away from each other.

Dorsal (dôr'sal). The outer surface of an organ; upon or relating to the back.

Dorsiventral (dôr-sĭ-vĕn'tral). Extending from the dorsal to the ventral side.

Echinate (ĕk'ĭ-nāt). Beset with prickles.

Ecology (ē-kŏl'ō-jĭ). The mutual relationship between plants and their environment.

Ellipsoid (ĕ-lĭp′soid). An elliptical solid.

Elliptic (ĕ-lĭp′tĭk). With the outline of an ellipse; oval or oblong with regularly rounded ends.

Emarginate (ē-mär′jĭ-nāt). Notched or indented at the apex. Obcordate is more deeply, and retuse more shallowly, notched. (See Ill.)

Embryo (ĕm′brĭ-ō). The rudimentary or undeveloped plant in a seed; on the side toward the lemma.

Emersed (ē-mērst′). Raised above the surface of the water instead of floating on it; said of aquatic plants.

Epidermis (ĕp-ĭ-dēr′mĭs). The thin layer of cells forming the external integument in seed plants.

Entire (ĕn-tīr′). Without teeth, lobes, divisions or any marginal cuttings; smooth in outline.

Erose (ē-rōs′). As if gnawed.

Excurrent (ĕks-kŭr′ĕnt). Running out; the midnerve of a leaf, vein or veins of a glume or lemma projecting beyond the glume or lemma.

Exserted (ĕk-sērt′ĕd). Projecting beyond the surrounding organs.

Extravaginal innovation (ĕks-trȧ-văj′ĭ-nal ĭn-ō-vā′shŭn). When the branch splits the sheath and grows outward like a stolon or rootstock.

Extrorse (ĕks-trôrs′). Facing outward.

Falcate (făl′kāt). Sickle-shaped.

Fascicle (făs′ĭ-kl). A close bundle or cluster; especially like organs having a common source.

Fascicled (făs′ĭ-kld). Arranged in fascicles.

Fastigiate (făs-tĭj′ĭ-āt). Branches erect and near together.

Ferruginous (fĕ-rōō′jĭ-nŭs). Color of iron-rust.

Fertile (fēr′tĭl). Fruit producing or capable of reproduction.

Flabellate (flȧ-bĕl′āt). Fan-shaped.

Flora (flō′rȧ). The vegetation of a given region, or a botanical manual treating thereof.

Fluted (flōōt′ĕd). Channeled or grooved.

Filament (fĭl′ȧ-mĕnt). The stalk of a stamen on which is borne the pollen sac or anther.

Filiform (fĭl′ĭ-fôrm). Thread-like; long, slender and cylindrical.

Fimbriate (fĭm′brĭ-āt). Fringed. Divisions finer than laciniate.

Floret (flō′rĕt). A small flower, especially the readily detachable flowers of a grass spikelet, consisting of the lemma and its palea together with the stamens and pistils.

Flaccid (flăk′sĭd). Lax, weak.

Flexuous (flĕk′shū-ŭs). Bending gently in opposite directions; slightly zigzag or wavy.

Foliaceous (fō-lĭ-ā′shŭs). Leafy or leaf-like in texture or appearance.

Fruit (frōōt). The ripened ovary of a seed plant with its contents and various envelopes.

Fuscous (fŭs′kŭs). Grayish-brown.

Fusiform (fū′zĭ-fôrm). Spindle-shaped; thickest in the middle and tapering toward each end.

Genetics (jē-nĕt′ĭks). The science of plant or animal breeding. The branch of biology dealing with heredity and all its phases.

Geniculate (jē-nĭk′ū-lāt). Knee-like, bent like a knee; said of stems, the awns of needle-grass, etc.

Genus (jē'nŭs). A group of related species showing similar characteristics. White pine, yellow pine, bristle pine, are parts of the species comprised in the genus *Pinus*.

Gibbous (gĭb'ŭs). Humped or swollen on one side.

Glabrate (glā'brāt). Becoming glabrous, or nearly so, in age.

Glabrescent (glā-brĕs'ĕnt). Tending to become glabrous.

Glabrous (glā'brŭs). Devoid of hairs; smooth in the sense of absence of all hairiness.

Gland (glănd). A secreting cell. Plant glands are usually small, often in the form of glandular hairs.

Glandular (glăn'dū-lẽr). Pertaining to or possessing glands. Viscid (sticky) plants are familiar examples of glandularity.

Glaucous (glô'kŭs). Covered with a whitish or bluish bloom as in the cabbage leaf or fresh bloom.

Globose (glō'bōs). Spherical or approximately so and round in cross-section.

Glomerate (glŏm'ẽr-āt). A compact cluster.

Glumaceous (glū-mā'shŭs). Resembling glumes.

Glumes (glŭms). The two lowest bracts of a grass spikelet which are empty, i. e. do not bear stamens or pistils in their axis. The lower is known as the first and the upper as the second glume.

Grass (grás). A member of the botanical family *Poaceae* (*Gramineae*). (See description.)

Grass-like plants. Plants which resemble true grasses superficially but which do not belong to that family. The most characteristic grass-like plants are the sedges (*Cyperaceae*) and rushes.

Gregarious (grē-gā'rĭ-ŭs). Growing in groups or colonies.

Habit (hăb'ĭt). Aspect; manner of growth.

Habitat (hăb'ĭ-tăt). The site or environment which a plant or plants natively occupy, and the study of which is the science of ecology.

Halophyte (hăl'ō-fīt). A plant adapted to existence in a saline environment, as *Distichlis spicata*.

Head (hĕd). A dense round cluster of sessile or nearly sessile spikelets.

Herbaceous (hẽr-bā'shŭs). Having the characteristics of an herb and free from woody tissue; leaf-like in texture and color.

Hermaphrodite (hẽr-măf'rō-dīt). In botany a plant with perfect flowers, i. e. one containing both pistils and stamens.

Hilum (hī'lŭm). The scar on the surface of a seed which shows the place of attachment; lies on side towards palea.

Hirsute (hẽr'sūt). Hairy with somewhat coarse, stiffish, rather straight beard-like hairs. (See Ill.)

Hispid (hĭs'pĭd). Bristly; beset with stiff, rough, bristle-like hairs.

Hispidulous (hĭs-pĭd'ū-lŭs). Minutely hispid.

Homonym (hŏm'ō-nĭm). The same name for different plants or groups.

Hyaline (hī'à-lĭn). Thin and translucent.

Hybrid (hī'brĭd). The offspring of a male of one race, variety, subspecies, species or sometimes genus, and the female of another.

Hydrophyte (hī'drō-fīt). A plant that grows in the water or wet and saturated soils. (See xerophyte and mesophyte.)

Imbricate (ĭm'brĭ-kāt). Partially overlapping like shingles on a roof.

Immersed (ĭ-mẽrst'). A term used for aquatic plants growing entirely under water.

Imperfect (ĭm-pẽr'fĕkt). Unisexual; wanting either stamens or pistils.

Included (ĭn-klūd'ĕd). Inclosed in and not protruding from the surrounding organs.

Incumbent (ĭn-kŭm'bĕnt). Leaning or resting upon.

Indigenous (ĭn-dĭj'ē-nŭs). Native.

Indurate (ĭn'dū-rāt). To make hard; hardened.

Inferior (ĭn-fē'rĭ-ẽr). Being in a lower position or having the base attached below some other organ.

Inflorescence (ĭn-flō-rĕs'ĕns). The flowering part of a plant, and especially its mode of arrangement.

Innovation (ĭn-ō-vā'shŭn). An offshoot from the main stem, which frequently becomes established as a new plant. (See intravaginal and extravaginal.)

Intercalary (ĭn-tẽr'ká-lā-rĭ). Growth which takes place elsewhere than at the apex or growing points, as at the internodes or base of leaf in grasses.

Internerves (ĭn'tẽr-nẽrvs). Space between the nerves.

Internodes (ĭn'tẽr-nōdz). The portion of the stem between the nodes or joints.

Interrupted (ĭn-tē-rŭpt'ĕd). Not continuous; not uniform.

Intramarginal (ĭn-trȧ-mär'jĭn-al). Within and near the margins.

Intravaginal innovation (ĭn-trȧ-văj'ĭ-nal ĭn-ō-vā'shŭn). Branch growing parallel to culm and emerging from the sheath as in bunch grasses.

Introrse (ĭn-trôrs'). Facing inward.

Involucel (ĭn-vŏl'ū-sĕl). A secondary involucre.

Involucre (ĭn'vō-lū-kẽr). A whorl of distinct or united bracts subtending a spikelet or cluster of spikelets.

Involute (ĭn'vō-lūt). Inrolled, i. e. with both edges rolled in toward the middle, as a grass blade, each edge presenting a spiral appearance in cross-section.

Jointed (joint'ĕd). See articulated.

Keel (kēl). A projecting ridge on a surface, like the keel of a boat. (See carinate.) (See drawing.)

Lacerate (lăs'ẽr-āt). Deeply and irregularly cut as if torn.

Laciniate (lā-sĭn'ĭ-āt). Narrowly incised or slashed; cut into narrow pointed lobes. Divisions coarser than fimbriate.

Lanate (lā'nāt). Woolly, with dense, long, soft, more or less entangled but not matted hairs. (Matted, tomentose.)

Lanose (lā'nōs). Densely lanate.

Lanceolate (lăn'sē-ō-lāt). Lance-shaped. (See Ill.)

Lateral (lăt'ẽr-al). Of or pertaining to a side of an organism.

Lemmas (lĕm'ȧz). Often called scales or flowering glumes; the chaffy bracts which, together with the paleas, inclose the stamens and pistils, the essential flowering organs. (See floret and Ill.)

Lenticular (lĕn-tĭk'ū-lẽr). Resembling a lens in shape.

Ligneous (lĭg'nē-ŭs). Woody.

Ligulate (lĭg'ŭ-lāt). Provided with a ligule.

Ligule (lĭg'ūl). The projecting, usually tongue-like, membranaceous end of the lining of the leaf sheath, seen at the base of a leaf blade, between it and the stalk. It is either membranaceous, ciliate-membranaceous, a ring of hairs, or a mere ridge, or sometimes wanting.

Linear (lĭn'ē-ẽr). Linelike; narrow and flat with the margins parallel or nearly so, as most grasses.

Littoral (lĭt'ō-ral). Inhabiting the sea-shore.

Lobed (lōbd). Incised, but with rounded rather than sharp margins or apex, and not deeper than about half-way.

Lodicule (lŏd'ĭ-kūl). One of three small hyaline scales, representing the corolla, found in the florets of most grasses inside the lemma and palea and subtending the floral organs, i. e. pistil and stamens; usually very small.

Lunate (lū'nāt). Half-moon-shaped.

Marcescent (mär-sĕs'ĕnt). Withering but not deciduous, as the dried persistent leaves of some bunch grasses.

Membranaceous (mĕm-brà-nā'shŭs). Thin and translucent, resembling a membrane; membranous.

Membranous (mĕm'brā-nŭs). Membrane-like; of or pertaining to a membrane.

Meter or metre (mē'tēr). 39.37 inches.

Midrib (mĭd'rĭb). The central or main rib of a leaf blade.

Millimeter or millimetre (mĭl'ĭ-mē-tēr). About 1/25th of an inch.

Monecious (mō-nē'shŭs). With the stamens (male) and the pistils (female) in separate flowers on the same plant. (See dioecious and hermaphrodite).

Monoecious. (See monecious).

Morphology (môr-fŏl'ō-jĭ). The science of form and structure, and is sometimes called structural botany; it deals with the forms of plants and their organs.

Mucro (mū'krō). A sharp straight point, especially if abrupt and short.

Mucronate (mū'krō-nāt). Ending in a mucro.

Muricate (mū'rĭ-kāt). Rough with short hard prominences.

Muticous (mū'tĭ-kŭs). Pointless or blunt.

Naked (nā'kĕd). Lacking parts or organs usually present.

Nerve (nērv). A name for ribs or veins approximately parallel, applied especially to leaves, glumes, lemmas and paleas of grass flowers.

Node (nōd). A joint or knot, said especially of culms whose nodes or joints are enlarged, often dark-colored, being the points where leaves and branches spring.

Ob (ŏb). A prefix signifying in an opposite direction or inversion.

Obcordate (ŏb-kôr'dāt). Reverse of heart-shaped.

Oblanceolate (ŏb-lăn'sē-ō-lāt). Reverse of lance-shaped; with the narrowed tapering point downward.

Oblique (ŏb-lēk'). Unequal sided; slanting.

Oblong (ŏb'lŏng). About two to four times as long as broad, and with the sides, though slightly rounded, approximately parallel.

Obovate (ŏb-ō'vāt). Reverse of ovate.

Obovoid (ŏb-ō'void). Reverse of ovoid, or egg-shaped with the broader end foremost or uppermost.

Obtuse (ŏb-tūs'). Blunt or rounded at the tip.

Orbicular (ôr-bĭk'ū-lēr). Circular in outline or nearly so, as an orbicular leaf.

Organ (ôr'gan). A member; a plant part having a special function or functions; e. g., a root, leaf, etc.

Oval (ō'val). Broadly elliptical. Some use it as a synonym of ovate.

Ovate (ō'vāt). Egg-shaped in longitudinal section, with the broad end downward. Used to describe surfaces.

Ovoid (ō'void). Egg-shaped with the broader end downward. A term used in describing solids, such as fruit.

Palea (pā'lē-à). A chaff-like bract, especially the bract in a grass floret opposite the lemma, and which together with the lemma and lodicules incloses the stamens and pistils and later the grain.

Palmate (păl'māt). Lobed or divided so that the sinuses point to or reach the apex of the petiole or insertion.

Panicle (păn'ĭ-kl). A compound more or less open inflorescence in which the lower branches are typically longer and blossom earlier than the upper branches. The term is sometimes applied to any irregular compound inflorescence.

Paniculate (pà-nĭk'ū-lāt). Arranged in panicles.

Papilla (pà-pĭl'à). A diminutive nipple-like or pimple-like protuberance; often at the base of hairs.

Papillose (păp'ĭ-lōs). Beset with papillae.

Pectinate (pĕk'tĭ-nāt). Pinnatified with narrow and closely set segments, like comb teeth.

Pedicel (pĕd'ĭ-sĕl). The footstalk or stem of an individual flower or fruit in an inflorescence consisting of more than one flower.

Pedicellate (pĕd'ĭ-sĕl-āt). Provided with a pedicel or stalk; not sessile.

Peduncle (pē-dŭn'kl). The stalk of a flower cluster, or of an inflorescence consisting of one flower.

Pedunculate (pē-dŭn'kū-lāt). Provided with a peduncle.

Pendulous (pĕn'dū-lŭs). Hanging down.

Perennial (pĕr-ĕn'ĭ-al). Lasting for three or more years; said especially of herbaceous plants that are neither annual nor biennial.

Perfect (pĕr'fĕkt). Said of a spikelet or flower having both stamens and pistils. Most flowers are perfect.

Perianth (pĕr'ĭ-ănth). The floral envelope.

Pericarp (pĕr'ĭ-kärp). The outer covering of a fruit and corresponding to the outer walls of the ovary from which it is fashioned.

Persistent (pĕr-sĭs'tĕnt). Remaining attached beyond the time such parts usually drop off.

Petiole (pĕt'ĭ-ōl). A leafstock whereby the blade of a leaf is attached to the plant stem or sheath.

Phylogeny (fī-lŏj'ē-nĭ). Race history of an animal or vegetable.

Pilose (pī'lōs). With long soft and rather distinct hairs.

Pistil (pĭs'tĭl). The female or seed-producing organ of the flower.

Pistillate (pĭs'tĭl-āt). With pistils; usually employed in the sense of without stamens.

Plano-convex (plā'nō-kŏn'vĕks). Plain or flat on one side and convex on the other.

Plumose (plū'mōs). Resembling a plume or feather.

Poaceae (pō-ā'sē-ē). The grass family.

Pollen, pollen-grain (pŏl'ĕn). Contents of an anther.

Polygamous (pō-lĭg'à-mŭs). Having both perfect and imperfect flowers on the same plant, i. e. a plant having not only flowers with both stamens and pistils, but having also flowers with only stamens or only pistils.

Polymorphous (pŏl-ĭ-môr'fŭs). Assuming various forms.

Posterior (pŏs-tē'rĭ-ēr). On side next to the axis.

Prickle (prĭk'l). A sharp pointed emergence from the bark and readily pulling off with it, as a rose prickle. (Spines or thorns partake of the nature of branches and are more deeply seated.)

Procumbent (prō-kŭm′bĕnt). Same as prostrate. Lying on the surface of the ground; said especially of culms.

Prostrate (prŏs′trāt). Same as procumbent.

Puberulent (pū-bĕr′ū-lĕnt). Very finely pubescent.

Pubescent (pū-bĕs′ĕnt). In a general sense, with hairs; in a restricted sense, downy.

Pulvinus (pŭl-vī′nŭs). A cushion-like appendage in the axils of the branches of an inflorescence.

Punctate (pŭnk′tāt). Dotted, especially if beset with minute holes or depressions.

Pungent (pŭn′jĕnt). Tipped with a hard, rigid, prickly point, as a pine-needle.

Pustulate (pŭs′tū-lāt). Beset with pimple-like or blister-like elevated and sharply defined areas (pustules).

Pyriform (pĭr′ĭ-fôrm). Pear-shaped.

Race (rās). A breed or strain, lower and less constant than a species.

Raceme (rā-sēm′). An elongated determinate flower cluster with each flower pediceled.

Racemose (răs′ē-mōs). Raceme bearing; having the characteristic of a raceme, or raceme-like.

Rachilla (rà-kĭl′à). The axis of the spikelet in grasses, prolongation of the pedicel.

Rachis (rā′kĭs). The axis of a spike or spike-like raceme. The racemes with long pediceled spikelets are usually called branches.

Radical (răd′ĭ-kăl). Belonging to or proceeding from the root or base of culm.

Recurved (rē-kûrvd′). Bent abruptly backward.

Reflex (rē-flĕks′). Abruptly bent or turned downward.

Regular (rĕg′ū-lēr). Uniform in shape or structure.

Reniform (rĕn′ĭ-fôrm). Kidney-shaped.

Reticulate (rē-tĭk′ū-lāt). Net-veined.

Retrorse (rē-trôrs′). Turned backward or downward.

Retuse (rē-tūs′). Having the apex rounded or obtuse, with a slight notch, as a leaf. Similar to emarginate, but notch more shallow.

Revolute (rĕv′ō-lūt). Rolled backward from margin of apex.

Rhizome (rī′zōm). Same as rootstock. Any prostrate or subterranean culm rooting at the nodes.

Root (rōōt). The underground part of a plant which supplies it with nourishment.

Rootstock (rōōt′stŏck). Same as rhizome.

Rudiment (rōō′dĭ-mĕnt). A very partially developed organ; a vestige.

Rufous (rōō′fŭs). Yellowish-red or brownish-red.

Rugose (rōō-gōs′). Wrinkled.

Runner (rŭn′ēr). A filiform or very slender stolon.

Saccate (săk′āt). With a sac or pouch.

Scabrous (skā′brŭs). Rough to the touch.

Scale (skāl). A minute or rudimentary leaf.

Scarious (skā′rĭ-ŭs). Thin, dry, translucent; not green.

Scorpioid (scôr′pĭ-oid). Coiled up in the bud or unrolling in expanding.

Secund (sē′kŭnd). Borne along one side of an axis.

Seed (sēd). Ripened ovule (See caryopsis).

Serrate (sĕr′āt). Having teeth pointed forward.

Serrulate (sĕr′ōō-lāt). Finely serrate.

Sessile (sĕs'ĭl). Without a stalk.

Setaceous (sē-tā'shŭs). Bristle-like.

Setiform (sē'tĭ-fôrm). Bristle-shaped.

Setose (sē-tōs'). Bristly.

Sheath (shēth). A tubular envelope; as the lower part of the leaf of grasses.

Sheathing (shēth'ĭng). Inclosed as by a sheath.

Sinus (sī'nŭs). A space between the lobes of a leaf.

Smooth (smōōth). Without roughness or pubescence.

Spathe (spāth). A large bract or pair of bracts inclosing an inflorescence.

Spatulate (spăt'ū-lāt). Spoon-shaped.

Species (spē'shēz). The unit of plant and animal classification; a group of individuals with so many characteristics in common as to indicate a very high degree of relationship and a common descent.

Spicate (spī'kāt). Like a spike.

Spike (spīk). An elongated flower cluster in which the flowers are sessile or nearly so.

Spikelet (spīk'lĕt). A name applied to each unit of a grass or sedge inflorescence. A grass spikelet usually consists of two empty glumes and one or more lemmas, subtending a palea, stamens and pistils.

Spine (spīn). A sharp-pointed, rigid, deep-seated emergence from a plant. Spines differ from prickles in not pulling off with the bark; they differ from thorns by absence of vascular tissue.

Squarrose (skwăr'ōs). Thickly crowded and rigid; as squarrose leaves.

Stamen (stā'mĕn). A male floral organ which bears pollen grains; usually consisting of a filament or stalk, and an anther or pollen-sac.

Staminate (stăm'ĭ-nāt). Male plant; bearing stamens. A staminate plant bears stamens only.

Stem (stĕm). Same as culm.

Sterile (stĕr'ĭl). Barren; said of shoots that bear leaves and no flowers; and of anthers that are rudimentary and bear no pollen; sometimes applied to spikelets with stamens only, i. e. imperfect.

Stigma (stĭg'mȧ). Usually the tip of a pistil through which fertilization by the pollen grain is accomplished. It is commonly sticky and hairy.

Stipe (stīp). A stalk-like support of an organ.

Stipitate (stĭp'ĭ-tāt). Having or borne on a stipe, as a pod.

Stolon (stō'lŏn). A trailing or reclining branch, above ground, which strikes root where its joints touch the soil, there sending up new shoots and new plants.

Stoloniferous (stō-lŏn-ĭf'ĕr-ŭs). Bearing stolons.

Stramineous (strā-mĭn'ē-ŭs). Straw-colored.

Striate (strī'āt). Marked with slender, longitudinal grooves; minutely channeled.

Strict (strĭkt). Very straight and upright.

Strigose (strī'gōs). Beset with appressed, rigid hairs.

Style (stīl). The stalk-like and often slender portion of the pistil connecting the stigma with the ovary.

Subacute (sŭb-ȧ-kūt'). Somewhat acute; acutish.

Subtended (sŭb-tĕnd'ĕd). Included in the axil.

Subulate (sū'bū-lāt). Awl-shaped.

Succulent (sŭk'ū-lĕnt). Juicy, watery or pulpy, as succulent culms.

Sulcate (sŭl'kāt). Grooved longitudinally.

Sulcus (sŭl'kŭs). A furrow, groove.

Swale (swāl). A slight depression or valley, as a plain.

Synonym (sĭn'ō-nĭm). Different name applied to the same group.

Tawny (tô'nĭ). Dull yellowish with a tinge of brown.

Taxonomy (tăks-ŏn'ō-mĭ). The science of classification. In botany synonymous with systematic botany, which is the classification of arrangement of plants according to their natural relationships and principles underlying such classification.

Taxonomic agrostology (tăks-ō-nŏm'ĭk). Treats of the botanical classification or natural relationship of grasses.

Terete (tē-rēt'). Elongated and round in cross-section; cylindrical except that terete may also be tapered.

Terminal (tĕr'mĭ-nal). Growing at the end of a branch or stem.

Ternate (tĕr'nāt). Arranged in threes.

Tomentose (tō'mĕn-tōs). With a dense wool-like covering of closely entangled, matted hairs.

Tortuous (tôr'chū-ŭs). Twisted or bent.

Transverse (trăns-vērs'). Crosswise.

Triquetrous (trī-kwē'trŭs). Three-sided, the sides channeled.

Truncate (trŭn'kāt). Squared at the tip; terminating abruptly as if cut off crosswise.

Tuberculate (tū-bĕr'kū-lāt). With rounded projections, or small, pimple-like prominences, tubercles.

Tumid (tū'mĭd). Swollen.

Turgid (tûr'jĭd). Swollen or tightly drawn; said of a membrane covering expanded from within.

Umbonate (ŭm'bō-nāt). Bearing an *umbo* or boss in the centre; a conical or rounded protuberance.

Undulate (ŭn'dū-lāt). With wavy margins.

Unisexual (ū-nĭ-sĕks'ū-al). One-sexed; having the flowers or organs of one sex only, either staminate or pistillate. E. g. the unisexual spikelets of buffalo grass.

Vaginate (văj'ĭ-nāt). Provided with or surrounded by a sheath, as the vaginate culm of a grass.

Variety (vȧ-rī'ē-tĭ). A group of plants related by descent, but distinguished from other similar groups only by characters considered too inconsistent or too trivial to entitle it to recognition as a species.

Vegetative (vĕj-ē-tā'tĭv). Pertaining to growth, opposed to reproduction.

Vein (vān). One of the branches of the woody portion of leaves or other organs.

Veinlet (vān'lĕt). A branch of a vein.

Ventral (vĕn'trăl). The opposite of dorsal; literally, pertaining to the abdomen.

Versatile (vĕr'sȧ-tĭl). An anther attached at or near its middle to the filament.

Verticillate (vĕr-tĭs'ĭ-lāt). With three or more branches or leaves at a node; whorled.

Verrucose (vĕr'ōō-kōs). Beset with wart-like projections.

Villous (vĭl'ŭs). Beset with long, soft, weak hairs.

Viscid (vĭs'ĭd). Sticky or gummy to the touch.

Whorl (hwûrl or hwôrl). Same as verticillate.

Wing (wĭng). A thin, wing-like expansion.

Xerophyte (zē'rō-fīt). A plant adapted to arid conditions; a desert plant.

Xerophytic (zē-rō-fīt'ĭk). Of or pertaining to xerophytes or desert plants.

POACEAE, THE GRASS FAMILY

Flowers perfect (rarely unisexual), small, with no distinct perianth, arranged in spikelets consisting of a shortened axis **(Rachilla)** and 2-to-many 2-ranked bracts, the lowest two (the **Glumes**) being empty (rarely one or both of these obsolete), the one or more upper ones **(Lemmas)** bearing in their axils a single flower, and, between the flower and the rachilla, a second 2-nerved bract (the **Palea**), the lemma, palea and flower together constituting the **Floret; Stamens** 1 to 6, usually 3, with very delicate **Filaments** and 2-celled **Anthers; Pistil** 1, with a 1-celled 1-ovuled ovary, 2 (rarely 1 or 3) **Styles**, and usually plumose **Stigmas; Fruit** a caryopsis with starchy endosperm and a small embryo at the base on the side opposite the hilum.

Herbs, or rarely woody plants, with usually hollow stems **(Culms)** closed at the nodes, and 2-ranked parallel-veined **leaves,** these consisting of 2 parts, the **Sheath,** enveloping the culm, its margins overlapping or sometimes grown together, and the **Blade,** usually flat; between the two, on the inside, a membranaceous hyaline or hairy appendage (the **Ligule**), rarely wanting.

The **Spikelets** are almost always aggregated in spikes or panicles at the ends of the main culms or branches. The **Perianth** is usually represented by 2 (rarely 3) small hyaline scales (the **Lodicules**) at the base of the flower inside the lemma and palea. The **Grain** or **Caryopsis** (the single seed and the adherent pericarp) may be free, as in wheat, or permanently inclosed in the lemma and palea, as in the oat. Rarely the seed is free from the pericarp, as in species of *Sporobolus* and *Eleusine*.

The fruit in a restricted sense is the ripened ovary and its contents, but in a wider sense it is the ripened ovary with the adjacent parts. In some of the genera, especially those of *Paniceae*, the indurate lemma firmly clasps the palea of like texture, the mature grain tightly inclosed within. In such cases the whole floret is usually designated as the fruit.

The culms are woody in the bamboos and solid in our species of the tribes *Tripsaceae* and *Andropogoneae*. The margins of the sheaths are grown together in species of *Bromus, Danthonia, Festuca, Melica, Glyceria,* and other genera.

The parts of the spikelet may be modified in various ways. The first glume, and more rarely also the second, may be wanting. The lemmas may contain no flower, or even no palea, or may be reduced or rudimentary. Rarely, as in species of *Agrostis* and *Andropogon,* the palea is obsolete.

The culms, branches, leaves, and roots form the vegetative part of the plant. The plant may be erect, spreading or creeping, simple or branching, with or without rootstocks and/or stolons, annual or perennial; the culm, sheaths, blades and ligules may be short or long, narrow or wide, glabrous or hairy, smooth or rough.

Branches are borne only at the nodes, appearing between the sheaths and the culm. The branching is called intravaginal if the branch grows up parallel with the culm until it emerges from the sheath, or if it diverges from the culm taking the sheath with it. The branching is called extravaginal if the branch splits the sheath and grows outward. Branches borne at the middle and upper nodes are commonly intravaginal, while those growing at the lower nodes are often extravaginal.

Many grasses produce underground culms called rootstocks or rhizomes, while others produce prostrate culms called stolons or runners. In a few cases plants produce both stolons and rhizomes, e. g., bermuda-grass. The culm and the usually reduced leaves of the stolons are green, while the culm and scales (much reduced leaves of the rootstocks) are pale. Rootstocks may be stout or quite slender.

Perennials are plants that, with or without rootstocks or stolons, live on from year to year although the culms may die down to the ground. Such plants often have old culms at their base, and are more difficult to pull up than annuals, often breaking at or near the surface of the ground.

Since the spikelet is so uniform in most of the grasses it is on the variations in its characters and those of its component parts that classification mainly depends, especially on the variations in the glumes, lemmas and paleas, their number, shape, size, venation, texture and relation to one another.

Most of the genera of grasses fall naturally into one of the two series or subfamilies. The remaining few are rather arbitrarily assigned to one or the other series. In the same manner most of the genera may be assembled into distinct and well-marked tribes; however, several are not closely allied to the other genera in the tribes to which they are assigned but are so placed for convenience in classification.

The *First Book of Grasses* by Agnes Chase, Associate Agrostologist, U. S. Department of Agriculture, and *A Text-book of Grasses* by A. S. Hitchcock, Principal Botanist in charge of Systematic Agrostology U. S. Department of Agriculture, the Macmillan Company, Publisher, are highly recommended by the author as invaluable aids to the student in the study of the structure of grasses.

HOW TO IDENTIFY THE GRASSES

Immediately following comes the division of the grasses into two sub-families, *Poatae* (*Poacoideae* or *Pooideae*) and *Panicatae* (*Panicoideae*), each embracing several tribes. Supplementing this key to the tribes are drawings of a representative panicle and spikelets of each tribe. Then comes a full description of each tribe followed by a key to the genera of that tribe.

For purposes of exemplification let us take rescue-grass (*Bromus catharticus*). See illustration and with a specimen of this species before you proceed as follows:

Find key to the subfamilies. Read the descriptions of the sub-families and observe the drawings. Spikelets laterally compressed or flattened. Hence *Poatae*.

Read the descriptions of the tribes under Poatae. The drawings show that the spikelets resemble those of *Bambuseae* and *Festuceae*. Plant not shrubby. Hence *Festuceae*.

Read the key to Festuceae. Observe the photographs of the plants of this tribe; this will eliminate most of the genera. The lemmas are 5-many-nerved and awn-pointed or short-awned from a bifid apex. Hence *Bromus*.

Read the key to Bromus. Observe the photographs. To prove your selection is right be sure to read the key. Spikelets strongly compressed or flattened laterally, sheaths and blades pubescent, lemma awn-pointed or short-awned. Hence *Bromus catharticus*.

If a collector is in doubt as to the correct classification of a specimen, an authoritative identification may be obtained from the Department of Agriculture at Washington. Take a specimen (including roots) that is in flower and place it in a press between heavy blotting paper 11.5 by 16.5 inches; dry and replace the paper every day or two until the specimen is thoroughly dry. Then send it to A. S. Hitchcock, Principal Botanist in charge of Systematic Agrostology, Smithsonian Institution, Washington, D. C. Specimens should be numbered consecutively for further reference, and duplicates with the same number should be kept by the collector.

In order to acquire early proficiency in classifying grasses it is very necessary to form the habit of always writing out the description of the specimen being classified, using the form adopted in this work. In no other way can one's powers of accurate and expeditious discrimination be developed within a relatively short time. This method will also greatly aid the memory in retaining the distinctive features of the species to which a specimen classified belongs.

Under the author's supervision his son, William I. Silveus, 832 Cambridge Oval, San Antonio, Texas, has collected and pressed specimens of various grasses growing at or near San Antonio (particularly rescue-grass), and will be pleased to fill orders on receipt of a small sum plus express or mail charges. If a specimen ordered is not on hand or in season the remittance will be returned, or, if desired, the order will be filled as soon as the plant is again in season.

DESCRIPTIONS OF THE SUBFAMILIES AND KEYS TO THE TRIBES

SUBFAMILY I. POATAE (pō-ā'te)

Spikelets 1 to many flowered, the reduced florets, if any, above the perfect florets (except in Phalarideae; sterile lemmas below as well as above in Campulosus, Uniola, and Blepharidachne); articulation usually above the glumes; spikelets usually more or less LATERALLY COMPRESSED.

KEY TO TRIBES OF POATAE

A. SPIKELETS IN OPEN OR CONTRACTED PANICLES; USUALLY ARTICULATE ABOVE THE GLUMES.

Tribe No.1. has WOODY perennial culms, and all the other tribes have HERBACEOUS annual culms.

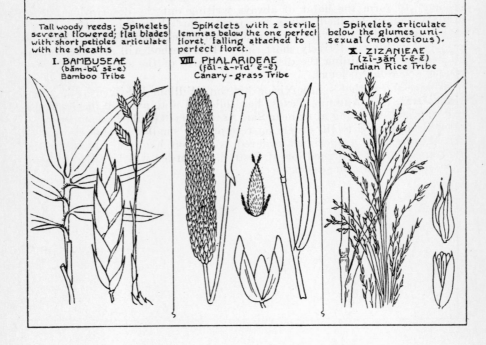

Tall woody reeds; Spikelets several flowered; flat blades with short petioles articulate with the sheaths

I. BAMBUSEAE
(băm-bū' sē-e)
Bamboo Tribe

Spikelets with 2 sterile lemmas below the one perfect floret, falling attached to perfect floret.

VIII. PHALARIDEAE
(făl-a-rĭd' ē-ē)
Canary-grass Tribe

Spikelets articulate below the glumes uni-sexual (monoecious).

X. ZIZANIEAE
(zĭ-zăn ĭ-ē-ē)
Indian Rice Tribe

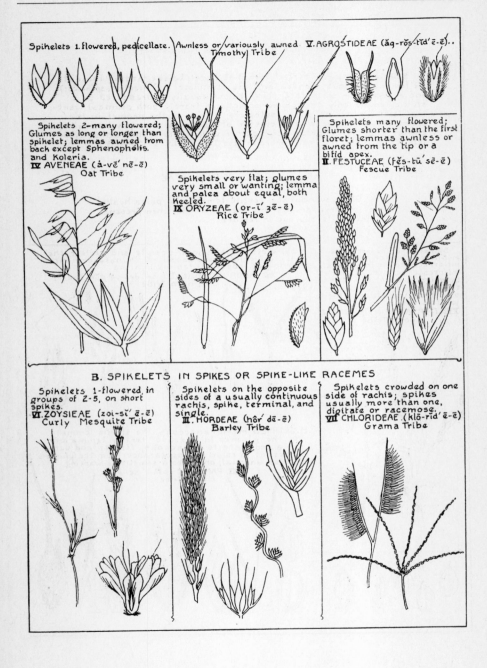

Spikelets 1.flowered, pedicellate. Awnless or variously awned **V.**AGROSTIDEAE (ăg-rŏs-tĭd'ē-ē)..
Timothy Tribe

Spikelets 2-many flowered;
Glumes as long or longer than
spikelet; lemmas awned from
back except Sphenopholis.
and Koleria.
IV AVENEAE (ă-vē'nē-ē)
Oat Tribe

Spikelets very flat; glumes
very small or wanting; lemma
and palea about equal, both
keeled.
IX ORYZEAE (or-ī'zē-ē)
Rice Tribe

Spikelets many flowered;
Glumes shorter than the first
floret; lemmas awnless or
awned from the tip or a
bifid apex.
II.FESTUCEAE (fĕs-tū'sē-ē)
Fescue Tribe

B. SPIKELETS IN SPIKES OR SPIKE-LIKE RACEMES

Spikelets 1-flowered in
groups of 2-5, on short
spikes.
VI.ZOYSIEAE (zoi-sī'ē-ē)
Curly Mesquite Tribe

Spikelets on the opposite
sides of a usually continuous
rachis, spike, terminal, and
single.
III.HORDEAE (hôr'dē-ē)
Barley Tribe

Spikelets crowded on one
side of rachis; spikes
usually more than one,
digitate or racemose.
VII CHLORIDEAE (klō-rĭd'ē-ē)
Grama Tribe

SUBFAMILY II, PANICATAE (păn-ĭ-kā′tē)

Spikelets with one perfect terminal floret (disregarding those of the few monoecious genera and the staminate and neuter spikelets) and a sterile or staminate floret below, usually represented by a sterile lemma only one glume sometimes (rarely both glumes) want-ing; articulation below the spikelets, either in the pedicel, in the rachis, or at the base of a cluster of spikelets, the spikelets falling entire, singly or in groups, or together with joints of the rachis; spike-lets, or at least the fruits, more or less DORSALLY COMPRESSED.

KEY TO TRIBES OF PANICATAE

A. Glumes indurate; fertile lemma and palea hyaline or membranaceous, the sterile lemma, when present, like the fertile one in texture.

Spikelets unisexual, the pistillate below, on the same inflorescence, or in separate inflorescences, the staminate in pairs at each joint of the spike-like raceme, the pistillate imbedded in the jointed rachis.
XIII. TRIPSACEAE (trĭp-sā′ ē-ē)
Corn Tribe

Spikelets in pairs, one sessile and perfect, the other pedicellate and usually staminate or neuter, sometimes obsolete; lemma hyaline.
XII ANDROPOGONEAE (ăn′-drō-pō-gŏn′ ē-ē)
Sorghum Tribe

B. GLUMES membranaceous, the sterile lemma like the glumes in texture, fertile lemma and palea indurate to coriaceous, firmer and very different in color and appearance from the glumes. Glumes unequal, one or both sometimes wanting.
XI PANICEAE (păn-ĭ′ sē-ē)
Millet Tribe

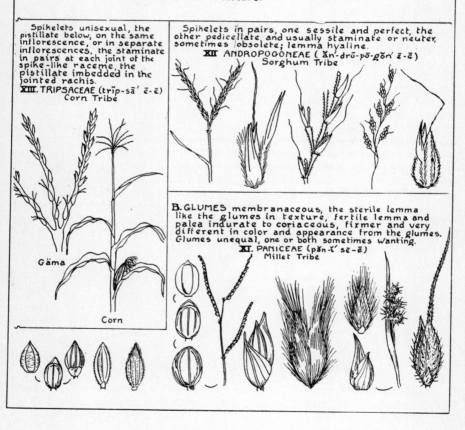

Gäma

Corn

DESCRIPTIONS OF THE TRIBES AND KEYS TO THE GENERA

TRIBE 1, BAMBUSEAE (băm-bū′sē-ē)

The tribe which includes the bamboos is for the most part confined to the tropics and subtropics. One genus extends into southern United States. The *bamboos* have woody-jointed, usually hollow culms either erect or vine-like. Some of the larger kinds are as much as a foot in diameter and 100 feet in height. The common economic species of the tropics, such as *Bambusa vulgaris* Schrad., (*Bambos bambos* (L.) Wight), because of the large hollow culms with hard partitions at the nodes found in most large species, can be used for a great variety of purposes. Many kinds of *bamboos* are culti-vated for ornament in the warmer parts of the United States, especially in Florida and California. *Arundinaria japonica* Sieb. & Zucc., with several-flowered spikelets, and a few species of *Phyllostachys*, are hardy as far north as Washington. They form dense masses of shoots, usually 8 to 20 feet high. *Phyllostachys* (fĭl-ō-stā′kĭs) does not usually flower in this country, but the plants can be distinguished by the internodes which are flattened on one side. *Bambusa* (băm-bū′sȧ) is a modified spelling of the original *Bambos*. Our genera of this tribe are grouped under *Arundinaria*.

CULMS CYLINDRIC.
    Branches in whorls at the nodes, distinctly smaller than the main culm, diverging from it.   1. Bambusa
    Branches appressed at the base and not in whorls, not much smaller than the main culm.   1. Arundinaria
CULMS NOT CYLINDRIC. The internodes (especially of the small branches) flat on one side, the branches mostly in twos, stiffly ascending from one side of the culm.   1. Phyllostachys

TRIBE 2, FESTUCEAE (fĕs-tū′sē-ē)

Spikelets more than 1-flowered, usually several-flowered, in open, narrow, or sometimes spikelike panicles; **Lemmas** awnless or awned from the tip, rarely from between the teeth of a bifid apex; **Rachilla** usually disarticulating above the glumes and between the florets.

A large and important tribe, mainly inhabitants of the cooler regions. The lemma is divided into several awns in *Pappophorum* and its allies, is deeply 2-lobed in *Triplasis* and in a few species of *Triodia*, 3-lobed in *Blepharidachne*, and slightly 2-toothed in *Bromus* and a few other genera, the awn, when single, arising from between the teeth. The paleas are persistent upon the continuous rachilla in most species of *Eragrostis*.

Scleropogon, Monanthochloë, Distichlis, and a few species of *Poa* and *Eragrostis,* are dioecious. *Gynerium, Cortaderia, Arundo* and *Phragmites* are tall reeds.   In *Blepharidachne* there is a pair of sterile florets at the base of the single fertile floret, and a rudiment above.   In some species of *Melica* there is, above the fertile florets, a club-shaped rudiment consisting of one or more sterile lemmas.   In *Uniola* there are one to four sterile lemmas below the fertile ones.

PLANTS DIOECIOUS, THE SEXES VERY DISSIMILAR.
  PISTILLATE LEMMAS with 3 long twisted divergent awns, the staminate
     lemmas awnless or mucronate.   20. Scleropogon
  PISTILLATE LEMMAS silky with long hairs, the staminate lemmas glabrous,
     plants very tall. (At end of *Arundo donax.*)
     Blades crowded at the base, less than 1′ wide.   11. Cortaderia
     Blades not crowded at the base, 2′ wide.   11. Gynerium
PLANTS WITH PERFECT FLOWERS, OR, IF DIOECIOUS, the sexes not
     dissimilar in appearance.
  LEMMAS DIVIDED at the summit into 9 or more awns or awnlike lobes.
     AWNS unmixed with awned teeth; all the florets falling attached, their
        awns forming a pappus-like crown, only the lowest floret fertile; panicle
        narrow.   22. Pappophorum
     AWNS mixed with awned teeth; florets not falling attached, the rachilla
        disarticulating between them; panicles somewhat open.   21. Cottea
  LEMMAS AWNLESS, with a single awn, or, if 3, the lateral awns minute.
     TALL stout reeds with large plume-like panicles; lemmas or rachilla with
        long silky hairs as long as the lemmas.
        Lemmas hairy; rachilla naked.   11. Arundo
        Lemmas naked; rachilla hairy.   12. Phragmites
     LOW or rather tall grasses, rarely over 5 feet tall.
       Plants dioecious; lemmas glabrous; grasses of salt or alkaline soils;
          perennials.
          Plants low and creeping; spikelets obscure, scarcely differentiated from
             the short crowded rigid leaves.   8. Monanthochloë
          Plants erect from creeping rhizomes; spikelets in a narrow simple ex-
             serted panicle.   9. Distichlis
       Plants not dioecious (except in a few species of *Poa* with villous lemmas
          and in an annual species of *Eragrostis*).
          Spikelets of two forms, sterile and fertile intermixed; fertile spikelets
             with 1 perfect floret, long-awned; sterile spikelets with many obtuse
             glumes; panicle branchlets short, nodding.   14. Lamarckia
          Spikelets all alike in the same inflorescence.
            Lemmas 3-nerved, the nerves prominent, often hairy.
              INFLORESCENCE A FEW-FLOWERED HEAD OR capitate panicle
                 overtopped by the leaves or partly concealed in them; lemmas
                 toothed or cleft; low plants of the arid regions.
              INFLORESCENCE HIDDEN among the sharp-pointed leaves, not
                 woolly; plants annual (*Chlorideae*).   71. Munroa
              INFLORESCENCE A CAPITATE woolly panicle, not concealed;
                 plants perennial.
                 Lemmas cleft either side of the midnerve to near the base, the
                    lower two sterile, the third floret fertile, the fourth reduced to
                    a 3-awned rudiment.   19. Blepharidachne
                 Lemma 2-lobed but not deeply cleft, all but uppermost fertile.
                                                       16. Triodia
              INFLORESCENCE AN EXSERTED OPEN OR SPIKELIKE panicle.
                LEMMAS PUBESCENT on the nerves or callus (except in *Triodia
                   albescens*), the midnerve usually exserted as an awn or mucro;
                   nerves hairy, at least below, the lateral ones often con-
                   spicuously so.
                   Palea long-ciliate on the upper half.   18. Triplasis
                   Palea sometimes villous but not long-ciliate on the upper half;
                      perennials.   16. Triodia

LEMMAS NOT pubescent on the nerves or callus (the internerves sometimes pubescent), awnless; glumes shorter than the lemmas; lateral nerves of lemma not marginal, the internerves glabrous.

Lemmas chartaceous; grain large and beaked at maturity forcing the lemma and palea open. 7. Diarrhena

Lemma membranaceous; if firm, the grain neither large nor beaked; acute or acuminate; spikelets 3-to-many-flowered; rachilla continuous, the palea usually persistent after the fall of the lemma. 6. Eragrostis

Lemmas 5-to-many-nerved, the nerves sometimes obscure.

SPIKELETS WITH 1 TO 4 EMPTY LEMMAS below the fertile florets; nerves obscure; lemmas firm. 10. Uniola

SPIKELETS WITH NO EMPTY LEMMAS BELOW THE fertile florets; nerves usually prominent; lemmas membranaceous (firm in a few species of *Bromus* and *Festuca*).

LEMMAS KEELED on the back.

SPIKELETS strongly compressed, crowded in one-sided clusters at the ends of the stiff, naked panicle branches. 13. Dactylis

SPIKELETS not strongly compressed, not crowded in one-sided clusters.

Lemmas awned from a minutely bifid apex (awnless or nearly so in *Bromus catharticus*); spikelets large. 2. Bromus

Lemmas awnless; spikelets small. 5. Poa

LEMMAS ROUNDED on the back (slightly keeled toward the summit in *Festuca* and *Bromus*).

GLUMES papery; lemmas firm, strongly nerved, scarious-margined; upper florets sterile, often reduced to a club-shaped rudiment infolded by the broad upper lemmas; spikelets tawny or purplish, usually not green. 15. Melica

GLUMES not papery; upper florets not unlike the others.

Nerves of the lemma parallel, not converging at the summit or but slightly so; lemmas awnless, mostly obtuse, nerves prominent; plants usually rather tall; growing in woods or fresh-water marshes. 4. Glyceria

Nerves of the lemma converging at the summit; lemmas awned or pointed.

Lemma entire, awned from the tip or pointed.

Glumes 1-3-nerved; lemmas lanceolate or narrower, 5-nerved. 3. Festuca

Glumes 5-9-nerved; lemmas broad, many-nerved, firm, entire or minutely lobed. 17. Vaseyochloa

Lemmas awned or awn-tipped from a minutely bifid apex. 2. Bromus

TRIBE 3, HORDEAE (hôr′dē-ē)

Spikelets 1-to-several-flowered, sessile on opposite sides of a jointed or continuous axis forming symmetrical (not one-sided) spikes.

This small but important tribe, found in the temperate regions of both hemispheres, includes our most important cereals, wheat, barley and rye. The rachis is flattened or concave next to the spikelets, or in some genera is thickened and hollowed out, the spikelets being more or less included in the hollows. In *Triticum* and its allies there is one spikelet at each node of the rachis; in *Hordeum* and its allies there are two or three at each node. In *Lolium* and its allies the spikelets are placed edgewise to the rachis, and the first or inner glume is suppressed except in the terminal spikelet. The rachilla of the spikelet disarticulates at maturity in several genera. In some species of *Elymus* and especially in *Sitanion* the glumes are very slender, extending into long awns, in the latter genus sometimes divided into several slender bristles. In this tribe the blades of the leaves bear on each side at the base a small appendage or auricle.

SPIKELETS SOLITARY AT EACH NODE OF THE RACHIS (rarely 2 in species
of *Agropyron*, but never throughout); spikelets 2-to-several-flowered, not
sunken in the rachis.
SPIKELETS PLACED edgewise to the rachis; first glume wanting except in
terminal spikelet.
29. Lolium
SPIKELETS PLACED flatwise to the rachis.
PLANTS perennial.
23. Agropyron
PLANTS annual.
Glumes ovate, 3-nerved.
24. Triticum
Glumes subulate, 1-nerved.
25. Secale
SPIKELETS MORE THAN 1 AT EACH NODE OF THE RACHIS.
SPIKELETS 3 AT each node of the rachis, 1-flowered, the lateral pair pediceled,
usually reduced to awns.
28. Hordeum
SPIKELETS 2 AT each node of the rachis, alike, 2-to-6-flowered; glumes
usually equaling the florets; spikelets appressed or ascending.
Rachis continuous (rarely tardily disarticulating); glumes broad or narrow,
entire.
26. Elymus
Rachis disarticulating at maturity; glumes subulate; extending into long
awns, these and the awns of the lemmas making the spike very bristly.
27. Sitanion

TRIBE 4, AVENEAE (ȧ-vē′nē-ē)

Spikelets 2-to-several-flowered, in open or contracted panicles, or
rarely in racemes; Glumes usually as long as or longer than the first
lemma, commonly longer than all the florets; Lemmas usually awned from
the back or from between the teeth of a bifid apex, the awn bent, often
twisted, the callus and rachilla-joints usually villous.

A rather small tribe widely distributed in both warm and cool regions.
In our genera the rachilla is prolonged beyond the upper floret as a slender
stipe (except in *Aira*). The lemma is awnless or nearly so in *Sphenopholis*
and in our species of *Koeleria*. These genera are placed in this tribe because they appear to be closely allied to *Trisetum*, with which they agree
in having oblanceolate glumes about as long as the first floret.

SPIKELETS AWNLESS OR THE UPPER MUCRONATE (rarely short-awned
in *Sphenopholis*).
Articulation below the glumes; glumes distinctly different in shape, the second
widened above.
32. Sphenopholis
Articulation above the glumes; glumes similar in shape.
30. Koeleria
SPIKELETS AWNED.
FLORETS 2, LOWER floret perfect, awnless, the upper staminate, the awn
hooked.
35. Holcus
FLORETS 2 OR MORE, all alike except the reduced upper ones.
AWN arising from between the teeth of a bifid apex, flattened, twisted;
inflorescence a simple panicle or reduced to a raceme.
36. Danthonia
AWN dorsal, not flattened; lemma often bifid at apex.
Spikelets large, the glumes over 10 mm. long.
33. Avena
Spikelets less than 10 mm. long.
Lemmas keeled, bidentate; awn arising from above the middle.
31. Trisetum
Lemmas convex; awn from below the middle; rachilla not prolonged;
lemmas tapering into 2 slender teeth.
34. Aira

TRIBE 5, AGROSTIDEAE (ăg-rŏs-tĭd′ē-ē)

Spikelets 1-flowered, usually perfect, arranged in open, contracted,
or spikelike panicles, but not in true spikes nor in one-sided racemes.

A large and important tribe, inhabiting more especially the temperate and cool regions. The articulation of the rachilla is usually above the glumes, the mature floret falling from the persistent glumes, but in a few genera the articulation is below the glumes, the mature spikelet falling entire (*Alopecurus, Cinna, Polypogon, Lycurus,* and *Limnodea*). The palea is small or wanting in some species of *Agrostis*. In a few genera the rachilla is prolonged behind the palea as a minute bristle, or sometimes as a more pronounced villous stipe (*Limnodea, Cinna,* three species of *Agrostis,* and *Gastridium*). In some genera the rachilla-joint between the glumes and the lemma is slightly elongated, forming a hard stipe, which remains attached to the mature fruit as a pointed callus. The callus is well marked in *Stipa* (especially in *S. spartea* and its allies) and in *Aristida,* the mature lemma being terete, indurate and convolute, the palea wholly inclosed. In many genera the lemma is awned either from the tip or from the back, the awn being trifid in *Aristida*.

ARTICULATION BELOW THE GLUMES, THESE FALLING WITH THE
  spikelet.
  SPIKELETS IN pairs in a spikelike panicle, one perfect, the other staminate or
    neuter, the pair falling together. 43. Lycurus
  SPIKELETS ALL alike.
    GLUMES long-awned. 42. Polypogon
    GLUMES awnless.
      Rachilla not prolonged behind the palea; panicle dense and spikelike; glumes
        united toward the base, ciliate on the keel. 41. Alopecurus
      Rachilla prolonged behind the palea; panicle narrow or open, not dense;
        glumes not united, not ciliate on the keel.
        Panicle narrow; lemma with a slender bent twisted awn from the bifid
          apex. 40. Limnodea
        Panicle open and drooping; lemma with a minute straight awn just below
          the entire apex. 39. Cinna
ARTICULATION ABOVE THE GLUMES; glumes persistent; fruit laterally com-
  pressed or terete, awned or awnless.
  FRUIT INDURATE, terete, awned, the nerves obscure; callus well-developed,
    oblique, bearded.
    AWN trifid, the lateral divisions sometimes short, rarely obsolete (when
      obsolete no line of demarcation between awn and lemma as in the next).
      52. Aristida
    AWN simple, a line of demarcation between the awn and lemma.
      Awn persistent, twisted and bent, several-to-many-times longer than the
        fruit.
        Edges of lemma overlapping, inclosing the palea, fruit slender, callus
          sharp-pointed. 51. Stipa
        Edges of lemma not meeting, exposing the indurate sulcus of the palea,
          this projecting from the summit as a minute point; fruit plump;
          callus short, acutish. 50. Piptochaetium
      Awn deciduous, not twisted, sometimes bent, rarely more than 3 or 4 times
        as long as the plump fruit; callus short, usually obtuse. 49. Oryzopsis
  FRUIT THIN or firm, but scarcely indurate; if firm, the nerves prominent or
    evident; callus not well developed.
    GLUMES longer than the lemma; panicle not feathery; spikelets not woolly.
      Glumes compressed-carinate, abruptly mucronate, stiffly ciliate on the
        keels; panicle dense, cylindric. 44. Phleum
      Glumes not compressed-carinate, not ciliate.
        Glumes saccate at base; lemma long-awned; inflorescence contracted,
          shining. 45. Gastridium
        Glumes not saccate at base; lemma awned or awnless; panicle open or
          contracted; palea usually small or wanting. 38. Agrostis
    GLUMES not longer than the lemma, usually shorter.
      LEMMA AWNED FROM THE TIP OR FROM JUST BELOW IT, or
        mucronate, 3-5-nerved (lateral nerves obsolete in *Muhlenbergia utilis*);
        floret not stipitate. 46. Muhlenbergia

LEMMA AWNLESS, HAIRY OR GLABROUS AT BASE.
  FLORET BEARING a tuft of hairs at the base from the short callus;
    lemma and palea chartaceous, awnless. Panicle open. 37. Calamovilfa
  FLORET WITHOUT hairs at base.
    LEMMA 3-nerved, the nerves densely silky.   48. Blepharoneuron
    LEMMA 1-nerved, the nerves glabrous; caryopsis at maturity falling
      from the lemma and palea; seed loose in the pericarp, this usually
      opening when ripe; inflorescence an open or contracted panicle.
                                                          47. Sporobolus

TRIBE 6, ZOYSIEAE (zoi-sǐ'ē-ē)
(Nazieae)

Spikelets subsessile in short spikes of 2 to 5 (single in *Zoysia*), each
spike falling entire from the continuous axis, usually 1-flowered, all perfect, or perfect and staminate together in the same spike; Glumes usually
firmer than the lemma and palea, sometimes awned, the lemma awnless.

This small and unimportant tribe is known also as *Nazieae*. In *Zoysia*
the spikelets are single and have only one glume, this coriaceous, much
firmer than the lemma and palea, the palea sometimes obsolete.

SPIKELETS SINGLE; first glume wanting.
SPIKELETS IN clusters of 2 to 5; first glume present.   54. Zoysia
  SPIKELETS bearing hooked spines on the second glume, the group forming a
    little bur.   53. Tragus
  SPIKELETS not bearing hooked spines, mostly cleft and awned; groups of
    spikelets erect, the spike not one-sided.   55. Hilaria

TRIBE 7, CHLORIDEAE (klō-rǐd'ē-ē)

Spikelets 1-to-several-flowered, in 2 rows on one side of a continuous
rachis forming one-sided spikes or spikelike racemes, these solitary, digitate,
or racemose along the main axis.

A large and rather important tribe, confined mostly to warm regions.
The group is heterogeneous, the only common character of the genera
(aside from the characters that place them in *Poatae*) being the arrangement of the spikelets in one-sided spikes. *Chloris* and the allied genera
form a coherent group, in which the spikelet consists of one perfect floret
and, above this, one or more modified or rudimentary florets. *Leptochloa,
Eleusine,* and their allies, with several-flowered spikelets, are more nearly
related to certain genera of *Festuceae*. The spike is reduced to two or three
spikelets or even to one spikelet, and is sometimes deciduous from the main
axis in *Cathestecum* and in some species of *Bouteloua*. In *Ctenium* there
are two sterile florets below the perfect one.

PLANTS DIOECIOUS; A LOW STOLONIFEROUS PERENNIAL. 72. Buchloë
PLANTS WITH PERFECT FLOWERS.
  SPIKELETS WITH more than one perfect floret.
    INFLORESCENCE a few-flowered head or capitate panicle hidden among
      the sharp-pointed leaves; a low spreading annual.   71. Munroa
    INFLORESCENCE exserted.
      Spikes solitary, the spikelets distant, appressed, several-flowered.
                                                                58. Tripogon
      Spikes more than one; lemma obtuse or acute, often 2-toothed or 2-lobed,
        and mucronate or short-awned from between the teeth or lobes.
        Spikes or racemes numerous, racemose along an elongated axis.
          Glumes usually shorter than the lower florets.   56. Leptochloa
          Glumes usually about equaling the upper florets.   57. Trichoneura
        Spikes few, digitate, or nearly so.
          Rachis of spike extending beyond the spikelets.   60. Dactyloctenium
          Rachis not prolonged.   59. Eleusine

SPIKELETS WITH only 1 perfect floret, often with additional imperfect florets above.
    SPIKELETS without additional modified florets, the rachilla sometimes prolonged.
        Articulation below the glumes, the spikelets falling entire; glumes unequal, narrow.
                64. Spartina
        Articulation above the glumes.
           Spikes digitate; rachilla prolonged.   61. Cynodon
           Spikes racemose along the main axis; rachilla not prolonged.
              Spikes slender, divaricate, the main axis elongating and becoming loosely spiral in fruit.   63. Schedonnardus
              Spikes short and rather stout, appressed, the axis unchanged in fruit.
                  62. Willkommia

SPIKELETS with 1 or more modified florets above the perfect one.
    Spikelets with 2 sterile florets below the perfect one; second glume bearing a squarrose spine on the back; spike single, recurved.   65. Ctenium
    Spikelets with no sterile florets below the perfect one; second glume without a squarrose spine; spikes usually several.
        Spikes digitate or nearly so.   67. Chloris
           Fertile lemma 1-awned or awnless.   68. Trichloris
           Fertile lemma 3-awned.
        Spikes racemose along the main axis.
           Spikelets distant, appressed; spikes slender, elongate.
                66. Gymnopogon
           Spikelets contiguous or crowded, not appressed; spikes usually short and rather stout.
              Spikelets 3 in each spike, the 2 lateral staminate or rudimentary; spikes falling entire.   70. Cathestecum
               Spikelets 2-to-many (rarely 1) in each spike, all alike; spikes usually persistent, the florets falling.   69. Bouteloua

TRIBE 8, PHALARIDEAE (făl-à-rĭd′ē-ē)

Spikelets with one perfect terminal floret and, below this, a pair of staminate or neuter florets.

A small tribe of about six genera, only three of which are found in the United States, two in Texas. In *Phalaris* the lateral florets are reduced to minute scalelike lemmas closely appressed to the edges of the fertile floret.

LATERAL FLORETS reduced to small awnless scalelike lemmas; spikelets much compressed laterally.   74. Phalaris
LATERAL FLORETS consisting of awned hairy sterile lemmas exceeding the fertile floret; spikelet terete.   73. Anthoxanthum

TRIBE 9, ORYZEAE (ō-rī′zē-ē)

Spikelets 1-flowered, perfect, strongly laterally compressed, paniculate; **Glumes** reduced or wanting; **Palea** apparently 1-nerved; **Stamens 6**.

A small tribe whose affinities are not evident. It includes rice, the important food plant.

GLUMES MINUTE; lemma often awned.   75. Oryza
GLUMES WANTING; lemma awnless.   76. Leersia

TRIBE 10, ZIZANIEAE (zī-zăn-ĭ′ē-ē).

Spikelets unisexual, the pistillate terete or nearly so; **Glumes** shorter than the lemma, usually one or both obsolete, the pedicel disarticulating below the spikelet.

A small tribe of uncertain affinities; the species aquatic or subaquatic, of no economic importance except Indian rice (*Zizania*).

PLANTS ANNUAL and perennial; pistillate spikelets on the ascending upper branches, the staminate on the spreading lower branches of the panicle.

78. Zizania

PLANTS PERENNIAL; pistillate spikelets at the ends, the staminate below on the same branches of the panicle.

77. Zizaniopsis

TRIBE 11, PANICEAE (păn-ĭ′sē-ē)

Spikelets with one perfect terminal floret and, below this, a sterile floret and two glumes; **Fertile Lemma** and **Palea** indurate, or at least firmer than the glumes and sterile lemma; articulation below the spikelet.

A large tribe, confined mostly to warm regions, and containing few economic species. The first glume is wanting in some genera, such as *Paspalum*. The spikelets are usually awnless, but the glumes and sterile lemma are awned in *Echinochloa* and *Oplismenus*, and the second glume and sterile lemma in *Tricholaena*. In *Eriochloa* and in some species of *Brachiaria* the fertile lemma is awn-tipped. In *Setaria* there are, beneath the spikelet, one or more bristles, these representing sterile branchlets. In *Pennisetum* similar bristles form an involucral cluster, falling with the spikelet. In *Cenchrus* the bristles are united, forming a bur.

SPIKELETS SUNKEN IN THE CAVITIES OF THE FLATTENED CORKY rachis.

83. Stenotaphrum

SPIKELETS NOT SUNKEN IN THE RACHIS.
  SPIKELETS SUBTENDED or surrounded by 1-to-many-distinct or more or less connate bristles, forming an involucre.
    BRISTLES persistent, the spikelets deciduous.

93. Setaria

    BRISTLES falling with the spikelets at maturity.
      Bristles not united at base, slender, often plumose.

94. Pennisetum

      Bristles united into a burlike involucre, the bristles retrorsely barbed.

95. Cenchrus

  SPIKELETS NOT subtended by bristles.
    GLUMES or sterile lemma awned (awn short and concealed in the silky hairs of the spikelet in *Tricholaena*, awn reduced to a point in *Echinochloa colonum*).
      Inflorescence paniculate; spikelets silky.

92. Tricholaena

      Inflorescence of unilateral simple or somewhat compound racemes along a common axis; spikelets smooth or hispid, not silky.
        Blades lanceolate, broad and thin; glumes 2-lobed, awned from between the lobes.
        Blades long and narrow; glumes awned from the tip.

90. Oplismenus

91. Echinochloa

    GLUMES and sterile lemma awnless.
      Fruit cartilaginous-indurate, flexible, usually dark colored, the lemma with more or less prominent white hyaline margins, these not inrolled.
        Spikelets covered with long silky hairs, arranged in racemes, these panicled.

80. Trichachne

        Spikelets glabrous or variously pubescent but not long-silky.
          Spikelets in slender racemes more or less digitate at the summit of the culms.

81. Digitaria

          Spikelets in panicles.
            Fruiting lemma boat-shaped; panicles narrow.

79. Anthaenantia

            Fruiting lemma convex; panicle diffuse.

82. Leptoloma

      Fruit chartaceous-indurate, rigid.
        Spikelets placed with the back of the fruit turned away from the rachis of the racemes, usually single or in pairs.
          First glume and the rachilla-joint forming a swollen ring-like callus below the spikelet.

84. Eriochloa

          First glume present or wanting, not forming a ringlike callus below the spikelet.
            First glume present; racemes racemose along the main axis.

85. Brachiaria

            First glume wanting; racemes digitate or subdigitate. 86. Axonopus

Spikelets placed with the back of the fruit turned toward the rachis of the spikelike racemes, or pedicellate in panicles; fruit not long-acuminate, at least one glume present.

First glume typically wanting; spikelets plano-convex, subsessile in spikelike racemes.   87. Paspalum

First glume present; spikelets usually in panicles.

Second glume inflated-saccate, this and the sterile lemma much exceeding the stipitate fruit.   89. Sacciolepis

Second glume not inflated-saccate.   88. Panicum.

TRIBE 12, ANDROPOGONEAE (ăn-drō-pō-gŏn′ē-ē)

Spikelets in pairs along a rachis, the usual arrangement being one of the pair sessile and fertile, the other pedicellate and staminate or neuter, or rarely wanting, only the pedicel present; **Fertile Spikelet** consisting of one perfect terminal floret and, below this, a staminate or neuter floret, the lemmas thin or hyaline, and two awnless glumes (rarely awned), one or usually both firm or indurate.

A large tribe, confined mostly to warm regions. The rachis is usually jointed, disarticulating at maturity, with the spikelets attached. In a few genera it is thickened. Sometimes the racemes are shortened to 1 or 2 joints and borne on branches, the whole forming a panicle (as in *Sorghum* and *Sorghastrum*) instead of a series of racemes. In a few genera the spikelets of the pair are alike. In *Trachypogon* the fertile spikelet is pedicellate and the sterile one nearly sessile.

SPIKELETS ALL PERFECT, SURROUNDED BY A COPIOUS TUFT OF SOFT hairs.

RACHIS CONTINUOUS, the spikelets falling; spikelets of the pair unequally pedicellate.

Racemes in a narrow spikelike panicle, spikelets awnless.   96. Imperata

Racemes in a broad fan-shaped panicle; spikelets awned.   97. Miscanthus

RACHIS BREAKING up into joints at maturity with the spikelets attached; one spikelet sessile, the other pedicellate.

Spikelets awnless.   98. Saccharum

Spikelets awned.   99. Erianthus

SPIKELETS UNLIKE, THE SESSILE PERFECT, THE PEDICELLATE sterile (sessile spikelet staminate, pedicellate spikelet perfect, in *Trachypogon*).

PEDICEL THICKENED, appressed to the thickened rachis-joint (at least parallel to it) or adnate to it; spikelets awnless, appressed to the joint.

RACHIS-joint and pedicel adnate, forming a short flat joint, this sunken in the open side of the globose first glume of the sessile spikelet; sterile spikelet conspicuous.   109. Hackelochloa

RACHIS-joint and pedicel distinct, the sessile spikelet appressed to them.

Racemes subcylindric; rachis-joints and pedicels glabrous; sterile spikelet rudimentary.

First glume lanceolate; spikelets sunken in the hollow rachis-joint.
                                                                       107. Manisuris

First glume oblong, winged; rachis-joint flattened. Our plant stoloniferous; introduced.   108. Eremochloa

Racemes flat; rachis-joints and pedicels woolly, not much thicker at the summit; sterile spikelet staminate or neuter; first glume of sessile spikelet lanceolate.   106. Elyonurus

PEDICEL NOT thickened (if slightly so the spikelets awned), neither appressed nor adnate to the rachis-joint, this usually slender; spikelets usually awned.

FERTILE spikelet with a hairy-pointed callus, formed of the attached supporting rachis-joint or pedicel; awns strong; racemes single of several-to-many joints.

Primary spikelet subsessile, sterile, persistent on the continuous axis after the fall of the fertile pedicellate spikelet, the pedicel forming the callus.
                                                                       105. Trachypogon

Primary spikelet sessile, fertile; pedicellate spikelet sterile; lower few-to-several pairs of spikelets all staminate or neuter.   104. Heteropogon

FERTILE spikelet without a callus, the rachis disarticulating immediately below the spikelet; awns slender.
Glumes muricate.
Primary branches of the panicle in whorls of 6-20 (in our species panicle elongated). 101. Vetiveria
Glumes not muricate.
Racemes of several-to-many joints, solitary, digitate or aggregate.
100. Andropogon
Racemes reduced to one or few joints, these mostly peduncled in a sub-simple or compound panicle.
Pedicellate spikelets staminate. 102. Sorghum
Pedicellate spikelet wanting; the pedicel only present.
103. Sorghastrum

TRIBE 13, TRIPSACEAE (trĭp-sā′sē-ē)

Spikelets unisexual, the staminate in pairs or sometimes in threes, 2-flowered, the pistillate usually single, 2-flowered, the lower floret sterile, imbedded in hollows of the thickened articulate axis and falling attached to the joints, or inclosed in a thickened involucre or sheath, or, in *Zea*, crowded in rows on a thickened axis (cob); **Glumes** membranaceous or thick and rigid, awnless; **Lemmas** and **Palea** hyaline, awnless. Plants monoecious.

This small tribe is scarcely more than a subtribe of *Andropogoneae*. It is also known as *Maydeae*.

STAMINATE AND pistillate spikelets in separate inflorescences, the first in a terminal tassel, the second in the axils of the leaves.
PISTILLATE spikes distinct, the spikelets imbedded in the hardened rachis, this disarticulating at maturity. 112. Euchlaena
PISTILLATE spikes grown together forming an ear, the grains at maturity much exceeding the glumes. 113. Zea
STAMINATE AND pistillate spikelets in separate portions of the same spike, the pistillate below.
SPIKES short, the 1-or-2-flowered pistillate portion inclosed in a beadlike sheathing bract. 110. Coix
SPIKES many-flowered, the pistillate portion breaking up into several 1-seeded joints; no beadlike sheathing bract. 111. Tripsacum

DESCRIPTIONS
OF THE
GENERA AND SPECIES

PHOTOGRAPHS
AND
DRAWINGS

DESCRIPTIONS OF THE GENERA AND SPECIES

I. BAMBUSEAE, THE BAMBOO TRIBE

1. ARUNDINARIA Michx. (à-rŭn-dĭ-nā′rĭ-à)

Spikelets few to many-flowered, large, compressed, the rachilla disarticulating above the glumes and between the florets; **Glumes** unequal, shorter than the lemmas, the first sometimes wanting; **Lemmas** acute or acuminate or mucronate, faintly many-nerved; **Palea** about as long as the lemma, prominently 2-keeled.

Shrubs or tall reeds, with *woody perennial* branching culms, flat blades with petioles articulate with the sheaths, and loose racemes or panicles. Species about 25, in the Tropics of both hemispheres; 2 species in the southern United States.

Our two species, *A. tecta* (Walt.) Muhl. and *A. gigantea* (Walt.) Chapm. (*A. macrosperma* Michx.), are the only native representatives of the tropical tribe *Bamboseae*, or *Bambuseae*, the bamboos. Our species are known respectively as small and large cane. Both flower infrequently. The first is rarely over 6 feet tall, with drooping blades, the inflorescence on leafless or nearly leafless shoots from the base of the plant. This is found from Maryland southward. The other species grows to a height of as much as 25 or 30 feet, and forms, in the alluvial river bottoms of the southern states, dense thickets called canebrakes. The racemes are borne on leafy branches, the species flowering less frequently than the small cane.

Stock are fond of the young plants and of the leaves and seeds, and both species furnish much forage in localities where they are abundant. The young shoots are sometimes used as a potherb. The stems or culms of the large cane are used for fishing rods, pipestems, baskets, mats, light scaffolding, and for a variety of other purposes. *Arundinaria japonica* Sieb. & Zucc. is sometimes cultivated in the southern states.

As these plants bloom infrequently their study is difficult. The writer's knowledge is necessarily limited, as he was unable to collect any plants of *A. tecta* (its location in Texas is doubtful), and having found in eastern Texas only a few patches of *A. gigantea*, two or three small plants having a few spikelets. Because of this limited knowledge the descriptions will be dispensed with. However, the artist has illustrated one of these plants, including the panicle and spikelets. There is also a photograph of a couple of culms of *A. gigantea*.

At the end of the description of the Tribe Bambuseae a key is given to three of our genera, which will enable the student to distinguish these genera. The artist has illustrated their characteristics.

Although there are several species of *Phyllostachys* in our southern states their specific identity is in doubt as they seldom bloom in cultivation. There is at least one species of this genus at several places in Brackenridge Park, San Antonio, Texas.

There is at least one species of *Bambusa*, *B. nana* Roxb., at Mercedes, Texas, which is used as a windbreak for orange groves. It is illustrated by a photograph.

In general aspect these plants look much alike. It is hoped that in the near future someone will give our plants of this tribe a more intensive study.

ARUNDINARIA GIGANTEA, Large or Giant Cane

BAMBUSA NANA

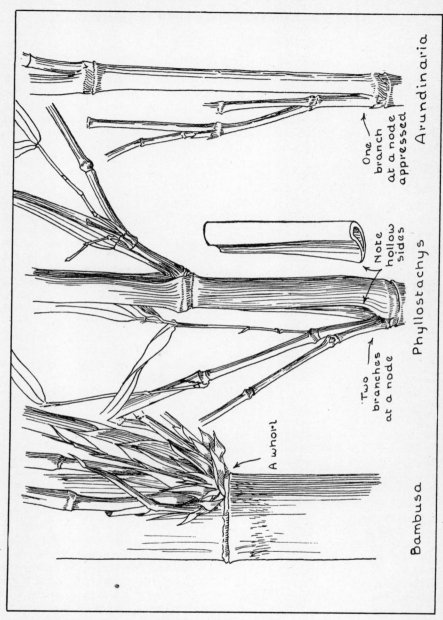

Drawings showing the distinguishing characteristics of the genera
BAMBUSA, PHYLLOSTACHYS AND ARUNDINARIA

II. FESTUCEAE, THE FESCUE TRIBE

2. BROMUS L. (brō′mŭs)
(The Brome-grasses)

Spikelets several to many-flowered, the rachilla disarticulating above the glumes and between the florets; **Glumes** unequal, acute, the first 1 to 3-nerved, the second 3-5-nerved; **Lemmas** convex on the back or keeled, 5-9-nerved, 2-toothed at the apex, awnless or usually awned from between the teeth; **Palea** usually shorter than the lemma. In this genus the grain adheres to the palea.

Annual or perennial, low or rather tall grasses, with closed sheaths, flat blades, and open or contracted panicles of large spikelets. Species about 43 in the United States, 13 in Texas.

Rescue grass or Schrader's grass, the best known bromus grass in Texas, is an annual or biennial, 1-3 feet tall, with the sheaths and blades usually conspicuously pubescent. It has a narrow erect, or in the larger plants spreading and drooping, panicle of green or purple-tinged flat spikelets often more than an inch long, the lemmas acuminate to short-awned. It is a native of South America, and is cultivated occasionally in the southern states for forage, often being the only green grass in the winter months, thereby supplying a great need. The name rescue grass is appropriate. It is plentiful in Texas, beginning to make its appearance in January of each year.

B. marginatus and *B. polyanthus,* perennials, also with flat spikelets, the former with lemmas pubescent and the latter with lemmas scabrous or smooth, are rather rare in Texas but common in California. These two species have been referred to *Bromus carinatus* Hook. & Arn.

B. ciliatus, known as a wild brome-grass, with lemmas pubescent on the margins; *B. purgans* with lemmas pubescent all over the back; *B. purgans* var. *incanus* with woolly sheaths; and *B. texensis,* with lemmas minutely scabrous; all with drooping panicles and the lower glume one-nerved, are closely related. *B. purgans* var. *incanus* has been collected on Black Mountain in west Texas, while *B. ciliatus* and *B. purgans* have a wide range. *B. texensis,* not so tall and robust as the other plants, is confined to southern Texas and Mexico. All are found growing in open woods and along the margins of thickets and woods.

B. anomalus, a mountain plant of west Texas, has closely drooping panicles with spikelets pubescent and both glumes 3-nerved.

B. secalinus, B. commutatus, B. japonicus and *B. mollis* are closely related annuals, the first two being classed by some European botanists as varieties of *B. arvensis* L.; *B. secalinus,* with glabrous sheaths and awns shorter than the lemmas, and *B. japonicus,* with pubescent sheaths and awns longer than the lemmas, are frequently found growing under similar conditions such as waste land and cultivated grain fields; *B. secalinus* was thought by the early farmers of the country to be degenerate wheat and called it "cheat" or "chess" and is sometimes grown in the northwest for hay; *B. mollis* has an erect compact panicle of short turgid pubescent spikelets.

B. rigidus, another annual called ripgut, is one of the most vicious of the grasses. The ripe florets, sharp-pointed at the base, get into the mouths and noses of stock and the scabrous awns then work into the flesh. The first collection of this species in Texas was made in 1933 at Marshall by the author. It should be exterminated promptly wherever found. It is common in Arizona and on the Pacific Slope.

B. *inermis,* awnless brome-grass, with an erect panicle and creeping rhizomes, is cultivated for hay in the northern portion of the Great Plains. While it is a well-known grass, it is not likely to be found in Texas.

SPIKELETS STRONGLY COMPRESSED-KEELED.
  SHEATHS AND BLADES commonly conspicuously pubescent, especially the lower ones (except in *B. polyanthus*).
    ANNUAL or biennial: panicles erect or drooping; lemmas and glumes glabrous, several-nerved, the awn of the lemma less than 1 mm. long or wanting.   1. B. catharticus
    PERENNIAL: panicles erect or nodding, narrow, lower glume 3-5-nerved, the upper 5-9-nerved; awn of the lemma 4-8 mm. long.
      Blades pubescent, at least the lower.   2. B. marginatus
      Blades glabrous, or merely scabrous.   3. B. polyanthus
  SPIKELETS NOT STRONGLY COMPRESSED-KEELED, more or less rounded, at least at the base.
    PLANTS PERENNIAL: panicles usually drooping; awn 2-8 mm. long or wanting in *B. inermis.*
      LOWER glume 1-nerved, the upper 3-nerved (or the first sometimes 3-nerved in *B. texensis*).
        Glumes glabrous or merely scabrous on the nerves.
          Sheaths glabrous or nearly so.
            Lemma pubescent at or near the margins only.   4. B. ciliatus
            Lemma glabrous, awnless or short-awned.   5. B. inermis
          Sheaths and nodes pubescent; lemmas scabrous.   6. B. texensis
          Sheaths densely pubescent; lemmas evenly pubescent all over the back.   7a. B. anomalus var. lanatipes
        Glumes pubescent; lemmas evenly pubescent over the back.
          Sheaths usually sparsely pubescent.   8. B. purgans
          Sheaths densely woolly.   8a. B. purgans var. incanus
      BOTH glumes 3-nerved, lemmas and glumes densely pubescent; sheaths pubescent or glabrous.   7. B. anomalus
    PLANTS ANNUAL.
      LOWER glume 3-nerved, the upper 5-9-nerved.
        Awn commonly shorter than the lemma; straight.
          Panicle erect, narrow, compact, 1-3' long; lemmas and glumes with soft appressed hairs, not dense.   9. B. mollis
          Panicle erect or finally drooping; glumes and lemmas glabrous, or very sparsely pubescent; sheaths commonly glabrous.   10. B. secalinus
        Awn commonly fully as long as or longer than the lemmas; panicle erect or finally drooping; glumes and lemmas glabrous, or very sparsely pubescent; sheaths commonly pubescent.
          Awn divergent at maturity.   11. B. japonicus
          Awn straight.   12. B. commutatus
      LOWER glume 1-nerved, the upper 3-5-nerved; lemmas about 22 mm. long, awn longer than the lemma and from between a bifid apex, the teeth 4-6 mm. long.   13. B. rigidus

1. B. CATHARTICUS Vahl (kȧ-thär′tĭ-kŭs); *B. unioloides* H. B. K.; RESCUE-GRASS OR SCHRADER'S GRASS.

Culms commonly 1-3 feet tall, tufted, erect or spreading, sometimes decumbent at the base, the smaller and younger plants usually conspicuously pubescent or pilose, the older ones often glabrous or nearly so; **Blades** 3-16′ long, 2-12 mm. wide, usually somewhat rough, especially on the upper surface, from pilose to pubescent, or sometimes glabrous; **Sheaths** shorter than the internodes, flattened, smooth to rough, pilose to pubescent, rarely glabrous; **Ligule** 2-5 mm. long, membranaceous, somewhat pubescent; **Panicle** narrow to pyramidal, erect or nodding, 2-15′ long, with few to many spikelets, the branches erect or spreading, those of the larger plants usually diffusely spreading, as much as 7′ long, with

2-5 spikelets at the extremities of each branch,, the main axis and pedicels scabrous; **Spikelets** green, sometimes tinged with purple, flattened, 5-11-flowered, 20-35 mm. long; **Glumes** subequal, 10-12 mm. long, acute, 7-9-nerved; **Lemmas** including the short awn 12-18 mm. long, two-toothed, acute, minutely scabrous, 7-11-nerved, merely acuminate or with an awn usually less than 1 mm. long; **Palea** usually more than two-thirds as long as its lemma, two-toothed; **Grain** 3-6 mm. long, oblong, grooved on one side. Texas to Florida, Colorado and California. February to August.

2. B. MARGINATUS Nees (mär-jĭ-nā'tŭs).

Culms 1-4 feet tall, simple, smooth or rough; **Blades** 6-13′ long, 4-9 mm. wide, flat, rough, pubescent especially the lower sometimes sparsely so; **Sheaths** the upper shorter than the internodes, at least the lower pubescent, the upper often only sparsely so; **Ligule** truncate, about 2 mm. long; **Panicles** large and open, sometimes reduced to a raceme, exserted, 5-12′ long, loosely and few-flowered, the branches spreading or drooping but not deflexed, the lower distant, 2-6′ long, slender with only a few spikelets to each branch, the spikelets on pedicels usually less than the length of the spikelet; **Spikelets** 7-11-flowered, 25-35 mm. long, lanceolate; **Glumes** 7-10 mm. long, acute, pubescent at least when young, or scabrous-puberulent, especially on the midnerves, the first 3-nerved (3-5), and the second slightly longer and broader, 5-7-nerved (5-9); **Lemmas** 11-13 mm. long, compressed-keeled above, acute, 7-nerved, usually pubescent, bearing a straight awn 4-7 mm. long; **Palea** about three-fourths as long as its lemma, hispid-ciliate.

Open woods and open ground, western Texas, northern Mexico, extending to Colorado, common on the Pacific Slope.

3. B. POLYANTHUS Scribn. (pŏl-ĭ-ăn'thŭs).

A stout perennial as much as 40′ tall, similar to *B. marginatus,* but differing in the glabrous sheaths, scabrous blades, erect or somewhat spreading panicle, and smooth or somewhat scabrous lemmas, the awn 4-6 mm. long. (See drawings of *B. marginatus.*)

Texas to Arizona, north to Colorado and Montana and west to Washington.

4. B. CILIATUS L. (sĭl-ĭ-ā'tŭs); WILD BROME-GRASS, FRINGED BROME-GRASS, OR SWAMP-CHESS.

Culms 2-4 feet tall, rather stout, erect, simple, glabrous to pubescent at the nodes; **Blades** 5-12′ long, 4-12 mm. wide, flat, often rough especially on the upper surface, glabrous or usually pubescent on the upper surface; **Sheaths** usually shorter than the internodes, smooth to rough, often pubescent, the lower sometimes sparsely hirsute; **Ligule** very short; **Panicle** exserted 4-12′ long, nodding, the slender rough branches widely spreading and usually drooping, the lower 2-5′ long; **Spikelets** 5-11-flowered, about 25 mm. long, somewhat terete; **Glumes** unequal, about two-thirds as long as the adjacent florets, acute, scabrous on the keels, the first 1-nerved, the second 3-nerved; **Lemmas** 8-12 mm. long, obtuse to acute, pubescent at or near the margin, especially below, 5-7-nerved, bearing an awn 3-8 mm. long from between the bifid apex; **Palea** slightly shorter than its lemma.

In woods and thickets, Texas, Minnesota to New York. Spring-summer.

5. B. INERMIS Leyss. (ĭn-ĕr'mĭs) ; AWNLESS BROME-GRASS, HUNGARIAN BROME-GRASS. *Has not been collected in Texas.*

Culms 2.5-3.5 feet tall, tufted, erect, rather stout, from creeping rhizomes; **Blades** 5-10' long, 4-6 mm. wide, flat; **Sheaths** mostly shorter than the internodes; **Ligule** membranaceous, about 1 mm. long; **Panicle** 4-10' long, exserted, erect, ovate to oblong, the axis scabrous above, the comparatively short branches erect or slightly spreading, several to a whorl, the lower distant; **Spikelets** purplish, erect, 10-30 mm. long, about 5 mm. wide, oblong, nearly terete; **Glumes** acute, 6-8 mm. long, the first 1-nerved, the second 1-2 mm. longer and 3-nerved; **Lemmas** 10-12 mm. long, obtuse, entire or emarginate, 5-7-nerved, typically glabrous, or slightly scabrous on some of the nerves, especially on the midnerve toward the apex, awnless, or rarely awn-pointed; **Palea** nearly as long as the lemma, ciliate. (See photograph of *Bromus anomalus* for drawings.)

In cultivation, or escaped in waste places and fields, mainly from northern Kansas to Minnesota and Montana, and to Colorado. Summer.

6. B. TEXENSIS (Shear) Hitchc. (tĕks-ĕn'sĭs) ; *B. purgans* var. *texensis* Shear.

Culms commonly 2-3 feet tall, tufted, rather slender, leafy, pubescent to puberulent, including the nodes; **Blades** 4-15' long, 2-10 mm. wide, flat, flaccid, soft, tapering toward the base, pubescent or puberulent; **Sheaths** shorter than the internodes, pubescent with the hairs mostly pointing downward; **Ligule** membranaceous, about 3 mm. long, edges fringed, pubescent or puberulent; **Panicle** usually exserted, 3-6' long, erect or nodding, loose and open, rather lax, the branches mostly in ones and twos, the lower as much as 4' long, 5-20 spikelets to a panicle, the pedicels short; **Spikelets** 7-10-flowered, 20-30 mm. long, terete-lanceolate when young, somewhat flattened and oblong or wedge-shaped when old; **Glumes** scabrous on the keel, acute, the first narrow, lanceolate, 5-7 mm. long, 1-nerved, or sometimes 2-3-nerved on the same panicle, the second broader, 7-9 mm. long, 3-nerved, sometimes mucronate; **Lemmas** about 10 mm. long, elliptic, 7-nerved, three strong nerves and the others obscure, minutely scabrous, with a scabrous awn 4-8 mm. long; **Palea** as long, shorter or longer than its lemma, two-toothed.

Texas and northeastern Mexico. (San Antonio, Texas.) Spring.

7. B. ANOMALUS Rupr. (à-nŏm'à-lŭs) ; *B. porteri* (Coult.) Nash.

Culms 18-36' tall, in small or medium sized tufts, erect, glabrous to pubescent, the nodes from slightly to densely pubescent; **Blades** 4-8' (3-12) long, 3-7 mm. wide, the basal narrow and longer, flat, rough; **Sheaths** shorter than the internodes, from glabrous to short pubescent, sometimes pilose or densely pubescent, the hairs often pointing downward; **Ligule** membranaceous, 1-2 mm. long, truncate; **Panicle** drooping, 3-6' long, the axis pubescent, the branches flexuous and drooping, pubescent, commonly two branches at each of the 3-5 nodes, about 1.5' distant, or less, the lateral flexuous pedicels much shorter than the spikelets; **Spikelets** 6-11-flowered, 16-32 mm. long, nearly terete; **Glumes** densely pubescent, both 3-nerved; **Lemmas** 11-13 mm. long, with three strong nerves and four faint ones, densely pubescent with long silky hairs, awns 2-4 mm. long, from a slightly emarginate apex. The pubescence on culms, including nodes and sheaths, is very variable.

Open hillsides or open woods, mountains of west Texas to Colorado.

7a. B. ANOMALUS var. LANATIPES (Shear) Hitchc. (lā-năt'ĭ-pēz);
B. porteri lanatipes Shear.

Similar to the species but more robust and with woolly sheaths, the blades broader. Western Texas to Arizona and Colorado.

8. B. PURGANS L. (pûr'găns); HAIRY WOOD-CHESS.

Culms 2-5, commonly 3-4 feet tall, erect or spreading, slightly rough, nodes and internodes more or less pubescent; **Blades** 5-17' long, 4-19 mm. wide, flat, narrowed toward both ends, rough or smooth below, glabrous or sometimes short-pilose on one or both surfaces; **Sheaths** shorter than the internodes, pubescent and often sparsely papillose, the lower retrorse pilose, the hairs short and rather stiff; **Ligule** membranaceous, 1-2 mm. long; **Panicle** exserted, open, 6-15' long, finally nodding, the axis scabrous toward the tip, branches commonly 2-3 at a node, lower distant as much as 3', upper gradually shorter, scabrous, capillary, the lower as much as 8' long, naked below, with one to each drooping branch; **Spikelets** 4-7-flowered (4-11), exclusive of the awns 18-25 mm. long, 3-4 mm. wide, almost terete, the pedicels 8-20 mm. long; **Glumes** sparsely pubescent, the first 1-nerved, about 6 mm. long, narrow, acute, the second 9-10 mm. long, broader, 3-nerved, abruptly acute, with short awns; **Lemmas** 11-12 mm. long, lanceolate, elliptic, acute, 5-7-nerved, very pubescent all over the back, the scabrous awn 4-7 mm. long; **Rachilla** about 3 mm. long, pubescent; **Palea** 8-9 mm. long, about 2 mm. shorter than its lemma, oblong, ciliate. (See photograph of *B. texensis* for drawings.)

In woods and borders of woods, Texas to Florida, north to New England and Wyoming. Summer.

8a. B. PURGANS var. INCANUS Shear (ĭn-kā'nŭs); *B. incanus* (Shear) Hitchc.

This variety is *similar to the species* except the blades are scarcely as wide and the sheaths densely woolly. The palea is as long as or slightly longer than the lemma. (See photograph of *B. texensis*.)

Woods, North Dakota, Penna., Delaware, Maryland, New Jersey, western Texas to Colorado. (Fowlkes Ranch, Black Mountains.)

9. B. MOLLIS L. (mŏl'ĭs) (has been referred to *B. hordeaceous* L. which is a European species not known in America); SOFT CHESS, HAIRY CHEAT.

Culms 10-30' tall, erect, rather slender, sparsely pilose, especially the nodes, or the upper internodes glabrous, the hairs usually pointing downward, the whole plant softly pubescent throughout; **Blades** 1-6' long, 2-6 mm. wide, flat, pilose to pubescent; **Sheaths** shorter than the internodes, usually more or less pilose; **Ligule** membranaceous, about 1 mm. long; **Panicle** exserted, 1.5-3.5' long, oblong to ovate-oblong, somewhat contracted, dense, usually 12-25 mm. wide, the branches commonly erect or slightly ascending; **Spikelets** 5-11-flowered, 12-17 mm. long, 4-6 mm. wide, lanceolate, the lateral pedicels from 1 to 5 mm. long, pilose; **Glumes** subequal, about 6 mm. long, acute, sparsely pubescent, the hairs appressed or ascending, the first narrow, 3-5-nerved, the second broader, slightly longer, sometimes awn-pointed, 5-7-nerved; **Lemmas** 6-9 mm. long, obtuse, 7-9-nerved, more or less pubescent, the hairs mostly appressed, bearing a straight scabrous awn 5-8 mm. long between the acute or obtuse teeth; **Palea** somewhat shorter than its lemma, prominently ciliate-hispid.

In fields and waste places, Texas, North Carolina, California, Nova Scotia to British Columbia. Late spring and summer.

10. B. SECALINUS L. (sĕk-à-lī′nŭs) ; CHEAT OR CHESS.

Culms 18-36′ tall, erect, simple, rather rigid, glabrous or the swollen nodes hispidulous; **Blades** 2.5-9′ long, 2-7 mm. wide, strongly nerved, flat, smooth or rough; often puberulent or pubescent on the upper surface; **Sheaths** about as long as the internodes, strongly nerved, glabrous or the lower puberulent; **Ligule** membranaceous, 1-2.5 mm. long, toothed or erose; **Panicles** exserted, 3-10′ long, at first erect and rather narrow, finally the branches somewhat spreading and drooping, especially so in the larger plants, the branches usually in whorls of 4-6, one long and the other short, commonly 1-3′ long, rarely 6′, the shorter bearing one spikelet and the longer 3-4 spikelets at their extremities; **Spikelets** 5-10-flowered, (5-15) 10-18 mm. long, 4-7 mm. broad, somewhat flattened, erect or slightly drooping, the glumes and lemmas scarious along the margins; **Glumes** minutely scabrous toward the apex, the first 4-5 mm. long, acute, 3-nerved, the second broader, obtuse, 5-6 mm. long, 7-nerved; **Lemmas** 6-8 mm. long, broad, turgid, emarginate or toothed, obtuse, somewhat rough toward the apex, 7-nerved, becoming at maturity convex with its margins inrolled, the nerves obscure, bearing a straight or finally spreading scabrous awn below the obtuse or emarginate apex, the awn mostly 3-6 mm. long, rarely 10 mm. long; **Palea** about as long as its lemma, ciliate-hispid.

In fields and waste places, almost throughout the United States. (Bellville, Texas.) Spring-summer.

11. B. JAPONICUS Thunb. (jā-pŏn′ĭ-kŭs) ; *B. patulus* M. & K. ; SPREADING BROME-GRASS.

Culms 1-2.5 feet tall, erect or spreading, rather weak, geniculate at the base, the swollen brown nodes glabrous or pubescent, usually growing in colonies; **Blades** 3-8′ long, 3-7 mm. wide, flat, harshly puberulent to densely pubescent, or often velvety, the grayish hairs often conspicuous; **Sheaths** about as long as or sometimes shorter or longer than the internodes, commonly densely pubescent, often conspicuously so, the hairs mostly reflexed; **Ligule** membranaceous, about 2 mm. long, erose; **Panicle** exserted, soon nodding, 6-12′ long, the axis and branches scabrous toward their extremities, the capillary branches ascending or spreading, or finally pendulous, mostly in half whorls of 2-6, the lower whorls 2-3′ distant, short branches intermixed with long ones, with 1-5 spikelets at their extremities, the scabrous capillary pedicels half as long as to longer than the spikelet; **Spikelets** 7-13-flowered, exclusive of the awns 18-26 mm. long, about 4-5 mm. wide, somewhat flattened, almost oblong, the nerves evident, glumes and lemmas often minutely and sparsely pubescent and papillose especially along the nerves; **Glumes** unequal, the first about 5 mm. long, acute, 3-5-nerved, the second broader, about 7 mm. long, obtuse, often emarginate, 5-9-nerved, both slightly scabrous especially toward the apex; **Lemmas** 7-9 mm. long, 9-nerved, wider above the base, scarious on the margins, emarginate or two-toothed, obtuse, bearing a scabrous awn from about 1.5 mm. below the apex, 5-13 mm. long, finally divaricately spreading at maturity, there being sometimes at the base of the lemma a tuft of kinky brown hairs; **Palea** about four-fifths as long as its lemma, obtuse, hispid-ciliate on the keels.

Low places among small trees. Texas, Colorado, Massachusetts.

12. B. COMMUTATUS Schrad. (kŏm-ū-tā′tŭs).

Culms 1-3.5 feet tall, tufted, erect or decumbent at the base, slender to stout, the sheaths and blades strongly nerved; **Blades** 2-9′ long, 2-7 mm. wide, flat, slightly rough, from sparsely to almost densely short-pubescent; **Sheaths** shorter than the internodes, sparsely to almost densely short-pubescent, the hairs usually retrorsely pilose, not so pubescent as in *B. japonicus;* **Ligule** membranaceous, about 2 mm. long; **Panicles** 4-7′ long, usually not over 1.5′ wide, finally drooping, the branches usually ascending, rather short, with 1-3 spikelets on pedicels commonly about as long as the spikelets, in aspect the panicle resembling that of *B. secalinus;* **Spikelets** 6-10-flowered, 13-25 mm. long, commonly about 6-7 mm. wide, somewhat flattened, the lemmas thinner, not inrolled at the margin, and the florets more closely imbricate so that in side view no openings are seen as in *B. secalinus;* **Glumes** subequal, the first narrow, acute, 3-nerved, about 5-6 mm. long, the second broader, subacute, 7-9-nerved, 7-8 mm. long; **Lemmas** less plump and more overlapping than in *B. secalinus,* 7-10 mm. long, thin, with broad, scarious puberulent margins widened about one-third the distance from the apex, acute, 7-9-nerved, minutely scabrous, the straight awn commonly 7-9 mm., rarely 13 mm. long; **Palea** nearly as long as its lemma, ciliate on the keels. (Illustrated with photographs of *B. secalinus.*)

In waste places, Texas, and perhaps here and there over much of the United States. (Palestine, Texas.) Summer.

13. B. RIGIDUS Roth (rĭj′ĭ-dŭs); RIPGUT.

Culms 1-2.5 feet tall, tufted, erect or spreading, often slightly decumbent at the very base, harshly puberulent below the panicle; **Blades** mostly 4-6′ long, 3-6 mm. wide, flat, sparsely short-hirsute, especially toward the base, somewhat rough; **Sheaths** the upper shorter than the internodes, the lower longer than the short internodes, usually sparsely short-hirsute, somewhat rough; **Ligule** membranaceous, 3-4 mm. long; **Panicle** with pale purplish tinge, loose, finally exserted and drooping, 4-8′ long, the axis and branches harshly short-pubescent, the branches in whorls of about 6, distant 1-2′, with 1-3 spikelets, often only 1, at the end of the flexuous branches; **Spikelets** 5-8-flowered, exclusive of the awns 1-1.5′ long, loosely-flowered, the rachilla 4-5 mm. long; **Glumes** acuminate, long-pointed or awned, hyaline-margined, 15-30 mm. long, the first about two-thirds as long as the second, 1-nerved, rarely 3-nerved at the very base, the second 3-5-nerved; **Lemmas** exclusive of the awn 15-27 mm. long, narrowed toward the indurate base, scabrous, 5-7-nerved, with a stout scabrous awn, mostly 20-45 mm. long from a bifid apex, the teeth 4-6 mm. long, margins hyaline; **Palea** nearly two-thirds as long as the lemma, hispid-ciliate.

Open ground, British Columbia to Idaho, south to southern California and Arizona. Also once in Texas, Virginia, Maryland. (Sandy land, Marshall, Texas.) Spring.

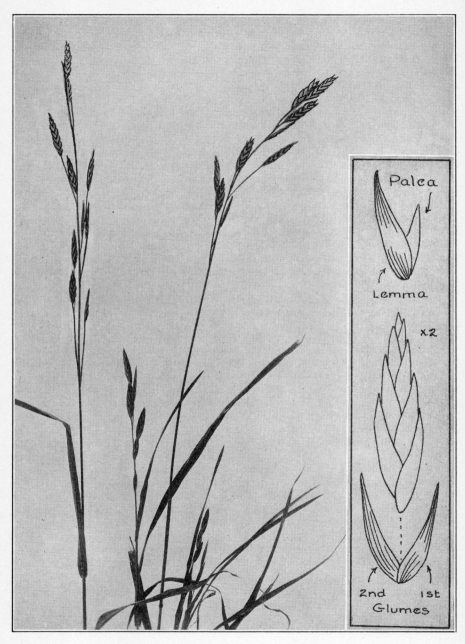

BROMUS CATHARTICUS, Rescue-grass

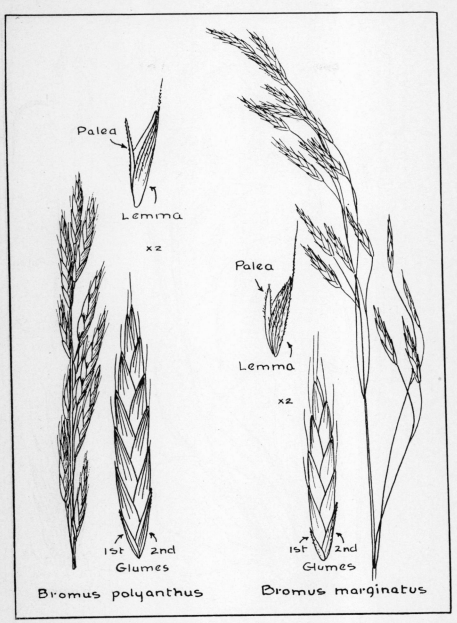

Palea

Lemma

x2

Palea

Lemma

x2

1st 2nd
Glumes

1st 2nd
Glumes

Bromus polyanthus

Bromus marginatus

BROMUS MARGINATUS AND B. POLYANTHUS

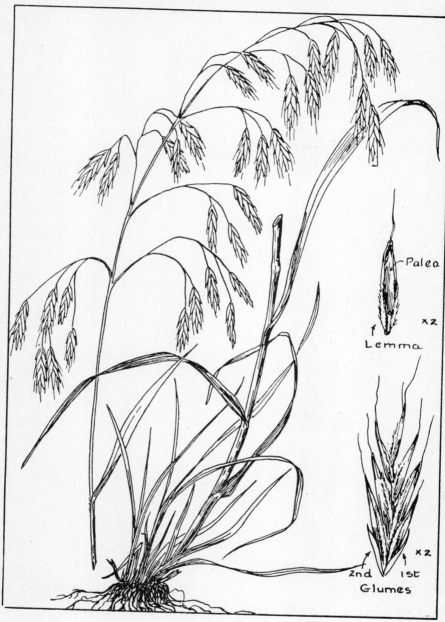

Palea

Lemma

×2

2nd   1st
Glumes

×2

BROMUS CILIATUS, WILD BROME-GRASS

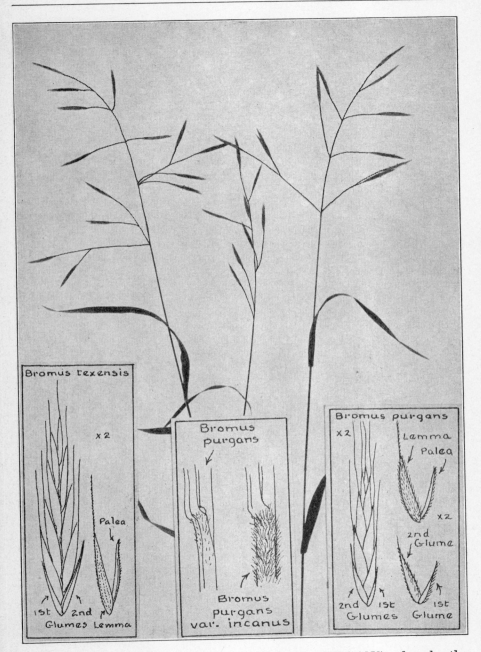

Bromus texensis

x 2

Palea

1st 2nd
Glumes Lemma

Bromus
purgans

Bromus
purgans
var. incanus

Bromus purgans

x2

Lemma
Palea

x2

2nd
Glume

2nd 1st
Glumes Glume

1st
Glume

BROMUS TEXENSIS; drawings of BROMUS PURGANS; also sheaths
of BROMUS PURGANS AND BROMUS PURGANS VAR. INCANUS.

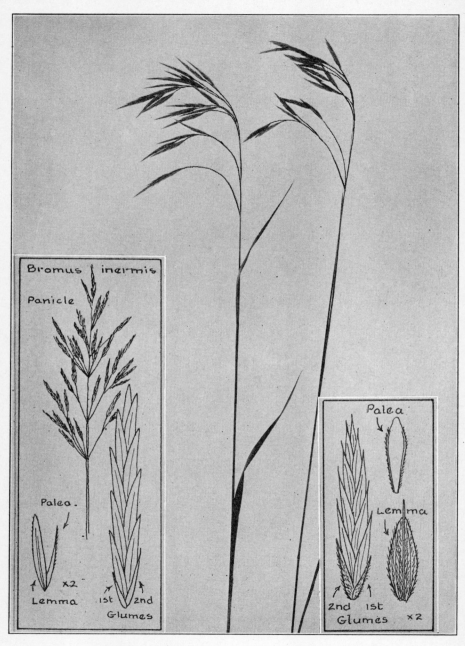

BROMUS ANOMALUS; BROMUS INERMIS

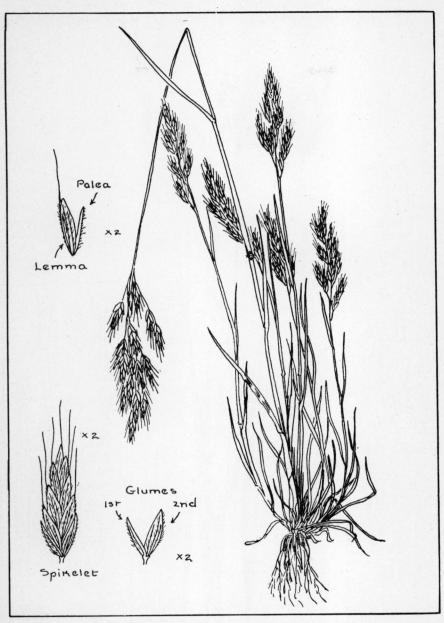

BROMUS MOLLIS, Soft or Hairy Chess

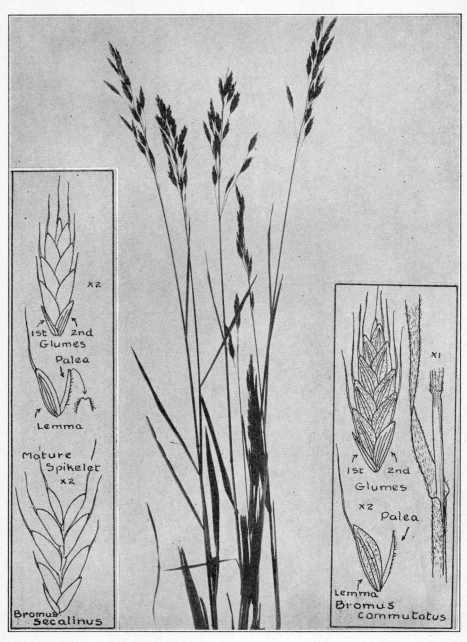

BROMUS SECALINUS, CHEAT OR CHESS; drawings of B. SECALINUS
AND B. COMMUTATUS

BROMUS JAPONICUS

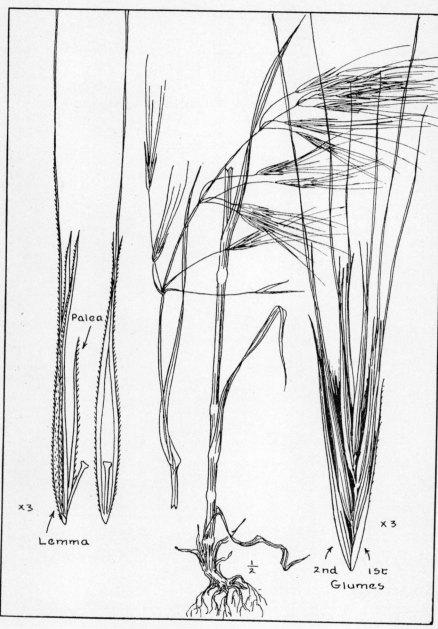

BROMUS RIGIDUS, Ripgut

3. FESTUCA L. (fĕs-tū'kà)
(The Fescue Grasses)

Spikelets few to several-flowered, the rachilla disarticulating above the glumes and between the florets; **Glumes** narrow, acute, unequal, the first sometimes very small; **Lemmas** rounded on the back, membranaceous or somewhat indurate, 5-nerved, the nerves often obscure, acute or rarely obtuse, awned from the tip or rarely from a minutely bifid apex.

Annual or perennial low or rather tall grasses of varied habit, the spikelets in narrow or open panicles. Species about 40 in the United States, 8 in Texas.

Slender fescue and southern fescue are the most important of the Texas annuals, both having slender panicles and awned lemmas, the former with a wide range, grows in dry sterile soil, the latter confined to the southern states, thrives in very sandy soil. *F. megalura* with ciliate lemmas and *F. myuros* with lemmas not ciliate are rare in Texas.

The Texas perennials: *F. versuta*, with a very open panicle and mucronate or short-awned lemmas; *F. obtusa* and *F. shortii* with open but rather narrow panicles of awnless spikelets, the former with a loosely flowered panicle, the branches spikelet-bearing at the end, and the latter with a more compact panicle, the branches spikelet-bearing usually below the middle; and *F. ligulata*, a west Texas grass, with a narrow panicle and awnless spikelets 2-3-flowered.

PANICLES NARROW, THE BRANCHES USUALLY ERECT, RARELY
SPREADING; stamens usually 1.
  PLANTS ANNUAL.
    BLADES flat or involute.
      Lemmas ciliate on the upper half.   1. F. megalura
      Lemmas not ciliate.   2. F. myuros
    BLADES involute or folded, less than 2 mm. wide.
      Awn shorter than the lemma; both glumes subulate; spikelets 5-13-flowered.
        Lemmas smooth or scabrous.   3. F. octoflora
        Lemmas hirtellus.   3a. F. octoflora var. hirtella
      Awn much longer than the lemma; spikelets 3-6-flowered; first glume more
        than half as long as the second; lemmas appressed-pubescent.
                                      4. F. sciurea
  PLANTS PERENNIAL; blades 1-2 mm. wide; lemmas awnless, 4 mm. long;
  ligule 2-4 mm. long.   5. F. ligulata
PANICLES MORE OPEN, THE BRANCHES FINALLY SPREADING; blades
flat, over 3 mm. wide; stamens usually 3; PERENNIALS.
  LEMMAS AWNLESS, about 4 mm. long; spikelet 4-6 mm. long.
    PANICLE loose, the elongated branches spikelet-bearing at their ends; spike-
      lets lanceolate, lemmas acute.   6. F. obtusa
    PANICLE more compact, the shorter branches spikelet-bearing at or below
      the middle; spikelets obovate, lemmas obtuse.   7. F. shortii
  LEMMAS MUCRONATE, 5-6.5 mm. long; spikelets 8-11 mm. long.
                                        8. F. versuta

1. F. MEGALURA Nutt. (mĕg-à-lū'rà).

Culms 1-2 feet tall, tufted, scabrous below the panicle, a pale green plant; **Blades** 2.5-4' long, 1.5 mm. wide or less, flat or involute; **Sheaths** shorter than the internodes, one margin at the summit wide and scarious; **Ligule** membranaceous, less than 0.5 mm. long; **Panicle** elongated, 2-8' long, narrow, often included at the base, green or tinged with purple, the axis triangular, scabrous on the margins, the branches erect and nearly appressed, commonly less than 1.5' long, the spikelets on short scabrous pedicels, appressed; **Spikelets** 4-6-flowered, 6.5-10 mm. long, narrow; **Glumes,** the first minute, less than 0.5 mm. (1.5-2 mm.) long, acute, subulate, the second 2-4 mm. long, acuminate, scabrous; **Lemmas,** the lower 4-6 mm. long, the upper shorter, narrow, obscurely 5-nerved, minutely scabrous and ciliate-hispid on the upper half, the cilia may be obscured by the inrolling of the lemma, with a straight scabrous awn 8-13 mm. long; **Palea** about two-thirds as long as its lemma, acute, ciliate; **Rachilla** scabrous and lengthened above the first or lower floret. (Illustrated on photograph of *F. octoflora*.)

Open dry soil, Texas, Arizona, California and Mexico. (Taylor, Texas, doubtless introduced in seed from the West.) Spring.

2. F. MYUROS L. (mī-ū'rŏs).

Differs from *F. megalura* chiefly in the absence of cilia on the upper portion of the lemma; **Panicle** usually smaller, and the first glume much shorter than the second, usually 1-2 mm. long. (See drawings of spikelets on photograph of *F. octoflora*.)

Open ground, coastal plain, Texas to Mississippi, Ohio, Pacific Coast.

3. F. OCTOFLORA Walt. (ŏk-tō-flō'rȧ); (Includes *F. parviflora* Ell.); SLENDER FESCUE.

Culms 2-16' usually about 7' tall, tufted, erect, rigid, slender, simple; **Blades** 1-3' long, less than 2 mm. wide, usually involute, bristle-pointed, soft, erect or ascending; **Sheaths** shorter than the internodes, loose; **Ligule** membranaceous, short; **Panicle** narrow, erect, 1-6' long, often one-sided, its short branches erect or ascending; **Spikelets** 3-13-flowered, 5-10 mm. long; **Glumes** subulate, acute, the first more than half as long as the second, about 2.5 mm. long, 1-nerved, the second about 4 mm. long, 3-nerved; **Lemmas** more or less divergent, about 3.5-5 mm. long, acuminate, involute, smooth or minutely scabrous toward the apex, the awns usually shorter than the body of the lemma, sometimes awnless or awn-pointed, the five nerves somewhat obscure; **Palea** nearly as long as its lemma. The anthers and stigmas remain within the floret at the time of the flowering, but at maturity of the grain you may see the tiny anthers at the summit of the grain. This species and a few others of this genus are said to be *cleistogamous*.

Dry or sterile soil, over most of the United States, extending north to Canada. Spring and summer.

3a. F. OCTOFLORA var. HIRTELLA Piper (hĕr-tĕl'ȧ).

This variety differs from the species in that the lemmas are minutely hirsute (hirtellus). Its range is given as the southwestern United States and Lower California in Mexico, probably in Texas.

4. F. SCIUREA Nutt. (sī-ū-rē'ȧ); SOUTHERN FESCUE-GRASS.

Culms 5-22' commonly about 12' tall, erect or spreading, solitary or a few culms to a tuft, slender, weak; **Blades** 1-3' long, commonly less than 2', less than 1 mm. wide, involute, often several very fine ones at the base; **Sheaths** shorter than or as long as the internodes; **Ligule** membranaceous, about 1 mm. long, irregularly truncate, decurrent along the margins of the sheath, wider than the blade; **Panicle** 1.5-10' long, erect or slightly nodding, slender, the slender branches appressed, usually 1' long and 1-3 short branches at each node, the lower distant, 3-4' long and naked at the base on the larger plants, the short pediceled spikelets crowded on the short-appressed branchlets; **Spikelets** 3-6 flowered, exclusive of the awns 4-4.5 mm. long; **Glumes** acuminate, the first about 2 mm. long, 1-nerved, the second about 3 mm. long, broader, 3-nerved; **Lemmas**

3-3.5 mm. long, upper shorter, narrow, involute, appressed-hirsute, the scabrous awns 2-3 times as long as the body of the lemmas; **Palea** about as long as the lemma; **Grain** about as long as the palea, oblong. The anthers and stigmas remain within the floret at the time of flowering, but at maturity of the grain you may see the tiny anthers at the summit of the seed. This species and a few other annuals of this genus are said to be *cleistogamous*.

Open woods, usually in very sandy soil, Texas to Florida, north to Virginia and Oklahoma. (Sutherland Springs, Texas.) Spring-summer.

5. F. LIGULATA Swallen (lĭg-ū-lā'tá).

Culms 18-26' tall, loosely tufted, slender, erect from a decumbent, often rhizome-like base, scabrous below the panicle, otherwise glabrous or nearly so; **Blades** 2.5-8' long, or those of the innovations as much as 12' long, 1-2 mm. wide, rather firm, scabrous on both surfaces, strongly nerved above; **Sheaths** minutely scabrous or smooth; **Ligule** membranaceous, hyaline, 3-3.5 mm. long; **Panicles** 2.5-4' long, the axis scabrous, the one or two branches stiffly ascending or spreading, few-flowered, naked below, scabrous; **Spikelets** 2-3-flowered, 6 mm. long, appressed to the branches; **Glumes** acute or subobtuse, scabrous especially on the mid-nerve, the first 3.5 mm. long, 1-nerved, the second 4 mm. long, 3-nerved; **Lemmas** 4 mm. long, awnless, acute or obtuse, scabrous, obscurely nerved; **Palea** equaling or exceeding slightly the lemma.

Moist shady slopes along creek, upper McKittrick Canyon, Guadalupe mountains, Culberson county, Texas; altitude about 6600 feet. Summer.

6. F. OBTUSA Spreng. (ŏb-tū'sá); *F. nutans* Willd.; NODDING FESCUE-GRASS.

Culms 1-3.5 feet tall, few to a tuft or solitary, erect, simple, a rather slender dark green plant; **Blades** 4-13' long, 4-7 mm. wide, flat, rough on the upper surface; **Sheaths** much shorter than the internodes, glabrous to sparsely pubescent; **Ligule** very short; **Panicle** exserted, loose, 4-10' long, finally nodding, the capillary scabrous branches mostly in pairs, few and distant, finally spreading, the lower as much as 5' long, the spikelets more or less secund, loosely scattered mostly towards the end of the branches, the capillary scabrous pedicels commonly 3-8 mm. long, ascending; **Spikelets** 3-5-flowered, 4-6 mm. long, lanceolate; **Glumes** firm, acute, scabrous on the keel, the first 1-nerved, 2.5-3 mm. long, the second 3-nerved, 3.5-4 mm. long; **Lemmas** oblong, 3.5-4 mm. long, subacute, obscurely nerved.

Rocky woods, Texas to Florida, north to Minnesota. Spring-summer.

7. F. SHORTII Kunth (shŏrt'ĭ-ī); NODDING FESCUE-GRASS.

Culms 2-4 feet tall, solitary or a few culms to a tuft, erect, simple; **Blades** 5-10' long, 2-6 mm. wide, flat, rough to smooth; **Sheaths** much shorter than the internodes, glabrous to sparsely short pubescent; **Panicle** 3-7' long, more compact than *F. obtusa*, spikelets somewhat aggregate but few, erect, or slightly nodding, the scabrous branches finally ascending or spreading, mostly in pairs, the lower as much as 3.5' long, densely flowered on the upper two-thirds or towards the ends, the scabrous pedicels 1-4 mm. long; **Spikelets** 3-6-flowered, 5-6 mm. long, obovate at maturity; **Glumes** unequal, firm, acute, scabrous, especially on the nerves, 2.5-3.5 mm. long, the first 1-3-nerved, and the second 3-nerved and longer; **Lemmas** 3.5-4 mm. long, obtuse or subobtuse, obscurely nerved.

In woods and thickets or open ground, Texas to Georgia, north to Pennsylvania and Iowa.   Spring-summer.

8. F. VERSUTA Beal (vĕr-sū'tà) ; *F. texana* Vasey.

Culms 2-4.5 feet tall, tufted, erect, rather stout; **Blades** 5-15' long, 5-9 mm. wide, those of the shoots as much as 20', flat, narrowed at both ends, long acuminate, rough, especially on the upper surface; **Sheaths** shorter than the internodes; **Ligule** a membranaceous or callus ring, very short; **Panicle** exserted, 5-10' long, open, pyramidal, slightly nodding, the upper part of the axis scabrous, the branches single or mostly in twos, the lower 2.5-6' long, somewhat distant, ascending to spreading, naked below, a few short branchlets near the end, commonly 1-4 spikelets, rarely a dozen to each branch; **Spikelets** 4-6-flowered, 8-11 mm. long, ovate, glaucous-green, the scabrous pedicels usually shorter than the spikelets; **Glumes** lanceolate-acuminate, rigid, scabrous on the midnerve, 3-nerved, the first 4-5 mm. long, and the second 5-6 mm. long; **Lemmas** 5-6.5 mm. long, 1.5 mm. wide, lanceolate, acute, obscurely 5-nerved, hispidulous, scabrous on the midnerve, rounded at the base, awnless, mucronate, or with a very short awn between the teeth of the minutely bifid apex; **Palea** about as long as the lemma, scabrous on the keels; **Grain** nearly as long as the palea, oblong, channeled.

Rich rocky soil, in open woods, Texas.   (Near turn of Scenic Loop about 25 miles northwest of San Antonio, Texas.) Spring.

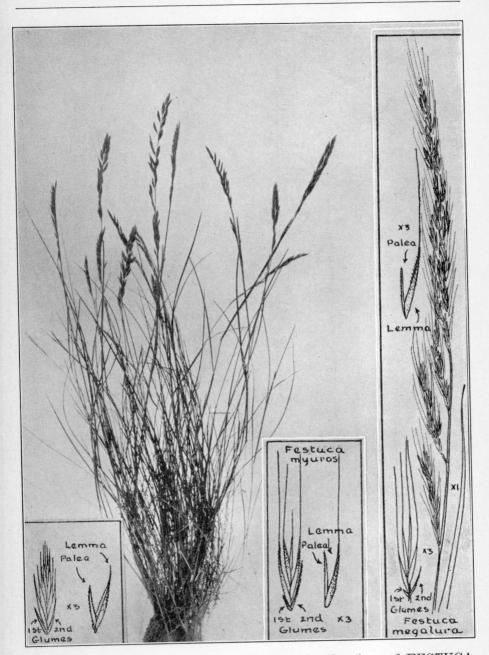

FESTUCA OCTOFLORA, Slender Fescue; also drawings of FESTUCA
MEGALURA AND FESTUCA MYUROS

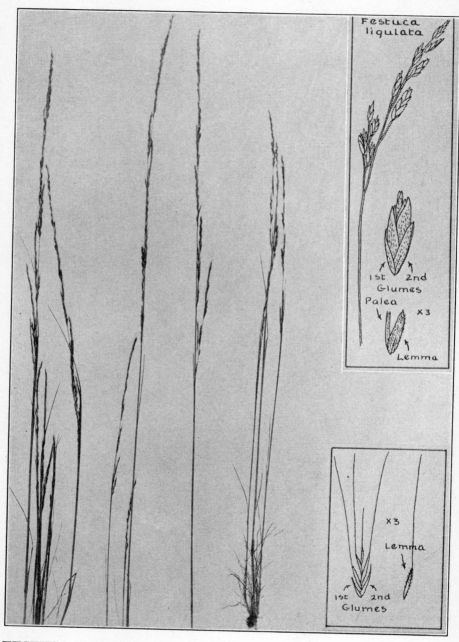

FESTUCA SCIUREA, Southern Fescue; also drawings of FESTUCA LIGULATA

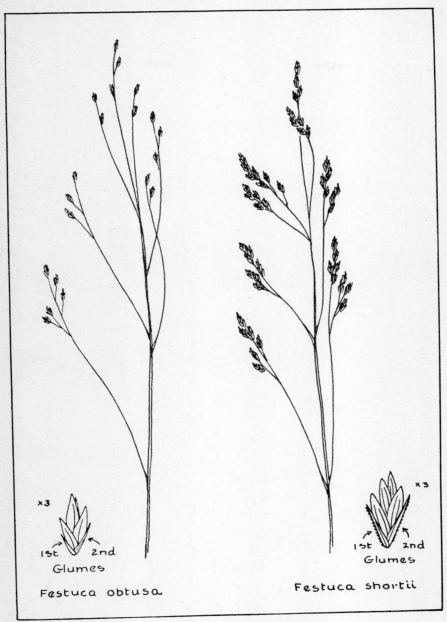

FESTUCA OBTUSA AND FESTUCA SHORTII

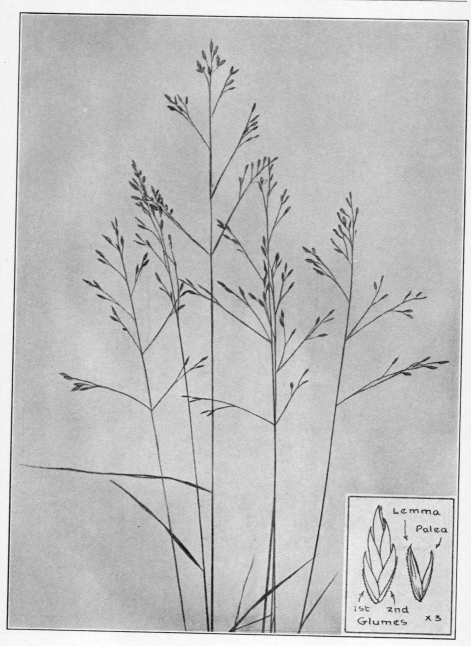

FESTUCA VERSUTA

4. GLYCERIA R. Br. (glī-sē′rĭ-à)
(Panicularia Heister)

Spikelets few to many-flowered, subterete or slightly compressed, the rachilla disarticulating above the glumes and between the florets; **Glumes** unequal, short, obtuse or acute, usually scarious, mostly 1-nerved; **Lemmas** broad, convex on the back, firm, usually obtuse, awnless, scarious at the apex, 5-9-nerved, the nerves parallel, usually prominent.

Usually tall aquatic or marsh grasses, with flat blades, closed or partly closed sheaths, and open or contracted panicles. Species about 35, in the temperate regions of both hemispheres; 16 species in the United States, two in Texas.

The two species in Texas, both *perennials,* are not important as they are limited to swampy regions.

Nerved manna grass, the most important species in the United States, with drooping panicles of small, strongly nerved green or purple spikelets, is our representative of the group with ovate or oblong spikelets usually less than 5 mm. long, and floating manna grass, with an erect panicle the branches appressed or stiffly ascending, one subsessile spikelet at the base of each branch, is our representative of the group with linear spikelets 8-20 mm. long.

SPIKELETS OVATE OR OBLONG, 3-4 mm. long; lemmas 2 mm. long, strongly
    7-nerved, obtuse at the apex; panicle and branches drooping.   1. G. striata
SPIKELETS LINEAR, compressed-cylindric, 8-20 mm. long; panicle erect;
    lemmas 3-4.5 mm. long, hispidulous, erose at the truncate apex.
                                             2. G. septentrionalis

1. **G. STRIATA** (Lam.) Hitchc. (strī-ā′tà); *G. nervata* (Willd.) Trin.; *Panicularia nervata* (Willd.) Kuntze; NERVED MANNA-GRASS, FOWL MEADOW-GRASS.

    Culms 2-4 feet tall, in small or large clumps, erect or spreading, simple; **Blades** erect or ascending, 6-12′ long, 4-10 mm. wide, flat, rough · toward the tip, the plant rather leafy especially at the base; **Sheaths** except the lower shorter than the internodes, closed nearly to the summit, rough; **Ligule** membranaceous, 1-3 mm. long, nearly truncate; **Panicle** pale-green or purple, 4-8′ long, exserted, pyramidal, erect or finally drooping, the axis rough, the slender branches rough, mostly in ones to threes, one usually shorter, naked below, ascending, spreading, or finally drooping, rarely erect, the lower as much as 6′ long; **Spikelets** green or purple, 3-7-flowered, 3-4 mm. long, ovate to oblong; **Glumes** oval, unequal, thin, 1-nerved, usually obtuse, rarely acute, both much shorter than the contiguous florets, 0.5-1.5 mm. long, the second usually longer; **Lemmas** 1.5-2 mm. long, obtuse or rounded at the apex, conspicuously 7-nerved, soon falling; **Palea** shorter than to exceeding the lemma, obovate-elliptic, obtuse, incurved; **Grain** about 1 mm. long, oval, apiculate.

Wet places or in water, Texas to Florida, north to Maine, and California. (Along stream below swimming pool at New Braunfels, Texas.) Spring-fall.

2. **G. SEPTENTRIONALIS** Hitchc. (sĕp-tĕn-trĭ-ō-nā′lĭs); *Panicularia septentrionalis* (Hitchc.) Bicknell; FLOATING MANNA-GRASS.

    Culms 2-5 feet tall, commonly stout, thick and soft, erect or decumbent, simple, flattened, often rooting at the lower nodes; **Blades** 5-12′ long, or more, 4-8 mm. wide, flat, slightly rough, often floating; **Sheaths**

mostly overlapping, smooth to rough, loose; **Ligule** 4-6 mm. long, decurrent; **Panicle** usually erect, 8-15' long, the few slender branches at first appressed, finally rather stiffly ascending, the lower 3-6' long, the spikelets subsessile or on short pedicels, usually one subsessile spikelet at the base of each branch; **Spikelets** green, 7-31-flowered, linear, compressed, 8-20 mm. long; **Glumes** 2-4.5 mm. long, unequal, the upper slightly longer, commonly obtuse or truncate, scarious at the apex; **Lemmas** green or pale, 3-4.5 mm. long, oblong, the obtuse scarious apex erose, often exceeded by the tip of the palea, more or less minutely scabrous, nerves evident; **Palea** two-toothed, hispidulous-ciliate.

Wet places, often in shallow water, Texas to South Carolina, north to Maine. (Near Hempstead, Texas.) Late spring and fall.

GLYCERIA STRIATA, Nerved Manna-grass or Fowl Meadow-grass

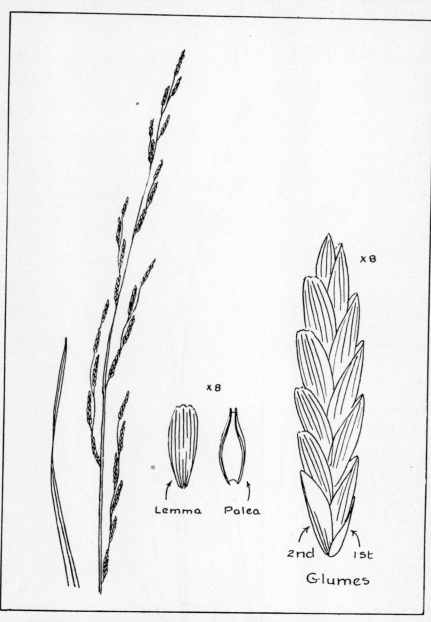

GLYCERIA SEPTENTRIONALIS, Floating Manna-grass

5. POA L. (pō'à)
(The Blue-grasses)

Spikelets 2 to several-flowered, the rachilla disarticulating above the glumes and between the florets, the uppermost floret reduced or rudimentary; **Glumes** acute, keeled, somewhat unequal, the first 1-nerved, the second usually 3-nerved; **Lemmas** somewhat keeled, acute or acutish, awnless, membranaceous, often somewhat scarious at the tip, 5-nerved, the nerves sometimes pubescent.

Annual, or usually perennial, species of low or rather tall grasses, with spikelets in open or contracted panicles, the narrow blades flat or folded, ending in a navicular point (boat-shaped). Species about 90 in the United States, especially numerous in the western mountains, 12 in Texas.

The blue-grasses are important in the United States as forage grasses, but are not very common in Texas. The lemmas of many of the species are webby at the base, i. e. tufts of loose cottony hairs, and often pubescent below or only on some or all of the nerves. A characteristic of the genus is the boat-shaped (navicular) apex of the blades.

Mutton grass, in the extreme western part of the State, and Texas blue-grass, a native of Texas and Oklahoma, are dioecious.

P. annua, P. bigelovii and *P. chapmaniana* are annuals, all the others being perennials, some with long rootstocks.

The most important in the State are Texas blue-grass, and annual blue-grass, both being early spring grasses. Texas blue-grass in south Texas is found only near or in the shade of trees and along the banks of streams, but is rather common in north central Texas. Patches of pistillate plants with hairy spikelets are likely to be found at one location, and nearby, or perhaps miles away, a patch of staminate plants with glabrous spikelets.

Annual blue-grass is a low soft, light green plant, growing on lawns, bare places, in gardens, and slightly shaded places where other grasses do not thrive. It often flowers when only 3-4' tall, and it is necessary to pull up a tuft for close examination. It is found over most of the United States, and in the northern states is one of the first grasses in the spring to make the fields and waysides green. In south Texas along with rescue-grass it begins to make its appearance in January or February of each year, but later in the year dies down leaving bare spots.

P. chapmaniana, resembling *P. annua* but more erect, with the blades narrower and shorter, mostly basal; *P. autumnalis,* a slender woodland species with the spikelets scattered at the ends of the spreading branches; and *P. sylvestris* with oblong-pyramidal panicle, the branches reflexed at maturity, are east Texas plants.

Kentucky blue-grass and Canada blue-grass, both perennials with long rootstocks, are occasionally planted in Texas. The former is the most important of the blue-grasses, and in many of the eastern states is the principal lawn and pasture grass in the more moist places where there is plenty of lime in the soil. The latter is blue-green in color and has about the same range as Kentucky blue-grass, but is confined to sandy or clay soil. It has flattened culms, geniculate at the base, and a shorter and narrower panicle than Kentucky blue-grass.

PLANTS ANNUAL; LOW, DENSELY TUFTED; spikelets 3-7-flowered, keeled, marginal nerves of lemma usually pubescent below.
BRANCHES OF THE panicle spreading; plants 3-8' tall, sheaths smooth.
BLADES usually more than 1.5' long, 1.5-4 mm. wide, a leafy plant; lemmas not webbed at the base; anthers 0.5-1 mm. long.   1. P. annua

BLADES usually less than 1.5′ long, 1.5 mm. wide; lemmas slightly webbed at the base; anthers 0.1-0.2 mm. long.   2. P. chapmaniana
BRANCHES OF THE panicle erect; plants 8-20′ tall; sheaths usually rough; cobweb scant at the base.   3. P. bigelovii
PLANTS PERENNIAL; USUALLY MORE THAN 12′ TALL.
RHIZOMES PRESENT.
CULMS strongly flattened; panicle 2-4′ long, open but branches usually less than 1.5′ long, spikelet-bearing nearly to the base; lemmas obtuse, the intermediate nerves faint or wanting, with short hairs or naked at the base.   4. P. compressa
CULMS cylindric or obscurely flattened.
Plants dioecious; the pistillate spikelets woolly, the hairs longer than the lemmas, the staminate glabrous; the branches of the dense contracted panicle appressed or narrowly ascending.   5. P. arachnifera
Plants not dioecious, the florets perfect; lemmas webbed at the base, pubescent on the keel and marginal nerves.
Lemmas glabrous on the internerves and prominent intermediate nerves; panicle larger, lower branches usually in whorls of 5, naked at the base and longer than in *P. compressa*.   6. P. pratensis
Lemmas pubescent on the lower part of the internerves, appearing webbed at the base; panicle long, narrow, dense, the branches short and erect, spikelet-bearing nearly to the base.   7. P. arida
RHIZOMES WANTING.
LEMMAS webbed at the base.
Lower panicle branches reflexed at maturity usually more than 3; spikelets scattered at the end of the branches; midnerve of lemma pubescent its whole length, the intermediate glabrous, prominent.   8. P. sylvestris
Lower panicle branches not reflexed, ascending; panicles open, but narrow; lemmas acute, somewhat webbed at the base.   9. P. interior
LEMMAS not webbed at the base.
Lemmas glabrous, scabrous at the base, 4 mm. long; spikelets 6-7 mm. long; plants leafy at the base, the involute blades long, 0.5 mm. thick.
                                                           10. P. involuta
Lemmas pubescent on the keel and marginal nerves.
Panicle open, loose, spikelets scattered toward end of the long spreading branches; internerves pubescent below.   11. P. autumnalis
Panicle narrow, oblong-pyramidal, rather dense, the branches usually ascending; spikelets 7-9 mm. long, lemmas 4-5 mm. long; plants dioecious, spikelets nearly alike on staminate and pistillate plants.
                                                           12. P. fendleriana

1. P. ANNUA L. (ăn′yū-à) ; ANNUAL BLUE-GRASS, LOW SPEAR-GRASS, DWARF MEADOW-GRASS.

Culms 3-9′ tall, tufted, usually branched at base, erect or decumbent, flattened, usually the leaves more numerous and longer than in *P. chapmaniana;* Blades 0.5-4′ long, 1.5-5 mm. wide, abruptly acute, flaccid, flat or folded, boat-shaped at the tip; Sheaths loose, usually overlapping; Ligule 2-3 mm. long, membranaceous; Panicle 0.5-3′ long, branches spreading in ones or twos, 8-35 mm. long; Spikelets 3-6 flowered, 3-5 mm. long, flattened, short pediceled; Glumes, first acute, 1-nerved, about 2 mm. long, second obtuse, 3-nerved, about 2.5 mm. long, broader above than the first, scabrous on keel toward apex; Lemmas 2.5-3 mm. long, distinctly 5-nerved, hairy below on the keel and marginal nerves, sparingly so on intermediate nerves, often tinged with purple; Palea about 2 mm. long, little shorter than lemma, narrow, pubescent on nerves; Grain about 1.5 mm. long; Stamens, anthers 0.5-1 mm long.

In waste and cultivated places throughout America.   (San Antonio, Texas.)   Late winter-fall.

2. P. CHAPMANIANA Scribn. (chăp-măn-ĭ-ā′nà) ; CHAPMAN'S SPEAR-GRASS.

Culms 3-6′ tall, rarely taller, erect or geniculate at the base, usually

more erect than *P. annua,* rigid, simple, tufted, light green; **Blades**
10-25 mm. long, 1.5 mm. wide or less, flat or conduplicate, mostly basal;
Sheaths longer or shorter than the internodes, mostly at the base of the
culm, close; **Ligule** 1-2 mm. long, truncate; **Panicle** 1-2' long, the branches
erect or ascending or spreading, 1.5' long or less, spikelet-bearing on outer
half; **Spikelets** 3-7-flowered, 2.5-4 mm. long; **Glumes** unequal, the second
about 2 mm. long, the first shorter, 3-nerved or the first rarely 1-nerved;
Lemmas about 2.5 mm. long, obtuse, 3-nerved, or sometimes with two additional obscure nerves, webbed at the base, the midnerve and marginal
nerves sometimes pubescent for three-fourths of their length; **Stamens**
anthers 0.1-0.2 mm. long.

In dry soil, Texas to Florida, Iowa, Georgia and Tennessee. Late
winter-fall.

3. P. BIGELOVII Vasey & Scribn. (bĭg-ē-lō'vĭ-ī).

Culms 8-20' tall, tufted, erect, slender; **Blades** 2-4' long, 1-4 mm. wide,
flat, flaccid, not abruptly acute; **Sheaths** mostly longer than the internodes, scabrous or smooth; **Ligule** lanceolate, 2-3 mm. long; **Panicle** 2-8'
long, erect, linear, the branches erect, mostly in pairs, the longest
30-40 mm. long, those below as much as 2' distant, densely-flowered, sometimes naked at the base, the pedicels very short; **Spikelets** flattened, 3-7-
flowered, 4-5 mm. long, ovate; **Glumes** subequal, acute, rather firm,
2.2-3 mm. long, scabrous on the keel, the first 1-nerved, rarely 3-nerved,
the second 3-nerved; **Lemmas** 2.5-4 mm. long, subacute, villous on the
midrib and marginal nerves except toward the apex, pubescent on the
internerves below, cobweb rather scant, the nerves on each side of the
midnerve obscure; **Palea** about three-fourths as long as its lemma.

Open ground, arid regions, western Texas, Oklahoma and Colorado
to Arizona and California.

4. P. COMPRESSA L. (kŏm-prĕs'å); CANADA BLUE-GRASS.

Culms 6-24' tall, erect from a decumbent base, from horizontal rootstocks, flattened, two-edged, wiry, bluish-green, smooth, not tufted;
Blades 1-4' long, 2-3 mm. wide, smooth beneath, rough above; **Sheaths**
shorter than the internodes, loose, flattened; **Ligule** membranaceous,
1-3 mm. long; **Panicle** exserted, open, rather oblong, 2-4' long, branches
erect or ascending, usually less than 1' long, sometimes the lower 1.5' long,
spikelet-bearing from near the base; **Spikelets** 3-7-flowered (3-9) 3-6 mm.
long, subsessile; **Glumes** 2-2.5 mm. long, 3-nerved, acute; **Lemmas**
2-2.5 mm. long, obscurely 5-nerved, or the intermediate nerves wanting
or obscure, more or less bronzed at the summit, subacute, the midnerve
and marginal nerves pubescent below or naked.

Waste places and cultivated grounds and woods over most of North
America. Spring-summer.

5. P. ARACHNIFERA Torr. (ăr-ăk-nĭf'ĕr-å); TEXAS BLUE-GRASS.

Pistillate Plants: Culms 1-3 feet high, somewhat tufted, with creeping rootstocks, the leaves of the sterile shoots numerous and long; **Blades**
of the culm about 2-3, 3-6' long, 3-6 mm. wide, those of the sterile shoots
numerous, as much as 12' long, and about 2-3 mm. wide, erect, rough above,
flat or involute; **Sheaths** long, somewhat flattened, loose, lower somewhat
rough; **Ligule** membranaceous, about 1 mm. long, ovate; **Panicle** 2-6' long,
oblong or linear-oblong, spikelike, dense, sometimes interrupted below,
rather light greenish, mostly long-exserted, branches in threes to fives,

lower as much as 2.5' long, naked at base, gradually shorter above, as short as 10 mm., spikelet-bearing to the base, crowded branches appressed or ascending; **Spikelets** 5-7 mm. long, usually 3-7-flowered, flat, short pediceled, rachilla about 0.7 mm. long; **Glumes** greenish, acute, scabrous on keel, the first about 2.5-3.5 mm. long, 1-nerved, narrow, the second about 3.5-4.5 mm. long, 3-nerved, broader; **Lemmas** 4.5-5.5 mm. long, 5-nerved, acuminate, awn-pointed, keel pilose on lower one-half to two-thirds, marginal nerves pilose on about the lower one-third, intermediate nerves glabrous, all but the midnerve extending only about two-thirds of distance to apex, long webby hairs at base of lemma. The spikelets, glumes and lemmas vary much in length.

Staminate Plant: Similar to the pistillate plant except the spikelets are staminate and the lemmas glabrous or occasionally with a few long hairs at the base.

Prairies, Texas to Louisiana and Florida, north to Kansas, west to New Mexico. (Austin, Gonzales, Texas.)   April-May.

6. P. PRATENSIS L. (prā-tĕn'sĭs) ; KENTUCKY BLUE-GRASS, JUNE-GRASS.

Culms 1-4 feet tall, erect from long running rootstocks, tufted, simple, with panicle much exceeding the leaves; **Blades** of the culm 2-6' long, basal often much longer, rarely 25' long, 1-6 mm. wide, smooth or slightly rough, often minutely pubescent on upper surface; **Sheaths** longer than the internodes or the lower overlapping, flattened, smooth or lower sometimes rough; **Ligule** membranaceous, truncate, usually less than 2 mm. long; **Panicle** 2.5-8' long, much exserted, on long slender peduncle, ovate to pyramidal, branches ascending, spreading or horizontal, the lower longer, as much as 3' long, and in half-whorls of 4-5, divided into branchlets and spikelet-bearing above the middle; **Spikelets** 3-6-flowered, ovate to lanceolate, 3.5-5 mm. long, flattened, exceeding their pedicels, crowded at the end of the branches; **Glumes** acute, slightly unequal, scabrous on keel; otherwise glabrous, the first 1-nerved, the second 3-nerved; **Lemmas** 2.5-3.5 mm. long, webbed at the base, acute, 5-nerved, the marginal and midnerves silky pubescent below, the intermediate naked and prominent.

Meadows, fields and woods; over most of North America. Spring-summer.

7. P. ARIDA Vasey (ăr'ĭ-dà); *P. andina* Nutt.; *P. pratericola* Rydb.; PRAIRIE OR BUNCH-GRASS.

Culms 1-2 feet tall, densely tufted, erect, rigid, simple; **Blades,** the basal 3-6', or those of the culm very short, usually less than an inch long, 1-3 mm. wide, erect, flat or folded, rough above; **Sheaths,** the upper shorter than the internodes, slightly rough; **Ligule** 2-4 mm. long; **Panicle** exserted, 2-5' long, narrow, the branches short, commonly less than 1.5' long, erect or sometimes ascending, spikelet-bearing to the base, or the lower longer ones naked at the base, the spikelets crowded, the pedicels mostly 1-3 mm. long; **Spikelets** 3-7-flowered, 5-7 mm. long; **Glumes** subequal, acute, 3-nerved, 3-4 mm. long; **Lemmas** 3-4 mm. long, acute or obtuse or erose-truncate at the apex, the intermediate nerves very obscure, from sparsely to densely pubescent below on the midnerve and marginal nerves and also between the nerves; **Palea** nearly equal to the lemma.

Prairies and meadows, Texas, New Mexico, Utah, Kansas, North Dakota. Summer.

8. **P. SYLVESTRIS** A. Gray (sĭl-vĕs'trĭs) ; SYLVAN SPEAR-GRASS.

Culms 1-3 feet tall, erect, slender, simple, slightly flattened; **Blades** of the culm 1.5-6′ long, the basal much longer, 2-6 mm. wide, rough above; **Sheaths** shorter than the internodes, smooth to rough, rarely pubescent; **Ligule** membranaceous, 1-1.5 mm. long more or less; **Panicle** 3-7′, oblong-pyramidal, open, the short flexuous filiform branches several to a node, ascending or spreading, often reflexed in age, 1.5-3′ long, spikelet-bearing beyond the middle, spikelets scattered; **Spikelets** 2-4-flowered, 2-4 mm. long, on slender pedicels; **Glumes** acute, the lower 1-nerved, the upper longer and 3-nerved, the first 2.3 mm. long, the second 2-2.7 mm. long, broad; **Lemmas** about 2.5 mm. long, obtuse, the midnerve pubescent to nearly the summit, the marginal nerves below the middle, webbed at the base, the intermediate nerves prominent, glabrous; **Palea** about as long as the lemma, pubescent on the keels.

Rich woods, thickets and meadows, Texas to Florida, New York to Wisconsin and Nebraska. Spring-summer.

9. **P. INTERIOR** Rydb. (ĭn-tē'rĭ-ēr) ; *P. nemoralis* Scribn. not L.; INLAND BLUE-GRASS.

Culms 8-24′ tall, tufted, erect, slender, somewhat rigid; **Blades** 1-3′ long, 1.5-2 mm. wide, rough or smooth; **Sheaths** longer or shorter than the internodes, smooth or rough; **Ligule** membranaceous, truncate, minutely ciliate, slightly less than 1 mm. long; **Panicle** finally exserted, open but narrow-oblong, 2-5′ long, the slender scabrous branches 1-2′ long, erect or ascending, rarely spreading, spikelet-bearing on the upper half; **Spikelets** 1-4-flowered, 3-4 mm. long, green but often tinged with purple; **Glumes** subequal, about 2 mm. long, acute, 3-nerved or the first 1-nerved, scabrous especially on the keel and toward the apex, the second with strong lateral nerves and broad scarious margins, much broader than the first; **Lemmas** 2-2.5 mm. long, somewhat webby at the base, scabrous toward the apex, the midnerve and the marginal nerves pubescent on the lower half, the intermediate nerves faint or obsolete; **Palea** 2-toothed, acute, equal or exceeding the lemma, often exceeding the lemma of the second floret.

Woods and open ground, Texas, New Mexico, Nebraska, Dakotas to Utah. (Ft. Smith to the Rio Grande, Texas.) Spring-summer.

10. **P. INVOLUTA** Hitchc. (ĭn-vō-lū'tà).

Culms 18′ tall, more or less, in small tufts, erect, slender, leafy at the base; **Blades** 4-7′ long, about 0.5 mm. wide, folded, involute, rough; **Sheaths** longer than the internodes, rough; **Ligule** membranaceous, about 0.5 mm. long; **Panicle** long, exserted, erect, open, about 4′ long, the slender branches mostly in twos, erect or ascending, or finally spreading, somewhat distant, spikelet-bearing mostly on the upper third; **Spikelets** 4-5-flowered, 6-7 mm. long; **Glumes** acute, the first 2-2.5 mm. long, 1-nerved, the second about 3 mm. long, 3-nerved; **Lemmas** 3-4 mm. long, acute or subacute, glabrous, scabrous at the base, otherwise more or less minutely scabrous, the scabrous rachilla about 1 mm. long; **Palea** equal to the lemma, ciliate.

On dry soil in brush, in small scattered clumps, Chisos Mountains, Texas, altitude 6,000-7,000 feet. Spring to summer.

11. **P. AUTUMNALIS** Muhl. (ô-tŭm-nā'lĭs) ; *P. flexuosa* Muhl.; FLEXUOUS SPEAR-GRASS.

Culms 8-24′ (12-36′) tall, one or a few culms to a tuft, slender, flattened, erect or spreading, simple; **Blades** 1-7′ long, the basal often longer, 1.5-3 mm. wide, flat, smooth or slightly rough; **Sheaths** shorter than the internodes; **Ligule** membranaceous, about 1 mm. long, truncate-lacerate; **Panicle** exserted, open, nodding, 2.5-8′ long, the longer branches as much as 4′, mostly in pairs, capillary, scabrous, distant, the few branches finally spreading, with 1-6 spikelets at their extremities; **Spikelets** 2-5-flowered, 4-6 mm. long, oval, pale green, on scabrous pedicels usually one to two times as long as the spikelet; **Glumes** scabrous on the keel toward the apex, the first about 2 mm. long, acute, 1-nerved, the second 2.5-3 mm. long, broader, 3-nerved, obtuse, sometimes emarginate; **Lemmas** 3-3.5 mm. long, oblong, conspicuously scarious toward the obtuse or emarginate apex, the 5 nerves evident, the midnerve and marginal nerves silky pubescent on the lower half, the internerves usually sparsely pubescent below; **Palea** shorter than its lemma, scabrous on the keels.

In woods, Texas to Florida, north to Kentucky and Pennsylvania. Spring-summer.

12. P. FENDLERIANA (Steud.) Vasey (fĕnd-lēr-ĭ-ā′nȧ); *P. californica* (Munro) Scribn.; Mutton-grass.

Plants Incompletely Dioecious: Culms 1-2 feet tall, densely tufted or in "bunches", erect, simple, rough or nearly smooth, leafy below; **Blades** 2-12′ long, 1-2 mm. wide, the basal and those of the sterile shoots very numerous and much longer than those of the culm, flat or condupli-cate, rough (rough beneath and hispid-puberulent above); **Sheaths** shorter than the internodes, rough above, or those of the sterile shoots smooth and scarious, rather loose and open near the throat; **Ligule** less than 1 mm. long; **Panicles** long-exserted, oblong, 1-3′ long, rather closely-flowered, erect or slightly nodding, the branches mostly in twos or threes, 1.5′ long or less, erect or somewhat spreading, subdivided and spikelet-bearing to the base or the longer ones naked at the base; **Spikelets** 5-6-flowered, 7-9 mm. long; **Glumes** 3-4 mm. long, the first slightly shorter, shorter than the lower lemmas, ovate, acute, carinate, minutely scabrous, 1-nerved or the second 3-nerved; **Lemmas** 4-5 mm. long, ovate-oblong, erose or emarginate at the obtuse apex, hispid on the keel toward the apex, more or less pubescent on the marginal nerves and midnerve below, only the midnerve extending to the apex, the intermediate nerves obscure; **Palea** oblong, emarginate, pubescent on the keels; **Stamens** 3, nearly sessile in the open, divergent staminate florets; **Pistillate Spikelets** with minute stamens, the anthers about 0.2 mm. long.

Hills and table lands, western Texas, New Mexico, Colorado and California. May-August.

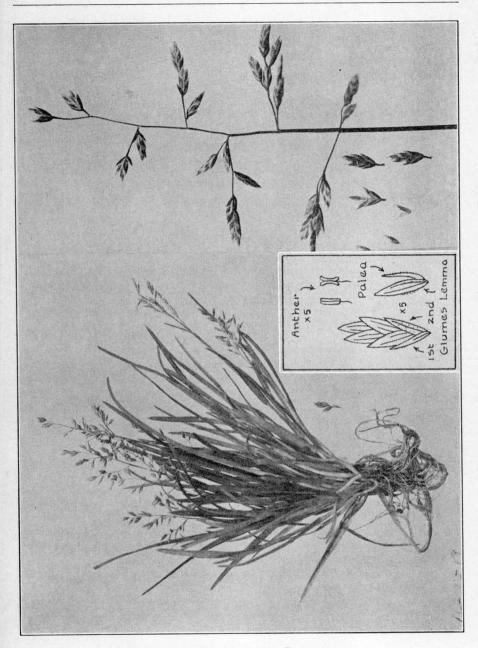

POA ANNUA, ANNUAL BLUE-GRASS

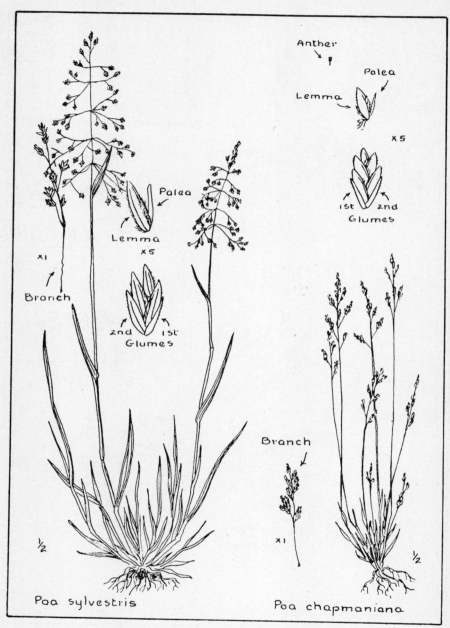

POA SYLVESTRIS AND **POA CHAPMANIANA**

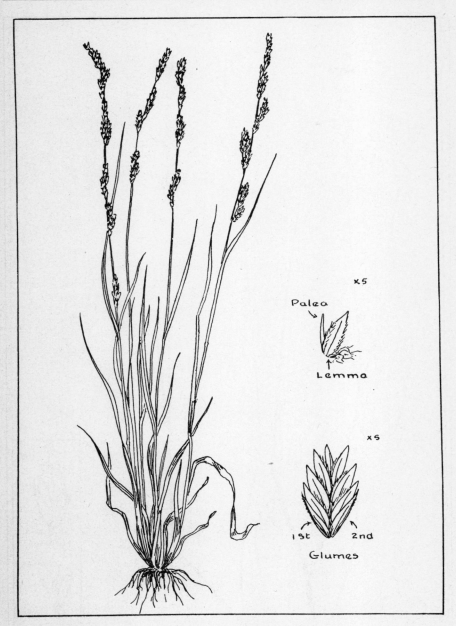

POA BIGELOVII

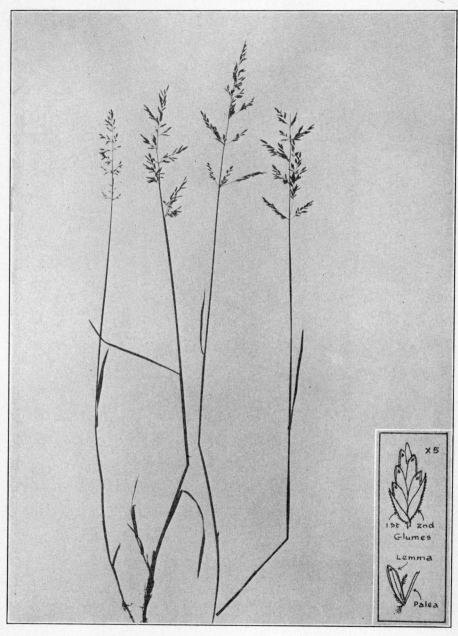

POA COMPRESSA, Canada Blue-grass

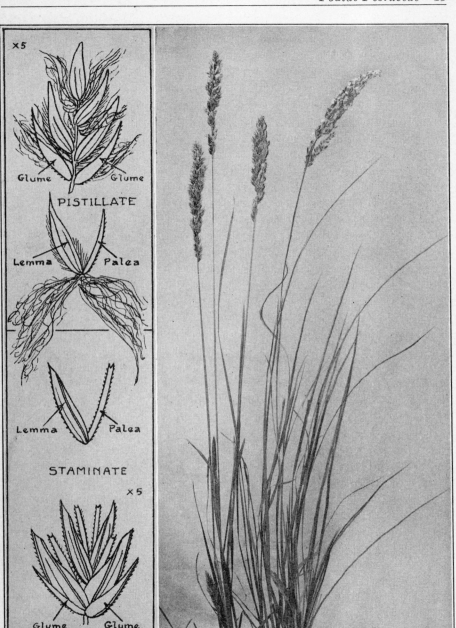

POA ARACHNIFERA, Texas Blue-grass

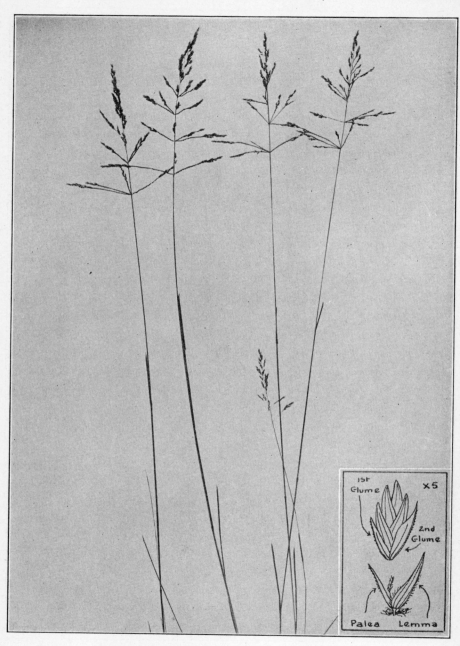

POA PRATENSIS, Kentucky Blue-grass

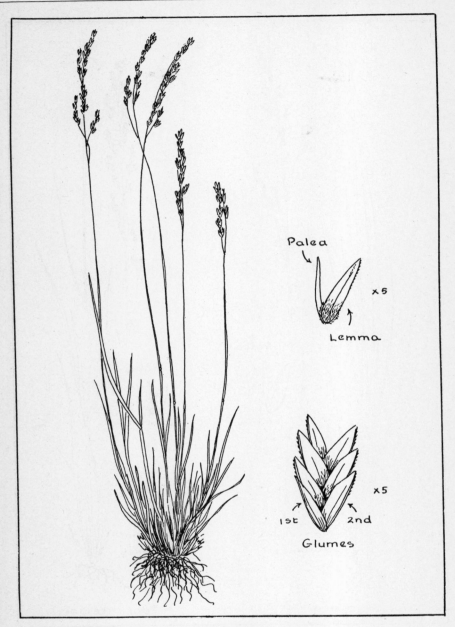

POA ARIDA

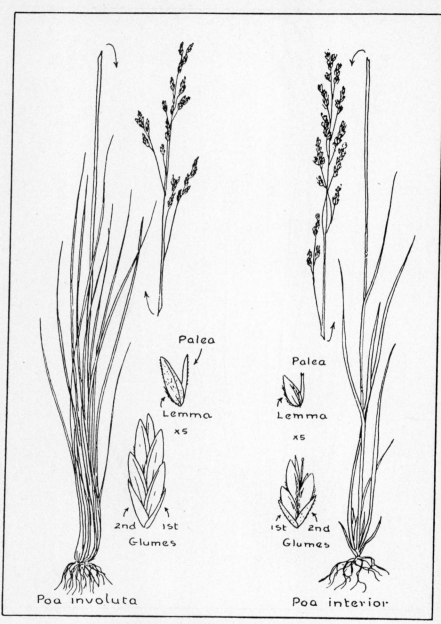

POA INVOLUTA AND POA INTERIOR

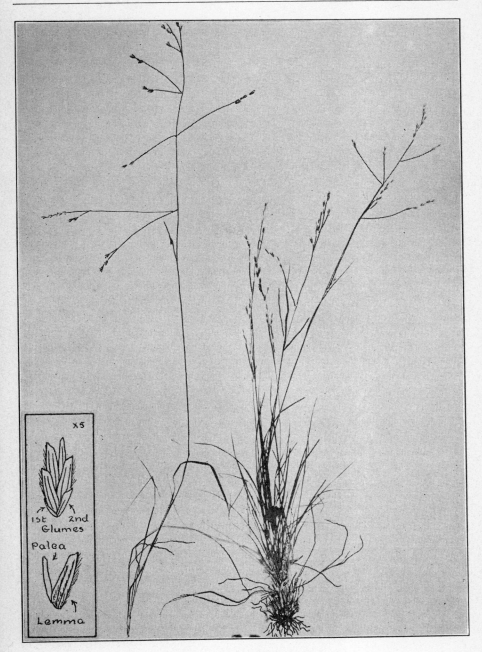

x5

1st 2nd
Glumes

Palea

Lemma

POA AUTUMNALIS

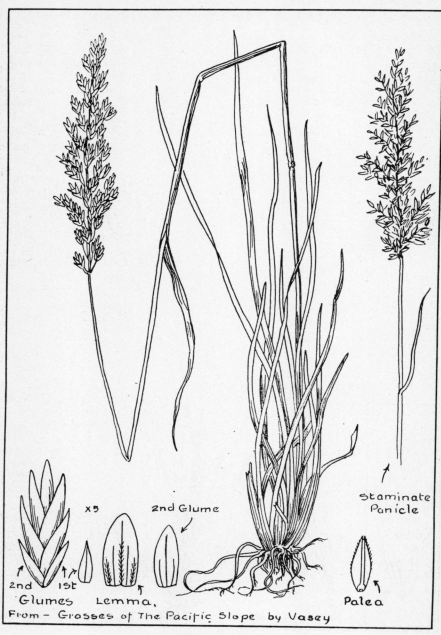

x 5   2nd Glume

2nd   1st
Glumes   Lemma.   Palea

staminate
Panicle

From — Grasses of The Pacific Slope by Vasey

POA FENDLERIANA

6. ERAGROSTIS Host (ĕr-à-grŏs'tĭs)

Spikelets few to many-flowered, the florets usually closely imbricate, the rachilla disarticulating above the glumes and between the florets, or continuous, the lemmas deciduous, the paleas persistent; **Glumes** somewhat unequal, shorter than the first lemma, acute or acuminate, 1-nerved or the second rarely 3-nerved; **Lemmas** acute or acuminate, keeled or rounded on the back, 3-nerved, the nerves usually prominent; **Palea** 2-nerved, the keels sometimes ciliate.

Annual or perennial grasses of various habit, the inflorescence an open or contracted panicle; about 37 species in the United States, mostly in the southern states.

This genus is well represented in Texas, having within its borders nearly all the species of the United States. They are often called stinkgrasses.

The distinguishing characteristics are the 1-nerved glumes, the second rarely 3-nerved, the 3-nerved lemmas, the nerves usually prominent, and the ciliate paleas.

In many of the species of this genus the rachilla is continuous and does not disarticulate as in most species of *Festuceae*. The grain is free and falls with the lemma, leaving the palea upon the rachilla. Among others in this group are *E. cilianensis* and *E. poaeoides*.

About half the species in Texas and the United States are annuals. *E. cilianensis* (*E. major* Host), a disagreeable smelling grass with a rather compact panicle of large spikelets about 3 mm. wide, and a closely related species, *E. poaeoides*, with smaller spikelets about 2 mm. wide, both with the keels of the glumes and lemmas more or less glandular-dotted, are allied to *E. pectinacea*, *E. neomexicana*, *E. mexicana*, *E. pilosa* and *E. diffusa*. In *E. pectinacea* the spikelets are dark-leadish-purple color about 1.5 mm. wide, the lateral nerves prominent, the spikelets appressed or nearly so to the branches; in *E. pilosa* the panicle is usually smaller, more delicate, more open, the spikelets being of a reddish-purple, the pedicels and spikelets ascending or spreading and about 1 mm. wide, the lateral nerves faint or wanting. *E. neomexicana* is very similar in appearance to *E. pectinacea* except the plant is much taller, the panicle elongated and spikelets larger, with the lemmas broader. In *E. diffusa* the panicle is more compound and the culms branch more freely than in *E. pectinacea*.

E. reptans, a dioecious plant, and *E. hypnoides*, with perfect flowers and a finer and more delicate grass, are extensively creeping plants rooting at the lower nodes, and growing mostly in moist soil along ditches, roads and streams, usually in dense small or large colonies. The pistillate plants are usually found at one location and the staminate at another which may be several miles away. The anthers of the staminate plants are about 2 mm. long, and those of the perfect flowers of *E. hypnoides* 0.2-0.3 mm. long.

Two low plants, *E. ciliaris*, with a spikelike panicle, and *E. amabilis*, with an open panicle, have conspicuously ciliate paleas.

E. glomerata, with a contracted elongated panicle of crowded subsessile spikelets rarely over 3 mm. long, is found along the banks of streams.

E. capillaris, branching only at the base, the branches and pedicels long and capillary, and *E. frankii*, branching above, the branches of the panicle short, are plants not over 20' tall, with the spikelets 3-5-flowered, the lateral nerves of the lemmas obscure.

E. barrelieri, with a glandular ring below the nodes, has a small panicle with the rather rigid ascending or spreading branches usually less than 2′ long, and *E. arida,* a taller plant without the glandular rings, has larger panicles, the branches much longer and not so stiff.

E. tephrosanthos, a rare plant closely allied to *E. pectinacea* with the aspect of a depauperate *E. pilosa,* is a delicate lacy plant 2-8′ tall. Its spikelets are more appressed than those of *E. pilosa* and less so than those of *E. pectinacea.*

The remaining species are perennials. *E. spicata,* with a very narrow elongated spikelike densely-flowered panicle, the very small spikelets 1-4-flowered, is rare. It is found south of Falfurrias and near Mercedes, Texas, and in Mexico.

E. secundiflora and *E. beyrichii* are plants of sandy soil, with contracted panicles more or less interrupted below, the former with the lemmas abruptly narrowed toward the apex, the anthers 0.2-0.3 mm. long, and the latter with longer lemmas gradually narrowed, the anthers 0.4-0.5 mm. long.

In all the other species of this genus the panicles are more or less open and have either the lateral nerves of the lemmas obscure or more or less prominent. Those with the lateral nerves obscure are *E. swalleni,* with pedicels glandular below the spikelets, sheaths glabrous, and spikelets 6-18-flowered; *E. hirsuta,* with pedicels and branches of the panicles long and capillary, sheaths usually hirsute and spikelets 3-5-flowered. In the closely related plants, *E. intermedia,* simple, with blades 3-7 mm. wide, and *E. lugens,* branching with blades 1-3 mm. wide, the axils of the branches of the panicles are conspicuously pilose, the former with spikelets 1.5 mm. wide, the panicle branches more or less rigid, and the latter with spikelets about 1 mm. wide, the branches of the panicle rather flexuous.

The following have the nerves of the lemmas more or less prominent. All of these except *E. sessilispica,* which has sessile spikelets along the rigid main branches of the panicle, have pediceled spikelets.

E. trichodes and *E. pilifera,* plants 3-6 feet tall, with oblong-elongated panicle sometimes half as long as the plant, the former with purple spikelets less than 10-flowered, the latter with bronze spikelets more than 10-flowered, have all the nodes close together at and near the base, the upper internodes very long.

E. silveana and *E. spectabilis* have reddish or dark-purple panicles, the first with panicles longer than broad, the branches viscid, not rigid, and glabrous sheaths, the latter with the panicle broader than long, often more than half as long as the plant, the branches slender but rigid, the sheaths pilose to glabrous.

E. elliottii and *E. erosa,* both with flattened spikelets, have lead-colored panicles, the former less than 20′ tall, the diffuse, few-flowered panicles with capillary fragile branches like spun glass, the latter 1.5-3 feet tall, densely tufted, with long open panicles. *E. palmeri,* somewhat similar to *E. erosa* in general appearance, has lower lemmas about 2 mm. long, shorter than those of *E. erosa,* and lacking the erose apex.

PLANTS ANNUAL; PANICLE CONTRACTED OR OPEN.
  CULMS EXTENSIVELY creeping; plants low.
    Plants dioecious; lemmas pubescent; anthers 2 mm. long.   1. E. reptans
    Plants not dioecious; lemmas glabrous; anthers 0.2-0.3 mm. long.
                                                                   2. E. hypnoides
  CULMS NOT EXTENSIVELY creeping; plants with perfect flowers.
    PALEA conspicuously ciliate.
      Panicle spikelike.   3. E. ciliaris
      Panicle open.   4. E. amabilis

PALEA not conspicuously ciliate.
  Panicle narrow, elongated, 4-8′ long; spikelet-bearing from the base; spike-lets crowded, subsessile, rarely over 3 mm. long.   5. E. glomerata
  Panicle open, usually diffuse.
    Keels of glumes and lemmas more or less glandular; spikelets 8-35-flowered; panicle usually less than 5′ long; the branches rather stiffly ascending or spreading, short.
      Spikelets about 3 mm. wide.   6. E. cilianensis
      Spikelets about 2 mm. wide.   7. E. poaeoides
    Keels of glumes and lemmas not glandular.
      Spikelets 2-5-flowered, 2-4 mm. long; lemmas 1.5 mm. long, lateral nerves obscure.
        Culms branching only at the base; pedicels and branches of the panicle long and capillary; culms slender, rarely over 20′ tall.
            8. E. capillaris
        Culms branching above the base; branches and pedicels short.
            9. E. frankii
      Spikelets 5-many-flowered; 3-18 mm. long.
        SPIKELETS ABOUT 1 mm. WIDE; lemma 1.5 mm. long, lateral nerves faint; panicle branches pilose in the axils.
            10. E. pilosa
        SPIKELETS ABOUT 1.5 mm. WIDE OR WIDER.
          SPIKELETS LINEAR at maturity or ovate linear in *E. pectinacea* and *E. diffusa.*
            PANICLE branches and pedicels rather stiffly ascending or spreading.
              Culms with a glandular ring below the nodes; plant usually 1-1.5 feet tall; panicle usually 3-5′ long, the branches less than 2′ long.   11. E. barrelieri
              Culms not glandular; plants usually 1.5-2.5 feet tall; panicle diffuse, usually 5-10′ long, the branches spreading as much as 6′ long.   12. E. arida
            PANICLE branches and pedicels usually appressed, branches naked at the base for 5-10 mm.; lower lemmas 1.5-2 mm. long.
              Primary panicle branches simple or the lower with a branch-let bearing 2-3 spikelets; spikelets loosely imbricate or sometimes not overlapping; plants slender, mostly less than 12′ tall, the culms slender at the base. Distribution chiefly east of the 100th meridian.   13. E. pectinacea
              Primary panicle branches usually bearing appressed branch-lets with few to several spikelets, the spikelets thus appearing imbricate and crowded along the primary branches; plants more robust, mostly more than 12′ tall, the culms stouter at the base. Distribution from Texas to California.   14. E. diffusa
          SPIKELETS OVATE to ovate-oblong or nearly linear.
            PLANTS comparatively robust, 1-3 feet tall; panicles large, branches many-flowered, ascending; blades as much as 10 mm. wide, but often not so wide.   15. E. neomexicana
            PLANTS usually less than 12′ tall; panicles smaller and more open, the spreading branches few-flowered.
              16. E. mexicana
          PLANTS delicate, 2-8′ tall; spikelets about 1.2 mm. wide.
            17. E. tephrosanthos

PLANTS PERENNIAL: PANICLE OPEN OR CONTRACTED.
  PANICLES CONTRACTED or spikelike.
    PANICLE spikelike, slender, 12′ long or less; spikelets mostly 2-3-flowered, 1.5-2.5 mm. long.   18. E. spicata
    PANICLE contracted, scarcely spikelike, the spikelets crowded in clusters on short, rarely elongated spreading branches.
      Lemmas 3-3.5 mm. long, abruptly narrowed; anthers 0.2-0.3 mm. long.
            19. E. secundiflora
      Lemmas 3.5-4.5 mm. long, gradually narrowed; anthers 0.4-0.5 mm. long.
            20. E. beyrichii

PANICLES OPEN, more or less diffuse.
NERVES of the lemma obscure.
Sheaths glabrous except at the summit; spikelets commonly less than 10-flowered, 6-18-flowered in *E. swalleni.*
Pedicels glandular below the spikelet, axils of the panicle branches glabrous or with a few hairs only.   21. E. swalleni
Pedicels not glandular; axils of the branches commonly strongly pilose.
Spikelets about 1.5 mm. wide, the panicle branches stiffly spreading; plant rarely branching.   22. E. intermedia
Spikelets about 1 mm. wide; panicle branches more flexuous; plant branching.   23. E. lugens
Sheaths hairy, especially the lower; pedicels and branches of the panicle long and capillary; spikelets 3-5-flowered.   24. E. hirsuta
NERVES of the lemma prominent, evident in *E. palmeri* and *E. erosa.*
Spikelets nearly sessile along the main branches of panicle, panicle often more than half as long as the plant, the branches finally widely and rigidly spreading; sheaths glabrous.   25. E. sessilispica
Spikelets on pedicels 1-2 mm. long; spikelets usually appressed.
Blades elongated; branches of the panicle long and slender; spikelets scattered at the end of the branches and branchlets, 6-25-flowered.
                                                                        26. E. refracta
Blades not elongated; branches of the panicle shorter and stout, rigid; spikelets crowded, 5-12-flowered.   27. E. curtipedicellata
Spikelets on pedicels usually more than 2 mm. long, often longer than the spikelet.
Panicle elongated, nearly oblong, usually more than half as long as the plant, the branches ascending or erect, the capillary pedicels often longer than the spikelet; plants usually 3-5 feet tall; sheaths pilose at the throat.
Spikelets mostly 6-10-flowered, purple.   28. E. trichodes
Spikelets mostly more than 10-flowered, stramineous or bronze.
                                                                        29. E. pilifera
Panicle not elongated; the branches spreading or ascending; spikelets 1-1.5 mm. wide, mostly less than 10-flowered.
Panicle mostly reddish-purple, the branches finally spreading.
Sheaths appressed-pilose or glabrous; panicle about as wide as long, often more than half as long as the plant, the branches slender but rigid; axils of the branches usually pilose.   30. E. spectabilis
Sheaths glabrous; panicle longer than broad, usually glabrous in the axils, the branches VISCID, more lax, and spikelets usually smaller than in *E. spectabilis.*   31. E. silveana
Panicle leadish-color, the branches ascending or spreading; sheaths glabrous.
PLANTS USUALLY 2-3.5 FEET TALL.
Lower lemma 2 mm. long; panicle narrowly pyramidal, the branches ascending; spikelets 4-8-flowered.   32. E. palmeri
Lower lemma 2-3 mm. long, erose at the apex; panicle usually longer and the branches more spreading than in *E. palmeri;* spikelets 6-14-flowered.   33. E. erosa
PLANTS USUALLY LESS THAN 20' TALL; pedicels spreading, mostly longer than the spikelet; spikelets 6-16-flowered, 5-10 mm. long, 1.5 mm. wide.   34. E. elliottii

1. **E. REPTANS** (Michx.) Nees (rĕp′tăns); *E. weigeltiana* (Reichenb.) Bush; CREEPING MEADOW-GRASS.

Staminate plants: Culms slender, with extensively creeping stolons, taking root at the nodes, freely branching, the flowering branches erect or ascending, only a few inches tall; **Blades** 10-40 mm. mostly 10-20 mm. long, 1-2 mm. wide, flat or involute, ascending or spreading, minutely pubescent; **Sheaths** very short, shorter than the internodes, loose, margins ciliate, minutely pubescent; **Ligule** a ring of hairs less than 1 mm. long; **Panicles** mostly a capitate or sub-capitate cluster less than an inch long, with few to many spikelets on short pedicels sparsely covered with capitate hairs; **Spikelets** 5-36-flowered, 5-22 mm. long, 2-2.5 mm. wide, flat, ovate to lanceolate-oblong, light-green turning pale; **Glumes** scabrous on the nerve, acute, hyaline, the first about half as long as the second, the second 1.5-2 mm. long; **Lemmas** 2-2.5 mm. long, the lateral nerves prominent, the midnerve scabrous, body pubescent or nearly glabrous; **Palea** nearly as long as its lemma, curved, ciliate; **Stamens,** anthers nearly 2 mm. long.

Pistillate Plant: Similar except lemmas more acute, sparsely pubescent; **Palea** somewhat shorter.

In sandy usually wet soil; Texas, Louisiana to Nebraska, also Mexico. (Hondo and Robstown, Texas.) Spring and summer.

2. E. HYPNOIDES (Lam.) B. S. P. (hĭp-noi′dēz) ; SMOOTH CREEPING-
GRASS.

Culms 2-8′ tall, densely-tufted, slender, usually prostrate or creeping or ascending from a decumbent base, rooting at the lower nodes, freely branching, the plant commonly having a more lacy aspect and less densely-flowered than shown in the photograph; **Blades** 7-25 mm. long, 1-2 mm. wide, flat or soon involute, aristate, glabrous or pubescent in some plants; **Sheaths** mostly shorter than the internodes, loose, sparsely-ciliate and papillose especially toward the base, otherwise glabrous or pubescent; **Ligule** a ring of hairs about 0.5 mm. long; **Panicles** numerous, often half the length of the plant, consisting of many subcapitate clusters, the several branches with one to several clusters to each branch or branchlet, the clusters often again subdivided into short-peduncled smaller clusters, often many spikelets to each, the scabrous and often pubescent pedicels 1-3 mm. long; **Spikelets** perfect, green, finally pale, 10-50 flowered, 6-20 mm. long, 1.5-1.8 mm. wide, flattened, the green nerves prominent, the glumes and lemmas glabrous or sparsely hispidulous, or pubescent in some plants; **Glumes** acute, scabrous on the nerve, the first narrow, usually 0.5-1 mm. long, the second broader, 1-1.5 mm. long; **Lemmas** about 2 mm. long, narrow, acuminate, scabrous on the midnerve, glabrous or sparsely hispidulous or pubescent; **Palea** about 0.8 mm. long, ciliate on the keels, persistent; **Grain** about 0.5 mm. long, oblong, amber; **Stamens,** anthers 0.2-0.3 mm. long.

Low moist soil, Texas to New England. (Sabine River, Marshall, Carthage, Orange, and at the mouth of the Rio Grande.) Summer and fall.

3. E. CILIARIS (L.) Link (sĭl-ĭ-ā′rĭs).

Culms 6-17′ tall, densely-tufted, slender, erect or ascending, often decumbent at the base, rather diffuse, often branching; **Blades** 1-3.5′ long, 2-4 mm. wide, flat or involute, smooth or rough on the upper surface, sometimes a few hairs on the upper surface near the base, often papillose; **Sheaths** shorter than the internodes, ciliate on the margins, with a tuft of long hairs at the throat; **Panicle** 1-4.5′ long, spikelike, often interrupted below, subcylindric, 5-7 mm. thick, the very short appressed branches crowded with spikelets, the scabrous pedicels less than the length of the spikelets; **Spikelets** 6-16-flowered, 2-3.5 mm. long, about 1.5 mm. wide, ovate to oblong; **Glumes** acute, scabrous on the keel, 0.8 to 1.2 mm. long, the second slightly longer; **Lemmas** about 1 mm. long, oblong-elliptic, the lateral nerves near the margin, mucronate, rough, sometimes ciliate on the back; **Palea** about as long as the lemma, *conspicuously* ciliate-hispid, the hairs about 0.7 mm. long.

In waste places and cultivated ground, Texas to Florida, widely distributed in tropical America. Summer and fall.

4. E. AMABILIS (L.) Wight & Arn. (ă-măb′ĭ-lĭs) ; *E. plumosa* Link.

Culms 4-15′ tall, densely-tufted, erect or ascending from a decumbent base, freely branching; **Blades** 0.5-1.5′ (0.5-4′) long, 2-4 mm. wide, flat, rough above; **Sheaths** mostly shorter than the internodes, ciliate, pilose at the throat; **Ligule** very short; **Panicle** usually exserted, open, usually diffuse, 1.5-3.5′ (1.5-6′) long, oblong-pyramidal, somewhat broader toward the base, the branches usually less than 15 mm. long, naked at the very base, freely branching nearly to the base, the branchlets numerous, commonly with 2-4 spikelets to a branchlet, the rather stiffly ascending pedicels about 1 mm. long; **Spikelets** purplish, 3-7-flowered, 1.5-2.2 mm. long, scarcely 1 mm. wide, flat-oblong; **Glumes** acute, scabrous on the keel, the first 0.5 mm. long, the second 0.8 mm. long; **Lemmas** purple, 0.6-0.8 mm. long, 0.3 mm. wide, obtuse, scabrous on the keel, minutely so over the back; **Palea** nearly as long as the lemma, *conspicuously ciliate*, the hairs about 0.3 mm. long.

In cultivated ground and waste places, eastern Texas, Georgia and Florida. Widely distributed in the tropical regions. (Waller County, Texas.) Spring-fall.

5. E. GLOMERATA (Walt.) L. H. Dewey (glŏm-ĕr-ā′tà) ; *E. conferta* Trin.

Culms 1-3 feet tall, tufted, erect, usually rather stout, freely branching; **Blades** 1.5-8′ long, 3-4 mm. (3-10) wide, flat, long-acuminate ; **Sheaths** shorter than the internodes; **Ligule** less than 1 mm. long; **Panicles** tawny, 3-10′ (4-24′) long, exserted, or some of the axillary included at the base, often 1-3 on the branches or in the axils of the sheaths, narrow, densely-flowered, the short branches numerous, clustered, erect or narrowly ascending, spikelet-bearing to the base, the short-pediceled spikelets appressed; **Spikelets** tawny, 5-10-flowered, 2.5-3.5 mm. long, 1.5 mm. wide, flattened; **Glumes** about 1 mm. long, the first shorter, acute or obtuse, thin, scabrous at the apex; **Lemmas**, the lower 1-1.2 mm. long, acute or subobtuse, minutely scabrous especially on the keel; **Palea** about four-fifths as long as the lemma, ciliate.

In damp or wet places, central Texas to Louisiana, Arkansas, South Carolina. (Texarkana.) Summer-fall.

6. E. CILIANENSIS (All.) Link (sĭl-ĭ-ăn-ĕn′sĭs) ; *E. megastachya* (Koel.) Link; *E. major* Host; STRONG-SCENTED LOVE-GRASS.

Culms 6-25′ tall, densely-tufted, at first erect, finally ascending from a decumbent or geniculate base, freely branching, rather flaccid, often ill-scented; **Blades** 2-6′ long, 2-6 mm. wide, flat, rough above; **Sheaths** shorter than the internodes, conspicuously pilose at the throat; **Ligule** a dense ring of short hairs; **Panicle** greenish-lead color, exserted, 2-6′ long, rather densely-flowered, the branches 1-2′ long, scabrous, solitary or rarely in twos, stiffly ascending or spreading, spikelet-bearing nearly to the base; **Spikelets** 8-37-flowered, 5-18 mm. long, about 3 mm. wide, flat, divergent on short pedicels, a few conspicuous glands on the keels of the glumes and lemmas; **Glumes** acute, the first 1-nerved, about 2 mm. long, the second 3-nerved, a little shorter than the first; **Lemmas** closely imbricate, 2-2.5 mm. long, the lateral nerves prominent, subacute, thin, scabrous; **Palea** about two-thirds as long as its lemma, linear-spatulate, ciliate, falling with the lemma and rachilla internodes; **Anthers** 0.5 mm. long.

In waste places, throughout the United States. Spring-fall.

7. E. POAEOIDES (L.) Beauv. (pō-ē-oi′dēz) ; *E. eragrostis* (L.) Karst.; *E. minor* Host; Low Love-grass.

Culms 6-15′ tall, tufted, erect or commonly decumbent and spreading, freely branching; **Blades** 1-2.5′ long, 1-4 mm. wide, flat, rough above, often somewhat pilose near the base; **Sheaths** shorter than the internodes, loose, sometimes sparingly pilose, especially at the throat, often more or less papillose; **Ligule** a ring of short hairs; **Panicle** finally exserted or those of the branches included at the base, 2-5′ long, oblong to oblong-pyramidal, the short branches rather rigidly ascending or spreading, commonly 0.5-2′ long, sometimes longer, the spikelets on rather rigid scabrous pedicels 1-2 mm. long, ascending or spreading; **Spikelets** lead-color, 6-18-flowered, 5-10 mm. long, about 2 mm. wide, the florets less densely imbricate than those of *E. cilianensis*, the rachilla-joints being visible at the base, the glumes and lemmas sparsely scabrous, usually glandular on the keel; **Glumes** acute, the first about 1.2 mm. long, the second about 1.8 mm. long; **Lemmas** about 1.5 mm. long, obtuse, the lateral nerves prominent; **Palea** nearly as long as the lemma, finely ciliate, persistent; **Stamens,** anthers 0.2 mm. long.

In waste places and cultivated ground, Texas, Pennsylvania, New York, Massachusetts. (Rather rare.) Summer-fall.

8. E. CAPILLARIS (L.) Nees (kăp-ĭl-ăr′ĭs) ; Tiny Love-grass, Love-grass.

Culms 4-20′ tall, tufted, erect or spreading from a decumbent base, sparingly branched at the very base; **Blades** 3-10′ long, 1.5-3 mm. wide, long acuminate, rough above, glabrous or sparingly pilose on the upper surface and margins at or near the base; **Sheaths** short, overlapping and crowded at the very base, the upper inclosing the base of the panicle, villous at the throat, ciliate, otherwise glabrous or sparingly pilose; **Ligule** a ring of hairs less than 0.5 mm. long; **Panicle** open, diffuse, 4-16′ long, often nearly four-fifths the entire length of the plant, the capillary branches ascending or spreading, 1.5-5′ long, mostly in ones to threes, glabrous in the axils, usually a few scattered spikelets at the end of the slender branchlets, the lateral on pedicels 5-15 mm. long; **Spikelets** 2-4-flowered, 2-3 mm. long, ovate to oblong, only slightly flattened; **Glumes** nearly equal, about half the length of the spikelet, narrow, acuminate, scabrous on the keel; **Lemmas** the lower about 1.5 mm. long, acute, the lateral nerves obscure, scabrous on the keel, the scabrous rachilla-joint about 0.5 mm. long; **Palea** about two-thirds as long as the lemma, fringed or erose at the obtuse apex.

In dry places, Texas to Georgia, north to Missouri and Kansas, Rhode Island to New Hampshire. Summer-fall.

9. E. FRANKII Steud. (frănk′ĭ-ī) ; Frank's Love-grass. (*Not in Texas.*)

Culms 6-18′ tall, tufted, erect or often decumbent at the base, branching above the base; **Blades** 2-7′ long, 2-4 mm. wide, flat, rough on the upper surface; **Sheaths** shorter than the internodes, loose, glabrous to long-pilose at the throat; **Ligule** a ring of hairs about 1 mm. long; **Panicle** dark-leadish color, finally exserted, 2-6′ long, commonly 1-1.5′ wide, oblong, those of the branches shorter and usually included at the base, open, the branches ascending, the lower 1-2′ long, the spikelets on pedicels as long to twice as long as the spikelets; **Spikelets** 1-5-flowered, 2-3 mm. long, ovate, dark; **Glumes** acute, pointed, scabrous toward the apex, the first about 1 mm. long, the second about 1.5 mm. long; **Lemmas** 1.5 mm. long, acute, the lateral nerves obscure, sparsely minutely scabrous.

In moist places, Louisiana and Mississippi to Kansas, Minnesota, Massachusetts. Fall.

10. E. PILOSA (L.) Beauv. (pī-lō′så).

Culms 6-20′ tall, tufted, slender, erect or ascending from a decumbent or geniculate base, branching; **Blades** 1-5′ long, 2 mm. or less wide, smooth or slightly rough above; **Sheaths** shorter than the internodes, usually pilose at the throat; **Ligules** a ring of short hairs; **Panicles** 2-6′ long, exserted or included at the base, finally open, mostly ovate, the capillary branches at first erect, finally ascending or spreading, 1-3′ long, often pilose in the lower axils, the ascending pedicels and spikelets solitary or a few to the ascending branchlets; **Spikelets** often purple, 5-12-flowered, 3-6 mm. long, linear, about 1 mm. wide, on pedicels mostly shorter than the spikelets; **Glumes** acute, the first about half as long as the second, the second about 1 mm. long; **Lemmas**, the lower about 1.5 mm. long, acute, the lateral nerves faint or wanting, sparingly minutely scabrous on the keel; **Grain** purplish, about 0.7 mm. long and 0.3 mm. wide, oblong. In cultivated ground and waste places, Texas to Florida, north to Kansas and southern New England. (Claude, Texline, Marble Falls, Jacksonville and Polytechnic, Texas.) Summer and fall.

11. E. BARRELIERI Daveau (băr-ĕl-ĭ-ăr′ī).

Culms 6-25′ tall, tufted, erect, ascending or spreading, sometimes prostrate, from a prominently geniculate base, rooting at the lower nodes, freely branching, *commonly a glandular ring below the nodes;* **Blades** commonly 2-3.5′ sometimes 7′ long, the upper short, 2-5 mm. wide, flat, rounded at the base, lanceolate or linear-lanceolate, ascending, upper surface, margins and under surface toward the tip rough, glabrous, or sparsely pilose on the upper surface near the base; **Sheaths** shorter than the internodes, slightly flattened, glabrous, or ciliate on the margins and pilose or villous at the throat, the hairs sometimes extending along the entire length of the collar; **Ligule** a dense ring of fine hairs; **Panicles**, the terminal usually exserted, 3-7′ long, ovate to narrowly-pyramidal, erect, often with 1-3 small axillary panicles, usually included at the base, the short branches commonly less than 2′ long, solitary or two or three at a node, rigidly ascending or spreading, branching near the base, the short branchlets and pedicels divergent, the pedicels usually less than half the length of the spikelets, and the main axis and branches smooth and glabrous; **Spikelets** linear-oblong, 5-22-flowered, 5-15 mm. long, 1.1-1.5 mm. wide, flattened, grayish-green; **Glumes** acute, scabrous on the keel, the first 1-1.3 mm. long, the second slightly longer; **Lemmas** nearly 2 mm. long, 3-nerved, the lateral prominent, obtuse, sometimes erose, scabrous on upper part of keel; **Palea** slightly shorter than its lemma, narrower, obtuse, ciliate on the upper portion of the keels, arched, persistent.

Waste places and fields, Texas; recently introduced from Europe; Common in central Texas. Spring to fall.

12. E. ARIDA Hitchc. (ăr′ĭ-då).

Culms mostly 8-16′ tall, rarely taller, erect or spreading, tufted, rather stout, often freely branching, a taller plant with a much longer panicle and longer branches than in *E. barrelieri;* **Blades** 3-7' long, 2-4 mm. wide, the upper short, flat; **Sheaths** shorter than the internodes, glabrous, or sparingly pilose at the throat; **Ligules** a ring of hairs nearly 1 mm. long; **Panicles,** the terminal 5-12' long, exserted, or those of the branches shorter and often included at the base, finally open, narrowly pyramidal or ovate, the lower axils often pilose, the slender branches mostly 1-3 at a node, the lower as much as 6' long, ascending or finally spreading, naked at the base, the divergent branchlets mostly 1-2' long, with 2-10 spikelets to each, the lateral spikelets longer than the divergent pedicels; **Spikelets** 5-15-flowered, 3-10 mm. long, linear, about 1.5 mm. wide, light-leadish-purple; **Glumes** acute, scabrous on the keel, the first about 0.7 mm. long, the second about twice as long; **Lemmas,** the lower 1.6-2 mm. long, acute, the lateral nerves evident, scabrous on the midnerve; **Palea** about three-fourths as long as the lemma, ciliate, persistent.

Dry prairies, Texas to Arizona and central Mexico. (Ft. Davis, Texas.) Summer and fall.

13. E. PECTINACEA (Michx.) Nees (pĕk-tĭ-nā'sē-à); *E. caroliniana* (Spreng.) Scribn.; *E. purshii* Schrad.; PURSH'S LOVE-GRASS.

Culms 8-12' tall, rarely taller, slender, densely-tufted, erect, ascending or spreading usually from a decumbent or geniculate base, branching below; **Blades** 2.5-7' long, 2-6 mm. wide, flat, soon becoming involute, margins slightly rough, upper surface rough; **Sheaths** shorter than the internodes, villous at the throat; **Ligule** a dense ring of hairs about 1 mm. long; **Panicles** exserted or partly included, 5-9' long, ovate or narrowly ovate-pyramidal, axis somewhat angular, scabrous toward the apex, flexuous, the primary branches simple or the lower with a branchlet bearing 2-3 spikelets, the spikelets loosely imbricate or sometimes not overlapping; **Spikelets** 5-13-flowered, 4-7 mm. long, about 1.5 mm. wide, linear-oblong or lanceolate-oblong, dark-leadish-green, shining; **Glumes** acute, minutely scabrous on the upper part of the keel, the first about 1.2 mm. long, the second 1.8 mm. long; **Lemmas** 1.5-2 mm. long, 3-nerved, the lateral nerves prominent, acutish, broadly ovate when spread open; **Palea** slightly shorter than its lemma, arched, ciliate, persistent.

Waste places; over most of the United States, common in Texas. Summer and fall.

14. E. DIFFUSA Buckl. (dĭf-ū'zà).

E. diffusa differs from *E. pectinacea* (*E. caroliniana*) in being taller, more robust especially towards the base, its more compound panicle, the primary branches usually with several appressed branchlets with few to several spikelets; while in *E. pectinacea* the primary branches are usually simple or occasionally with a short branchlet at the base.

Culms 5-28', commonly more than 12' tall, densely-tufted, usually decumbent at the base and spreading, freely branching; **Blades** 1.5-5' commonly 2-3' long, 2-3 mm. wide, flat, rough above; **Sheaths** shorter than the internodes, commonly villous at the throat; **Ligule** a ring of hairs 0.5 mm. long or less; **Panicles** numerous, 2-9' long, oblong to pyramidal, dark-leadish color, the larger exserted, often two or three on the branches or from the axils of the sheaths, often included at the base, the branches, branchlets and spikelets at first appressed but finally open and spreading, the capillary branches commonly in ones or twos, freely branching especially the lower to the very base, the numerous short branchlets commonly longer than in *E. pectinacea,* usually bearing 1-6 spikelets, the pedicels on the lateral spikelets 3-10 mm. long; **Spikelets** 5-17-flowered, 4-9 mm. long, linear-lanceolate, those of the larger panicles about 1.5 mm. wide, those of the smaller ones about 1 mm. wide; **Glumes** acute, scabrous on the keel, the first about 1.2 mm. long, the second about 1.5 mm. long; **Lemmas** 1.7 mm. long, acute, scabrous toward the apex, especially on the keel, the three nerves prominent; **Palea** nearly as long as the lemma, curved, somewhat ciliate.

Sandy land, Texas, Oklahoma to southern California; also Missouri, South Carolina, Alabama and Louisiana.   Fall.

15. E. NEOMEXICANA Vasey (nē-ō-mĕks-ĭ-kā′nả).

Culms 1.5-3.5 feet tall, erect or spreading, tufted, often branching near the base; **Blades** 4.5-12′ long, 4-8 mm. wide, rough except near the base on the under surface; **Sheaths** shorter than the internodes, villous at the throat, margins sometimes ciliate; **Ligule** a dense ring of ciliate hairs nearly 1 mm. long; **Panicles** finally exserted, oblong, 6-16′ long, light-lead color, main axis, branches and pedicels scabrous, branches solitary or in twos, mostly ascending or narrowly spreading, commonly less than 5′ long, naked about one-fifth the distance from the base, the numerous branchlets more or less appressed, the slender pedicels mostly longer than the spikelets, sometimes two or three times as long; **Spikelets** 5-14-flowered, 4-9 mm. long, 1.5-2 mm. wide, linear or linear-lanceolate, somewhat flattened, mostly ascending; **Glumes** acute, scabrous on the keel and sometimes toward the apex, the first about 1.5 mm. long, the second nearly 2 mm. long; **Lemmas,** the lower about 2 mm. long, the prominent nerves more or less scabrous, sometimes slightly scabrous toward the acute apex; **Palea** nearly as long as its lemma, curved, ciliate on the keels, obtuse, persistent; **Grain** reddish, about 0.7 mm. long, 0.5 mm. wide, oblong, truncate at both ends, minutely grooved.

Mountains of west Texas to California and Mexico.   (In orchard just north of Ft. Davis.)   Summer.

16. E. MEXICANA (Hornem.) Link (mĕks-ĭ-kā′nả).

Similar to *E. neomexicana*, but lower, erect or spreading, often simple; **Panicle** erect, comparatively small and few-flowered, less compound, the branches and pedicels spreading; **Spikelets** usually not more than 7-flowered, 3-6 mm. long.

Open ground, Texas to Arizona, also Delaware and Iowa.

17. E. TEPHROSANTHOS Schult. (tĕf-rō-săn′thŏs).

Culms 2-10′ tall, tufted, erect or ascending from a decumbent base, a slender delicate plant; **Blades** 1-3.5′ long, 1-2.5 mm. wide, flat or soon involute; **Sheaths** commonly longer than the internodes, pilose at the throat, the hairs 2-3 mm. long; **Ligule** a ring of hairs less than 0.5 mm. long; **Panicle** open, usually erect, narrowly ovate or pyramidal, finally exserted, 1-3′ long, sparsely pilose in the lower axils, the branches commonly less than 1′ long, ascending, naked at the very base, the spikelets rather crowded, scarcely appressed, on scabrous pedicels 1.5 mm.-2 mm. long; **Spikelets** 5-11-flowered, 3-6 mm. long, 1.2 mm. wide, ovate to ovate-oblong; **Glumes** acute, scabrous on the keel, the first 0.8 mm. long, the second 1.2 mm. long; **Lemmas** 1.5 mm. long, subobtuse, scabrous on the upper half of the keel and tips, the nerves prominent, not more than 0.5 mm. from keel to margin; **Palea** four-fifths to as long as the lemma, ciliate.

Dry ground along railway right-of-way, Brownsville, Texas. Late spring-summer.

18. E. SPICATA Vasey (spī-kā'tà).

Culms 2-4 feet tall, densely-tufted, erect, with numerous sterile shoots; **Blades** 5-15' long, the upper short, 3-6 mm. wide, flat or involute with long filiform tips, margins and upper surface rough, sometimes a few hairs on the upper surface near the base; **Sheaths** longer than the internodes, open at the summit, sometimes slightly rough; **Ligule** a ring of hairs about 1 mm. long; **Panicle** finally pale, spikelike, exserted or included at the base, 10-15' long, usually 2-5 mm. thick, cylindric, dense, sometimes a few of the branches slightly projecting, the small spikelets crowded on very short appressed branchlets, the very short pedicels hispidulous; **Spikelets** 1-4 mostly 2-flowered, about 1.5-2.5 mm. long; **Glumes** oval, about 1-1.2 mm. long, the first slightly shorter, broad, obtuse, thin, pale, scabrous on the nerve; **Lemmas** 1.3-1.5 mm. long, broad, pale, thin, obtuse, the lateral nerves obscure, the midnerve scabrous often slightly excurrent; **Palea** about equal to its lemma, scabrous on the keels, obtuse, thin.

Low places, in prairies, or along railway rights-of-way. Extreme southwest Texas and Mexico. (Falfurrias and Mercedes, Texas.) Summer and fall.

19. E. SECUNDIFLORA Presl (sē-kŭn-dĭ-flō'rà); *E. oxylepis* Torr.; *E. interrupta* (Nutt.) Trelease. (See *E. beyrichii*, a closely related plant.)

Culms 10-36' tall, tufted, branching, the plant, panicle and spikelets variable; **Blades** 2.5-20' long, mostly 8-12' long, 2-5 mm. wide, flat, soon becoming involute toward the apex, with a long narrow tip; **Sheaths** shorter or longer than the internodes, a tuft of hairs at the throat; **Ligule** a ring of very short hairs; **Panicles** usually purplish, the terminal exserted 8-18' long, narrow or ovate-pyramidal, the branches sometimes longer and spreading, short panicles often included or partly hidden in the second and third sheaths, the main axis and branches scabrous, the lower branches often distant, mostly 1-3 rarely 6' long, usually erect or ascending sometimes spreading or even horizontal, naked at the base, sometimes sparsely-pilose in the axils, the spikelets in more or less capitate clusters, interrupted or irregularly arranged along the branches or branchlets, the spikelets on short scabrous pedicels; **Spikelets** tinged with purple, 8-40-flowered, mostly 10-15 mm. long, 3-4 mm. wide, flat; **Glumes** shorter than the lower lemma, subequal, 2-3 mm. long, acute, scabrous on the nerve; **Lemmas,** the lower 3 mm. the middle sometimes 3.5 mm. long, abruptly-narrowed, acute, the green nerves prominent, scabrous on the midnerve; **Palea** about one-fourth shorter than its lemma, 2-toothed, curved, obtuse, ciliate on the keels; **Stamens,** anthers 0.2-0.3 mm. long.

Sandy land; middle and southern United States to Mexico. Spring to fall.

20. E. BEYRICHII J. G. Smith (bā-rĭk'ĭ-ī).

This plant is closely related to *E. secundiflora*, and like it, the plant, panicles, and spikelets vary much.

In this species the gradually narrowed lemmas are longer, with paleas slightly over half as long as the lemma, anthers 0.4-0.5 mm. long while in *E. secundiflora* the shorter lemmas are abruptly narrowed, the paleas about one-fourth shorter than the lemmas, anthers 0.2-0.3 mm. long.

Culms 4-20′ tall, tufted, rather slender, erect, ascending or spreading from a geniculate or decumbent base, branching; **Blades** 2-12′ long, mostly 3.5-5′, 1-5 mm. wide, flat or involute, a few hairs on the upper surface near the base, the basal blades numerous; **Sheaths** mostly shorter than the internodes, usually villous at the throat; **Ligule** a dense ring of short and long hairs intermixed; **Panicles** more or less purplish, turning pale, exserted, 1-6′ long, usually oblong, ovate or capitate, the short branches overlapping above, often interrupted below, commonly less than 1.5′ long, erect or ascending, spikelet-bearing to the base, crowded in dense ovate or oblong clusters, the spikelets sub-sessile or on very short scabrous pedicels, arranged along a scabrous axis; **Spikelets** pale, often tinged with purple, 6-28-flowered, 6-20 mm. long, commonly 3.5-6 mm. wide, flat, ovate to oblong; **Glumes** unequal, shorter than the lower lemmas, the first about 1.8 mm. long, the second about 2.2 mm. long, acute, scabrous on the nerve; **Lemmas** the lower 3.5 mm., the middle sometimes 3.5-4.5 mm. long, acuminate, gradually narrowed, the three nerves prominent, scabrous on the midnerve and slightly so on the margins; **Palea** about half as long as its lemma, elliptic, curved, ciliate, the emarginate or erose apex truncate or obtuse; **Stamens**, anthers 0.4-0.5 mm. long.

In sandy places, Texas to Mexico. Spring to fall.

21. E. SWALLENI Hitchc. (swäl′ĕn-ī).

Culms 1-2 feet tall, densely-tufted, erect; **Blades** 1.5-3.5′ long more or less, 1.5 mm. wide more or less, flat or involute, rough above; **Sheaths** mostly longer than the internodes, pilose at the throat; **Ligule** a ring of hairs less than 0.5 mm. long; **Panicle** exserted, 10′ long more or less, pyramidal, the axils of the branches glabrous or with a few long hairs, the branches in ones to threes, ascending or spreading, the lower mostly 3-5′ long, rather loosely-flowered, the pedicels 4-10 mm. long, with a *glandular ring* below the spikelet; **Spikelets** 6-18-flowered, 5-11 mm. long, 1.5 mm. wide, linear-lanceolate; **Glumes** acute, the first 1 mm. long, the second broader, about 2 mm. long; **Lemmas** 2 mm. long, narrowly obtuse, the nerves evident; **Palea** about two-thirds as long as the lemma, curved, finely-ciliate.

Texas. (Sarita, Texas.) Spring-summer.

22. E. INTERMEDIA Hitchc. (ĭn-tẽr-mēd′ĭ-à).

Culms 1-3 feet tall, commonly in rather large dense tufts, erect or spreading, simple or very rarely branching; **Blades** 3-14′ rarely 20′ long, 3-7 mm. wide, slightly narrowed at the base, flat or involute at the tip, margins and upper surface rough, hirsute at the base on the upper surface, otherwise glabrous or sparsely pilose with long hairs on the upper surface, more or less papillose; **Sheaths** mostly longer than the internodes, especially below, hirsute at the throat, the long spreading hairs extending part or all the way across the collar, commonly ciliate or papillose-ciliate, or the lower sparsely papillose-hirsute; **Ligule** a ring of very short hairs, often hidden by the long hairs back of the throat; **Panicles** finally exserted, 5-18′ rarely 24′ long, pyramidal, scabrous toward the apex, pilose in the main axils, as well as those of the branchlets, especially the lower, the branches mostly solitary or as many as 4 to a node, the lower as much as 7′ long, stiffly ascending, spreading or horizontal, scabrous, naked or branching to the base, the spikelets on scabrous divergent pedicels, the lateral mostly 2-3 times as long as the spikelets, 1-10 spikelets to each divergent branchlet, the panicle breaking loose and rolling before the wind as a tumble weed; **Spikelets** 2-9-flowered, 2.5-6 mm. long, at maturity about 1.5 mm. wide, more or less purple, the spikelets turning somewhat pale-green, dark with age; **Glumes** scabrous on the nerve, narrow and acute, equal or the first 1.2-1.5 mm. long, the second 1.5-2 mm. long, broader; **Lemmas** about 2-2.5 mm. long, 0.6 mm. wide, broadly acute, the three nerves obscure, sparsely minutely scabrous, margins scarious; **Palea** persistent, nearly as long as the lemma, curved, obtuse, scabrous on the keels; **Grain** 0.8 mm. long, dark amber, striate.

In rather rich soil on rocky, gravelly or sandy land, Texas. Florida and Mexico. Spring to fall.

23. E. LUGENS Nees (lū′gĕns).

Culms 1-3 feet tall, in small or large tufts, erect or geniculate at the base, especially in the large tufts, simple or branching, often growing in rather large colonies, the panicles, especially when young, as well as the nodes and the internodes, often tinged with purple, giving the colonies or fields a purplish tinge; **Blades** 1.5-9′ long, 1-3 mm. wide, flat or involute toward the tip, rough and often very sparsely-pilose on the upper surface; **Sheaths** shorter than the internodes, often a tuft of long hairs at each end of the collar; **Ligule** a dense ring of hairs about 0.5 mm. long, the hairs of the same ligule varying in length; **Panicles** purplish, especially when young, finally exserted, pyramidal, 12′ long or less, about half as wide, axis rough toward the tip, the lower axils more or less pilose, the panicles on the branches usually smaller and often included at the base, the panicles soon breaking away and rolling before the wind, the capillary scabrous branches ascending or spreading, or sometimes horizontal, not so stiff as in *E. intermedia*, the lower as much as 6′ long, naked at the base, in ones to fours, often branching near the base, the capillary scabrous pedicels 1-3 times as long as the divergent spikelets; **Spikelets** 3-8-flowered, 3-5 mm. long, about 1 mm. wide, linear-oblong, dark-purple, turning pale or grayish-purple with age; **Glumes** acute, the first nearly 1 mm. long, the second about 1.5 mm. long; **Lemma** 1.5-1.8 mm. long, about 0.4 mm. wide, acute, 3-nerved, the lateral nerves obscure; **Palea** persistent, curved, about two-thirds the length of its lemma, finely-ciliate; **Grain** about 0.5 mm. long, half as wide, oblong, rather dark-amber.

Sandy land, waste places and cultivated fields. (Goliad and Rio Grande Valley.) Spring.

24. E. HIRSUTA (Michx.) Nees (hẽr-sū′tȧ) ; Stout Love-grass.

Culms 2-4.5 feet tall, densely-tufted, erect or spreading, rather stout, branching only at or near the base; **Blades** crowded near the base, mostly 1-2 rarely 3 feet long, 3-10 mm. wide, flat or involute toward the tip, long-acuminate, tough, glabrous or a few hairs on upper surface near the base; **Sheaths** overlapping, at least the lower ones papillose-hirsute, with a tuft of hairs on each side at the summit; **Ligule** less than 1 mm. long, ciliate; **Panicles** purplish, 10-30′ long, oblong-pyramidal, at first narrow, finally exserted and widely spreading or those of the branches included at the base, the lower axils often pilose, the scabrous pedicels and branches long and capillary, naked at the base, ascending to spreading, as long as 10′, the branchlets 1-3′ long, the scabrous, divergent pedicels 6-20 mm. long, or the lateral mostly 2-5 mm. long, with 1-10 spikelets to each branchlet; **Spikelets** purplish, ovate to oblong, 2-5-flowered, 2.5-4 mm. long, 1.5-2 mm. wide; **Glumes** 1.2-2 mm. long, the second sometimes slightly longer, acute, scabrous on the keel and often sparsely on the body; **Lemmas** 1.5-2.5 mm.

long, acute, the lateral nerves rather obscure, scabrous on the midnerve and sparsely so on the body, especially toward the apex; **Palea** from equal to one-third shorter than its lemma, ciliate on the keels.

In dry fields, thickets and woodlands, Texas to Florida, north to South Carolina. (Near Marshall and Tyler, Texas.) Summer and fall.

25. E. SESSILISPICA Buckl. (sĕs-ĭl-ĭ-spī′ká); *Diplachne rigida* Vasey; *Eragrostis rigida* (Vasey) Scribn.; *Leptochloa rigida* Munro.

Culms 1-2.5 feet long, slender, rigid, erect or ascending, loosely-tufted; **Blades** 4-12′ mostly 6-8′ long, 2 mm. or less wide, flat or involute, 2-4 to the culm, acuminate, some rough, glabrous except a few scattered long hairs; **Sheaths** longer than the internodes; **Ligule** prominent tufts of spreading silky hairs; **Panicle** long exserted, often over one-half as long as the plant sometimes 2 feet long, open, pyramidal, broad, rigid, wídely spreading, the tips of the nodding panicles often touching the ground, the branches alternate, 2-10′ long, usually single but freely branching at the very base, spreading or horizontal, two inches or less distant, with tufts of long hairs in axils; **Spikelets** usually 6-8-flowered, 7-9 mm. long, sessile, appressed, distant, alternate on the opposite sides of triangular branches, often purplish; **Glumes** lanceolate, acute, rigid, slightly scabrous on keel, the first 2.5-3 mm. long, 1-nerved, the second 3-4 mm. long, 3-nerved; **Lemmas** lanceolate, acute, rigid, 3 mm. (3-4) long, the two lateral nerves vanishing before reaching the margins, narrow, scabrous on keel; **Palea** firm, much arched, slightly shorter than the lemma, about 2.5 mm. long, oblong, obtuse, ciliate.

Mostly sandy land, dry prairies and along river banks; Texas to New Mexico, north to Kansas. Spring to fall.

26. E. REFRACTA (Muhl.) Scribn. (rē-frăk′tá); *E. campestris* Trin.; MEADOW LOVE-GRASS.

Culms 1-3 feet tall, tufted, branching only at the very base; **Blades** 1.5-12′ long, 2-4 mm. wide, flat or involute, slightly rough above, some-what villous toward the base; **Sheaths** mostly overlapping, sparingly villous at the throat; **Ligule** a ring of short hairs; **Panicle** light-lead color or purplish, loosely-flowered, usually included at the base, 8-20′ long; the slender scabrous branches at first ascending but finally widely spreading, 4-11′ long, the axils often villous, naked at the base, the long slender scabrous branchlets bearing toward their ends a few scattered appressed spikelets, the pedicels 1-2 mm. long; **Spikelets** 4-13-flowered (6-30), 3-6 mm. (4-12) long, linear-lanceolate; **Glumes** acuminate, 1.5-2 mm. long, the second slightly longer; **Lemmas** 1.5-2 mm. long, narrowed or concave above the middle into an acuminate point, the lateral nerves prominent; **Palea** about three-fourths as long as the lemma, linear, incurved, ciliate.

In sandy rather moist soil, eastern Texas to Florida, north to Delaware and Maryland. Summer-fall.

27. E. CURTIPEDICELLATA Buckl. (kûr-tĭ-pĕd-ĭ-sĕl-ā′tá); SHORT-STALKED LOVE-GRASS.

The comparatively short culms have very large rigid panicles, as long as 18′, often curved and drooping, sometimes reclining. *The sheaths and lower surface of the blades are often glandular-viscid.*

Culms 1-3 feet tall, tufted, with numerous sterile shoots, from a bulbous base, erect or decumbent at the base, rigid, rarely branching, often growing in rather large patches or colonies; **Blades** mostly 3-7′

long, 2-7 mm. wide, flat or involute toward the apex, rather rigid, margins and upper surface rough; **Sheaths** longer than the internodes, open and rather loose above, throat and each end of the collar villous, the hairs 3-6 mm. long, otherwise glabrous or a few scattered hairs along the exposed margins; **Ligule** a ring of short hairs; **Panicle** included at the base or finally exserted, 4-18' long, oblong-pyramidal, diffuse, erect or finally nodding or reclining, the rigid branches 3-7' long, widely-spreading, naked at base, pilose in the axils, the main axis smooth, the branches scabrous, the several short branchlets spikelet-bearing nearly to the base, the *appressed* spikelets on pedicels 1-2 mm. long; **Spikelets** 5-12-flowered, 4-6 mm. long, 1.5 mm. wide, oblong-linear, purplish or pale; **Glumes,** the first about 1.5 mm. long, the second about 2 mm. long, ovate, acute, keeled, minutely scabrous on the keel; **Lemmas** about 1.7 mm. long, lanceolate, subacute, lateral nerves prominent, scabrous on the keel; **Palea** about 1.5 mm. long, linear, obtuse, curved so that its two hispid nerves appear outside of the lemmas.

Prairies, Texas to Kansas. Summer and fall.

28. E. TRICHODES (Nutt.) Nash (trī-kō'dēz).

Culms 2-4 feet tall, tufted, erect, simple, comparatively slender, all the internodes being very short and at the base except the upper which extends from near the base to the panicle; **Blades** 6-36' long, 2-7 mm. wide, flat, narrowed toward the base, attenuate into a long slender point, somewhat rough on the upper surface toward the tip, margins rough or smooth, the upper surface hirsute near the base or a few scattered hairs toward the apex; **Sheaths** longer than the internodes, confined mostly toward the base, hirsute at the throat, otherwise glabrous or almost glabrous; **Ligule** a dense ring of short hairs; **Panicle** purplish, usually exserted, sometimes included at the base, 10-36' long, often over half the length of the culm, finally nodding, comparatively narrow, oblong, interrupted below, the axis rigid and somewhat scabrous, the lower axils sometimes pilose, the scabrous capillary branches erect or ascending, mostly 3-7' long, naked below, often solitary below and whorled above, the scabrous, divergent branchlets usually less than 1.5' long, the flexuous scabrous pedicels twice to several times as long as the spikelets; **Spikelets** pale or purplish, 3-10-flowered, 3-9 mm. long; **Glumes** 2-4 mm. long, the second slightly longer, acute, scabrous on the keel and sometimes sparsely so on the body; **Lemmas,** the lower 2.5-3 mm. long, acute, scabrous on the midnerve, the lateral nerves manifest; **Palea** about as long as the lemma, obtuse, ciliate. As this plant is similar to *E. pilifera* except, perhaps, not so tall and spikelets smaller, the photograph and illustrations are omitted.

Dry sandy soil, Texas and New Mexico to Arkansas, thence to Illinois and Ohio. Summer and fall.

29. E. PILIFERA Scheele (pī-lĭf'ẽr-à); *E. grandiflora* Smith & Bush.

This species is so closely related to *E. trichodes* that perhaps it should be determined as a variety of that species. It is usually taller and stouter, with a larger panicle; **Spikelets** bronze rather than purplish, larger, usually more than 10-flowered (4-18). In this species the upper florets keep on developing after the lower have begun to fall from the rachilla.

Very sandy land, Texas to Nebraska and Illinois. (Between Ballinger and Abilene.) Fall.

30. **E. SPECTABILIS** (Pursh) Steud. (spĕk-tăb'ĭ-lĭs); *E. pectinacea* of most American authors, not Michaux's species; LOVE-GRASS, PURPLE LOVE-GRASS.

Culms 1-3 feet tall, tufted, erect or ascending, rigid, simple; **Blades** 8-18′ long, 3-8 mm. wide, flat, rough on the margins and both surfaces except below near the base, glabrous or hirsute at the base and pubescent or pilose toward the apex on the upper surface, and pubescent on the under surface near the base, more or less papillose; **Sheaths** longer than the internodes, throat prominently hirsute, glabrous or pubescent below to papillose-hirsute toward the summit; **Ligule** a ring of hairs 2-4 mm. long; **Panicle** reddish-purple, loosely-flowered, included or finally exserted, ovate to pyramidal, widely diffuse, 8-25′ long, the rigid branches 10′ long or less, ascending, horizontal or even reflexed, the branchlets mostly 2-3′ long, main axis, branches and branchlets scabrous and glabrous to pilose, the axils from pilose to copiously villous; **Spikelets** purplish, 4-11-flowered, 4-8 mm. long, 1.5-2 mm. wide, flat, linear-oblong, the scabrous pedicels slightly shorter than or about as long or twice as long as the spikelets, the terminal ones often very long; **Glumes** about equal, 1.5 mm. long, ovate, acute, more or less scabrous especially on the keel; **Lemmas** 1.5-2 mm. long, the nerves prominent, acute, minutely scabrous especially on the keel; **Palea** nearly as long as its lemma, incurved, obtuse, ciliate on the nerves.

Dry or sandy land, Texas to Florida and north. Summer and fall.

31. **E. SILVEANA** Swallen (sĭl-vē-ā'nȧ).

This is a new species first collected by the author near Taft and Port Arthur, Texas. The branches of the panicle are glandular-viscid, and sometimes the sheaths and blades.

Culms 1-2.5 feet tall, densely-tufted, erect, the tufts often large, erect or spreading from a knotty base, smooth and glabrous throughout except where noted; **Blades** 3.5-10′ long, 4-7 mm. wide, flat, soon involute when dry, acuminate, narrowed into a slender point, slightly rough on the upper surface near the tip; **Sheaths** longer than the internodes; **Ligule** a ring of short hairs less than 0.5 mm. long; **Panicle** usually somewhat included at the base, 8-15′ long, ovate-pyramidal to oblong, about half as wide as long, the axis scabrous toward the summit, the slender scabrous *viscid* branches single or a few in a whorl, stiffly ascending or spreading, naked at the base, mostly 3-4′ sometimes even more than 6′ long, the numerous divergent branchlets short, with several appressed or somewhat spreading spikelets, the pedicels scabrous, the lateral usually less than half as long as the spikelet, the terminal often 2-3 times as long as the spikelet; **Spikelets** 4-9-flowered, 2-5 mm. long, about 1 mm. wide, oblong, bright-to-dark-purplish; **Glumes** about 1 mm. long, the first slightly shorter, acute, scabrous on the keel; **Lemmas** 1-1.3 mm. long, 0.4-0.5 mm. wide, the lateral nerves prominent and parallel, acute, more or less minutely scabrous; **Palea** slightly longer than its lemma, curved, the keels ciliate-hispid, the stiff hairs exposed at the sides of the lemma.

Low black sandy loam, usually near the coast, many places along the coast from Taft to Port Arthur. Fall.

32. **E. PALMERI** S. Wats. (päm'ĕr-ī).

Culms 2.5-3.5 feet tall, densely-tufted, erect, simple, from rootstocks; **Blades** 5-14′ mostly 7-10′ long, the sterile long, 2-4 mm. wide, flat at the base, involute at the long narrow tip, more or less rough and hairy on the upper surface near the base, especially hairy near the ligule; **Sheaths** shorter than the internodes, usually villous at the throat, the long hairs extending partly across the collar; **Ligule** a ring of very short hairs; **Panicles** 5-12' long, narrowly pyramidal, long-exserted, the axils glabrous, the capillary slightly scabrous branches in ones to threes, mostly solitary, scattered, the lower commonly 4-6' long, ascending or somewhat spreading, usually branching to near the base, a few spikelets on the numerous branchlets, the spikelets and pedicels ascending or spreading, slightly scabrous, the lateral 1.5-3 mm. long, the terminal 3-6 mm. long; **Spikelets** 4-8-flowered, 3-6 mm. long, slightly flattened, linear-lanceolate; **Glumes** acute, scabrous on the keel toward the apex, the first 1-1.5 mm. long, the second 1.5-2 mm. long; **Lemmas,** the lower about 2 mm. long, acute, scabrous on the keel toward the apex, the lateral nerves evident towards the base of the lemma; **Palea** nearly as long as the lemma, slightly curved. (Illustrated on photograph of *E. erosa.*)

Rio Grande Valley, Texas, and Mexico. (Harlingen, Texas.) Fall.

33. E. EROSA Scribn. (ē-rō'sà).

Culms 1-3.5 feet tall, usually rather densely-tufted, erect or spreading, simple; **Blades** 4-15' long, 1-5 mm. wide, flat or involute toward the long slender point, rather erect, sometimes with a few hairs on the upper surface near the base; **Sheaths** usually shorter than the internodes, glabrous or sparsely-pilose at the throat on each end of the collar; **Ligule** a ring of short soft hairs less than 0.5 mm. long; **Panicle** finally exserted, diffuse, 4-18' long, often more than half as wide, narrowly to broadly pyramidal, loosely-flowered, the axils glabrous or the lower with few hairs, the somewhat capillary branches mostly in ones or twos sometimes threes, naked at the base, the lower 4-8' long, the branchlets commonly 1-3' long, the ultimate subdivisions usually less than an inch long, the branches, branchlets and ultimate subdivisions ascending or spreading, the scabrous pedicels of the lateral spikelets 1-2 mm. long, sometimes as long as the spikelet, the terminal longer than spikelet; **Spikelets** 3-15-flowered, 3-10 mm. long, 1-1.5 mm. wide, linear, rather flat and compact, olive-green or finally light-lead color; **Glumes** scabrous on the nerve, acute, 1.5-2 mm. long, the second slightly longer and broader and sometimes obtuse; **Lemmas** tardily deciduous, 2-2.5 mm. (3) long, acute or obtuse, more or less scabrous toward the apex, the nerves evident or obscure, the apex often fringed or erose, and margins, especially above, more or less scarious; **Palea** about as long as its lemma, persistent, curved, ciliate on the keels and sometimes at the apex, often truncate or lobed, sometimes erose; **Grain** about 1 mm. long and half as wide, narrowed slightly at one end, purplish.

Rocky or sandy soil, Texas to Mexico. (Riviera, and Devil's River on San Antonio-Alpine Road, Texas.) Spring to fall.

34. E. ELLIOTTII S. Wats. (ĕl-ĭ-ŭt'ĭ-ī); *E. nitida* (Ell.) Chapm.

Culms 10-28' usually less than 20' tall, tufted, firm, erect; **Blades** 15' long more or less, 3-5 mm. wide, long-acuminate, rough above; **Sheaths** mostly longer than the internodes; **Ligule** a short ciliate membrane; **Panicle** 15' long more or less, usually about half the length of the plant, diffuse, comparatively few-flowered, the branches ascending or somewhat spreading, capillary and fragile, the lower as much as 12' long, the spikelets spreading, on fragile pedicels mostly 5-15 mm. long; **Spikelets** 6-16-flowered, 5-10 mm. long, about 1.5 mm. wide, linear-oblong; **Glumes** acute, sometimes slightly scabrous on the nerve, the first about 1 mm. long and the second about 1.5 mm. long; **Lemmas** ovate, acute, 1.5-1.75 mm. long, the lateral nerves prominent; **Palea** about as long as its lemma, hispid-ciliate.

Southern United States, Gulf coast and west Indies, and Mexico. (Timbalier Island, Texas.)   Summer and fall.

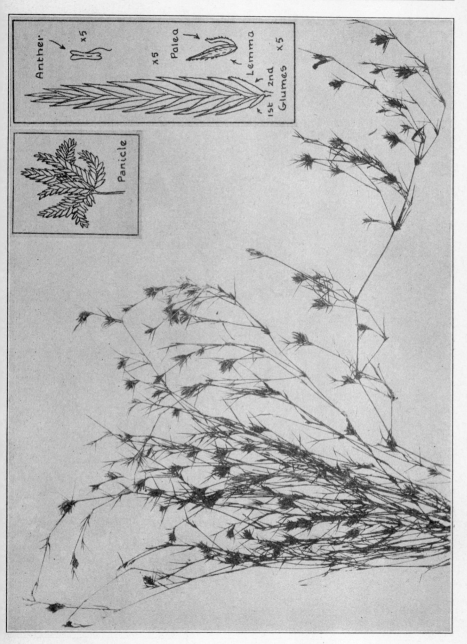

Anther. x5

x5 Palea

Lemma

1st / 2nd Glumes x5

Panicle

ERAGROSTIS REPTANS; Creeping Meadow-grass

ERAGROSTIS HYPNOIDES; Meadow Creeping-grass

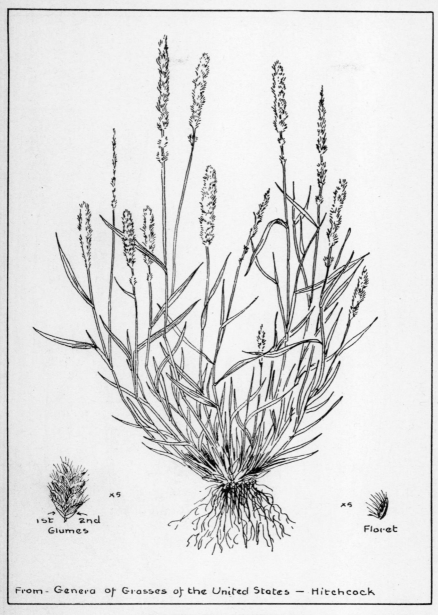

From - Genera of Grasses of the United States — Hitchcock

ERAGROSTIS CILIARIS

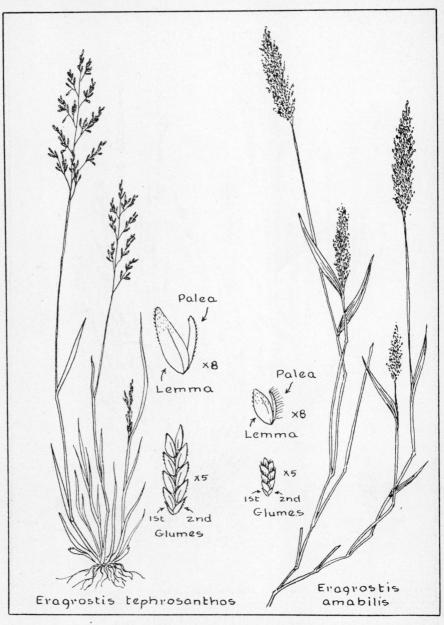

ERAGROSTIS TEPHROSANTHOS AND ERAGROSTIS AMABILIS

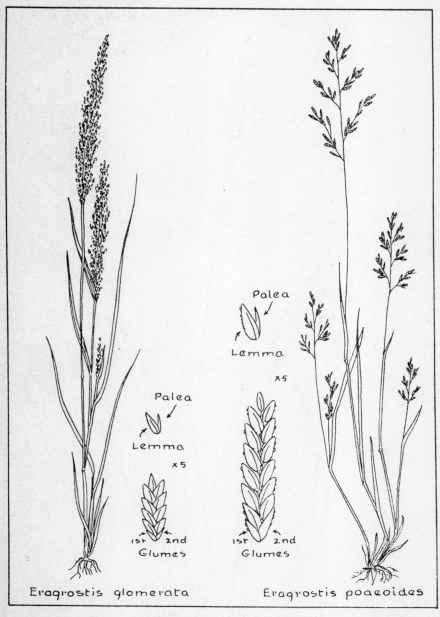

Palea

Lemma

x5

Palea

Lemma

x5

1st 2nd
Glumes

1st 2nd
Glumes

Eragrostis glomerata

Eragrostis poaeoides

ERAGROSTIS GLOMERATA AND **ERAGROSTIS POAEOIDES**

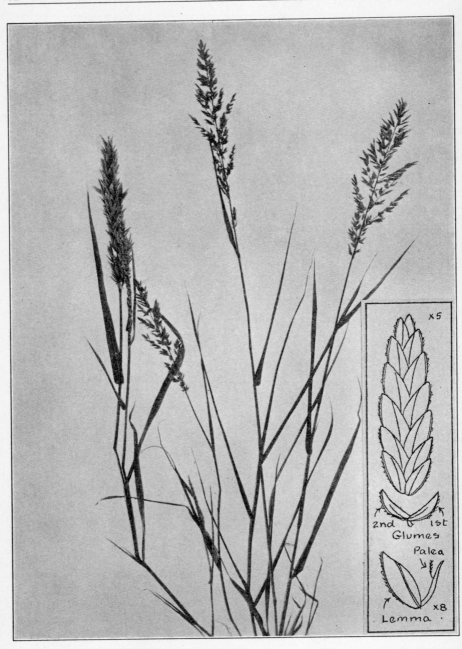

ERAGROSTIS CILIANENSIS; STRONG-SCENTED LOVE-GRASS

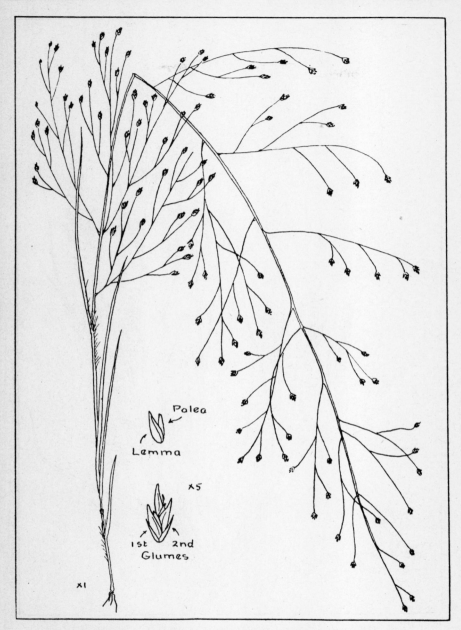

ERAGROSTIS CAPILLARIS, Tiny Love-grass, Lace-grass

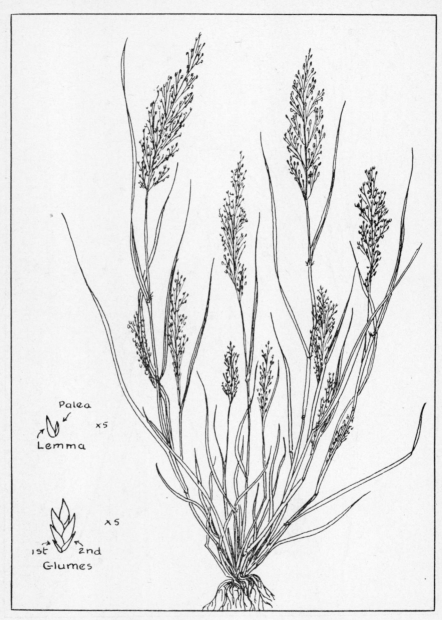

ERAGROSTIS FRANKII, Frank's Love-grass

ERAGROSTIS PILOSA

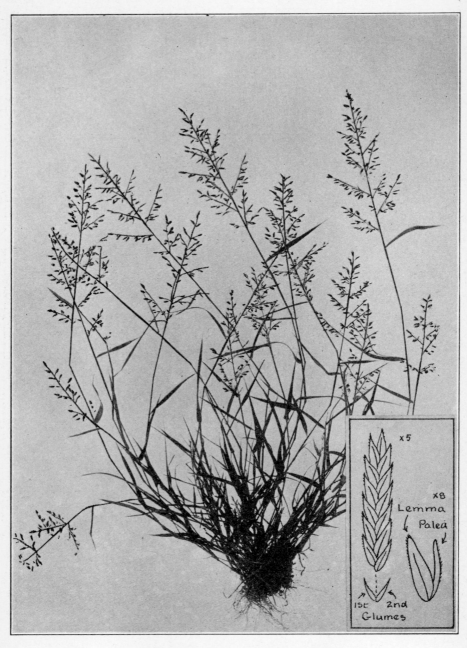

ERAGROSTIS BARRELIERI

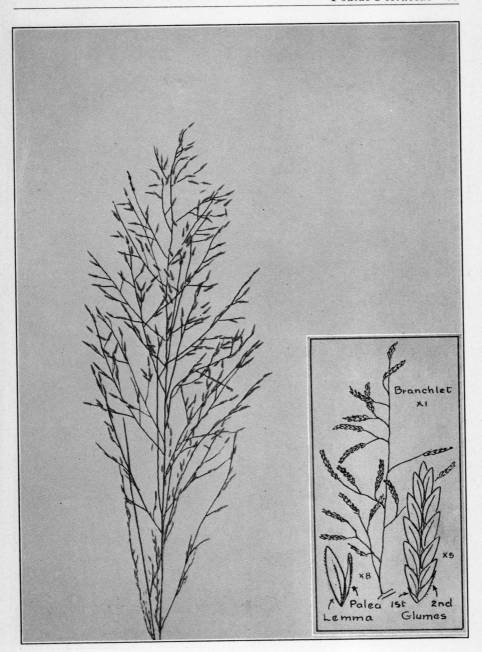

ERAGROSTIS ARIDA

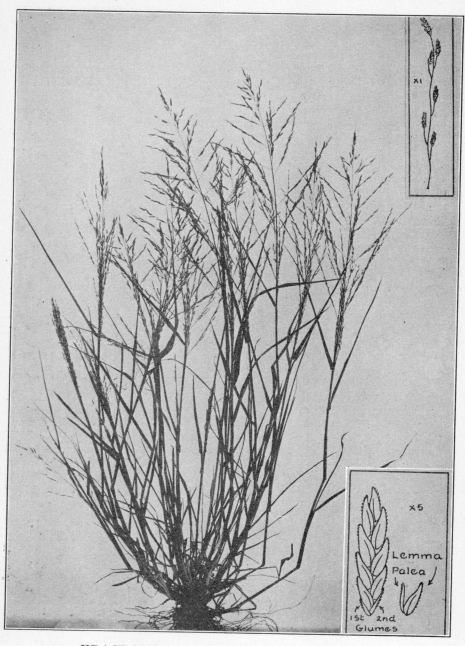

ERAGROSTIS PECTINACEA (E. caroliniana)

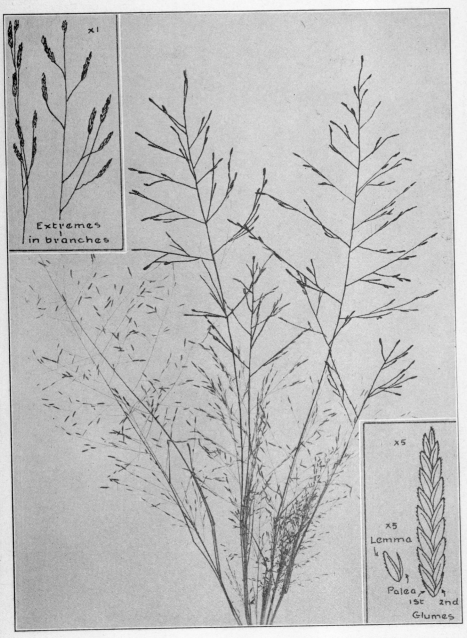

ERAGROSTIS DIFFUSA, formerly included in E. pectinacea
(E. caroliniana)

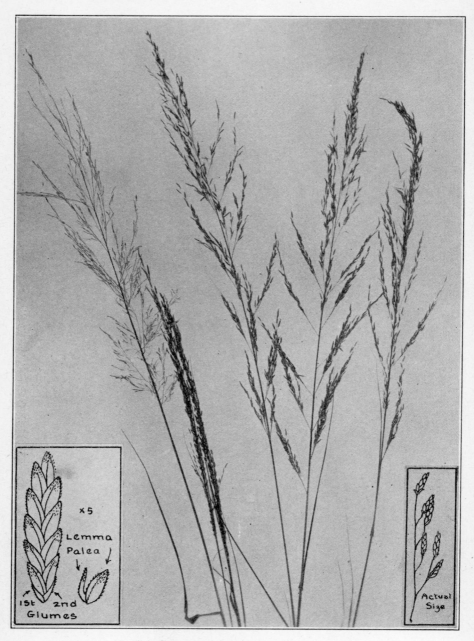

ERAGROSTIS NEOMEXICANA

ERAGROSTIS SPICATA

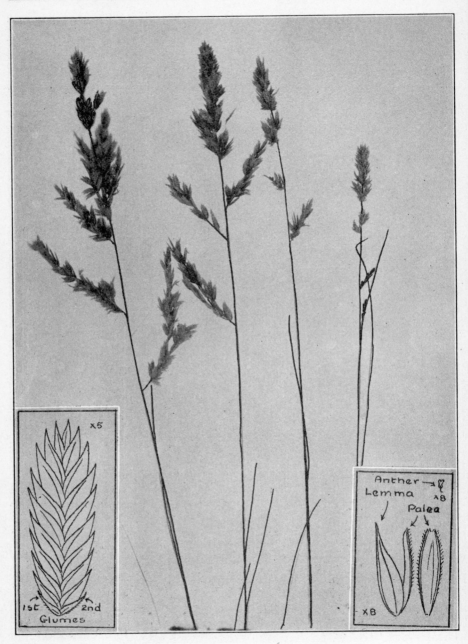

ERAGROSTIS SECUNDIFLORA

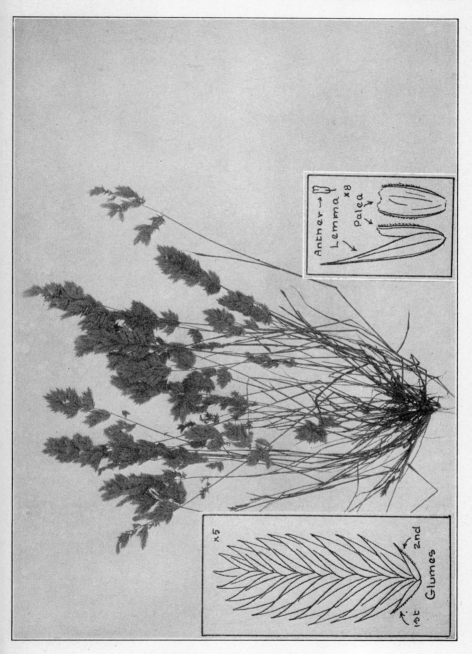

ERAGROSTIS BEYRICHII

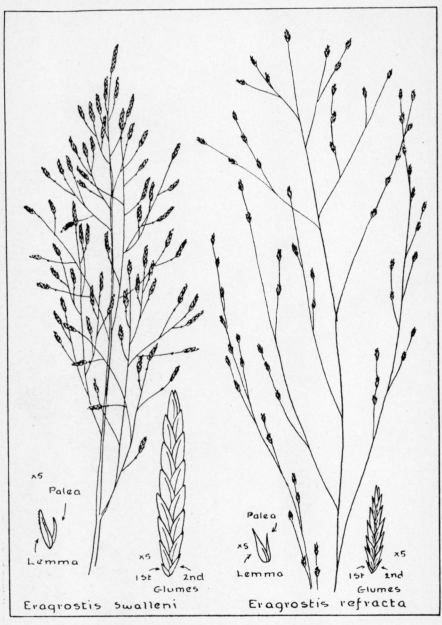

ERAGROSTIS SWALLENI AND ERAGROSTIS REFRACTA

ERAGROSTIS INTERMEDIA

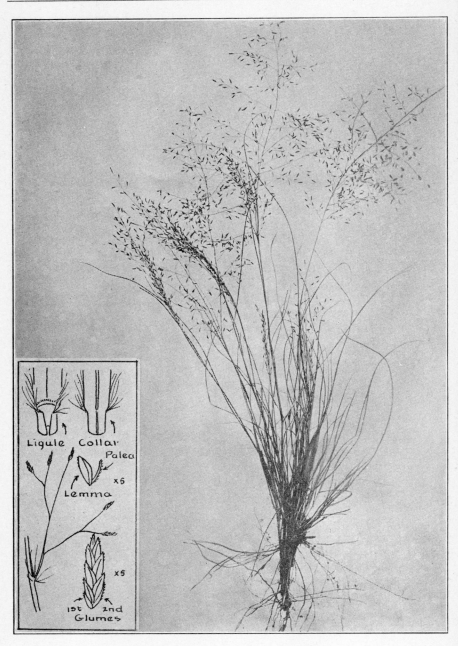

ERAGROSTIS LUGENS

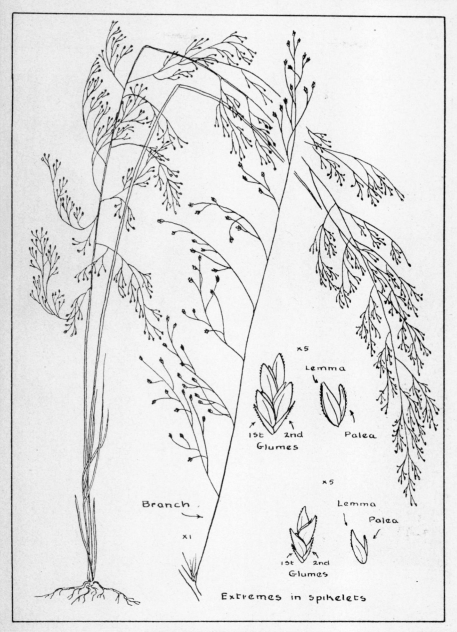

x5

Lemma

1st 2nd   Palea
Glumes

x5

Lemma
Palea

1st 2nd
Glumes

Branch

x1

Extremes in spikelets

ERAGROSTIS HIRSUTA

ERAGROSTIS SESSILISPICA

ERAGROSTIS CURTIPEDICELLATA

ERAGROSTIS PILIFERA (E. grandiflora)

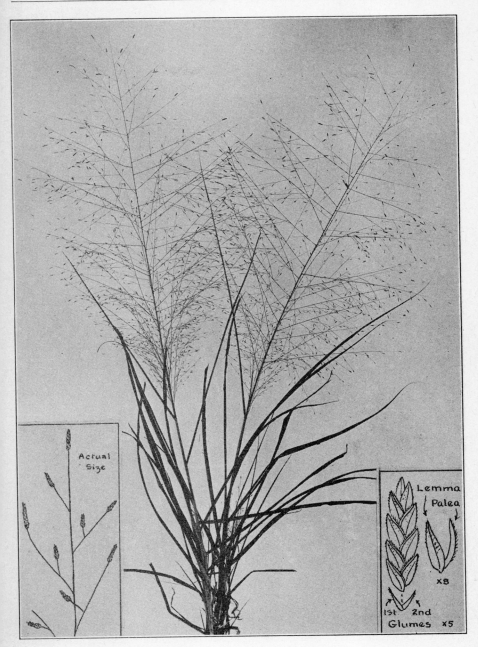

ERAGROSTIS SPECTABILIS, Purple Love-grass; formerly known as
E. pectinacea

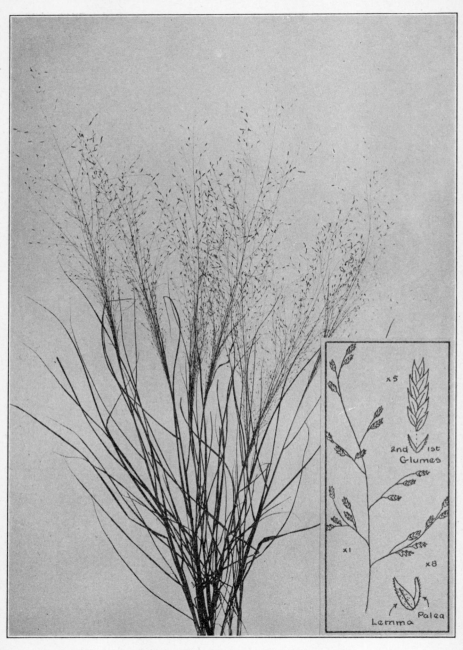

ERAGROSTIS SILVEANA

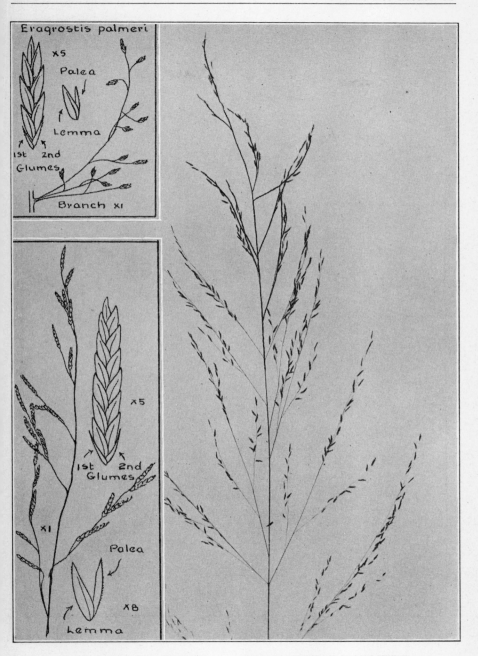

ERAGROSTIS EROSA AND ERAGROSTIS PALMERI

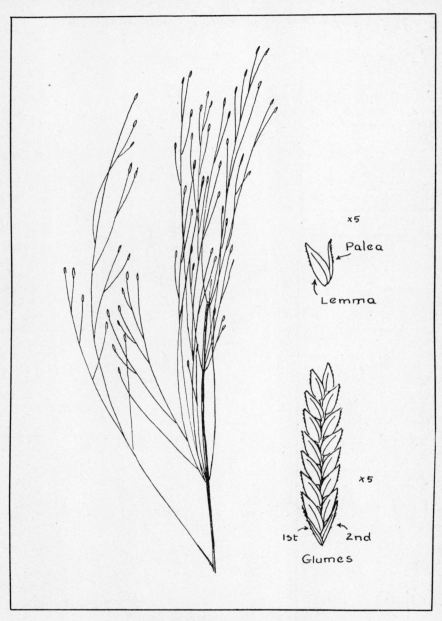

Palea

Lemma

×5

1st   2nd

Glumes

×5

ERAGROSTIS ELLIOTTII

7. DIARRHENA Beauv. (dī-à-rē′nà)
(Diarina Raf.)

Spikelets few-flowered, the rachilla disarticulating above the glumes and between the florets; **Glumes** unequal, acute, shorter than the lemmas, the first 1-nerved, the second 3-5-nerved; **Lemmas** chartaceous, pointed, 3-nerved, the nerves converging in the point, the upper floret reduced; **Palea** chartaceous, 2-nerved, obtuse, at maturity the lemma and palea widely spread by the large turgid beaked caryopsis with hard shining pericarp.

Perennials, with slender rhizomes, broadly linear, flat blades, long-tapering below, and narrow, few-flowered panicles.

Our single species, *D. americana,* is too rare to be of importance as a forage grass. Having failed to collect this species the artist made a copy from a drawing in Hitchcock's *Genera of Grasses of the United States.*

In rich woods, Texas to Oklahoma, Kansas, east to Ohio. Summer-fall.

1. **D. AMERICANA** Beauv. (à-měr-ĭ-kā′nà); *Diarina festucoides* Raf.; *D. diandra* (Michx.) Wood; *Korycarpus arundinaceus* Zea; *K. diandrus* (Michx.) Kuntze.

Culms 2-4 feet tall, erect, simple, rough below the panicle; **Blades** 6-24′ long, 10-18 mm. wide, flat, usually rough, leafy below; **Sheaths** longer than the internodes, smooth or slightly rough or pubescent near the summit; **Ligule** very short; **Panicle** long-exserted, narrow, 4-12′ long, drooping, the branches few, 1-2′ long, erect or somewhat ascending, few, the short-pediceled spikelets few; **Spikelets** 10-18 mm. long, at first narrow; **Glumes** unequal, the first about 2-2.5 mm. long, the second about 3.5 mm. long; **Lemmas** 4-6 mm. (6-10 mm.) long, somewhat abruptly acuminate, often exceeded by the beaked fruit; **Palea** shorter than the lemma, often exceeded by the beaked fruit. The size of spikelet as well as the lemmas vary much in this species.

In rich woods or along river banks, Texas to Oklahoma and Kansas, east to Ohio and West Virginia. Summer-fall.

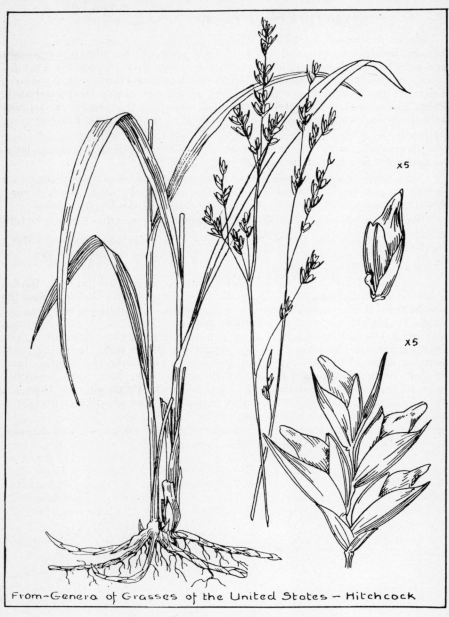

x5

x5

From-Genera of Grasses of the United States — Hitchcock

DIARRHENA AMERICANA

8. MONANTHOCHLOË Engelm. (mŏn-ăn-thŏk′lō-ē)

Plants dioecious; Spikelets 3-5-flowered, the uppermost florets rudimentary, the rachilla disarticulating tardily in pistillate spikelets; **Glumes** wanting; **Lemmas** rounded on the back, convolute, narrowed above, several-nerved, those of the pistillate spikelets like the blades in texture; **Palea** narrow, 2-nerved, in the pistillate spikelets convolute around the pistil, the rudimentary uppermost floret inclosed between the keels of the floret next below.

A creeping wiry *perennial,* with clustered short subulate leaves, the spikelets at the ends of the short branches only a little exceeding the leaves. One species in the United States.

Our species is a low *stoloniferous* plant, commonly 4-6′ tall, growing in small tufts or extensive patches or colonies, often in a tangled mass, the long stolons taking root at the numerous nodes and producing new plants. In general appearance it much resembles creeping juniper.

Often a patch of staminate plants is found and near by or at some distance a patch of pistillate. As the inflorescence is inconspicuous it will require close examination to find the stamens or stigmas projecting from the cluster of very short leaves at the apex of the culm.

M. LITTORALIS Engelm. (lĭt-ō-rā′lĭs) ; SALT CEDAR.

Culms 1-15′, usually 4-6′ tall, rigid, erect or prostrate with long stolons, internodes short, half to two inches usually about 1′ long, taking root at the numerous nodes and producing new plants, wiry, densely tufted; **Blades** in close clusters 5-9 mm. long, 1.5 mm. wide, conduplicate, widely spreading, curved, rigid, prominently nerved and scabrous on the margins; **Sheaths** crowded, overlapping, shorter than the internodes or blades; **Ligule** a ring of very short ciliate hairs; **Pistillate Plants: Spikelets** 8-9 mm. long, usually 2-3-flowered, upper rudimentary, mostly sessile and in pairs, or stipitate and single, in the leaf fascicles, slightly exceeding the leaves; **Glumes** wanting; **Lemmas** 6-7 mm. long, convolute, obtuse, lanceolate, several-nerved above, each lemma clasping the floret above; **Palea** 5-6 mm. long, lanceolate but upper part narrowed abruptly, the two green nerves ending about two-thirds the distance from the base, the margins about the middle serrate; **Stigmas** plumose, long; **Staminate Plants:** In general appearance the same as the pistillate. **Spikelets** 2-3-flowered; **Stamens** 3, with long filaments projecting from the apex of the culm.

Tidal flats or salt marshes along Gulf of Mexico, Texas to Florida, California. (Corpus Christi, Texas.) Spring-fall.

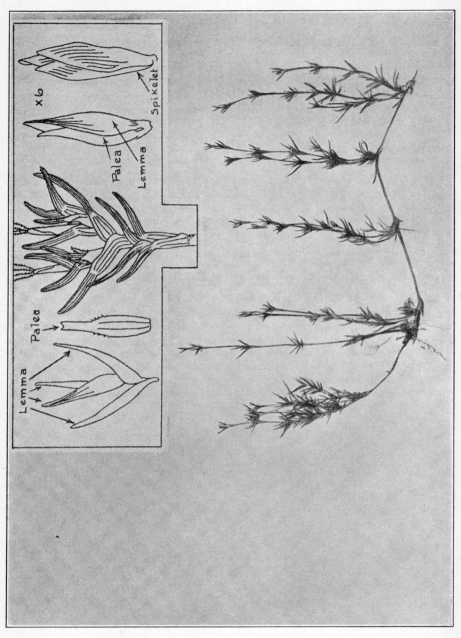

MONANTHOCHLOË LITTORALIS, Salt Cedar

9. DISTICHLIS Raf. (dĭs-tĭk'lĭs)

Plants Dioecious; Spikelets several to many-flowered, the rachilla of the pistillate spikelets disarticulating above the glumes and between the florets; **Glumes** unequal, broad, acute, keeled, mostly 3-nerved, the lateral nerves sometimes faint or obscured by striations and intermediate nerves; **Lemmas** closely imbricate, firm, the pistillate coriaceous, the margins bowed out near the base, acute or acutish, 3-nerved, several intermediate nerves or striations; **Palea** as long as the lemma or shorter, the pistillate coriaceous, inclosing the grain.

Low or tall *perennials,* with extensively creeping scaly rhizomes, erect, rather rigid culms, or in *D. texana* stoloniferous, and rather narrow dense pale panicles; three species in the United States, all in Texas.

D. spicata, a coast plant, and *D. stricta,* a plant of the interior, both usually about a foot tall, are much alike in aspect. They are erect or decumbent at the base, and from creeping scaly rootstocks. *D. texana,* a much taller and stouter grass, the culms often prostrate and stoloniferous, has longer and looser panicles and larger spikelets less compressed. It is mainly confined to the Big Bend district of western Texas and northern Mexico.

The pistillate and staminate plants may be found close together, but usually in separate or isolated, small or extensive patches or colonies.

PANICLE 1-2.5′ LONG, erect; spikelets 5-18-flowered, 6-13 mm. long; lemmas 3.5-4 mm. long.
    PANICLE condensed; spikelets mostly 5-9-flowered, imbricate.   1. D. spicata
    PANICLE loose; spikelets mostly 9-15-flowered, less imbricate, plainly visible.
                                                     2. D. stricta
PANICLE 4-10′ LONG, sometimes nodding; spikelets 5-9-flowered, 12-21 mm. long; lemmas about 10 mm. long; plants stoloniferous.   3. D. texana

1. D. SPICATA (L.) Greene (spĭ-kā'tà) ; SALT-GRASS.

Culms 6-24′ tall, erect or decumbent, from creeping, scaly rootstocks, freely branching, rigid, often glaucous; **Blades** stiffly ascending, mostly 2-3′ long, 2-4 mm. wide, flat or involute, usually crowded, conspicuously distichlis; **Sheaths** overlapping, glabrous except a few long hairs at the throat at each end of the ligule; **Ligule** membranaceous, about 0.5 mm. long; **Panicle** 1-2.5′ long, dense, oblong or ovoid; **Staminate Spikelets** 5-9-flowered, 6-10 mm. long, flat, pale green, subsessile or short pediceled; **Glumes** acute, the first about two-thirds as long as the second, 2-3 mm. long, the second 3-4 mm. long, 3-nerved, sometimes with intermediate green streaks or nerves; **Lemmas** 3.5-4 mm. long, many-nerved, or 3 green nerves and intermediate green streaks; **Pistillate Spikelets** similar to the staminate except less flattened, the lemmas bowed out below, and palea coriaceous.

Salt marshes or flats along the coast of most of the United States. Summer.

2. D. STRICTA (Torr.) Rydb. (strĭk'tà).

Resembling *D. spicata;* **Panicle** congested, the individual spikelets easily distinguished; **Spikelets** especially the staminate with more florets and usually stramineous.

Alkaline soil of the interior; Texas, Oklahoma, Mexico and California, north to Washington and Canada.

3. D. TEXANA (Vasey) Scribn. (tĕks-ā′nȧ).

Culms 1-3 feet tall, simple or branching, erect or spreading from decumbent-geniculate base, often producing stout prostrate culms and stolons as much as 10 feet long, from stout, knotty, scaly rootstocks, commonly growing in dense colonies; **Blades** 7-18′ long, 3-6 mm. wide, stiffly erect or ascending, the leaves crowded at the short upper internodes, flat or involute toward the tip, attenuate into a long narrow tip, rough except on the under surface toward the base; **Sheaths,** the upper short, crowded, overlapping, the lower sometimes shorter than the internodes, slightly ciliate at the summit; **Ligule,** a very short membrane with rather stiff hairs about 1 mm. long; **Panicle** included at the base or finally exserted, commonly 4-10′ long, narrow, loose, erect or slightly nodding, the appressed or ascending branches mostly 1-3′ long, a few subsessile or short-pediceled appressed or slightly spreading spikelets to each branch; **Pistillate Spikelets** 5-9-flowered, 12-21 mm. long, about 3 mm. wide, pale, rigid, less compressed than those of *D. spicata,* the glumes and lemmas with intermediate nerves or striations in addition to the three nerves; **Glumes** subequal, acute, scabrous on the keel, the first 7-11 mm. long, the second 9-12 mm. long; **Lemmas** 10-11 mm. long, broad near the base, margins papery, rigid, more or less scabrous toward the apex and on the three strong nerves; **Palea** half to two-thirds as long as its lemma, wide at the base and narrowed toward the apex, margins ciliate, closely inclosing the grain; **Staminate Spikelets** (unable to find any staminate plants).

Cultivated and waste meadow lands or sand flats, Big Bend country to El Paso, Texas south into Mexico.   (Castalon, near Terlingua, and Presidio, Texas.)

DISTICHLIS TEXANA

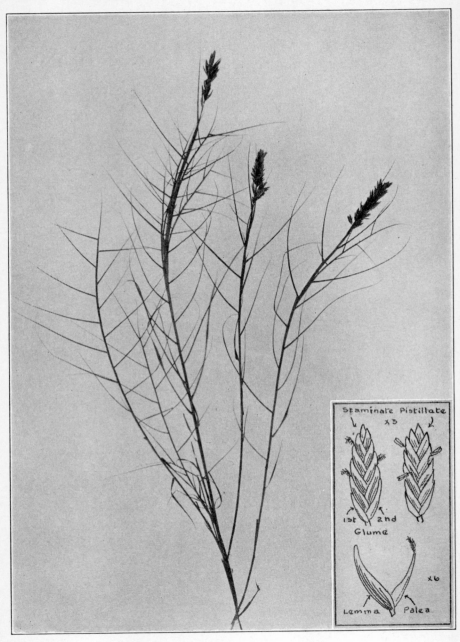

DISTICHLIS SPICATA, Salt-grass

10. UNIOLA L. (ū-nī'ō-là)

Spikelets 3-many-flowered, the lower 1-4 lemmas empty, the rachilla disarticulating above the glumes and between the florets; **Glumes** compressed-keeled, rigid, usually narrow, nerved, acute or acuminate, or rarely mucronate; **Lemmas** laterally compressed, sometimes conspicuously flattened, chartaceous, many-nerved, the nerves sometimes obscure, acute or acuminate, the empty ones at the base usually successively smaller, the uppermost usually reduced; **Palea** rigid, sometimes bowed out in the winged keels.

Perennial, rather tall, erect grasses, with flat or sometimes convolute blades and narrow or open panicles of compressed, sometimes very broad and flat, spikelets. Six species in the United States, four in Texas.

Seaside oats, a tall, stout grass with long attenuate tough blades, and large, heavy, rather compact drooping panicles of large flat, pale spikelets, is an excellent sand binder by reason of its extensively creeping rootstocks. It is common on the coastal sand dunes from Texas to Virginia.

Broad-leaved spike-grass, usually 3-4 feet tall, has broad flat blades and open drooping panicles of large, very flat, green spikelets.

These two grasses are strikingly ornamental, the former in isolated patches or colonies, giving life and beauty to the almost barren waste of the shifting sand dunes, and the latter giving added beauty to the borders of woodlands and shaded margins of winding streams and ditches. They are often collected and used to decorate homes and public buildings, the spikelets being colored or used in their natural state.

U. laxa and *U. sessiliflora,* rather slender grasses with very long and narrow panicles, the former with narrow blades, glabrous collars and sheaths, the latter with broader blades 5-10 mm. wide and pubescent collars and sheaths, are both sandy land grasses. In Texas they are confined mostly to sandy woodlands.

As *U. laxa* and *U. sessiliflora* are similar in general appearance, a photograph of *U. laxa,* since it would not show any distinguishing characteristics, is dispensed with.

PANICLES OPEN; spikelets very flat, more than 12 mm. long.
  PANICLES drooping, the branches and long capillary pedicels pendulous.
                                                                1. U. latifolia
  PANICLES slightly drooping, compact, the branches erect and rigid; spikelets
    on short pedicels.   2. U. paniculata
PANICLES NARROW, strict; spikelets less than 8 mm. long.
  COLLAR of sheaths pubescent, sheaths commonly loosely pubescent; blades
    5-10 mm. wide.   3. U. sessiliflora
  COLLAR and sheaths glabrous, or nearly so, blades 3-6 mm. wide.   4. U. laxa

1. U. LATIFOLIA Michx. (lăt-ĭ-fō'lĭ-à); Broad-leaved Spike-grass.

Culms 2-5 feet tall, rather stout, erect or spreading from short strong rhizomes; **Blades** 4-10' long, 8-27 mm. wide, flat, lanceolate, tapering toward both ends, rough on the margin, commonly with a few hairs on the upper surface at base or ciliate at the base; **Sheaths** usually shorter than the internodes; **Ligule** membranaceous, short, truncate, fringed with very short hairs; **Panicle** 5-12' long, loose and lax, drooping, axis and branches scabrous, the long, slender, few-flowered branches drooping, the spikelets on long capillary pendulous pedicels; **Spikelets** green, many-flowered, usually 10-15-flowered, commonly 20-30 mm. rarely 40 mm. long, much flattened, ovate to ovate-lanceolate, acute; **Glumes** subequal, 5-6 mm. long, linear-lanceolate, acute; **Lemmas** 9-13 mm. long (the lower 1-2 sterile), strongly keeled, the keel winged and rough-ciliate, acute, many-nerved; **Palea** shorter than its lemma, keels winged, bowed out; **Stamen** 1.

Moist open woods and borders of streams and ditches, Texas to Florida and north to Kansas and Pennsylvania. (Brackenridge Park, Mission Burial Park, San Antonio, Texas.)   Spring-fall.

2. U. PANICULATA L.   (pȧ-nĭk-ū-lā′tȧ) ; SEASIDE OATS, BEACH-GRASS.

Culms 3-8 feet tall, erect, simple, stout, woody, pale, from extensively creeping rootstocks; **Blades** 12-30′ long, 8-13 mm. wide, flat or on drying soon involute or convolute, attenuate into a long slender point, tough and rigid, slightly rough on the upper surface; **Sheaths** shorter than the internodes; **Ligule** a ring of hairs about 1 mm. long; **Panicle** exserted, commonly 9-12′ long, sometimes much longer, comparatively narrow, compact, heavy, pale, somewhat drooping, the branches erect or ascending, the lower 2.5-3′ long, densely flowered, the pedicels short; **Spikelets** pale, many-flowered, commonly 12-15-flowered, 12-25 mm. long, rarely 25-flowered and 50 mm. long, much flattened, ovate to ovate-lanceolate when mature; **Glumes** shorter than the lemmas, 1-nerved or the second 3-nerved; **Lemmas** 8-10 mm. long (the lower 1-4 sterile, shorter, acute), strongly keeled, 7-9-nerved, the midnerve often slightly excurrent, obtuse, scabrous on the keel; **Palea** nearly as long as its lemma, broad at the base, ciliate on the margin; **Stamens** 3.   Spikelets examined by the author early and late in the season did not produce any grain (seed).

Very sandy land, usually shifting sand, along seacoast, especially coastal islands, Texas to Florida and north to Virginia. (Padre Island.) Summer-fall.

3. U. SESSILIFLORA Poir. (sĕs-ĭl-ĭ-flō′rȧ) ; *U. longifolia* Scribn.

Culms 2-4 feet tall, simple, solitary or a few culms to a tuft, erect, slender, naked beneath the panicles, leafy below, the lowermost leaves short, from short knotted rootstocks; **Blades** 3-16′ long, 4-11 mm. wide, flat, much narrowed toward the base, attenuate into a long slender tip, smooth or rough on the upper surface toward the tip, sparsely to densely pubescent, usually densely so on the upper surface toward the base; **Sheaths** mostly longer than the internodes, villous at the throat and collar, otherwise glabrous to papillose-pubescent or villous, the lower and those of the sterile shoots often hirsute or papillose-hirsute; **Ligule** a very short membrane, finely ciliate; **Panicles** commonly long-exserted, 5-18′ rarely 30′ long, slender, erect or slightly nodding at the summit, the erect or appressed branches as long as 2′, usually shorter, often distant as much as 2′, the spikelets subsessile on the slender main axis or branches; **Spikelets** 3-7-flowered, 6-8 mm. long, wedge-shaped; **Glumes** much shorter than the lemmas, about 1.5 mm. long, the first slightly shorter, acute; **Lemmas** 3-5 mm. long (the lower sterile), rigid, acuminate, involute at the beak-like points, spreading in fruit, many-nerved; **Palea** about three-fourths as long as the lemma, arched, scabrous on the keels; **Grain** about 3 mm. long, 1.5 mm. thick, dark purple; **Stamen** 1.

Sandy soil in well drained woodlands, eastern Texas to Florida, north to Tennessee. (Houston and Hempstead, Texas.)   Summer.

4. U. LAXA (L.) B. S. P. (lăks′ȧ) ; *U. gracilis* Michx. ; SLENDER SPIKE-GRASS.

Similar to *U. sessiliflora*, except: **Blades** 3-6 mm. wide, glabrous or sparsely pubescent toward the base; **Sheaths** and collar glabrous or nearly so. (See photograph of *U. sessiliflora*.)

Open ground and damp woods, eastern Texas to Florida. (Houston and Tyler, Texas.)   Summer.

UNIOLA PANICULATA, Seaside Oats

UNIOLA LATIFOLIA, Broad-leaved Spike-grass

UNIOLA SESSILIFLORA and drawings of spikelets of UNIOLA LAXA

11. ARUNDO L.   (a-rŭn'dō)

Spikelets several-flowered, the florets successively smaller, the summits of all about equal, the *rachilla glabrous,* disarticulating above the glumes and between the florets; **Glumes** somewhat unequal, membranaceous, 3-nerved, narrow, tapering into a slender point, about as long as the spikelet; **Lemmas** thin, 3-nerved, densely long-pilose, gradually narrowed at the summit, the nerves ending in slender teeth, the middle one longer, extending into a straight awn.

One species in southern United States, in Texas.

Our giant reed is a tall, woody perennial commonly 10-20 feet tall sometimes much taller, with broad flat blades clasping at the base, and very large panicles. It has been much used for lawn groups or borders and hedges in the southwestern States. It has escaped from cultivation, forming dense growths along ditches and streams. There is also a cultivated variety with white-striped blades, *A. donax versicolor* (Mill.) Kunth.

It is plentiful at many places along the streams and ditches of Texas.

A. DONAX L. (dō'năks) ; Giant Reed.

Culms 10-30 feet tall, growing in small or large colonies, from stout and knotty rootstocks, sometimes branched above, stout, woody, erect or ascending; **Blades** 7-30′ long or longer, the upper shorter and narrow, 15-70 mm. mostly 30-50 mm. wide, flat, lanceolate-acuminate, clasping, margins rough, otherwise smooth except slightly rough toward the apex; **Sheaths** mostly shorter than the internodes, sometimes overlapping, collar pale; **Ligule** membranaceous, less than 1 mm. long, fringed; **Panicle** commonly 20-32′ long, oblong, usually tawny, finally copiously hairy, dense, plume-like, branches as much as 18′ long, ascending, with numerous branchlets several inches long, naked at the base, main axis smooth, axis of branches and branchlets scabrous; **Spikelets** numerous, crowded, 10-13 mm. long, on slender scabrous pedicels nearly as long as the spikelet, 2-3-flowered, narrow, lanceolate; **Glumes** 8-10 mm. long, the second slightly longer, acute, 3-nerved, purplish, about as long as the spikelet; **Lemmas** 9-10 mm. long, 3-nerved, thin, the awns sometimes extending above the glumes, slender, acuminate, lower hairs nearly as long as the lemma, awn often 1-2 mm. long between two teeth, longer than the teeth; **Rachilla,** internodes *glabrous;* **Palea** nearly one-half as long as its lemma, truncate, ciliate on the keels.

Along streams, ditches, yards and parks, in the southern States. (San Antonio, Texas.)   Summer-fall.

GYNERIUM and CORTADERIA

Gynerium sagittatum, known as uva grass, and *Cortaderia selloana,* known as pampas grass, are giant dioecious reeds closely related to *Arundo donax.* For convenience they are described in connection with *Arundo donax.*

GYNERIUM SAGITTATUM (Aubl.) Beauv. (jĭn-ĕr'ĭ-ŭm săj-ĭ-tā'tŭm). Uva grass is found along streams in tropical America, and is cultivated occasionally in greenhouses in the southern states. It grows to a height of 30-40 feet, with sharp edged blades as much as 6 feet long and 2 inches wide, the culms clothed below with old sheaths from which the blades have fallen, and pale, plumy, densely-flowered panicles three feet long, the main axis erect, the branches drooping. The spikelets are several-flowered, the pistillate with long attenuate glumes and smaller long-silky lemmas, the staminate with shorter glumes and glabrous lemmas.

CORTADERIA SELLOANA (Schult.) Aschers & Graebn. (kôr-tå-dē'rĭ-å sĕl-ō-ā'nå); *C. argentea* (Nees) Stapf.; PAMPAS GRASS.

Pampas grass is an erect dioecious perennial, growing in large bunches with numerous long, narrow, basal blades, very rough on the margins, the stout flowering culms commonly 6-10 feet tall, sometimes as much as 20 feet, with beautiful feathery, silvery white or pink panicles or plumes, commonly 1-2 feet long. The numerous spikelets are 2-4-flowered, *the pistillate silky with long hairs, the staminate naked;* the glumes long, slender and papery.; the lemmas bearing a long slender awn. It is cultivated as a lawn ornamental in the warmer parts of the United States, and also for the plumes which are used for decorative purposes. It is a native of Argentina.

Staminate Plant: Culms 6-12 sometimes even 20 feet tall, in large bunches, erect, stout, internodes short except the upper which is very long; **Blades** 1-5 feet and even longer on larger plants, upper shorter, 5-14 mm. wide, crowded at the base of the culm, margins very scabrous, the midrib and both surfaces scabrous except toward the base, flat, soon becoming involute when dry, attenuate into a very long narrow point, the upper often exceeding the panicle; **Sheaths** longer than the internodes, glabrous or pubescent especially toward the summit, villous at the throat; **Ligule** a ring of dense hairs 1-2 mm. long; **Panicle** (unisexual) exserted or included at the base, commonly 1.5-2 feet sometimes 3 feet long, oblong-pyramidal, feathery, silvery white or pink, axis smooth, about every 1-3' a half whorl of many branches, often one large branch 6-10' long and many slender short ones with numerous branchlets, spikelet bearing nearly to the base, branches erect, ascending or slightly spreading; **Spikelets** 12-14 mm. long, naked, on flexuous and slightly scabrous pedicels usually shorter than the spikelet, numerous, 2-4-flowered, rachilla 1-1.5 mm. long; **Glumes** 8-12 mm. long, the first slightly shorter, narrow, 1-nerved, papery, thin, attenuate into a rather long point, mostly 2-toothed; **Lemmas** including awns about 10-12 mm. long, the awns usually about 4.5 mm. long, 3-nerved, *glabrous,* hyaline, narrow; **Palea** about 4 mm. long, hyaline, slightly 2-keeled, downy at the apex. **Stamens** 3. **Pistillate Plant:** Similar to the staminate except the lemmas are *villous,* the hairs usually longer than the body of the lemma and shorter than the awns.

ARUNDO DONAX, GIANT REED-GRASS

CORTADERIA SELLOANA, Pampas-grass

12. PHRAGMITES Adans.   (frăg-mī'tēz)

(The Reeds)

Spikelets several-flowered, the *rachilla clothed with long silky hairs,* disarticulating above the glumes and at the base of each joint between the florets, the lowest floret staminate or neuter; **Glumes** 3-nerved, or the upper 5-nerved, lanceolate, acute, unequal, the first about half as long as the upper, the second shorter than the florets; **Lemmas** narrow, long-acuminate, glabrous, 3-nerved, the florets successively smaller, the summits of all about equal; **Palea** much shorter than the lemma.

Perennial reeds, with broad, flat, linear blades and large terminal panicles. A single species in the United States known as tall reed grass, a stout, erect plant, 5-10 feet tall, from creeping rhizomes, or sometimes with leafy stolons, with broad flat blades, and an open slightly nodding and often purplish panicle 6-20′ long. It is found growing in isolated patches of a few culms or in large colonies in marshes and along the borders of ponds, lakes and streams. It has a range over most of the United States. It is very common from Galveston to Orange, Texas.

P. COMMUNIS Trin. (kŏm-ū'nĭs) ; *P. phragmites* (L.) Karst.; TALL REED-GRASS.

Culms commonly 5-10 feet sometimes 15 feet tall, stout, erect from creeping rhizomes, sometimes with leafy stolons; **Blades** 6-18′ or even longer, commonly 12-25 mm. or even 50 mm. wide, flat, lanceolate, narrowed and rounded at the base, ascending, smooth or sometimes slightly rough; **Sheaths** longer than the internodes, crowded, loose; **Ligule** a ring of very short hairs; **Panicle** finally exserted, erect or slightly nodding, often purplish, 6-20′ long, open and spreading, pyramidal, main axis rigid and scabrous, branches ascending, numerous, alternate, solitary or in whorls, divided at the very base, those in the lower whorl very numerous, as much as 10′ long, woolly at the nodes, the upper glabrous at the nodes, naked one-fourth to one-half distance from the base, scabrous, the branchlets rather long and numerous, also naked at the base, capillary and scabrous, the spikelets numerous on slender scabrous pedicels much shorter than the spikelets; **Spikelets** 3-7-flowered, 12-15 mm. long, the silky hairs on the rachilla about as long as the lemmas, the rachilla-joint disarticulating at the base leaving the *copious long hairs* with the florets next above; **Glumes** unequal, lanceolate, acute, reticulate toward the summit, the first 3-4 mm. long, the second about twice as long, but shorter than the florets; **Lemmas, the lowest somewhat longer than the others,** slightly shorter or equaling the uppermost floret, the upper progressively shorter, long-acuminate, narrow; **Palea** short.

In swamps and water, over most of the United States. (Mercedes, Houston to Orange, Texas.) Summer-fall.

PHRAGMITES COMMUNIS, Tall Reed-grass

13. DACTYLIS L.   (dăk'tĭ-lĭs)

Spikelets few-flowered, compressed, finally disarticulating between the florets, nearly sessile in dense one-sided fascicles, these borne at the ends of the few branches of a panicle; **Glumes** unequal, carinate, acute, hispid-ciliate on the keel; **Lemmas** compressed-keeled, mucronate, 5-nerved, ciliate on the keel.

One species in the United States. Orchard grass is a rather coarse, erect, *perennial* bunchgrass, 2-4 feet tall, soon forming large tussocks, with panicles 3-8' long, the dense one-sided clusters of spikelets at the end of the few stiff branches, spreading in flower and appressed in fruit. It is very suitable for shaded situations, and is well known as a meadow and pasture grass, being cultivated in the humid regions over most of the United States.

D. GLOMERATA L. (glŏm-ēr-ā'tà) ; ORCHARD GRASS.

Culms 2-4 feet tall, tufted, erect, simple, flattened; **Blades** 3-24' long, 3-9 mm. wide, flat, both surfaces and margins rough, long acuminate; **Sheaths,** upper shorter than the internodes, lower longer, flattened, smooth to rough; **Ligule** membranaceous, 2-5 mm. long; **Panicle** 3-8' long, branches spreading or ascending in flower, erect and contracted in fruit, the lower branches 1-4.5' long, naked below, stiff, spikelets in dense one-sided clusters at the end of the branches; **Spikelets** 5-9 mm. long, 2-5-flowered, subsessile; **Glumes** 1-3-nerved, the first slightly shorter, acuminate, awn-pointed, often mucronate, about three-fourths as long as the spikelet; **Lemmas** 4-6 mm. long, mucronate or short-awned, ciliate on the keel, especially above, more or less hispidulous, about 5-nerved.

Fields, especially shaded situations, Colorado, Georgia, Canada. (Likely to be found in north or northwest Texas.)   Summer.

DACTYLIS GLOMERATA, Orchard-grass

14. LAMARCKIA Moench (lä-mär′kĭ-à)
(Achyrodes Boehmer)

Spikelets of two kinds, in fascicles, the terminal one of each fascicle fertile, the others sterile; **Fertile Spikelet,** with one perfect floret, the rachilla produced beyond the floret, bearing a small awned empty lemma or reduced to an awn; **Glumes** narrow, acuminate or short-awned, 1-nerved; **Lemma** broader, raised on a slender stipe, scarcely nerved, bearing just below the apex a delicate straight awn; **Sterile Spikelets** linear, 1 to 3 in each fascicle, consisting of 2 glumes similar to those of the fertile spikelet, and numerous distichously imbricate, obtuse, awnless, empty lemmas.

A low, erect *annual*, with flat blades and oblong, one-sided, compact panicles, the crowded fascicles drooping, the fertile being hidden, except the awns, by the numerous sterile ones. Species one, a native of southern Europe, naturalized in southern California.

L. AUREA (L.) Moench (ô′rē-à) ; GOLDENTOP.

Culms 4-16′ tall, erect or decumbent at the base; **Blades** 3-7 mm. wide, soft; **Panicle** golden-yellow to purplish, linear-oblong, 20-70 mm. long, 10-20 mm. wide, dense, shining, the branches short, the branchlets capillary, flexuous, the pedicels fascicled, pubescent; **Fertile Spikelets** exclusive of the awns 2-3.5 mm. long; **Glumes** acuminate or short-awned, about equal, somewhat exceeding the lemma, sparsely scabrous; **Fertile Lemma** 2-3 mm. long, or about 4 mm. long including the stipe about 1 mm. long, the awn about twice as long as the lemma, the sterile lemma with an awn nearly as long as that of the lemma; **Sterile Spikelets** usually 5-8 mm. long, and with 5-10, rarely 15, empty lemmas.

Open ground and waste places, Texas, Arizona, southern California. Sometimes cultivated for ornament.

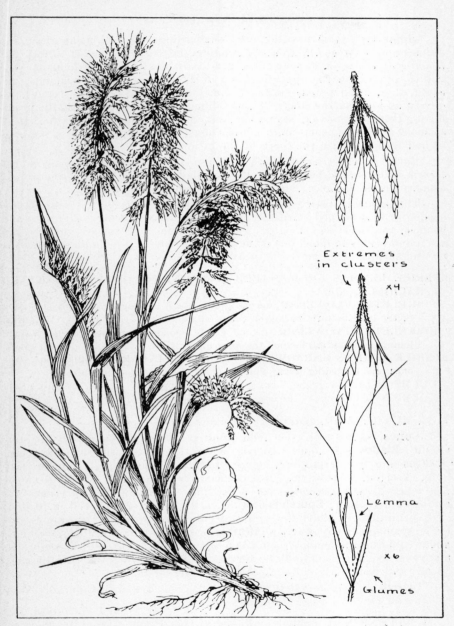

LAMARCKIA AUREA, Goldentop-grass

15. MELICA L. (mĕl′ĭ-kȧ)

Spikelets 2 to several-flowered, the rachilla disarticulating above the glumes and between the florets, prolonged beyond the perfect florets and bearing at the apex two or three gradually smaller sterile lemmas, convolute together or the upper inclosed in the lower; **Glumes** somewhat unequal, thin, often papery, scarious-margined, obtuse or acute, sometimes nearly as long as the lower floret, 3-5-nerved, the nerves usually prominent; **Lemmas** convex, several-nerved, membranaceous or rather firm, scarious-margined, sometimes conspicuously so, awnless or sometimes awned from between the teeth of the bifid apex.

Rather tall *perennials,* with the base of the culm often swollen into a corm, with closed sheaths, usually flat blades, narrow or sometimes open, usually simple panicles of relatively large spikelets.

This genus is distinguished from the allied genera by the more or less hooded or club-shaped sterile lemmas, the scarious margins of glumes and lemmas, and the closed sheaths. The four species in Texas are awnless, and are found mostly in moist places along the margins of woodlands, in thickets, around shrubs, or on banks of rocky ravines.

STERILE LEMMAS CLUB-SHAPED (PROMINENT) ON AN ELONGATED RACHILLA.
  SPIKELETS 2-FLOWERED; second glume about as long as the spikelet; apex of the lemmas terminating on the same plane. 1. M. mutica
  SPIKELETS 3-FLOWERED; second glume shorter than the spikelet; second lemma terminating beyond the apex of the first. 2. M. nitens
STERILE LEMMAS NARROWLY CONICAL OR LINEAR, much like the fertile ones and exceeding them; glumes much shorter than the spikelet.
  CULMS BULBOUS at the base; spikelets 3-9-flowered. 3. M. bulbosa
  CULMS NOT bulbous at the base; spikelets 4-5-flowered. 4. M. porteri

1. M. MUTICA Walt. (mū′tĭ-kȧ) ; NARROW MELIC-GRASS.

Culms 1-3 feet tall, erect from knotted rootstocks, commonly slender, simple; **Blades** 4-10′ long, 4-10 mm. wide, flat, rough, the lower shorter; **Sheaths** mostly overlapping, rough; **Ligule** 2-4 mm. long; **Panicle** 3-10′ long, exserted, narrow, the filiform branches single or in twos, one short, 1-2′ long, distant, ascending or spreading, few-flowered, sometimes reduced to a raceme; **Spikelets** falling entire, about 2-flowered, 6-10 mm. long, pendulous on short flexuous and pubescent pedicels, the glumes and lemmas conspicuously scarious; **Glumes** broad, acutish or obtuse, subequal, about equaling the lemma; **Lemmas** 6-8 mm. long, broad, obtuse, scabrous, many nerved, the intermediate nerves vanishing above, the rachilla prolonged and bearing 2 or 3 club-shaped sterile lemmas.

In rich soil, open woods and thickets, east Texas to Colorado, Wisconsin and Pennsylvania. Summer.

2. M. NITENS Nutt. (nī′tĕns) ; *Melica diffusa* Pursh; TALL MELIC-GRASS.

Culms 30-45′ tall, in small or rather large tufts, erect, simple, with rather long and numerous roots; **Blades** 5-12′ long, 4-12 mm. wide, narrowed towards the base, rough above, smooth or rough below, acuminate; **Sheaths** shorter than the internodes above, overlapping below, mostly smooth; **Ligule** membranaceous, less than 1 mm. long, lacerate; **Panicle** 3-9′ long, pyramidal, open, branches mostly in twos, one branch much longer than the other, as much as 4′ below to 1′ above, erect, spreading or drooping, naked at the base, spikelets racemose, hanging by slender pendulous pedicels, abruptly bent, enlarged and pubescent at the apex; **Spikelets** about 3-flowered, 10-12 mm. long, single, at first terete, finally spreading, the glumes and lemmas conspicuously scarious; **Glumes** broad at top, thin, with scarious margins, the first 5-nerved sometimes with two additional obscure nerves, about 7 mm. long, the second about 9 mm. long, 5-nerved, obtuse; **Lemmas** 5-7-nerved, scabrous, lower about 9 mm. long, with its palea about 7 mm. long, upper about 7 mm. long with palea about 5 mm. long, both obtuse, with palea broader at the top, pubescent on marginal nerves; the rachilla extending beyond the flowers and bearing two or three club-shaped convolute lemmas.

In rich rocky ravines or margins of thickets. Texas to Mexico and New Mexico, extending north to Nebraska and Pennsylvania. (Plentiful in San Antonio, Texas.) Early spring-summer.

3. M. BULBOSA Geyer (bŭl-bō'sà) ; *M. bella* Piper; ONION-GRASS.

Culms 1-2 feet tall, erect, single or densely tufted, simple, bulbous at the base; **Blades** 4-10′ long, 2-4 mm. wide, flat to involute, scabrous especially the upper surface, or nearly smooth; **Sheaths** about equal or longer than the internodes, scabrous or nearly smooth.; **Ligule** about 4 mm. long; **Panicle** narrow, 4-6′ long, erect, more or less interrupted below, densely-flowered, the branches short, rather stiff, appressed, mostly imbricate; **Spikelets** 3-9-flowered, rather turgid, lance-oblong, mostly 7-15 mm. long, papery with age, the stout pedicels stiffly erect; **Glumes** the first oblong, obtuse, thin, 3-5-nerved, 6 mm. long, the second oblanceolate, obtuse, minutely scabrous, 5-7-nerved, 7-8 mm. long, as long as the first floret; **Lemmas** 7-8 mm. long, broadly oblanceolate, obtuse or barely acute, or slightly emarginate, 7-nerved, with some shorter, obscure nerves.

Rocky woods and hills, western Texas to Utah and California, Colorado and north to Montana and British Columbia. Spring-summer.

4. M. PORTERI Scribn. (pōr'tĕr-ī).

Culms 15-40′ tall, tufted, erect or spreading, simple, from slender rootstocks; **Blades** 5-15′ long, 2-7 mm. wide, flat, rough, especially toward the apex; **Sheaths,** the upper shorter than the internodes, the lower overlapping, grown together, upwardly scabrous; **Ligule** membranaceous, 2-4 mm. long, wider than the blade, decurrent; **Panicle** 5-13′ long, narrow, slightly nodding, the branches 1-3.5′ long, 1-3 at each node, one long and one or two short, erect or spreading in anthesis, the spikelets racemose, pendulous, on abruptly bent short-pubescent pedicels; **Spikelets** 4-5-flowered, 10-13 mm. long, linear-oblong, slightly compressed, narrowed toward both ends; **Glumes** unequal, obtuse or acutish, shorter than the spikelet, the first about 5-6 mm. long, bluntly acute, the second 6-8 mm. long, acute; **Lemmas** 6-8 mm. long, subacute, scabrous, narrowed at the base and apex, about 7-nerved with some faint internerves, all converging toward the hyaline apex, the upper empty lemmas like the fertile ones and exceeding them.

Bluffs and rocky hillsides; Texas to Mexico, New Mexico to Colorado. Summer.

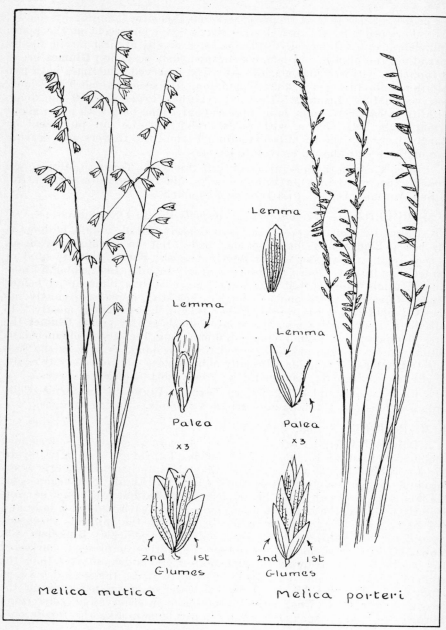

MELICA MUTICA AND MELICA PORTERI

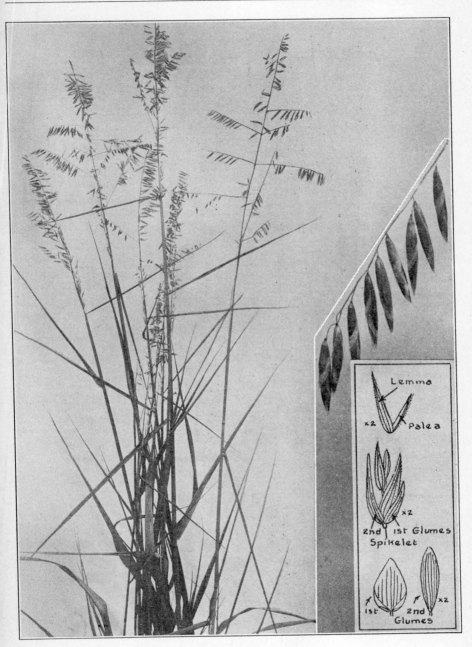

MELICA NITENS, Tall Melic-grass

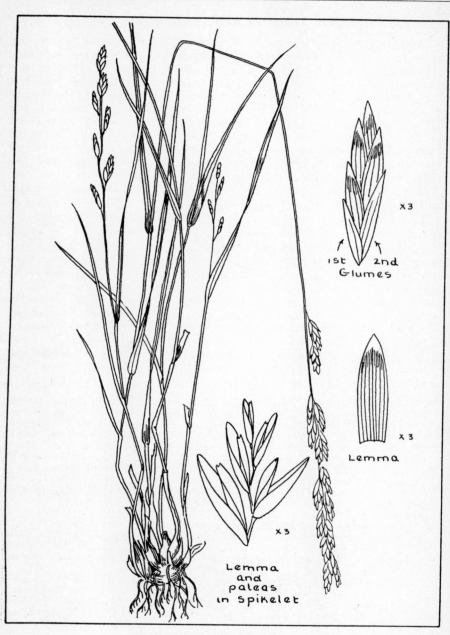

X3

1st   2nd
Glumes

Lemma
X3

X3

Lemma
and
paleas
in spikelet

MELICA BULBOSA

16. TRIODIA R. Br. (trī-ō'dĭ-à)

Spikelets several-flowered, the rachilla disarticulating above the glumes and between the florets; **Glumes** membranaceous, often thin, nearly equal in length, the first sometimes narrower, 1-nerved or the second rarely 3 to 5-nerved, acute or acuminate; **Lemmas** broad, rounded on the back, the apex from minutely emarginate or toothed to deeply and obtusely lobed, 3-nerved, the lateral nerves near the margins, the midnerve excurrent between the lobes as a minute point or as a short awn, the lateral nerves often excurrent as minute points, all the nerves pubescent below (subglabrous in one species), the lateral ones sometimes conspicuously so throughout; **Palea** broad, the two nerves near the margin, sometimes villous.

Erect, tufted *perennials*, rarely rhizomatous or stoloniferous, the blades usually flat, the inflorescence an open or contracted panicle, or a cluster of few-flowered spikes interspersed with leaves.   Species about 25, mostly in America; about 15 species in the United States, most of them in Texas.

T. pulchella, a low stoloniferous plant, usually less than 4' tall, a west Texas grass, and *T. pilosa*, commonly 5-8' tall, with acuminate lemmas, have subcapitate panicles.   *T. flava, T. texana, T. eragrostoides* have open usually drooping panicles, while *T. langloisii* has a narrowly open panicle.   In all the other species the panicles are either slender or oblong.   *T. pulchella, T. grandiflora, T. mutica* and *T. pilosa* agree in having woolly lemmas, the lower part of the three nerves being villous, and having paleas villous on the wings, the first two species also having deeply lobed lemmas.

T. pulchella, a low stoloniferous plant with deeply lobed lemmas, and *T. flava*, a tall plant with three nerves of the lemma extending into three mucros, are the two extremes of this genus.

LEMMAS GLABROUS ON THE BACK; CALLUS PUBESCENT; panicle narrow, long, its branches appressed or erect, dense; spikelets ovate-oblong, 4-6 mm. long; lemmas rounded at the erose apex.   1. T. albescens
LEMMAS PUBESCENT ON THE BACK, AT LEAST TOWARD THE BASE.
  PANICLE IN UMBELLATE clusters, terminating the leafy branches; plants usually less than 4' tall, stoloniferous.   2. T. pulchella
  PANICLE SHORT, DENSE, subcapitate on the simple nearly naked culms; blades with thick white margins; spikelets commonly 3-8.   3. T. pilosa
  PANICLE NARROW, SOMETIMES spikelike, its branches erect or appressed, spikelets usually purplish, sub-compressed.
    SECOND glume 1-nerved.
    Lateral nerves of the lemma usually excurrent into a minute point.
      Panicles elongated, exceeding 6'; glumes longer than the lemmas; palea linear-oblong.   4. T. stricta
      Panicles short, oblong, usually less than 4'; spikelets sessile, crowded, 6-12 mm. long.
      Palea about three-fourths as long as the lemma, gibbous at the base; spikelets 10-15-flowered.   5. T. congesta
      Palea about half as long as the lemma, broadly lanceolate; spikelets 4-8-flowered; lemma lobed.   6. T. grandiflora
    Lateral nerves of the lemma not excurrent into a minute point; panicle slender 4-8' long; spikelets terete, 8-10 mm. long.   7. T. mutica
    SECOND glume 3-5-nerved, or 1-nerved in *T. buckleyana;* lateral nerves of the lemma not excurrent.
      Panicle narrow, 5-12' long, the branches appressed; spikelets 6-10-flowered.   8. T. elongata
      Panicle usually open, 4-13' long, the branches ascending or narrowly spreading; spikelets 3-7-flowered.   9. T. buckleyana
  PANICLE OPEN, USUALLY ample, the branches spreading, often drooping, narrowly open in *T. langloisii;* spikelets compressed, usually purplish.

LATERAL nerves of the lemma excurrent into a minute point; glumes 1-nerved; spikelets 4-8-flowered.
Spikelets linear-oblong, more than twice as long as broad; axis and branches of the panicle viscid.   10. T. flava
Spikelets oval or ovate, less than twice as long as broad; panicle narrowly open.   11. T. langloisii
LATERAL nerves of the lemma not excurrent in a minute point; panicle open, drooping; spikelets 6-11-flowered.
Spikelets 4-6 mm. long; palea linear-elliptic; lemma 2 mm. long.
                                                               12. T. eragrostoides
Spikelets 7-11 mm. long; palea gibbous at the base; lemma 4 mm. long.
                                                               13. T. texana

1. T. ALBESCENS Vasey (ăl-bĕs'ĕns); *Sieglingia albescens* (Munro) Kuntze; *Tridens albescens* (Vasey) Wooton & Standley.

Culms 1-3 feet tall, loosely tufted, solid, usually simple; **Blades,** radical 4-12', those of culm shorter, 4-9' long, 3-6 mm. wide, flat soon becoming involute, slender, pointed, smooth except somewhat rough above; **Sheaths** shorter than the internodes; **Ligule** a dense ring of short hairs; **Panicle** greenish or purplish, usually exserted, contracted, somewhat interrupted below, erect or slightly nodding, 3-8' long, usually less than half inch wide, branches unequal, about 0.5-1.5' long, appressed, with crowded short pediceled spikelets; **Spikelets** 7-10-flowered, 5-6 mm. long, 2-3 mm. wide, pale green or purplish tinged, oval, flattened; **Glumes** nearly equal, first about 3.5 mm. and second about 4 mm. long, broadly ovate, acute, 1-nerved, keeled, hyaline; **Lemmas** 3-3.5 mm. long, 3-nerved, broadly elliptical, emarginate, more or less erose at apex, hyaline, midnerve slightly excurrent into a mucro, lateral nerves not marginal, a little pubescent at the very base; **Palea** broadly ovate, obtuse, about 2.5 mm. long, two-toothed, nearly equal to its lemma.

Prairies, especially along ditches; southern Texas to New Mexico. Spring to fall.

2. T. PULCHELLA H. B. K. (pŭl-chĕl'á); *Dasyochloa pulchella* (H. B. K.) Willd.; *Sieglingia pulchella* (H. B. K.) Kuntze.

This is a low tufted grass somewhat resembling false buffalo grass (*Munroa squarrosa*).

Culms usually 4' tall or less, densely tufted, arising from slender creeping rootstocks, fasciculately branched at the extremity of comparatively long naked internodes, often stoloniferous, very slender, scabrous; **Blades** 10-30 mm. long, about 0.5 mm. thick, involute, setaceous, rough, numerous, those of the sterile shoots recurved, clustered at the base and around the fascicles of branches, leaving the internodes naked; **Sheaths** short, open, tapering, scarious, villous at the throat; **Ligule** ciliate; decurrent as membranaceous margins of sheath; **Panicle,** small clusters of pale spikelets terminating the short clustered branches, sometimes almost hidden by the leaves; **Spikelets** mostly 5-10-flowered, sessile or pediceled, ovate-lanceolate, flattened, 5-10 mm. long, about 4 mm. wide; **Glumes** unequal, keeled, lance-ovate, acuminate, hyaline, 1-nerved, sometimes shorter than and sometimes as long as the spikelet, the second slightly longer than the first, 4-7 mm. long; **Lemmas** 4-5 mm. long, oblong, the apex cleft about half way to the base making two long narrow lobes with a straight awn between and exceeding the lobes, the two lateral nerves nearly marginal, ciliate, villous below; **Palea** oblong-spatulate, truncate, thin, pubescent below and on the keels.

On sandy mesas; western Texas and New Mexico to southern California. Summer-fall.

3. T. PILOSA (Buckl.) Merr. (pī-lō'sà); *Triodia acuminata* (Benth.) Vasey; *Sieglingia pilosa* Nash; *S. acuminata* (Benth.) Kuntze; *Erioneuron pilosum* (Buckl.) Nash.

Culms 4-12' tall, tufted, erect or spreading, slender, not branched, naked above, sterile shoots about 4' long; **Blades** 1-3' long, 2 mm. or less wide, culm leaves shorter than the numerous radical ones, only 2 or 3 on culm, strict or curved, flat, or folded (conduplicate) linear; abruptly pointed, more or less villous, papillose-hairy along the margins at base, with one white nerve in middle and white borders of uniform width, edges serrulate; **Sheaths** shorter than the internodes, villous with tufts of hairs at the summit, basal leaves with short tapering sheaths; **Ligule** a ring of very short hairs; **Panicle** narrow dense, short, almost capitate, usually 1-2' long, simple, oblong, long-exserted, few very short branches with 3-4 spikelets to a branch, in all about 4-20 spikelets, light colored or purplish; **Spikelets** crowded 8-12 mm. long, 4-6 mm. wide, lanceolate, flattened; **Glumes** acuminate, awn-pointed, 1-nerved, boat-shaped, smooth except keel scabrous, the first about 4.5 mm. long and the second 5.5 mm. long; **Lemmas** ovate-acuminate, obtuse or somewhat 2-toothed at apex, including awns 5.5-6 mm. long, awn about 0.5-0.7 mm. long, villous at base and base of three nerves, lateral nerves also long-villous near the tip, middle nerve excurrent into a short awn; **Palea** oval or spatulate, curved, ciliate on keels, villous at base, 2.5-3.5 mm. long. (Drawings with *T. buckleyana.*)

In dry gravelly soil; Texas to Kansas, Colorado and Arizona. Spring-summer.

4. T. STRICTA (Nutt.) Benth. (strĭk'tà); *Tridens strictus* (Nutt.) Nash.

Culms 2-5 feet tall, mostly in small tufts, rigid, slender or stout, erect, sometimes branched; **Blades** 1.5-20' long, 3-7 mm. wide, flat, smooth except the margins, glabrous except pubescent on upper surface near the base; **Sheaths** longer or shorter than the internodes; **Ligule** a ring of loose hairs 1-2 mm. long; **Panicle** exserted, spikelike, 4-12' long, 8-15 mm. wide, often interrupted below, dense, rigid, erect, pale or purplish, the branches appressed, the lower 1-2' sometimes 3' long, naked below, progressively shorter above, the uppermost very short, rarely with an axillary panicle; **Spikelets** 4-6 mm. long, about 3 mm. wide, 5-10-flowered, on short pedicels, crowded; **Glumes** 4-6 mm. long, longer than the lower lemmas to as long as the spikelet, equal, 1-nerved, acuminate or irregularly toothed at the apex, glabrous; **Lemmas** 2-3 mm. long, oblong, obtuse, toothed, membranaceous, 3-nerved, the middle nerve produced into a mucro or awn as much as 1.5 mm. long, the lateral nerves nearly marginal and often slightly excurrent, all pubescent on the lower two-thirds, the hairs rather coarse and about 0.7 mm. long; **Palea** about as long as its lemma, elliptic, obtuse, thin, softly pubescent on the keels and margins.

In moist soil, eastern Texas to Kansas and Louisiana. Spring to fall.

5. T. CONGESTA (L. H. Dewey) Bush (kŏn-jĕs'tà); *Sieglingia congesta* Dewey.

Culms 8-36' tall, solitary or a few culms to a tuft, erect, somewhat flattened, the nodes and collar of striate sheaths usually purple; **Blades** 2-15' long, 2-6 mm. wide, the basal and those of the sterile shoots longer, ascending, flat or soon involute, long-acuminate, margins and upper surface rough; **Sheaths** shorter than the internodes; **Ligule** a ciliate ring; **Panicle** 1.5-3.5' long, 7-20 mm. thick, oblong, dense, purplish but finally pale with age, the branches short, erect or appressed, the spikelets nearly sessile and crowded; **Spikelets** 6-13-flowered, 7-13 mm. long, 3-4 mm. wide, over 2 mm. thick, ovate or ovate-lanceolate to oblong; **Glumes** subequal, 3-3.5 mm. long, 1-nerved, broadly oval, subacute, mucronate; **Lemmas** about 4 mm. long, subcircular when spread, short-pubescent on keel and lateral nerves near the base, the midnerve excurrent in a short point or awn and lateral nerves also sometimes excurrent into a short point, sometimes an extra nerve near the midnerve; **Palea** slightly shorter than its lemma, deltoid-ovate before spreading, the broad infolded margins strongly gibbous at the base, sparsely hispid-ciliate on the nerves or keels.

Low black sandy land, Texas. (Railroad right-of-way, St. Paul, Texas.) Spring to fall.

6. **T. GRANDIFLORA** Vasey (grăn-dĭ-flō'rà); *T. nealleyi* Vasey; this species has been wrongly classified as *T. avenacea* H. B. K., a Mexican plant.

Culms 8-20' tall, rarely taller, tufted, simple, erect or sometimes geniculate at the base, nodes hairy, the internodes sparsely pubescent to glabrous; **Blades** 0.5-4' rarely 6' long, 2.5 mm. wide or less, flat or folded (conduplicate), abruptly pointed, the midnerve and margins white, from sparsely to densely-appressed pubescent, especially toward the base, often papillose around the base, the upper blades of the culm short, those of the sterile shoots long and recurved; **Sheaths** about half as long as the internodes, close, ciliate, slightly pubescent or glabrous, the lower numerous, overlapping, hairy-fringed; **Ligule** a ring of short dense hairs; **Panicles** usually much exserted, dense, linear or ovoid, 1-2.5' long, composed of numerous nearly sessile branches mostly about 1-1.5' long, erect, purple, turning pale; **Spikelets** 4-6-flowered, 8-10 mm. long, flattened, subsessile or with pedicels about 1 mm. long, crowded on the scabrous or pubescent branches; **Glumes** 1-nerved, lanceolate, acuminate, minutely scabrous on the keel, the first about 6 mm. long and the second about 7 mm. long, awn-pointed; **Lemmas** 4-6 mm. long, lance-ovate, with two narrow subacute or truncate minutely ciliate lobes at the apex, villous on the three nerves below, copiously ciliate, the scabrous midnerve excurrent into an awn 1-2 mm. long; **Palea** broadly lanceolate, about half as long as the lemma, villous at the base and ciliate on the two prominent keels.

Rocky banks in mountains or foothills, western Texas to Arizona and Mexico. (10 miles west of Van Horn, Texas, rocky foothills.) Late summer-fall.

7. **T. MUTICA** (Torr.) Scribn. (mū'tĭ-kà); *Tridens muticus* (Torr.) Nash; *Tricuspis mutica* Torr.

Culms 8-22' tall, tufted, erect, rigid, rather slender, very rough, nodes and internodes from sparsely pubescent to glabrous; **Blades** 1-5' mostly 2-4' long, commonly 1-3 mm. wide, flat or involute, ascending or erect, rigid, smooth or rough, glabrous to sparsely pilose, sometimes sparingly papillose; **Sheaths** longer than the internodes, smooth to rough, glabrous to papillose-pilose, sometimes prominently so, often villous at the throat; **Ligule** a ring of ciliate hairs about 1 mm. long, sometimes much longer at ends of ligule; **Panicle** 3-8' long, spikelike, erect, often interrupted, the short branches appressed, purplish, finally turning pale; **Spikelets** 5-11-flowered, 8-14 mm. long, linear-lanceolate, nearly terete; **Glumes** shorter than the lower lemmas, 3-6 mm. long, the second slightly longer and broader than the first, 1-nerved; **Lemmas** 4-6 mm. long, somewhat oblong, entire or emarginate at the rounded apex, the lobes usually irregular, the lateral nerves vanishing short of the apex, the midnerve rarely excurrent into a minute point, the callus and nerves prominently villous on the lower half, the hairs 1-2 mm. long; **Palea** about half as long as its lemma, elliptic, two-toothed, long ciliate on the keels.

Dry hills and plains, west and southwest Texas to Mexico and Arizona. Spring to fall.

8. T. ELONGATA (Buckl.) Scribn. (ē-lŏn-gā'tà); *T. trinerviglumis* Benth.; *Tridens elongatus* (Buckl.) Nash.

Culms 1.5-3 feet tall, slender, tufted, erect, rough, nodes often pubescent; **Blades** 3-12' long, 2-4 mm. wide, soon involute, rough, more or less pubescent; **Sheaths** longer than the internodes, rough, more or less pubescent, lower often papillose-pilose, pubescent to villous at the throat; **Ligule** a ring of hairs less than 1 mm. long; **Panicle** 5-12' long, narrow, the lower branches usually less than 3', appressed, with a few short pediceled spikelets on each branch; **Spikelets** oblong or oblanceolate, somewhat compressed, 6-9-flowered, 6-12 mm. long, pale or purplish; **Glumes** vary much as to length and number of nerves, with apex ranging from acute to obtuse, the first usually 1-nerved, sometimes several nerved, usually shorter than the second, the second 3 to several nerved, sometimes shorter than the first glume, both 3-7 mm. long; **Lemmas** 3-5.5 mm. long, oblong-ovate, obtuse, emarginate, mucronate or entire at the apex, the three nerves pubescent below, the lateral vanishing before reaching the margins; **Palea** ovate, obtuse, pubescent on the 2 keels, about three-fourths as long as the lemma; **Grain** ovate-conical, deeply hollowed on one side, punctate, brownish, slightly shorter than the palea.

On prairies; Texas to Colorado and Arizona. Summer to fall.

9. T. BUCKLEYANA (L. H. Dewey) Vasey (bŭk-lē-ā'nà).

Culms 1.5-3.5 feet tall, tufted, erect, simple, solid, rough; **Blades** 3-10' long, the upper short, 2-6 mm. wide, narrowed at the base, flat or involute toward the tip, rigidly ascending, rough; **Sheaths** overlapping, smooth to rough; **Ligule** membranaceous, short-ciliate, all less than 1 mm. long; **Panicles** exserted, 4-13' long, erect or slightly nodding, finally open, the axis, branches and branchlets rough, the branches ascending or spreading, commonly 4-7, mostly solitary, the lower as much as 6' long and as much as 3' distant, the longer naked at the base, the somewhat inflated and flattened sheaths often inclosing short racemes, the spikelets slightly overlapping, appressed, on scabrous pedicels 1.5-3 mm. long; **Spikelets** purplish, 3-7-flowered, 6-11 mm. long, oblong-linear, somewhat flattened; **Glumes** 1-nerved, acute to obtuse, thin, the first about 3.5 mm. long, the second 4-5 mm. long; **Lemmas** the lower 4-5 mm. long, about 1.4 mm. wide, 3-nerved, the lateral near the margin, villous at the base and lower half of the midnerve and lower three-fourths of the lateral nerves, obtuse, usually lobed at the apex, the lobes obtuse and minutely ciliate, all of the nerves stopping short of the margins except the midnerve sometimes excurrent into a short mucro; **Palea** about four-fifths as long as its lemma, two-toothed, elliptic, the nerves scabrous and villous on the lower half, the hairs about 0.5 mm. long; **Grain** elliptic, 2-3 mm. long, 1 mm. wide, hollow on one side.

Rocky open woods, central and southern Texas. (Austin, New Braunfels and Kyle, also in Kendall County, Texas.) Fall.

10. T. FLAVA (L.) Hitchc. (flā'và); *Tridens flavus* (L.) Hitchc.; *Poa flava* L.; TALL RED-TOP, PURPLE-TOP.

Culms 3-5.5 feet tall, tufted or 1 or 2 in a tuft, flattened, especially below; **Blades** 6-36' long, upper shorter, 3-12 mm. wide, flat, narrowed and convolute toward the base, scabrous on the margins and on surface toward the apex especially above, sparsely hairy above near the base; **Sheaths** shorter than the internodes except overlapping at the base, flattened, especially the lower ones, pubescent at the throat and collar; **Ligule** a ring of very short hairs; **Panicle** erect, finally open and spreading and even drooping, pyramidal, as much as 15' long, the lower branches as much as 7' long, mostly single or in twos, naked for one-third or more of its length, axis and branches smooth, erect, but finally spreading or drooping, the branchlets 1.5' long or less with a few short-pediceled spikelets; the plant often exudes a *sticky substance* below and on the axis and main branches of the panicle to which dirt adheres; **Spikelets** 3-7-flowered, 5-9 mm. long, slightly compressed, green or purplish; **Glumes** subequal, thin, 2-4 mm. long, 1-nerved, glabrous, obtuse or acutish, often slightly two-toothed; **Lemmas** about 3-4 mm. long, oblong, pubescent on the lower half of the three projecting nerves, the midnerve excurrent into a minute awn between a bifid apex; **Palea** nearly as long as its lemma, 2-toothed, ciliate on the nerves.

In dry soil, mostly in shaded situations; Texas to Kansas, east to Florida and New York. Summer to fall.

11. T. LANGLOISII (Nash) Bush (lăng-loi'sĭ-ī); *T. ambigua* (Ell.) Vasey; *Sieglingia ambigua* (Ell.) Kuntze.

Culms 2-3 feet tall, tufted, erect; **Blades** 2-14' long, 2-4 mm. wide, the uppermost short, flat, or soon involute, glabrous or pubescent on the upper surface toward the base; **Sheaths** shorter than the internodes, flattened, pubescent at the throat and collar; **Ligule** a ring of short hairs; **Panicle** exserted, loose and narrowly open, 3-7' long, the slender branches erect or ascending, 1.5-4' long, mostly solitary, rarely branching, the nearly sessile scattered spikelets usually on the upper half or three-fourths; **Spikelets** purplish, flattened, 4-7-flowered, 4-6 mm. long, 3-4 mm. wide, more than half as broad as long; **Glumes** about 3 mm. long, the lower slightly shorter, rather broad, acute, 1-nerved or the second 3-nerved; **Lemmas** 3-3.8 mm. long, scabrous toward the apex, the lateral nerves slightly excurrent and midnerve produced into a short awn from between two teeth, the apex more or less erose, the three nerves short-villous on the lower half, the hairs about 0.5 mm. long; **Palea** nearly as long as its lemma, 2-toothed, ciliate, elliptic, the folded margins wide. (Illustration with photograph of *T. eragrostoides*.)

In pine lands, eastern Texas to Florida, South Carolina. Summer-fall.

12. T. ERAGROSTOIDES Vasey & Scribn. (ĕr-à-grŏs-toi'dēz); *Tridens eragrostoides* (Vasey & Scribn.) Nash; *Sieglingia eragrostoides* (Vasey & Scribn.) L. H. Dewey.

Culms 1-4 feet tall, tufted, erect, solid, branching; **Blades** 4-12' long, 4-7 mm. wide, flat or involute toward the long tapering point, rough; **Sheaths** longer than the internodes, flattened, striate, rough, usually loose at the summit; **Ligule** membranaceous, 2-3 mm. long, lacerate; **Panicles** 6-12' long, open, lance-ovate or pyramidal, scarcely exserted, erect or drooping, the branches mostly single, slender, scabrous, distant, ascending or spreading, the lower as much as 6' long, spikelet-bearing nearly to the base, the spikelets loosely arranged, more or less appressed, on the branches or the few short branchlets, pedicels scabrous, about the length of the spikelets; **Spikelets** 7-11-flowered, 4-6 mm. long, 1.5 mm. wide, flattened, ovate-lanceolate, tinged with purple; **Glumes** about equal to the lower lemmas, subequal, the second broader and slightly longer, 1-nerved, acuminate, scabrous on the keel and the second somewhat on the body; **Lemmas** 2-2.3 mm. long, about 0.8 mm. wide, oblong, rounded on the back, minutely two-lobed, mucronate, pubescent below on the three nerves, the lateral nerves vanishing at the margins; **Palea** nearly as long as its lemma, obtuse, elliptic, ciliate, not gibbous below.

Plains and hillsides, Texas to Florida. (Meadow land near Bexar-Medina county line on Devine Road.)

13. T. TEXANA S. Wats. (tĕks-ā'nà); *Tridens texanus* (S. Wats.) Nash; *Sieglingia texana* (S. Wats.) Kuntze.

Culms 1-2 feet tall, tufted, simple or sparingly branched, erect or slightly geniculate at the base, from a somewhat bulbous base, more or less pubescent, the lower internodes sometimes papillose-pubescent; **Blades** 3-12' long, the basal numerous and shorter than the upper, 3-7 mm. wide, flat, acuminate, villous on the upper surface at the base, otherwise glabrous to sparingly pubescent on both surfaces, sometimes papillose or papillose-pubescent; **Sheaths,** the upper shorter than the internodes, the lower overlapping, collar and throat villous, otherwise glabrous to pubescent or papillose-pubescent; **Ligule** a ring of very short hairs; **Panicle** purplish, 3-6' long, loose and open, gracefully nodding, the main axis, branches and branchlets more or less pubescent, the flexuous branches commonly single or in pairs, usually 1-2' long, few and distant, each branch with 3-12 spikelets on short branchlets toward the extremities, the pedicels commonly less than the length of the spikelets; **Spikelets** 6-10-flowered, 6-11 mm. long, oblong, somewhat compressed, purplish; **Glumes** shorter than the adjacent lemmas, 1-nerved, thin, rather broad, acute or irregularly toothed, the first 2-3 mm. long, the second slightly longer and broader; **Lemmas** about 4 mm. long, oval when spread open, obtuse, 2-toothed, the three nerves pubescent toward the base, the midnerve slightly excurrent, the lateral nerves not marginal and usually not excurrent; **Palea** nearly as long as its lemma, broad at the base, narrowed above, obtuse, 2-keeled.

On dry hills, Texas east to Louisiana, west to New Mexico, and south to Mexico. Spring to fall.

TRIODIA ALBESCENS

TRIODIA PULCHELLA

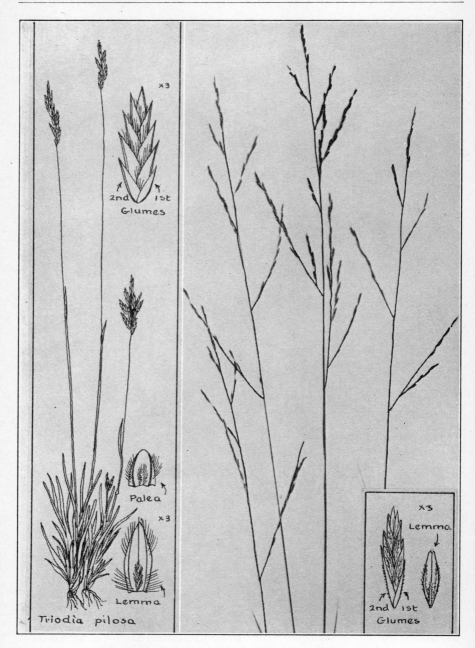

TRIODIA PILOSA; TRIODIA BUCKLEYANA

TRIODIA STRICTA

TRIODIA CONGESTA

TRIODIA GRANDIFLORA, the illustrations show the variations in the
Lemmas

TRIODIA MUTICA

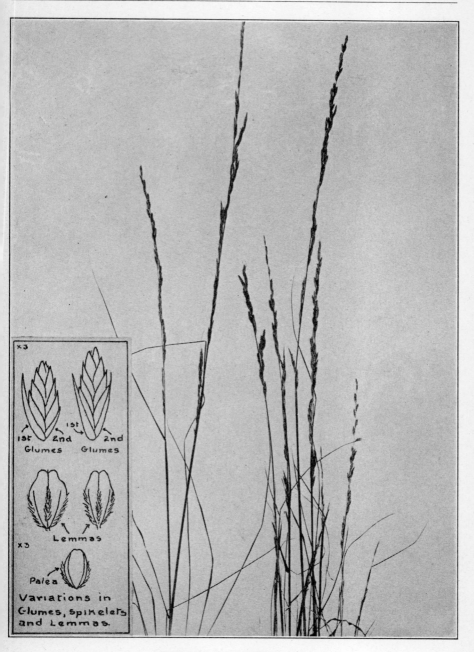

x3

1st Glumes   2nd Glumes   1st   2nd Glumes

Lemmas

x3

Palea

Variations in Glumes, spikelets and Lemmas.

TRIODIA ELONGATA

TRIODIA FLAVA

TRIODIA ERAGROSTOIDES (photograph); **TRIODIA LANGLOISII**
to the right

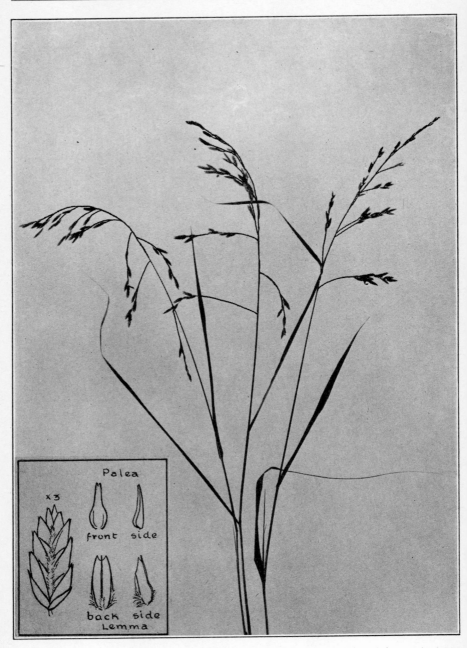

TRIODIA TEXANA

17. VASEYOCHLOA Hitchc. (vă-zē-ŏk'lō-à)

Spikelets subsessile or slightly compressed, several-flowered, the rachilla disarticulating above the glumes and between the florets; the **Joints** very stout; **Glumes** rather firm, unequal, much shorter than the lemmas, the first 3-5-nerved, the second 7-9-nerved; **Lemmas** rounded on the back, firm, closely imbricate, 7-9-nerved, broad, narrowed to an obtuse narrow apex, and with a stipe-like hairy callus, pubescent on the lower part of back and margins; **Palea** shorter than the lemma, splitting at maturity, the arcuate keels strongly wing-margined; **Caryopsis** concave-convex, oval, black, the base of the styles persistent as a 2-toothed crown.

Slender *perennials* with elongated blades and open panicles.

V. MULTINERVOSA (Vasey) Hitchc. (mŭl-tĭ-nēr-vō'sà); *Melica multinervosa* Vasey; *Triodia multinervosa* (Vasey) Hitchc.; *Distichlis multinervosa* (Vasey) Piper.

Culms 2-3 feet tall, tufted, sometimes densely so, simple, erect, often from a decumbent base, with short slender rootstocks; **Blades** 5-20' long, 2-6 mm. wide, the basal long, flat or involute, rough on the margins and toward the tip, especially on the upper surface; **Sheaths** longer than the internodes, somewhat flattened, those at the very base sparsely to densely villous, sometimes pilose at the throat and sparsely pubescent at the collar; **Ligule** membranaceous, very short, with hairs about 1 mm. long; **Panicle** exserted, 4-8' long, linear-oblong or ovate to pyramidal, axis scabrous toward the apex, erect or slightly nodding, the branches mostly single, usually 5-15, sometimes 2-5, the lower 2-5' long, alternate, ascending or spreading, naked about one-third the distance from the base, scabrous above, the spikelets on scabrous pedicels usually less than half the length of the spikelet, single on the branches or 2 or 3 on short branchlets, commonly 5-15 spikelets to a branch; **Spikelets** 5-12-flowered, 8-18 mm. long, somewhat flattened or nearly terete, about 3 mm. wide, rachilla very short, silky pubescent; **Glumes** shorter than the lower lemmas, 3.5-4.5 mm. long, the second slightly longer, rather broad, subacute or obtuse, sometimes minutely two-lobed and mucronate, both scabrous on the midnerve; **Lemmas** 4.5-5.5 mm. long, broad, ovate, 5-9-nerved, entire and acute, or obtuse and slightly two-lobed, often with a mucro at the apex, the callus villous, from sparsely to densely pubescent on the lower half, ciliate on the lower margins; **Palea** usually about four-fifths as long as its lemma, ovate-lanceolate, densely short pubescent, the nerves near the margins splitting open at maturity; **Grain** about 2-3 mm. long, 1.7 mm. wide, oval to obovate, hollowed out on one side, a cross section being the shape of a horseshoe; **Stamens** 3.

In sandy soil, open woods or open ground along the Coast, southern Texas. (Goliad, Falfurrias, mouth of Rio Grande.) Summer-fall.

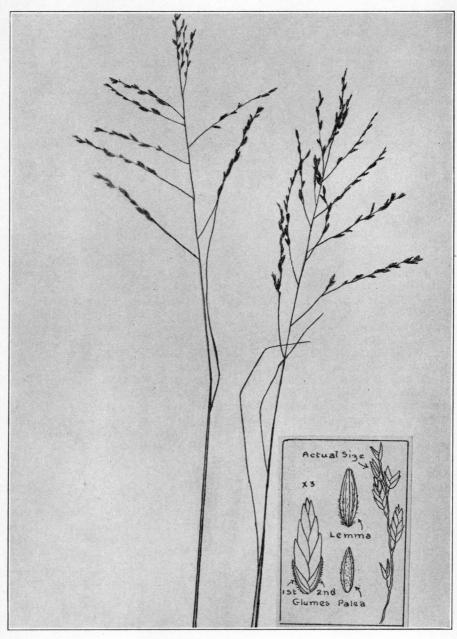

VASEYOCHLOA MULTINERVOSA

18. TRIPLASIS Beauv. (trĭp′lā-sĭs)

Spikelets few-flowered, the florets remote, the rachilla slender, terete, disarticulating above the glumes and between the florets; **Glumes** nearly equal, smooth, 1-nerved, acute; **Lemmas** narrow, 3-nerved, 2-lobed, the nerves parallel, pubescent or villous, the lateral pair near the margin, the midnerve excurrent as an awn, as long as or longer than the lobes; **Palea** shorter than the lemma, 2-keeled, the keels densely long-ciliate on the upper half.

Slender tufted *annuals* or *perennials,* with short blades, short, open, few-flowered purple panicles terminating the culms, and *cleistogamous* narrow panicles in the axils of the leaves. One species in Texas.

One species, known as sand-grass, is a tufted annual 12-30′ tall, with a small open panicle, and has additional *cleistogamous* spikelets reduced to a single large floret at the base of the lower sheaths.

T. PURPUREA (Walt.) Chapm. (pûr-pū′rē-à); SAND-GRASS.

Culms 12-32′ tall, in small tufts, erect or widely spreading, or ascending, sometimes decumbent, smooth and glabrous except the pubescent nodes; **Blades,** those of upper part of the culm very short, 6-20 mm. long, less than 2 mm. wide, the lower 1-6.5′ long, 4 mm. wide or less, flat or involute, rigid, erect, often sparsely ciliate toward the base, sometimes papillose-ciliate, rough; **Sheaths** shorter than the internodes, almost smooth to rough, the very lowest often pubescent, often villous at the throat; **Ligule** a ring of hairs less than 1 mm. long; **Panicle** finally exserted, 1.5-3′ long, open, branches few, short, the lower 20-40 mm. long, stiffly spreading, commonly in ones or twos, often with smaller panicles hidden in the sheaths, the lower sheaths with a single cleistogamous spikelet (see illustration); **Spikelets** 4-8 mm. long, 2-5-flowered, on short hispidulous pedicels; **Glumes** 2-4 mm. long, shorter than the lower lemmas, about equal, acute or subacute; **Lemmas** about 4 mm. long, 1.75 mm. wide when spread out, divided about one-fourth the way down, the lobes rounded or truncate, irregularly minutely toothed at the apex, the awn from the sinus equaling or exceeding the lobes, less than 2 mm. long, the three nerves pubescent; **Palea** shorter than its lemma, broad, the nerves nearly marginal, densely villous from the middle to the apex.

In sandy land, Texas to Maine. Summer-fall.

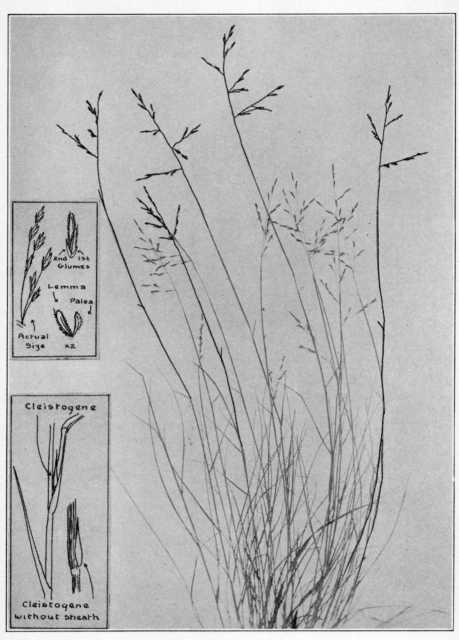

TRIPLASIS PURPUREA, Sand-grass

19. BLEPHARIDACHNE Hack. (blĕf-ăr-ĭ-dăk′nē)
(Eremochloë S. Wats.)

Spikelets 4-flowered, the rachilla disarticulating above the glumes but not between the florets; **Glumes** nearly equal, about as long as the spikelet, compressed, 1-nerved, thin, acuminate, smooth 2-lobed; **Lemmas** deeply 3-nerved, the first and second sterile, containing a palea but no flower, the third fertile, the fourth reduced to a 3-awned rudiment.

Low *annuals* or *perennials,* with short, congested, few-flowered panicles scarcely exserted from the subtending leaves; two species in the United States, one in Texas. Both *perennials,* apparently rare.

B. kingii, mostly less than 4′ tall, has much the aspect of *Triodia pulchella* H. B. K., but is not stoloniferous. It has been collected a few times on the plains and hills of Nevada, and, perhaps, in Utah and Arizona. *B. bigelovii,* 4-8′ tall, has only been collected on the rocky hills near El Paso.

The author made a fruitless search for these grasses in western Texas and southern New Mexico. It is hoped more material may be collected for further study.

To aid in the search for these grasses (though *B. kingii* has not been collected in Texas) the illustrations of *B. kingii* in Hitchcock's *Genera of Grasses of the United States* and of *B. bigelovii* in Vasey's *Grasses of the Southwest* have been copied.

GLUMES a little longer than the florets, acuminate, foliage scaberulous.
1. B. kingii
GLUMES a little shorter than the florets, subacute, foliage densely grayish harsh-puberulent.
2. B. bigelovii

1. B. KINGII (S. Wats.) Hack. (kĭng′ĭ-ī) ; *not in Texas.*

Culms mostly less than 4′ tall, branching below, tufted; **Blades** 10-30 mm. long, less than 1 mm. wide, involute, sharp-pointed; **Sheaths** with broad hyaline margins; **Panicles** subcapitate, pale or purplish, 10-20 mm. long, often exceeded by the upper blades, sheathed at the base; **Spikelets** flabellate; **Glumes** acuminate, exceeding the florets, about 8 mm. long; **Sterile Lemmas** about 6 mm. long, all the lemmas about the same height, long-ciliate on the margins, pilose at the base and on the callus, cleft nearly to the middle, the lateral lobes narrow, obtuse awn-tipped, the central lobe consisting of an awn, ciliate below, somewhat exceeding the lateral lobes; **Palea** much narrower and somewhat shorter than the lemma; **Fertile Lemma** similar to the sterile ones, the palea broad and as long as the lemma; the upper **Sterile Lemma** or rudiment on a rachilla-joint about 3 mm. long, reduced to three plumose awns; **Grain** compressed, about 2 mm. long.

Deserts, apparently rare, Nevada.

2. B. BIGELOVII (S. Wats.) Hack. (bĭg-ē-lō′vĭ-ī).

Culms 4-8′ tall, stiff, branching below, the culms and foliage harsh-puberulent, naked above except just below the panicle; **Blades** coarser than in *B. kingii;* **Sheaths** broad, firm; **Panicle** 10-30 mm. long, oblong, dense, the blades not exceeding the panicle; **Spikelets** about 7 mm. long; **Glumes** about 6 mm. long, subacute, a little shorter than the florets; **Fertile Lemma** and rudiment similar to those of *B. kingii.*

Known only from rocky hills at Frontera about 4 miles above El Paso, Texas.

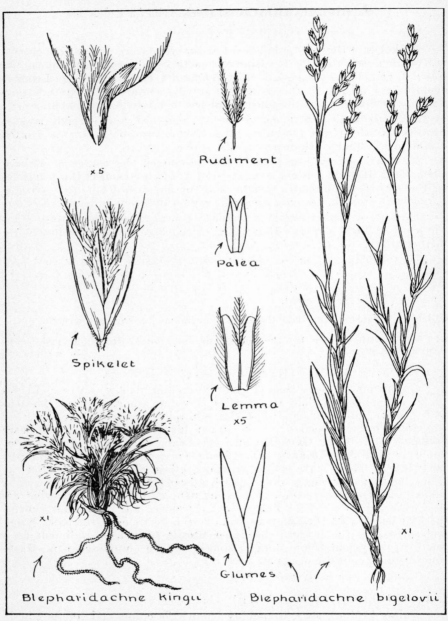

×5

Rudiment

Palea

Spikelet

Lemma
×5

×1

Glumes

Blepharidachne kingii   Blepharidachne bigelovii

×1

BLEPHARIDACHNE KINGII AND BLEPHARIDACHNE BIGELOVII

20. SCLEROPOGON Philippi (sklē-rō-pō′gŏn)

Plants dioecious. Staminate Spikelets several-flowered, pale, the rachilla not disarticulating; **Glumes** about equal, a perceptible internode between, membranaceous, long-acuminate, 1-nerved or obscurely 3-nerved, nearly as long as the first lemma; **Lemmas** similar to the glumes, somewhat distant on the rachilla, 3-nerved or obscurely 5-nerved, the apex mucronate; **Palea** obtuse, shorter than the lemma. **Pistillate Spikelets** several-flowered, the upper florets reduced to awns, the rachilla disarticulating above the glumes but not separating between the florets or only tardily so; **Glumes** acuminate, 3-nerved, with a few fine additional nerves, the first about half as long as the second; **Lemmas** narrow, 3-nerved, the nerves extending into 3 slender, scabrous, spreading awns, the florets falling together forming a cylindric many-awned fruit, the lowest floret with a sharp-bearded callus as in *Aristida;* **Palea** narrow, the two nerves near the margin produced into short awns.

The one species, a *stoloniferous perennial,* commonly 8-10′ tall, with flexuous blades and narrow few-flowered racemes or simple panicles, while usually dioecious, is sometimes monoecious or polygamous. It is called burro-grass.

Burro-grass tends to become established on overstocked ranges or on sterile soil, and is useful in preventing erosion. It is inferior to many other grasses as forage.

The plants usually grow in patches or colonies, sometimes covering whole fields, the staminate commonly less plentiful.

The numerous pale green or reddish-purple long spreading awns give the pistillate plant a strikingly different appearance from that of the staminate of pale awnless spikelets. The mature pistillate spikelets break away and form "tumbleweeds" that are blown before the wind.

From June to November on the semi-arid plains and open valleys west of the Pecos River acre upon acre of burro-grass may be seen glistening in the sunlight in varying tones of pale green, purple or red, giving new color and bloom to the seemingly grassless landscape.

S. BREVIFOLIUS Philippi (brĕv-ĭ-fō′lĭ-ŭs) ; *S. karwinskyanus* Benth.;
Burro or False Needle-grass.

Pistillate Plant; Culms 6-12′ tall, from a horizontal rootstock, often stoloniferous, the old rootstocks with pubescent scales, erect or spreading from a tufted leafy base, branching below, slender; **Blades** usually about 0.5-1.5′ sometimes 2′ long, about 2 mm. wide, flat or conduplicate, commonly 2-3 to a culm, hispid on the back of midnerve toward the apex, sparsely pubescent; **Sheaths** shorter than the internodes, often sparingly pilose at the throat; **Ligule** a dense row of stiff hairs about 1 mm. long; **Panicle** narrow, the spikelets few, the awns spreading; **Spikelets** 3-7-flowered, 12-17 mm. long, usually subtended by a bract, the internodes of the rachilla about 2 mm. long; **Glumes,** the first 7-12 mm. long, the second 12-17 mm. long; **Lemmas** 8-10 mm. long, with bearded callus about 1.5 mm. long, the three nerves produced into three subequal slightly scabrous and twisted straight awns, flattened at the base, 1-4′ long, with a membranaceous lobe outside of each lateral awn and sometimes one on each side of the middle awn; **Staminate Plant,** similar except the spikelet; **Spikelets** short-pediceled, commonly 5-8, each often subtended by a bract, 12-18, and sometimes 30-flowered, 0.5-1.5′ long and 4-5 mm. wide; **Glumes** 4-5 mm. long about equal, the first sometimes slightly shorter, keeled, acute; **Lemma** 5-8 mm. long, often with a mucro and 2-4 teeth.

On semi-arid plains and open valleys, southern Colorado to Texas and Arizona. It is plentiful west of the Pecos River. Spring to late fall.

SCLEROPOGON BREVIFOLIUS, Burro or False Needle-grass
Pistillate plant to the left; staminate to the right.

21. COTTEA Kunth (kŏt'ē-à)

Spikelets several-flowered, the uppermost reduced, the rachilla disarticulating above the glumes and between the florets; **Glumes** two, about equal, nearly equaling the lower lemma, with several parallel nerves; **Lemmas** rounded on the back, villous below, prominently 9-11-nerved, the nerves extending partly into awns of irregular size and partly into awned teeth; **Palea** awnless, a little longer than the body of the lemma.

An erect tufted branching *perennial*, with oblong open panicles. Species one; western Texas to southern Arizona and southward to Argentina.

This genus is allied to *Pappophorum* but differs in that the several-flowered spikelets separate between the florets and the awns are interspersed with the awned teeth.

Cottea pappophoroides Kunth is not abundant enough to have agricultural importance in the United States. *Cleistogenes* are produced in the lower sheaths and at the base. (Chase, Amer. Journ. Bot. 5:256. 1918.)

C. PAPPOPHOROIDES Kunth (păp-ō-fō-roi'dēz).

Culms 1-2 feet tall, loosely tufted, erect, light green or panicles somewhat purplish, pubescent; **Blades** 3-7′ long, 3-5 mm. wide, flat or involute toward the tapering points, slightly rough, noticeably pubescent; **Sheaths** mostly longer than the internodes, striate, pubescent; **Ligule** a ring of hairs nearly 1 mm. long; **Panicles** rather loose, narrowly lanceolate, 3-6′ long, short exserted or included at the base, rachis and branches pubescent, branches mostly solitary, 1-2′ long, ascending, spikelet-bearing nearly to the base, the nearly appressed spikelets on hairy pedicels one-fourth to one-half the length of the spikelet; **Spikelets** flattened, 4-9-flowered (7-10), including the awns 7-10 mm. long, the awns 1-3 mm. long, flat; **Glumes** about equal, 4-5 mm. long, broad, margins hyaline, more or less pubescent, the first irregularly three-toothed at the apex, the second acutish or short-awned, both about 13-nerved or the second about 9-nerved; **Lemmas** exclusive of the awns, the lower 3-4 mm. long, the upper progressively shorter, about 9-15-nerved, about five of the nerves extending into awns 2-3 mm. long, and many of the others produced into short awns or awned-teeth, pubescent on the back, the outer lobes being deeper and longer, ciliate; **Palea** 2.5-3 mm. long, two-toothed and the nerves nearly marginal, ciliate. *Cleistogenes* are produced in the lower sheaths and at base.

Rocky hills or mountains, Texas to Arizona and Mexico. (Base of large boulders near Shafter, Texas.) Fall.

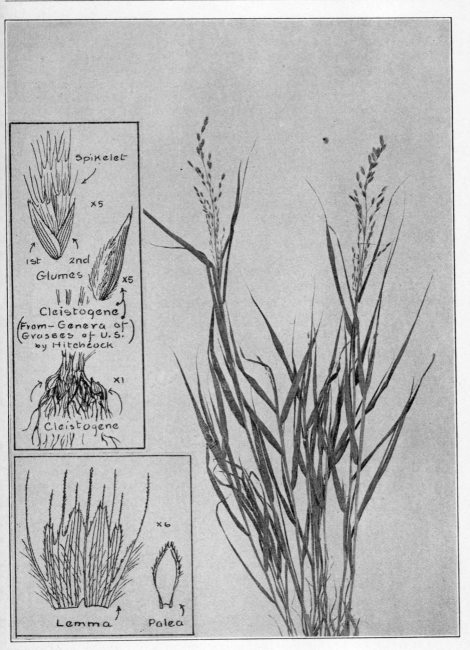

COTTEA PAPPOPHOROIDES. The illustrations show the cleistogenes from the sheaths and also the small hairy knots among the roots which are also cleistogenes.

22. PAPPOPHORUM Schreb.   (păp-ō-fō'rŭm)

Spikelets 2 to 5-flowered, the upper reduced, the rachilla disarticulating above the glumes but not between the florets, the internodes very short; Glumes nearly equal, keeled, thin-membranaceous, as long as or longer than the body of the florets, 1 to several nerved, acute; Lemmas rounded on the back, firm, obscurely many-nerved, dissected above into numerous spreading scabrous or plumose awns, the florets falling together, the awns of all forming a pappuslike crown; Palea as long as the body of the lemma, 2-nerved, the nerves near the margin.

Erect, cespitose *perennials*, with narrow or spikelike tawny or purplish panicles. Three species in the United States, all in Texas, Texas to Arizona. *P. bicolor* and *P. mucronulatum*, each 2-3 feet tall, the former with rather loose purplish panicle, the latter with a pale rather narrow densely flowered panicle, are often found growing at the same location and under the same conditions. *P. wrightii*, only about a foot tall, with a lead-colored spikelike panicle, the lemmas with nine equal plumose awns, produces cleistogamous spikelets in the lower sheaths, the *cleistogenes* being larger than the normal florets and the awns almost wanting. The culms disarticulate at the lower nodes as in other grasses producing *cleistogenes* in the lower sheaths.

PLANTS ABOUT A FOOT TALL, decumbent; nodes bearded; panicle lead-colored; glumes 3-7-nerved, awns of the lemmas plumose.   1. P. wrightii
PLANTS 2-3 FEET TALL, erect; glumes 1-nerved.
  PANICLE PURPLISH, loosely flowered; lower 2-3 florets fertile.
                                                                  2. P. bicolor
  PANICLE PALE, much narrowed above, densely flowered; lowermost floret fertile.   3. P. mucronulatum

1. P. WRIGHTII S. Watson (rī'tĭ-ī).

Culms 8-24' usually about 12' tall, solitary or densely tufted, erect or ascending from a geniculate base, slender, commonly freely branching, from a bulbous base, pubescent at the nodes or the upper sometimes glabrous, the internodes sometimes sparsely pubescent, often slightly rough; Blades commonly 1-3' long, 1-3 mm. wide, flat or involute, erect, puberulent or sometimes glabrous; Ligule a dense ring of hairs less than 1 mm. long; Panicles lead-colored or pale, exserted or included at the base, especially the lateral, compact, spikelike, often interrupted below, 2-4' long, 5-10 mm. in diameter, simple or with numerous short appressed branches, the spikelets crowded on short and puberulent pedicels; Spikelets 1-3-flowered, including the awns 4-6 mm. long; Glumes, the first 3.5-4.5 mm. long, the second about 1 mm. longer, 3-7-nerved, acute or slightly toothed, thin, scarious, sparingly pubescent; Lemmas, the *lower* 2-2.5 mm. long, oval, the nine prominent nerves terminating in nine ciliate-feathery awns (glabrous toward the apex) about twice as long as the body of the lemma, the body of the lemma hirsute or glabrous toward the apex; Sterile Lemmas raised on a long internode of the rachilla, smaller, otherwise similar to the lower.

On rocky banks, foothills and mountains of west Texas to Arizona. Late summer-fall.

2. P. BICOLOR Fourn. (bī'kŭl-ēr).

Culms 2-3 feet tall, erect or ascending, rather slender, branching; Blades 2-15' long, upper about 2' long, 2-5 mm. wide, flat or convolute, rough above; Sheaths shorter than the internodes, villous at the throat and collar, hairs 2-3 mm. long, otherwise glabrous; **Ligule** a ring of hairs about 1 mm. long; **Panicle** purplish, loose, 5-10′ long, exserted, branches at base about 2′ long, gradually shorter toward the apex, appressed or slightly spreading; **Spikelets** oblong, about 8 mm. long including the awns, excluding awns about 3.5 mm. long, on short puberulent pedicels, rachis minutely hispid, several-flowered, the two to three lower florets fertile, upper rudimentary; **Glumes** 1-nerved, the first about 3.5 mm. long, the second about 4 mm. long, hyaline, scabrous on the nerve, acute or with short teeth; **Lemmas,** the lower about 3-3.5 mm. long, villous with silky hairs 2-3 mm. long, 7-9-nerved, extending into scabrous awns or bristles, usually a shorter bristle alternate with them, many of them branched, the middle and marginal nerves villous below, hairs gradually shorter above; **Palea** nearly as long as its lemma, toothed, ciliate on the margins, hispidulous near the apex.

Sandy and gravelly soil, southern and western Texas. (On Devine road, Natalia, Texas.) Spring and fall.

3. **P. MUCRONULATUM** Nees (mū-krŏn-ū-lā′tŭm); *P. vaginatum* Buckl.

Culms 20-40′ tall, tufted, erect or spreading, solid, terete, branching toward the base; **Blades** 4-12′ long, some of the blades of the sterile shoots 24′ long, 3-5 mm. wide, flat or convolute, tapering into long slender points, rough above and on the margins; **Sheaths** shorter or longer than the internodes, rough or smooth, sometimes on the sterile shoots sparsely pilose at the throat; **Ligule** of many loose hairs 1-3 mm. long; **Panicle** pale, 5-12′ long, spikelike, usually tapering toward the top, the short branches appressed, the upper very short; **Spikelets** including the awns 6-8 mm. long, excluding the awns about 3 mm. long, on short hispid pedicels about 1 mm. long, commonly about 3-flowered (3-5), the lower fertile and the upper sterile; **Glumes** about equal, the first about 3.5 mm. long, the second about 3.5-4 mm. long, boat-shaped, hyaline, 1-nerved, scabrous on the nerve, the first sometimes and the second often three-toothed at the apex; **Lemmas,** the lower exclusive of the awns 2.5-3 mm. long, including awns about 6-7 mm. long, 7-nerved, the nerves extending into awns, and alternate with these 7-8 shorter awns, single or split near the base, densely villous at the base, on the margins and on each side of the middle nerve nearly to the apex; **Palea** lanceolate, hyaline, 3-toothed or lacerate at the apex; **Grain** about 2 mm. long, narrowly lanceolate, brown, falling with the fertile floret, to which the upper similar but sterile florets remain attached, the spreading awns of the whole aiding in dispersal of grain.

Gravelly or sandy soil, usually rich well-drained soil, southern and western Texas to Arizona. (Devine road near Natalia, Texas.) Spring and fall.

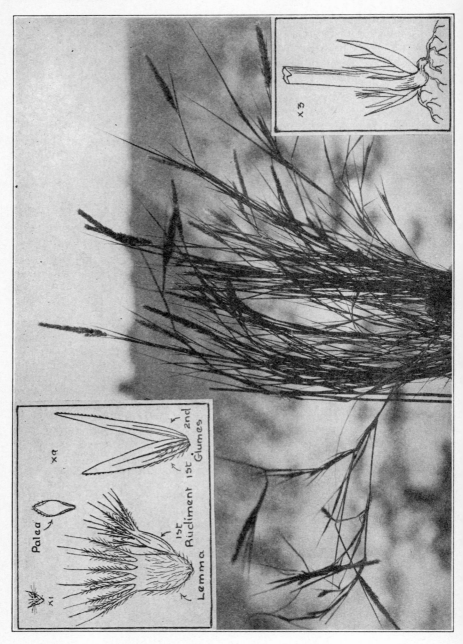

PAPPOPHORUM WRIGHTII, the drawing to the right shows the
cleistogenes in the lower sheaths.

PAPPOPHORUM BICOLOR

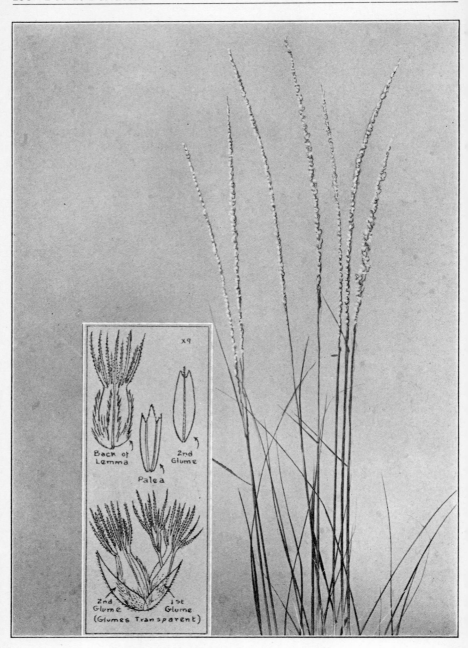

PAPPOPHORUM MUCRONULATUM

III. HORDEAE, THE BARLEY TRIBE

23. AGROPYRON Gaertn. (ăg-rō-pī′rŏn)

Spikelets several-flowered, solitary (or rarely in pairs), sessile, placed flatwise at each joint of a continuous (rarely disarticulating) rachis, the rachilla disarticulating above the glumes and between the florets; **Glumes** two, equal, firm, several-nerved, usually shorter than the first lemma, acute or awned, rarely obtuse or notched; **Lemmas** convex on the back, rather firm, 5-7-nerved, usually acute or awned from the apex; **Palea** shorter than the lemma.

Perennials or sometimes *annuals*, often with creeping rhizomes, with usually erect culms, and green or purplish usually erect spikes. About 25 species in the United States, about 5 in Texas.

All of our species are *perennials*, two with creeping rhizomes.

Quack- or couch-grass, often a troublesome weed in grain fields and meadows, especially in wheat-growing territory, has made itself well known by its pestiferous qualities. It is distinguished by its greenish-yellow rhizomes, thin flat blades, usually somewhat pilose above and smooth beneath. Bluestem, or western wheat-grass, has pale rhizomes and firm bluish-green blades, soon involute, rough on both surfaces, the nerves very prominent, and has the spikelets sometimes in pairs approaching the genus *Elymus*. It is common west of the Mississippi River where it is one of the most important forage grasses.

Of the group without rhizomes there are three species: two, *A. spicatus* and *A. arizonicum*, both with long-awned lemmas, the awns divergent, the former with awnless glumes and blades 1-2 mm. wide, and the latter with glumes awned and blades 4-6 mm. wide; one, *A. pauciflorum*, known as slender wheat-grass, with glumes nearly as long as the spikelet, the lemmas awnless or sometimes awned. The last is an excellent forage grass and produces a good quality of hay.

CULMS DENSELY-TUFTED. WITHOUT ROOTSTOCKS.
  LEMMAS CONSPICUOUSLY awned, awns divergent; spikelets flattened, distant.
    Spikes 3-6′ long; blades 1-2 mm. wide; glumes awnless.　　1. A. spicatum
    Spikes 6-12′ long; blades 4-6 mm. wide; glumes awned.　　2. A. arizonicum
  LEMMAS AWNLESS or short-awned; spikelets nearly cylindric.
　　　　　　　　　　　　　　　　　　　　　　　　3. A. pauciflorum
CULMS NOT DENSELY-TUFTED, WITH CREEPING ROOTSTOCKS. Lemmas awnless or with a very short awn; spikelets spreading.
    Blades flat, thin, scarcely prominent nerves, under surface smooth; rhizomes a bright greenish-yellow.　　　　　　　　　　　　　　4. A. repens
    Blades flat or involute, thick, the nerves prominent, rough above; rhizomes pale or gray.　　　　　　　　　　　　　　　　5. A. smithii

1. A. SPICATUM (Pursh) Scribn. & Smith (spī-kā′tŭm); *A. divergens* Nees; BUNCH-GRASS.

　　Culms 1-3 feet tall, densely-tufted, slender, rather wiry; **Blades** 2-8′ long, 1-3 mm. wide, involute or sometimes flat, the upper short; **Sheaths** about the length of the internodes; **Ligule** very short; **Spike** 3-7′ long, very slender, the spikelets remote, 10-20 mm. distant, erect or somewhat spreading; **Spikelets** 3-6-flowered, 12-20 mm. long, flattened; **Glumes** 10-14 mm. long, the first 3-nerved, about 2 mm. shorter than the 5-nerved second, usually acute or obtuse, awnless; **Lemmas** 8-10 mm. long, lanceolate, acute, scabrous toward the apex, 5-nerved, terminating in a stout diverging awn 12-25 mm. long.

Dry rocky hills, Texas to Colorado and Arizona. (Davis Mountains, Jeff Davis county, Texas.)   Spring-fall.

2. A. ARIZONICUM Scribn. & Smith (ăr-ĭ-zŏn'ĭ-kŭm).

Resembling A. spicatum; **Culms** usually taller and coarser; **Blades** 4-14′ long, commonly 4-6 mm. wide; **Spike** 6-12′ long, flexuous, the rachis more slender; **Spikelets** mostly 3-5-flowered, distant; **Glumes** short-awned; **Lemmas** 10-15 mm. long, acuminate, scabrous above, awns of the lemmas stouter, usually 20-30 mm. long.

Rocky slopes, western Texas, New Mexico, to Nevada and Colorado. Summer-fall.

3. A. PAUCIFLORUM (Schwein.) Hitchc. (pô-sĭ'flō'rŭm) ;   *A. tenerum* Vasey; *A. pseudo-repens* Scribn. & Smith; SLENDER WHEAT-GRASS.

Culms 2-3.5 feet tall, tufted, slender, erect, simple, rather rigid; **Blades** 3-10′ long, 2-6 mm. wide, flat or involute, prominently-nerved, mostly rough; **Sheaths** mostly shorter than the internodes, glabrous or the lower sometimes pubescent; **Ligule** membranaceous, about 1.5 mm. long; **Spike** 3-10′ long, slender, sometimes unilateral; **Spikelets** 3-7-flowered, 10-20 mm. long, remote to closely imbricate; **Glumes** equaling or somewhat shorter than the spikelet, lanceolate-acuminate, often awn-pointed, 3-7-nerved; **Lemmas** 8-13 mm. long, acuminate, awnless or sometimes tipped with an awn 1-4 mm. long, rough toward the apex, 5-nerved.

Dry soil, mountains, prairies and river valleys. Texas to Nebraska, Kansas, Colorado, Arizona, New England, and Canada.   Spring-summer.

4. A. REPENS (L.) Beauv. (rē'pĕns) ; QUACK-GRASS, COUCH- QUITCH- OR QUICK-GRASS.

Culms 1-4 feet tall, the creeping rootstocks and the lower portion of the culms a bright yellowish-green; **Blades** 4-12′ long, 2-10 mm. wide, flat, thin, with scarcely prominent nerves, scabrous or sparingly pilose on the upper surface, smooth beneath; **Sheaths** usually shorter than the internodes, glabrous or the lower sparsely pilose; **Ligule** very short; **Spike** 2-7′ long, stout or slender; **Spikelets** 3-7-flowered, 10-15 mm. long, nearly terete; **Glumes** 8-10 mm. long, acuminate or awn-pointed, 3-7-nerved; **Lemmas** about 10 mm. long, the upper progressively shorter, *strongly-nerved*, glabrous to scabrous, pointed or terminating in a short awn 1 mm. to as long as the lemmas.

Fields, roadsides, waste places, over much of the United States, mostly in wheat-growing country. (Gainesville, Texas.)   Summer-fall.

5. A. SMITHII Rydb. (smĭth'ĭ-ĭ) ; *A. occidentale* Scribn.; WESTERN WHEAT-GRASS OR BLUESTEM.

Culms 1-4 feet tall, rigid, glaucous, mostly solitary with sterile shoots from the very base, erect from slender creeping rootstocks, the lower portion of the culm and the rootstocks grayish or pale, often forming a turf; **Blades** 2-8′ long, the lower longer, 4-6 mm. wide, flat, becoming involute on drying, bluish-green, glaucous, rigid, spreading, rough above, smooth below, nerves prominent on upper surface; **Sheaths** shorter than the internodes, glaucous; **Ligule** a short membranaceous ring, slightly ciliate; **Spike** long-exserted, 3-7′ long, erect, strict, rachis scabrous on the margins; **Spikelets** 7-13-flowered, 12-25 mm. long, rarely in pairs, overlapping, slightly divergent, flattened, lanceolate when closed; **Glumes** one-half to two-thirds as long as the spikelet, acuminate, awn-pointed, scabrous on the keel, faintly 1-3 or sometimes 5-nerved; **Lemmas** 8-12 mm. long, lanceolate, mostly awnless, mucronate or awn-pointed, or sometimes with an awn 1 mm. or less long (lemmas on some spikelets awnless or short-awned), faintly 5-7-nerved.

In moist land, west of the Mississippi River. (Abilene, Lubbock, Texline, Texas.) Spring-summer.

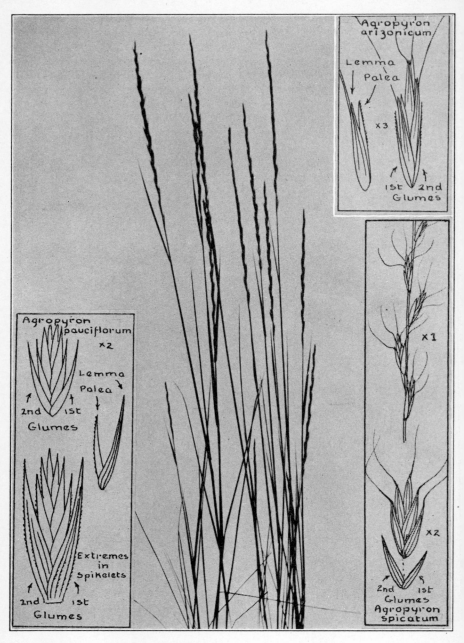

AGROPYRON PAUCIFLORUM, Slender Wheat-grass; drawings of
Agropyron spicatum and Agropyron arizonicum

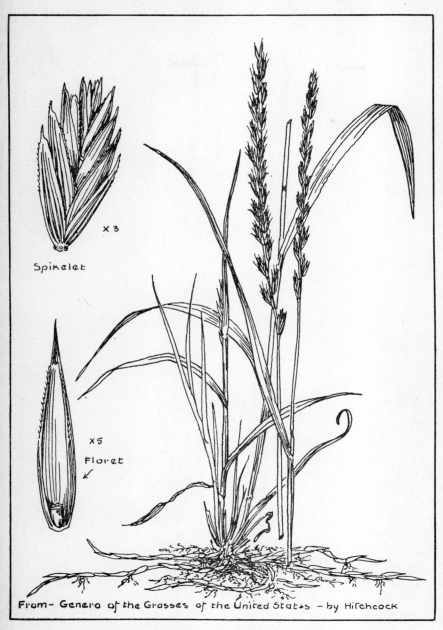

Spikelet

x 3

x 5

Floret

From- Genera of the Grasses of the United States — by Hitchcock

AGROPYRON REPENS, Quack-grass

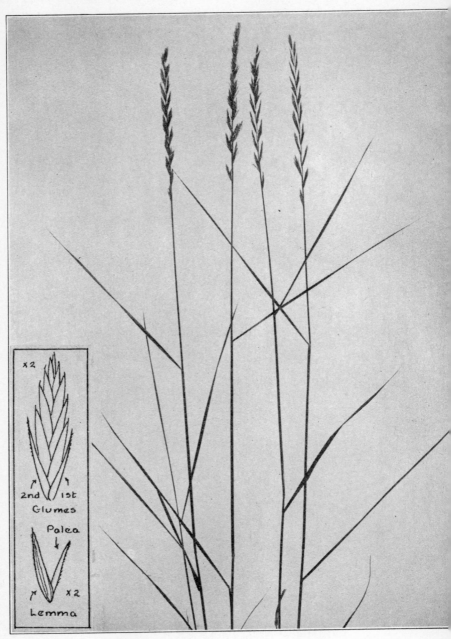

AGROPYRON SMITHII, WESTERN WHEAT-GRASS OR BLUESTEM

24. TRITICUM L. (trĭt′ĭ-kŭm)

Spikelets 2-5-flowered, solitary, sessile, placed flatwise at each joint of a continuous or articulate rachis, the rachilla disarticulating above the glumes and between the florets or continuous; **Glumes** rigid, 3-several-nerved, the apex abruptly mucronate or toothed or with one to many awns; **Lemmas** keeled or rounded on the back, many-nerved, ending in one to several teeth or awns.

Annual, low or rather tall grasses, with flat blades and terminal spikes. Species about 10, southern Europe and western Asia, one in the United States—the cultivated wheat.

There are many varieties of wheat, differing as to length of awns, color of head and of the grain, and the presence or absence of pubescence on the spikelet. Those varieties with long awns are called bearded wheat, and those with short awns or awnless beardless wheat.

For further information as to wheat consult the numerous government bulletins, and also *"A Text-book of Grasses"* by A. S. Hitchcock, Systematic Agrostologist, United States Department of Agriculture, published by *The Macmillan Company.*

T. AESTIVUM L. (ĕs-tī′vŭm) ; *T. vulgare* Vill.; *T. sativum* Lam.; WHEAT.

Culms commonly 2-3 feet tall, erect, tufted, smooth or pubescent at the nodes, hollow; **Blades** 12′ long more or less, 12 mm. wide more or less, flat, smooth or slightly scabrous on the upper surface, auricled at the base, especially in the young blades, ciliate; **Sheaths** smooth to slightly scabrous, or the lower pubescent; **Ligule** membranaceous, about 1 mm. long; **Spike** usually exserted, 1-5′ long, dense, more or less 4-sided, the spikelets single at the nodes, in two rows, alternating on the zigzag continuous rachis, overlapping; **Spikelets** commonly 3-5-flowered, ovate, somewhat flattened; **Glumes** shorter than the spikelet, one-sided, the outer side broader, the sharp keel ending in a short awn or point; **Lemmas** more or less 3-toothed, the middle tooth sometimes extending into a long awn.

Cultivated over most of the United States except the extreme southern portion. May to August.

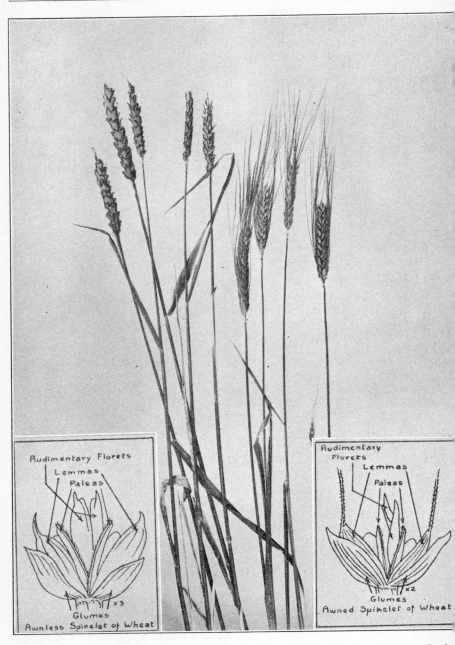

TRITICUM AESTIVUM, Cultivated Wheat, a bearded variety and also a beardless variety.

25. SECALE L. (sē-kā'lē)

Spikelets usually 2-flowered, solitary and sessile, placed flatwise against the rachis; the rachilla disarticulating above the glumes and produced beyond the upper floret as a minute stipe; **Glumes** narrow, rigid, acuminate or subulate-pointed; **Lemmas** broader, sharply keeled, 5-nerved, ciliate on the keel and exposed margins, tapering into a long awn.

Erect, mostly annual grasses, with flat blades and dense terminal spikes.

One species in the United States, a cultivated *annual*, often escaped in waste places and fields.

Secale cereale, common rye, is cultivated extensively in Europe and to some extent in the United States for the grain, but here it is frequently grown as a forage crop. Rye is used for winter forage in the south and for fall and spring pasture in the intermediate region, and for green feed farther north. It is also used for green manure and as a nurse crop for lawn mixtures, especially on public grounds when it is desired to cover the ground quickly with a green growth. In the wild species of *Secale* the rachis disarticulates, but in *S. cereale* it is continuous.

S. CEREALE L. (sē-rē-ā'lē) ; CULTIVATED RYE.

Culms 3-5 feet tall, usually glaucous, erect, pubescent below the spike; **Blades** 12' long more or less, 6-13 mm. wide, flat, rough, auricled on each side at the base; **Ligule** membranaceous, about 1 mm. long; **Spike** somewhat nodding, 3-5' long; **Rachis**-joints pubescent on the edges; **Spikelets** 2-flowered or a third rudimentary floret above; **Glumes** shorter than the lemmas, narrow, nearly subulate, 1-nerved, scabrous on the keel; **Lemmas** unsymmetrical, lanceolate, 5-nerved, ciliate-hispid on the keel and margins, the awn about an inch long. Cultivated here and there over most of the United States. Spring-summer.

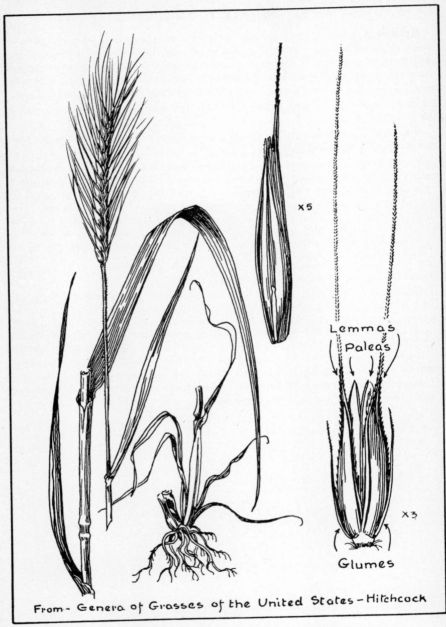

Lemmas

Paleas

Glumes

From- Genera of Grasses of the United States - Hitchcock

SECALE CEREALE, Cultivated or Common Rye

26. ELYMUS L. (ĕl′ĭ-mŭs)

Spikelets 2-6-flowered, sessile in pairs (rarely 3 or more or solitary) at each node of a continuous rachis, the florets dorsiventral to the rachis; rachilla disarticulating above the glumes and between the florets; **Glumes** equal, usually rigid, sometimes indurate below, narrow, sometimes subulate, 1-several-nerved, acute to aristate, somewhat asymmetric and often placed in front of the spikelets; **Lemmas** rounded on the back or nearly terete, obscurely 5-nerved, acute or usually awned from the tip.

Erect, usually rather tall grasses, with flat or rarely convolute blades and terminal spikes, the spikelets usually crowded, sometimes somewhat distant. About 25 species in the United States, 5 in Texas, all *perennials.*

In our Texas species, as well as in many others of this genus, the asymmetric glumes stand in front of the spikelet rather than at each side, so that the contiguous glumes of the pair are usually in pairs at each node, but in *E. triticoides* and *E. canadensis* var. *robustus* there are often three or four at each node. Some species of this genus have spikelets solitary toward the apex or base, being a transition to *Agropyron,* while *Agropyron smithii* with some of the spikelets in pairs at or near the middle of the spike may be considered a transition to *Elymus.*

All of our species except one have rather long-awned lemmas; *E. triticoides* has awnless or short-awned lemmas.

In *E. virginicus* and its varieties the broad glumes are prominently bowed out at the pale base, while in our other species the narrower glumes are straight or only slightly bowed out. As a rule in this genus the uppermost florets and awns are much reduced.

Most of our species thrive in open woods or thickets, or along streams. *E. triticoides* is usually found in meadows or on hillsides.

LEMMAS MERELY ACUTE OR SHORT-AWNED, BROADLY LANCEOLATE.
  Plants with horizontal rootstocks; first glume subulate, 1-nerved, second
  broader, 3-nerved; lemma 7-nerved above, glabrous.   1. E. triticoides
LEMMAS LONG-AWNED, THE AWN AS LONG AS OR LONGER THAN
  the lemma.
  GLUMES LINEAR-lanceolate to linear.
    GLUMES manifestly indurated, commonly bowed out at the base.
      Awn usually less than one and a half times the length of the lemma;
        awn of the glumes usually short; spikes usually included in the broad
        inflated upper sheath, stout, erect.
        Lemmas glabrous, spikelets 2-3-flowered.   2. E. virginicus
        Lemmas short-hirsute; spikelets 2-5-flowered.
                  2a. E. virginicus var. intermedius
      Awn more than twice the length of the lemma. Spikes exserted, erect or
        nodding.
        Glumes and lemmas hirsute or strongly scabrous.
                  2b. E. virginicus var. australis
        Glumes and lemmas glabrous or slightly scabrous.
                  2c. E. virginicus var. glabriflorus
    GLUMES not manifestly indurated, straight at the base; awn commonly more
      than twice as long as the lemma.
      Lemmas hirsute to nearly glabrous; blades 4-20 mm. wide.
        Spike rather loosely-flowered, long-exserted, commonly nodding; spike-
          lets in pairs.   3. E. canadensis
        Spike robust, densely-flowered, usually included at the base; spikelets
          mostly in threes and fours.   3a. E. canadensis var. robustus
      Lemmas glabrous to scabrous. Spike slender, long-exserted; blades 4-10
        mm. wide.   3b. E. canadensis var. brachystachys

GLUMES SETACEOUS or awl-shaped; spikes commonly slender, often nodding; awn of the lemma more than twice as long as its body.

Spikelets 1-3-flowered.

Awn not flexuous; glumes and lemmas hirsute, sometimes hispidulous or the lemmas glabrous.   4. E. villosus

Awn flexuous; lemmas sparsely hirsute or minutely scabrous toward the apex.   5. E. interruptus

1. **E. TRITICOIDES** Buckl. (trĭt-ĭ-koi'dēz); BEARDLESS WILD-RYE.

Culms 3-5 feet tall, erect, often branching at the base, leafy throughout, from horizontal rootstocks; **Blades** 6-12′ long, 4-8 mm. wide, flat or involute toward the tips, rough and often thinly pubescent above; **Sheaths** usually exceeding the internodes; **Ligule** usually less than 1 mm. long; **Spike** 4-8′ long, erect, usually somewhat interrupted or loosely-flowered, with 1-3 spikelets at each node, usually exceeding the internodes; **Spikelets** 5-10-flowered, 14-20 mm. long; **Glumes** 8-14 mm. long, the 3-nerved broader second about 1-2 mm. longer than the 1-nerved subulate first, both rigid and scabrous; **Lemmas** 8-10 mm. long, lance-ovate, acute or short-awned, glabrous, scabrous near the apex, 7-nerved (or 9), the nerves indistinct below; **Palea** about two-thirds as long as the lemma, lance-oblong, obtuse or emarginate, hispid on the prominent green keels and minutely ciliate on the margins above.

Meadows and hillsides, west Texas to Arizona and California, Washington.   Late spring-summer.

2. **E. VIRGINICUS** L. (vĕr-jĭn'ĭ-kŭs); TERRELL-GRASS, VIRGINIA WILD-RYE.

Culms 2-3 feet tall, simple, erect, rigid, often stout; **Blades** 5-12′ (5-14′) long, 4-8 mm. (4-16) wide, auricled, flat, rough, especially toward the tip; **Sheaths** mostly shorter than the internodes, the lower overlapping, the uppermost often inflated and enclosing the base of the spike, glabrous or sometimes the lower sparsely pubescent; **Ligule** a rather rigid short membrane, truncate; **Spike** 2-7′ long, included in the inflated sheath at the base or sometimes short-exserted, erect, rather rigid, dense; **Spikelets** usually 2 at each node, 3-5-flowered; **Glumes** about 12 mm. long, awn-pointed or with an awn as much as 8 mm. long, the thick, broadened prominently-nerved glumes conspicuous, 5-7-nerved, glabrous or the margins and nerves scabrous toward the apex; **Lemmas,** the lower 6-8 mm. long with scabrous awn 5-18 mm. long, glabrous; **Palea** elliptic, ciliate, slightly shorter than its lemma.

In moist soil, Texas to Florida and north. (Bellville and San Antonio, Texas.)   Spring-summer.

2a. **E. VIRGINICUS** var. **AUSTRALIS** (Scribn. & Ball) Hitchc. (ôs-trā'lĭs).

Differing from *E. virginicus* var. *intermedius* in the stouter bristly spike and larger awns; differing from *E. virginicus* var. *glabriflorus* in the hirsute or strongly scabrous glumes and lemmas.

Prairies and rocky hills; Texas and Florida, north to Virginia and Iowa.

2b. **E. VIRGINICUS** var. **INTERMEDIUS** (Vasey) Bush (ĭn-tĕr-mē'dĭ-ŭs); *E. virginicus* var. *hirsutiglumis* (Scribn.) Hitchc.; *E. hirsutiglumis* Scribn.; STRICT WILD-RYE.

Culms 2-3 feet tall, erect, more or less tufted; **Blades** 6-12′ long, 6-8 mm. (8-18) wide, flat, acuminate, very rough; **Sheaths** usually longer than the internodes, the uppermost often inflated and inclosing the base of the spike, the lower often pubescent to hispid; **Ligule** a very short membrane; **Spike** included or short exserted, 2.5-6′ long, stout, erect, rachis pubescent; **Spikelets** 2-5-flowered in pairs, crowded; **Glumes** including the awns 18-24 mm. long, acuminate into a scabrous awn about as long as or shorter than the glume, 3-5-nerved, the nerves hispid, prominently thickened and bowed at the pale base; **Lemmas** exclusive of the awns 8-10 mm. long, acuminate into a scabrous awn 12-18 mm. long, appressed-hirsute.

River banks, thickets and open fields, Texas to Nebraska, Virginia, Tennessee. (San Antonio, Texas.) Late spring and summer.

2c. E. VIRGINICUS var. GLABRIFLORUS (Vasey) Bush (glā-brĭflō′rŭs); SMOOTH SOUTHERN WILD-RYE.

Culms 2-4 feet tall, tufted, erect, rather stout; **Blades** mostly 6-12′ long, 8-16 mm. wide, narrowed at both ends, flat, acuminate, thin, rough, sometimes sparsely hirsute on one or both sides at the base; **Sheaths,** upper shorter and lower longer than the internodes, loose, ciliate, otherwise glabrous to pubescent or hirsute, mostly rough; **Ligule** membranaceous, truncate, about 1 mm. long; **Spike** exserted, 5-7′ long, stout, erect or nodding, spikelets finally divergent, usually in twos or sometimes threes; **Spikelets** 3-5-flowered; **Glumes** including the hispid awns 18-26 mm. long, awns shorter or longer than the body of the glumes, prominently bowed and thickened at the pale base, sometimes hispid-ciliate on the margins and scabrous on the nerves; **Lemmas** exclusive of the awns, the lower about 9 mm. long, the hispid awn 18-36 mm. long, the body glabrous or hispidulous especially toward the apex; **Palea** nearly as long as its lemma, elliptic, obtuse, ciliate on the margins.

Woods or thickets, Texas, New Mexico, Florida to Pennsylvania and Iowa. (Plentiful in Texas.) Spring.

3. E. CANADENSIS L. (kăn-ȧ-děn′sĭs); NODDING WILD-RYE.

Culms 2-5 feet tall, simple, slender to rather stout; **Blades** 5-12′ long, 6-18 mm. wide, flat, slightly narrowed toward the base, very rough, sometimes glaucous; **Sheaths** mostly longer than the internodes, smooth or slightly rough; **Ligule** membranaceous, truncate, about 1 mm. long; **Spike** commonly much exserted, 4-9′ long, rather stout, often interrupted below, finally nodding; **Spikelets** 3-5-flowered, divergent mostly in pairs; **Glumes** including the slender rough awns 15-30 mm. long, narrowly lanceolate, rigid, 3-nerved, hirsute, hispidulous on the nerves; **Lemmas** excluding the awns 8-14 mm. long, hirsute to hispidulous or nearly glabrous, the slender scabrous divergent awn 10-50 mm. long, usually curved when dry, often with lateral awns 1-2 mm. long.

On river banks, Texas to Arizona, Missouri to New Jersey and north. Summer.

3a. E. CANADENSIS var. ROBUSTUS (Scribn. & Smith) Mack. & Bush (rō-bŭs′tŭs).

This differs from *E. canadensis* in the more robust plant and spike, the spike sometimes 1.5′ thick, the **Spikelets** crowded, 2-4 at each node, the **Lemma** hispidulous-scabrous to glabrous, the awn usually somewhat shorter than that of the species.

On river banks, Texas to Arkansas, thence to the Rocky Mountains. (Natalia and Eastland, Texas.) Spring-summer.

3b. E. CANADENSIS var. BRACHYSTACHYS (Scribn. & Ball) Farwell (bră-kǐs'tà-kǐs).

Blades 4-10 mm. wide; **Glumes** and **Lemmas** glabrous, or merely scabrous (not hirsute).

Moist open or shady ground; Texas to New Mexico, Arkansas and Oklahoma.

4. E. VILLOSUS Muhl. (vǐl-ō'sǔs); erroneously referred to *E. striatus* Willd.; SLENDER WILD RYE.

Culms 2-3 feet tall, tufted, slender, simple, glabrous or sparsely short-hairy below; **Blades** 5-10' long, 4-10 mm. wide, smooth to rough, short-pubescent above; **Sheaths** shorter or longer than the internodes, smooth to rough, glabrous or usually sparsely to almost densely short-hirsute; **Ligule** membranaceous, less than 0.5 mm. long; **Spike** exserted, sometimes nodding, 2.5-5' long, dense; **Spikelets** somewhat divergent, 1-3-flowered; **Glumes** including the slender awns 18-24 mm. long, awl-shaped, 1-3-nerved, hirsute; **Lemmas** 6-7 mm. long, hirsute, bearing a slender but not flexuous awn 18-30 mm. long.

In woods and on banks, Texas, North Carolina, Maine to North Dakota. Late spring-summer.

A form with hispidulous glumes and glabrous or hispidulous lemmas has been published as *Elymus villosus forma arkansanus* (Scribn. & Ball) Fernald, *E. arkansanus* Scribn. & Ball. In woods and on banks, Texas to Arkansas, Iowa and New Jersey. (Balanced rock near Fredericksburg.) Spring-fall.

5. E. INTERRUPTUS Buckl. (ǐn-tĕr-ŭp'tǔs); *E. diversiglumis* Scribn. & Ball.

Culms 2-3.5 feet tall, tufted, erect, leafy; **Blades** 5-10' long, 5-12 mm. wide, flat, rough; **Sheaths** shorter than the internodes, or the lower over-lapping, glabrous or ciliate; **Ligule** membranaceous, about 1 mm. long; **Spike** 4-6' long, flexuous, finally exserted and nodding; **Spikelets** 2-4-flowered (2-flowered); **Glumes** setaceous or nearly so, scabrous, usually narrowed into a long slender flexuous awn (varying from a mere point to more than 15 mm. long); **Lemmas**, the lower about 9 mm. long, 5-7-nerved, sparsely hirsute, especially toward the apex, to scabrous, the awn flexuous, divergent, of the lower floret often 15-30 mm. long.

Thickets and open woods, Texas, Wisconsin and Minnesota to North Dakota and Wyoming. (Rocky banks of creeks, Davis Mountains, Jeff Davis county, and Llano, Texas.)

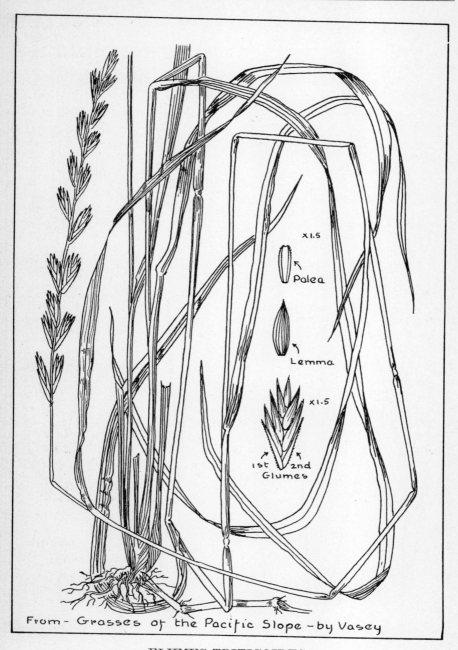

x1.5

↑ Palea

Lemma

x1.5

1st   2nd
Glumes

From - Grasses of the Pacific Slope - by Vasey

ELYMUS TRITICOIDES

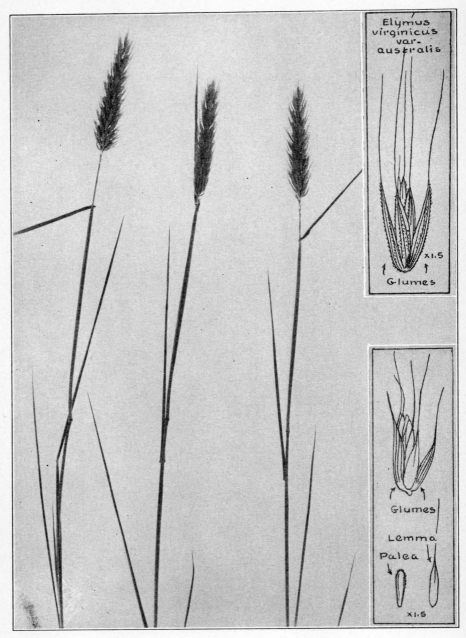

ELYMUS VIRGINICUS, Terrell-grass, Virginia Wild-rye; drawings of
ELYMUS VIRGINICUS var. AUSTRALIS.

ELYMUS VIRGINICUS VAR. GLABRIFLORUS to the left; ELYMUS
VIRGINICUS VAR. INTERMEDIUS to the right.

ELYMUS CANADENSIS, Nodding Wild-rye; drawings of
Elymus interruptus.

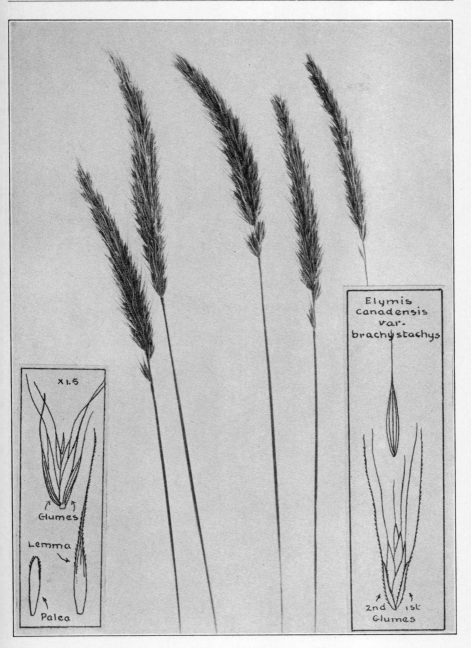

ELYMUS CANADENSIS var. ROBUSTUS; drawings of E. canadensis var. brachystachys.

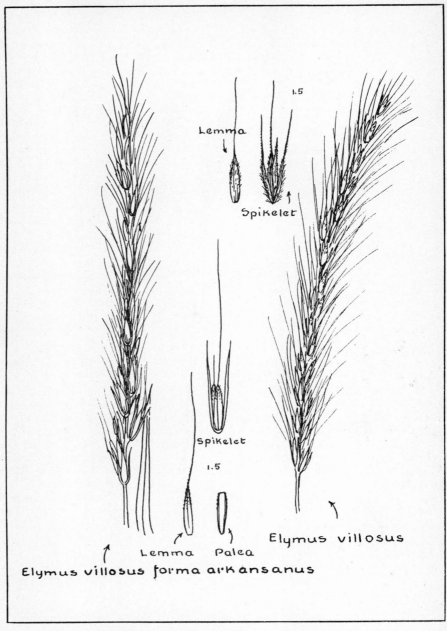

Lemma

1.5

Spikelet

Spikelet

1.5

Lemma   Palea

Elymus villosus

Elymus villosus forma arkansanus

ELYMUS VILLOSUS AND ELYMUS VILLOSUS FORMA
ARKANSANUS

27. SITANION Raf. (sī-tăn′yŭn)

Spikelets 2-to-few-flowered, the uppermost floret reduced, sessile, usually 2 at each node of a disarticulating rachis, the rachis breaking at the base of each joint, remaining attached as a pointed stipe to the spikelets above; **Glumes** narrow or setaceous, 1-3-nerved, the nerves prominent, extending into one-to-several awns, these (when more than one) irregular in size, sometimes mere lateral appendages of the long central awn, sometimes equal, the glume being bifid; **Lemmas** firm, convex on the back, nearly terete, the apex slightly 2-toothed, 5-nerved, the nerves obscure, the central nerve extending into a long, slender, finally spreading awn, sometimes one or more of the lateral nerves also extending into short awns; **Palea** firm, nearly as long as the body of the lemma, the two keels serrulate.

Low or rather tall cespitose *perennials,* with bristly spikes. Species about six, in the dry regions of western United States, one in Texas.

This genus is closely related to *Elymus,* and until recent years has been almost universally included in it. The characters which separate *Sitanion* are the disarticulating rachis together with the slender glumes and long-awned lemmas.

When young all the species furnish forage, but at maturity the disarticulated joints of the spike, with their pointed rachis-joints and long-awned spikelets, are blown about by the wind and often cause injury to stock, penetrating the nose and ears, working in by means of the forwardly roughened awns, and causing inflammation. The species are generally known as squirreltail or foxtail grasses.

S. HYSTRIX (Nutt.) J. G. Smith (hĭs′trĭks); *Elymus elymoides* (Raf.) Swezey; LONG-BRISTLED WILD RYE.

Culms 8-22′ tall, tufted, erect; **Blades** 1.5-6′ long, 2-7 mm. wide, flat, soon becoming involute, somewhat stiffly ascending, rough above, smooth below; **Sheaths** usually overlapping, the upper one often inflated and enclosing the base of the spike, sometimes rough; **Ligule** membranaceous, less than 1 mm. long; **Spikes** green or tinged with purple, 3-8′ long, including awns, usually two spikelets at each node, at maturity the awns spreading and rachis-joint disarticulating; **Spikelets** 2-6-flowered; **Glumes** entire, awl-shaped, with scabrous awns 2-3.5′ long; **Lemmas** 8-10 mm. long, scabrous, bearing a long scabrous awn 1.5-3.5′ long, at maturity divergent, the apex of lemma sometimes 2-toothed, the upper lemma usually short-awned.

In dry soil, Texas to Missouri, west to Colorado, Wyoming and Arizona. Late spring-summer.

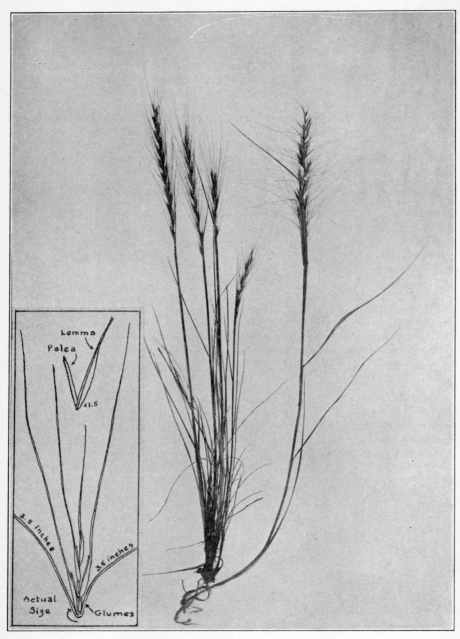

SITANION HYSTRIX, Long-bristle Wild-rye

28. HORDEUM L. (hôr'dē-ŭm)

Spikelets 1-flowered, 3 (sometimes 2) together at each node of the articulate rachis (continuous in *Hordeum vulgare*), the back of the lemma turned from the rachis, the middle one sessile or subsessile, the lateral ones pediceled; **Rachilla** disarticulating above the glumes and, in the central spikelet, prolonged behind the palea as a bristle and sometimes bearing a rudimentary floret; **Lateral Spikelets** usually imperfect, sometimes reduced to bristles; **Glumes** narrow, often subulate and awned, rigid, standing in front of the spikelet; **Lemma** rounded on the back, 5-nerved, usually obscurely so, tapering into a usually long awn.

Annual or *perennial* low or rather tall grasses, with flat blades and dense terminal cylindric spikes. 10 species in the United States, 5 in Texas.

Cultivated barley, an annual, with its many varieties, is the most important species of the genus, and resembles bearded wheat, the awns being as long as 6'. Beardless barley is a variety of *H. vulgare*. When all the spikelets of each cluster are fertile the barley is 2-rowed. In common or 4-rowed barley all the spikelets are fertile, but the lateral spikelets on the opposite sides of the spike being imbricate in a row so that the spike appears to be 4-rowed.

Little barley (*H. pusillum*), a small tufted annual with a narrow pale green spike 1-4' long, has both glumes of the central spikelet and the first glume of both lateral spikelets dilated above the base, the other glumes being bristle-like. *H. pusillum* var. *pubens* has pubescent spikelets.

H. nodosum, resembling little barley, differs in being a perennial, and in having uniformly awn-like glumes. *H. jubatum*, squirreltail, a perennial, has soft brushlike spikes, commonly purplish, with long-awned spikelets, the awns finally spreading, giving the spike a bushy appearance. *H. murinum*, barley-grass, an annual, differs from the other wild barleys in that both glumes of the central spikelet and the first glume of the lateral spikelets are ciliate on the margins with bristly hairs.

LATERAL SPIKELETS SESSILE; CULTIVATED ANNUALS.
  Lemma awned.   1. H. vulgare
  Lemma awnless.   1a. H. vulgare var. trifurcatum
LATERAL SPIKELETS STALKED; LEMMA AWNED.
  LEMMA OF THE middle spikelet sessile.
    SPIKES narrow with nearly erect or ascending awns.
      Glumes bristle-like; perennials.   2. H. nodosum
      Four glumes of cluster dilated above the base; annuals.
        Spikelets glabrous.   3. H. pusillum
        Spikelets pubescent, broader.   3a. H. pusillum var. pubens
    SPIKES bushy, with long spreading awns; perennials.   4. H. jubatum
  LEMMA OF THE middle spikelet stalked; glumes or some of them ciliate; annuals.   5. H. murinum

1. H. VULGARE L. (vŭl-gā'rē); *H. sativum* Jessen; CULTIVATED BARLEY.

Culms usually 2-3 feet tall, coarse but weak, erect; **Blades** 5-15' long more or less, about a half inch wide, flat, broad at the base, pointed, the under surface rough, with long glabrous auricles; **Ligule** membranaceous, short, truncate; **Spikes** excluding awns 3-4' long, dense, the rachis not disarticulating at maturity; **Spikelets** in clusters of three, all perfect; **Glumes** narrow, about 8 mm. long, with awns 7-10 mm. long, glabrous to pubescent; **Lemmas** 10-12 mm. long, fusiform, narrowed into a scabrous awn as long as 6 inches, the rachilla extended into a short hairy pedicel; **Palea** about as long as its lemma.

Cultivated lands, waste places, over most of the United States. Spring to summer.

1a. H. VULGARE var. TRIFURCATUM (Schlecht.) Allfeld (trī-fûr-kā'tŭm) ; BEARDLESS BARLEY.

Beardless barley is a cultivated variety of *H. vulgare* in which the **Awns** are suppressed and the **Lemmas** have only irregular short teeth or lobes. (See drawings of spike with *H. vulgare*.)

2. H. NODOSUM L. (nō-dō'sŭm) ; *H. pratense* Huds.; MEADOW BARLEY.

Culms 8-25′ tall, tufted, erect or decumbent at the base; **Blades** 1.5-5′ long, 2-6 mm. wide, flat, usually rough; **Sheaths** shorter than the internodes; **Ligule** membranaceous, about 6 mm. long, truncate; **Spike** 1-3.5′ long, finally exserted; **Spikelets** usually in threes; **Glumes** of all of the spikelets setaceous or awnlike; **Lemma** of the middle spikelet exclusive of the awns 6-8 mm. long, the awn usually 6-12 mm. long, the corresponding lemma in the lateral spikelets much smaller and stalked, awn-pointed.

In meadows and waste places, especially in saline soil, Texas to Tennessee and north. Late spring-summer.

3. H. PUSILLUM Nutt. (pū-sĭl'ŭm) ; LITTLE BARLEY.

Culms 4-24′ tall, in small tufts, erect or sometimes decumbent at the base; **Blades** 0.5-5′ long, 1-6 mm. wide, rough above, flat or involute when dry; **Sheaths** shorter than the internodes; **Ligule** membranaceous, short, truncate; **Spike** finally exserted, 1-4′ long, about 5-10 mm. thick, usually erect; **Spikelets** usually in threes, middle sessile and perfect, lateral on short pedicels, imperfect; **Glumes** scabrous, the first glume of each lateral spikelet and both glumes of the middle spikelet dilated above the base, the other two bristle-like, 8-15 mm. long, about equal to the awned lemma of the middle spikelet; **Lemma** of the middle spikelet exclusive of the short awn 6-8 mm. long, the corresponding parts of the lateral spikelets shorter, awnless or awn-pointed, on a short curved stipe; **Palea** of the middle spikelet about as long as its lemma, awn-pointed.

In dry soil, over most of the United States. Spring-summer.

3a. H. PUSILLUM var. PUBENS Hitchc. (pū'bĕns).

This variety differs from the species in that the **Spikelets** are pubescent and broader, and the dilated **Glumes** wider.

4. H. JUBATUM L. (jū-bā'tŭm) ; SQUIRRELTAIL-GRASS; FOXTAIL BARLEY.

Culms 8-30′ tall, tufted, erect, slender; **Blades** 1.5-5′ long, 2-5 mm. wide, flat, erect, scabrous; **Sheaths** shorter than the internodes, loose; **Ligule** membranaceous, about 1 mm. long; **Spikes** 2-4.5′ long, nodding, green or purplish, turning pale with age, the numerous long awns soon spreading; **Spikelets** three at each node of the articulate rachis, the middle sessile and perfect, the lateral stalked and abortive; **Glumes** setaceous, 1-2.5′ long, scabrous, finally spreading; **Lemma** of middle spikelet 6-8 mm. long, lanceolate, scabrous toward the apex, with scabrous awns 1.5-2.5′ long, the corresponding parts of the lateral spikelets similar but reduced, the lemma about 6 mm. long including the pedicel, sometimes much reduced, short-awned.

In dry soil, common in the western states, extending into the southern states. Summer.

5. H. MURINUM L. (mū-rī′nŭm); BARLEY-GRASS, WALL-BARLEY, MOUSE-BARLEY, FOXTAIL AND SEA-BARLEY.

Culms 12-30′ tall, erect or decumbent at the base; **Blades** 1.5-9′ the upper blades 1.5-3′ long, 3-7 mm. wide, flat, rough; **Sheaths** mostly shorter than the internodes, on small plants much crowded, loose; **Ligule** membranaceous, truncate, about 1 mm. long; **Spike** 2-3.5′ long, exserted or included at the base, spikelets in clusters of threes, the middle spikelets sessile and the lateral on stipes about 1.5 mm. long; **Spikelets, Glumes,** both glumes of the middle spikelet and the first glume of the lateral lanceolate and ciliate on the margins, the second glumes of the lateral spikelets awl-shaped, all with awns 18-30 mm. long; **Middle Spikelet, Lemma** exclusive of awn 9-12 mm. long, stalked, scabrous toward the apex, the scabrous awns about 25 mm. long; **Palea** about equal to its lemma, narrow, 2-toothed, the two nerves more or less pubescent; **Lateral Spikelets** imperfect, the lemmas and paleas well developed, these and the awns about equal to those of the middle spikelet, the awns sometimes longer; **Rachilla** of the lateral spikelets also extending behind the palea into a bristle shorter than that of the middle spikelet.

In waste places, sparingly over most of the United States. Spring and summer.

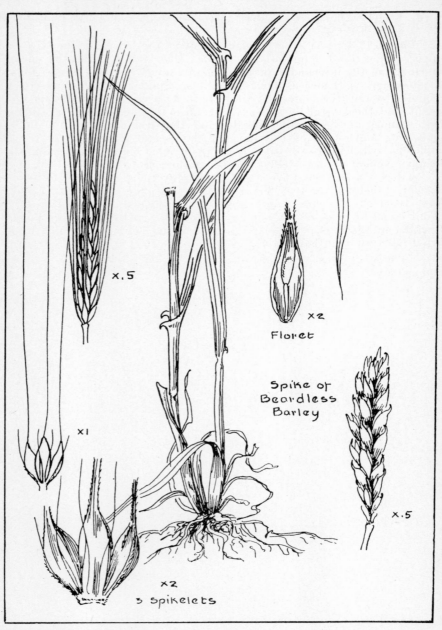

x.5

x2
Floret

Spike of
Beardless
Barley

x1

x.5

x2
3 spikelets

HORDEUM VULGARE, Cultivated Barley, and to the right a Spike of
Beardless Barley.

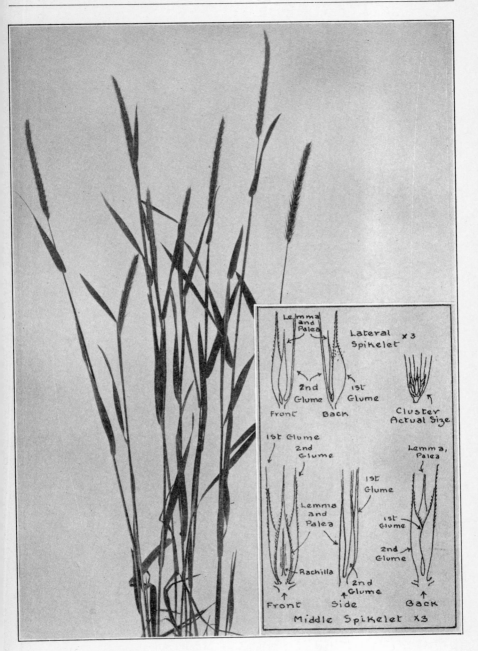

HORDEUM PUSILLUM, LITTLE BARLEY

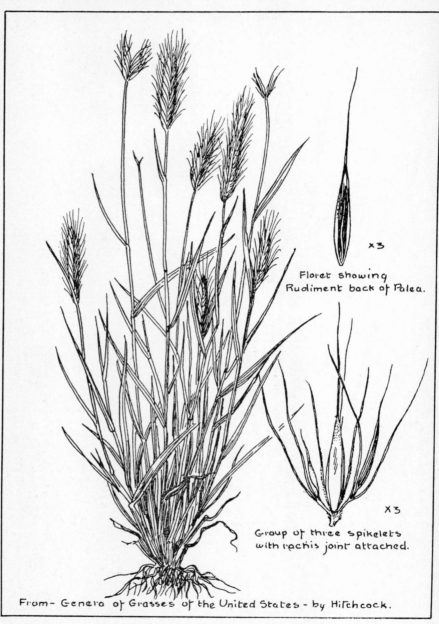

×3

Floret showing
Rudiment back of Palea.

×3

Group of three spikelets
with rachis joint attached.

From- Genera of Grasses of the United States - by Hitchcock.

HORDEUM NODOSUM, MEADOW BARLEY

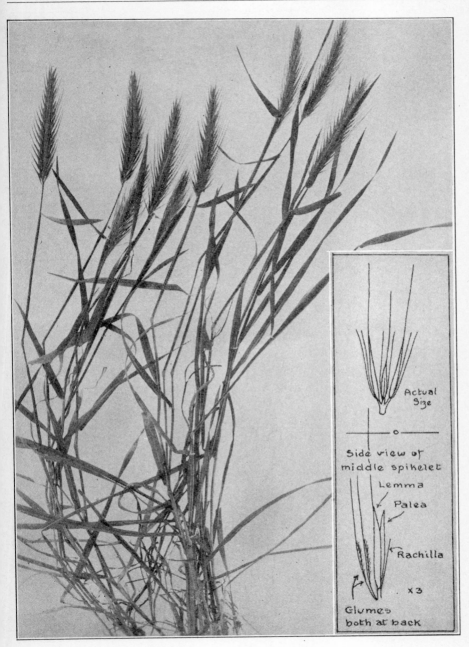

HORDEUM MURINUM, Sea-barley

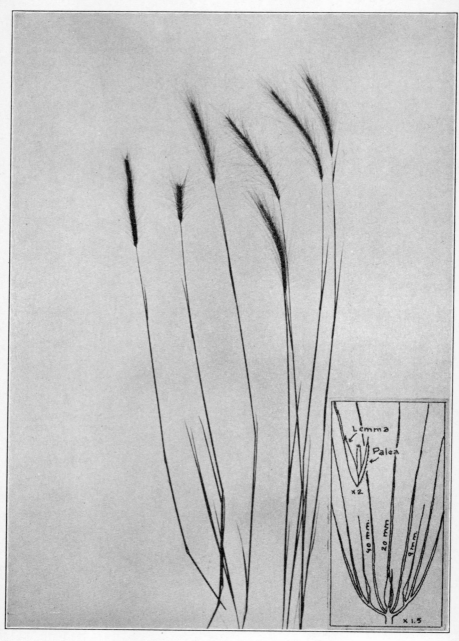

HORDEUM JUBATUM, Sǫᴜɪʀʀᴇʟᴛᴀɪʟ-ɢʀᴀss

29. LOLIUM L. (lō'lĭ-ŭm)

Spikelets several-flowered, solitary and sessile, placed edgewise to the continuous rachis, one edge fitting to the alternate concavities, the rachilla disarticulating above the glumes and between the florets; **First Glume** wanting (except on the terminal spikelet), the second outward, strongly 3-5-nerved, equaling or exceeding the second floret; **Lemmas** rounded on the back, 5-7-nerved, obtuse, acute, or awned.

Annuals or *perennials*, with flat blades, and simple terminal flat spikes.

This genus is easily distinguished by the position of the spikelets, edgewise to the rachis, and the usual absence of the first glume (the one next to the rachis) except in the terminal spikelet.

The three species in Texas, with a range covering most of the United States, have long narrow spikes.

English rye-grass and Italian rye-grass, closely related perennials, the first with awnless lemmas and the second with awned lemmas, are frequently used for lawns, meadows and pastures. They are of some importance in the south as winter forage. Cross-fertilization often takes place between these two species giving rise to plants with both awned and awnless spikelets. Darnel, the awned form being known as *Lolium temulentum* and the awnless form as *Lolium temulentum* var. *leptochaeton*, is supposed to be the plant referred to in Scripture in the parable of the tares. Because of the presence in the fruit of a narcotic poison, said to be due to a fungus, it is in bad repute.

SECOND GLUME shorter than the spikelet; plants perennial.
Lemmas awnless.   1. L. perenne
Lemmas awned.   2. L. multiflorum
SECOND GLUME equaling or exceeding the florets; plants annual.
Lemmas awned.   3. L. temulentum
Lemmas awnless.   3a. L. temulentum var. leptochaeton

1. L. PERENNE L. (pĕr-ĕn'nē) ; ENGLISH OR PERENNIAL RYE-GRASS, RAY-GRASS.

Culms 1-2.5 feet tall, tufted, erect; **Blades** commonly 4-6' long, 2-6 mm. wide, rough above, glossy; **Sheaths** about as long as or longer than the internodes, flattened, auriculate at the base, loose above, rough or smooth; **Ligule** membranaceous, about 1 mm. long; **Spike** slender, commonly 4-10' long; **Spikelets** 6-10-flowered, 10-14 mm. long, flattened; **Glumes,** the first, next to the rachis, wanting except in the terminal spikelet, the second commonly shorter than the florets, 6-12 mm. long, 5-nerved, rigid, obtuse; **Lemmas** 4-6 mm. long, 5-nerved, thin, obtuse, lanceolate; **Palea** about as long as its lemma, elliptic, acute, hyaline, the nerves near the ciliate margins.

In waste places and cultivated grounds, throughout most of the United States, especially the northern portion. Spring-summer.

2. L. MULTIFLORUM Lam. (mŭl-tĭ-flō'rŭm) ; *L. italicum* A. Br.; ITALIAN RYE-GRASS.

Culms commonly 2-3 feet tall, sometimes 3.5 feet, stout, tufted, erect, dark-green, with dark swollen nodes, sometimes geniculate at the base, rough above; **Blades** 4-12' long, 6-8 mm. wide, flat, acuminate, the base extended into an auricle on each side, rough, especially the margins and upper surface; **Sheaths** about as long as or shorter than the internodes, flattened, smooth or rough; **Ligule** membranaceous, about 1 mm. long;

Spike commonly 6-10′ as much as 18′ long; **Spikelets** 10-20-flowered, including awns 12-25 mm. long, linear or lanceolate; **Glumes**, the first, next to the rachis, wanting except in the terminal spikelet, the second shorter than the florets (as long as or longer than the lower florets), rigid, 5-nerved, obtuse, dark-green; **Lemmas** about 6 mm. long, lanceolate, rounded on the back, with five green nerves vanishing in the scarious margin at the apex, except the middle nerve which usually extends into an awn 1-8 mm. long (many plants have most of the lemmas awnless or with just the lower lemma awnless); **Palea** nearly as long as the lemma, acute, lanceolate-elliptic, the two green nerves near the ciliate margins, hyaline.

In fields and waste places, over much of the United States. Spring-summer.

3. L. TEMULENTUM L. (tĕm-ū-lĕn′tŭm) ; DARNEL, POISON-DARNEL.

This species is similar to the variety *L. temulentum* var. *leptochaeton* A. Br. except for the awned lemmas. A drawing of the spikelet accompanies the photograph of the variety.

Waste and cultivated ground, introduced from Europe, not so plentiful as Italian rye-grass or English rye-grass. Spring-summer.

3a. L. TEMULENTUM var. LEPTOCHAETON A. Br. (lĕp-tō-kē′tŏn) ; DARNEL, POISON-DARNEL.

Culms 2-3 feet tall, sometimes taller, erect, simple; **Blades** 4-10′ long, 2-7 mm. wide, flat, acuminate, rough on the upper surface; **Sheaths** longer or shorter than the internodes; **Ligule** membranaceous, less than 2 mm. long; **Spike** 4-10′ long, spikelets equaling or exceeding the intervals; **Spikelets** 4-7-flowered, 18-20 mm. long (10-20) ; **Glumes,** the first wanting except in the terminal spikelets, the second equaling or exceeding the florets, rigid, acuminate, green; **Lemmas** about 6 mm. long, broad, rounded on the back, turgid, obscurely 5-7-nerved, awnless; **Palea** about as long as its lemma, obovate.

In waste places and cultivated ground, introduced from Europe, perhaps, with about the same range as the species. Spring-summer.

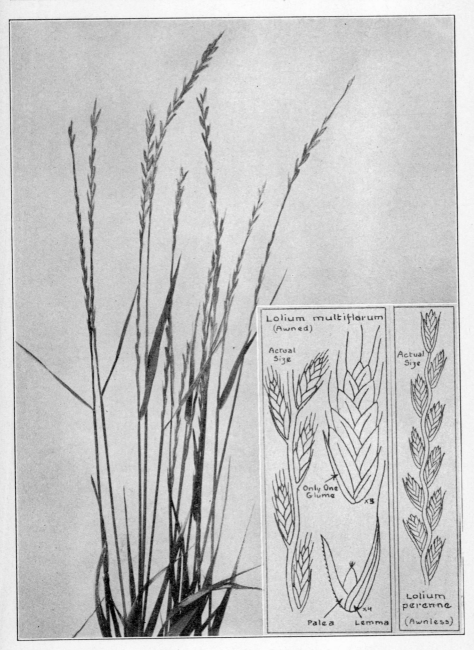

LOLIUM MULTIFLORUM, Italian Rye-grass; also drawing of
LOLIUM PERENNE, English Rye-grass, to the right.

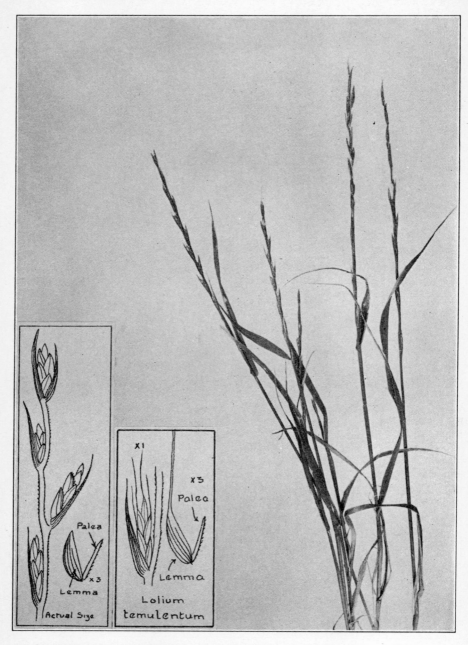

LOLIUM TEMULENTUM VAR. LEPTOCHAETON.   Also drawing of
Spikelet of L. temulentum, Darnel or Poison Darnel.

IV. AVENEAE, THE OAT TRIBE

30. KOELERIA Pers. (kĕl-ē'rĭ-à)

Spikelets 2-4-flowered, compressed, the rachilla disarticulating above the glumes and between the florets, prolonged beyond the perfect florets as a slender bristle or bearing a reduced or sterile floret at the tip; **Glumes** usually about equal in length, but unequal in shape, the lower narrow and sometimes shorter, 1-nerved, the upper somewhat broader above the middle, wider than the lower, 3-5-nerved; **Lemmas** somewhat scarious and shining, the lowermost a little longer than the glume, obscurely 5-nerved, acute or short-awned, the awn, if present, borne just below the apex.

Annual or *perennial*, slender, low or rather tall grasses, with narrow blades and spikelike panicles. Two species in the United States, one in Texas and one in California. Our only grass of this genus is a tufted perennial, a foot or two high, with slender, erect culms, with a pale shining, densely-flowered panicle, 2-5' long, the short branches appressed except when flowering. It thrives on prairies, plains and in open woods from northern Mexico through Texas north to Canada. It is a good forage grass and is a constituent of much of the native pasture throughout the western states.

K. CRISTATA (L.) Pers. (krĭs-tā'tà); *K. gracilis* Pers.; KOELER'S GRASS.

Culms 1-2.5 feet tall, tufted, erect, rigid, simple, densely short-pubescent below the panicle, leafy at the base; **Blades** 2.5-3' long, 1-3 mm. wide, flat or involute, the basal leaves somewhat longer, stiffly ascending or erect, usually more or less rough, and more or less puberulent (or hirsute); **Sheaths** mostly longer than the internodes, smooth to scabrous (or hirsute); **Ligule** membranaceous, fringed, about 1 mm. long; **Panicle** exserted, 2-7' long, pale-green, usually contracted or spikelike, when flowering the branches more or less ascending or spreading, the lower branches 1.5' or less long, gradually shorter above, often interrupted at the base, the main axis and branches minutely pubescent; **Spikelets** 2-4-flowered, 4-6 mm. long, the glumes and lemmas minutely scabrous; **Glumes** nearly as long as the lowest florets; **Lemmas** 3-4 mm. long, the lower a little longer than the glumes, obscurely 5-nerved, shining, acute or short-awned just below the apex, margins scarious. This species seems to be very variable as to pubescence and otherwise.

Prairies and plains, Texas, Colorado, California, south to Mexico. Summer.

KOELERIA CRISTATA, Koeler's Grass

31. TRISETUM Pers. (trī-sē′tŭm)

Spikelets usually 2-flowered, sometimes 3-5-flowered, the rachilla prolonged behind the upper floret, usually villous; **Glumes** somewhat unequal, acute, awnless, the second usually longer than the first floret; **Lemmas** usually short-bearded at the base, 2-toothed at the apex, the teeth often awned, bearing from the back below the cleft apex a straight and included or usually bent and exserted awn.

Tufted *perennials* with flat blades and open or usually contracted or spikelike panicles. Eight species in the United States, mostly in the mountains, one in Texas.

The name *Trisetum* refers to the three awns of the lemma of many of the species, one from the back and one from each of the teeth. Our only species, *T. interruptum,* has glabrous lemmas, the articulation being below the spikelets. This species is closely related to *Sphenopholis.*

Formerly our plants were divided into two species—*T. interruptum,* a freely branching plant with the awn of the lower lemma long and bent like those of the upper lemmas, the teeth extended into short scabrous awns, and *T. hallii,* usually simple, with the awn of the lower lemma short and straight (not long and bent like those of the upper lemma), the teeth wedge-shaped. But Dr. Hitchcock on examination of a great deal of material found that these two intergrade, the characters used to distinguish them being inconstant, and therefore reduced *T. hallii* to *T. interruptum.*

T. **INTERRUPTUM** Buckl. (ĭn-tĕr-ŭp′tŭm); including *T. hallii* Scribn.
Culms 6-18′ tall, tufted, erect or ascending from a geniculate base, slender, glabrous or puberulent, especially the lower internodes, and below the nodes simple or branching; **Blades** 1-5′ mostly 2-3′ long, 1.5-3 mm. wide, flat or involute toward the tip, rough, or the under surface smooth, the basal leaf-blades short and often numerous; **Sheaths** about as long as the internodes, rough, the lower sometimes puberulent; **Ligule** membranaceous, about 2 mm. long; **Panicle** 1.5-5′ long, slender, finally exserted, somewhat interrupted, erect or slightly nodding, the branches mostly in twos or threes, 0.5-1.5′ long, usually appressed, the sessile or short-pediceled spikelets crowded along their entire length; **Spikelets** 3-4-flowered, exclusive of the awns 4-5 mm. long, the uppermost floret abortive or reduced to a small rudiment; **Glumes** subequal, 3-4 mm. long, oblanceolate, acute or short awn-pointed, hispid on the keel, the first 3-nerved, the second broader, 5-7-nerved; **Lemmas,** the lower including the awn-like teeth 4-4.5 mm. long, 3-nerved, scabrous on the midnerve, carious on the margins toward the apex, finely tuberculate, *glabrous,* the teeth wedge-shaped or extended into short scabrous awns, bearing from the back an awn from one-fourth to one-third the distance from the apex, 2-6 mm. long, that of the lower lemma often straight and short, all of the other awns longer and more or less twisted and bent about one-third the distance above the insertion.

Dry or moist soil, prairies and hills, central Texas to southern New Mexico. Spring.

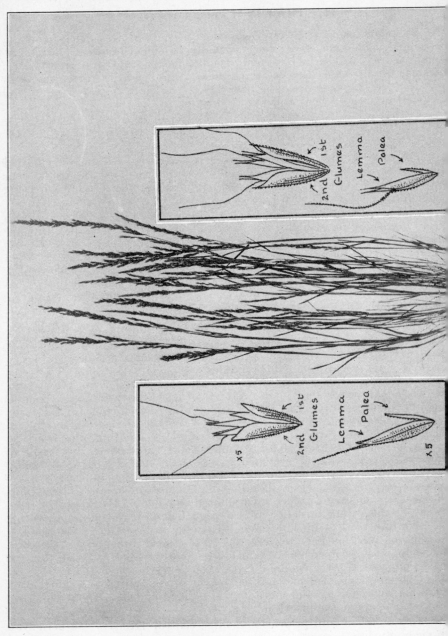

TRISETUM INTERRUPTUM, the drawings showing the two forms

32. SPHENOPHOLIS Scribn. (sfē-nŏf'ō-lĭs)
(Eatonia of Authors, not Raf.)

Spikelets 2-3-flowered, the pedicel disarticulating below the glumes, he rachilla produced beyond the upper floret as a slender bristle; **Glumes** unlike in shape, the first narrow, acute, 1-nerved, the second broadly bovate, 3-5-nerved, somewhat coriaceous; **Lemmas** firm, scarcely nerved, wnless, the first a little shorter or a little longer than the second glume.

Perennial grasses with usually flat blades and shining pale-green or ale-purplish narrow panicles.

S. obtusata, with rather dense panicle, the second glume obovate and ubcucullate, is found at random over much of the United States.

Our other species have rather loose, lax and nodding panicles; *S. longiflora* and *S. intermedia* with oblanceolate acute or acutish second glume not nuch wider than the lemmas; *S. nitida* and *S. filiformis* with an obovate econd glume broadly rounded at the summit.

PANICLES DENSE, USUALLY SPIKELIKE, ERECT OR NEARLY SO; the first glume shorter and not more than one-fifth as wide as the obovate-subcucullate second. 1. S. obtusata
PANICLES NOT DENSE, LAX, NODDING, contracted but loose, often slender, but not spikelike.
  SECOND GLUME oblanceolate, acute or subacute, not much wider than the lemmas; panicles many-flowered.
    Second glume about 2.5 mm. long; first glume subulate, about 2 mm. long; lemma 2.5 mm. long. 2. S. intermedia
    Second glume about 3.5 mm. long; first glume linear; lemma 3.5 mm. long. 3. S. longiflora
  SECOND GLUME obovate, broadly rounded at the summit.
    Blades rarely more than 4' long, flat, 2-5 mm. wide. 4. S. nitida
    Blades elongate, flat to subinvolute, mostly less than 2 mm. wide; first glume linear. 5. S. filiformis

. S. OBTUSATA (Michx.) Scribn. (ŏb-tū-sā'tȧ); *S. obtusata* var. *lobata* (Trin.) Scribn.; *S. pubescens* (Scribn.) Heller.

Culms 10-30' tall, solitary or a few culms to a tuft, simple, erect or lecumbent at the base, often scabrous just below the panicle; **Blades** .5-7' long, 2-9 mm. wide, flat, somewhat narrowed toward the base, rough, glabrous or pubescent; **Sheaths** shorter than the internodes, rather loose, mooth or rough, glabrous or pubescent; **Ligule** membranaceous, 1.5-3 mm. ong, erose; **Panicles** light-green or purplish, finally exserted, 2-7' long, ontracted, usually erect, densely-flowered, the branches 1.5' long or less, erect or appressed, the spikelets crowded, the scabrous pedicels about . mm. long; **Spikelets** 2.5-3 mm. long; **Glumes** scabrous on the keels, the irst about one-fifth as wide as and somewhat shorter than the second, he second about one-third shorter than the lower lemma, broad, obovate, btuse or truncate, subcucullate, minutely scabrous; **Lemmas** 2-2.3 mm. ong, obtuse, extending beyond the glumes, smooth or minutely scabrous, r much so on the keel toward the apex; **Palea** slightly shorter than the emma, narrow.

In dry or moist soil, Texas west to Arizona and east to Florida, 1orth to Maine. Spring-summer.

2. S. INTERMEDIA (Rydb.) Hitchc. (ĭn-tēr-mē'dĭ-ȧ); formerly erroneously determined as *S. pallens* (Spreng.) Scribn.

Culms 2-2.5 feet tall, slender, erect; **Blades** 2.5-7' long, 2-6 mm. wide, usually flat; **Panicles** 3-6' long, contracted, not dense or spikelike, lax, nodding; **Spikelets** 3-3.5 mm. long; **Glumes,** the first 2 mm. long, subulate scabrous on the keel, the second about 2.5 mm. long, oblanceolate, acute or subacute; **Lemmas** about 2.5 mm. long.

Meadows and damp woods, Texas, Georgia, Maine to Wisconsin (Palestine, Texas.)   Spring-summer.

3. S. LONGIFLORA (Vasey) Hitchc. (lŏn-jĭ-flō′rà); *S. pallens* var *longiflora* (Vasey) Scribn.

Culms 2-3.5 feet tall, in small tufts, erect or ascending; **Blades** 2.5-7 long, 4-8 mm. wide, flat, thin and lax, rough; **Sheaths** shorter than the internodes, smooth or slightly rough; **Ligule** membranaceous, about 2 mm long; **Panicles** linear-lanceolate, exserted, 4-9′ long, nodding, loose shining, the branches 1-2′ distant, in half whorls, 3.5′ long or less, usually appressed; **Spikelets** 1-2-flowered, 3.5-4.5 mm. long; **Glumes** more or less scabrous, especially on the keels, subequal, the first narrow, about 3.1 mm long, acute, the second about 3.5 mm. long, broader, oblanceolate, acute when spread; **Lemmas** about 3.5 mm. long, acute, scabrous on the kee toward the apex, margins scarious; **Palea** about three-fourths as long a its lemma, 2-toothed.

Along the banks of streams, in open woods, Texas and Louisiana (Chico Bayou, near Alvin, Texas.)   Spring.

4. S. NITIDA (Spreng.) Scribn. (nĭt′ĭ-dà); *Eatonia nitida* (Spreng. Nash; *E. dudleyi* Vasey; *S. glabra* (Nash) Heller; SLENDER SPHENO PHOLIS.

Culms 1-2 feet tall, very slender, erect, tufted; **Blades** 0.5-3′ long (o those of the sterile shoots 3-6′ long and 2-4 mm. wide), 2 mm. wide or less the upper short, abruptly acute, often pubescent; **Sheaths** shorter than th internodes, glabrous to softly pubescent; **Ligule** membranaceous, abou 0.5 mm. long; **Panicle** exserted, pale-green, 2-6′ long, loosely-flowered, it branches 1-2.5′ long, spreading at flowering time, finally erect; **Spikelet** 2-3-flowered, about 3 mm. long, on short pedicels; **Glumes** smooth o nearly so, equal or subequal, about 2 mm. long, the first not less than one third as wide as the second, the second rounded or abruptly apiculate a the summit; **Lemmas** narrow, 2-2.5 mm. long, oblong, obtuse or acutish the lower smooth or nearly so, the upper scabrous especially near the ti and on the keel; **Palea** slightly shorter than its lemma.

In dry soil, east Texas, Georgia, Mississippi, Vermont to Michigar (Kuntz, Texas.)   Spring-fall.

5. S. FILIFORMIS (Chapm.) Scribn. (fĭl-ĭ-fôr′mĭs); *Eatonia penn sylvanica* var. *filiformis* Chapm.; *E. filiformis* (Chapm.) Vasey.

Culms 1-2 feet tall, densely-tufted, erect, very slender; **Blades** of th culm 1.5-2′ long, of the sterile shoots as much as 20′ long, mostly less tha 2 mm. wide, flat or subinvolute; **Panicle** 2-6′ long, slender, often nodding the slender branches rather distant, erect or ascending; **Spikelets** 3-4 mm long, the two florets rather distant; **Glumes** about 2 mm. long, the secon broadly rounded at the summit; **Lemmas** about 2.8 mm. long, obtuse o subobtuse, rarely with a short spreading awn, the lower smooth, the uppe minutely roughened.

Dry plains, North Carolina to Florida, Tennessee, and eastern Texas (Colmesneil, Tyler County, Texas.)   Spring.

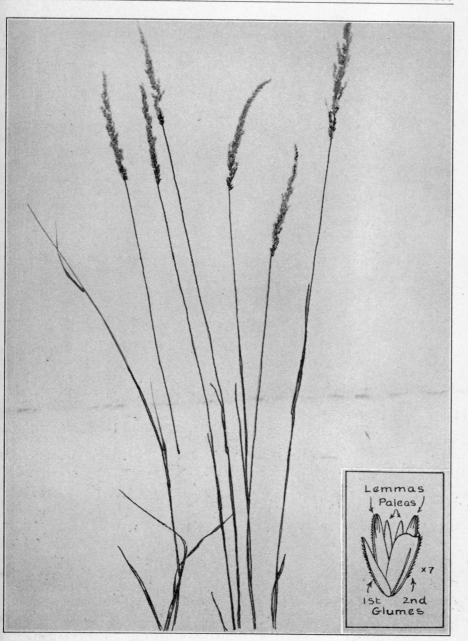

Lemmas
Paleas
×7
1st   2nd
Glumes

SPHENOPHOLIS OBTUSATA

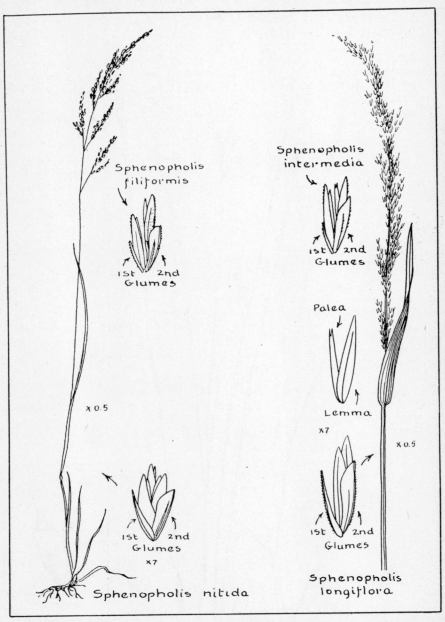

Sphenopholis
filiformis

1st 2nd
Glumes

Sphenopholis
intermedia

1st 2nd
Glumes

Palea

Lemma
×7

X 0.5

1st 2nd
Glumes
×7

1st 2nd
Glumes

X 0.5

Sphenopholis nitida

Sphenopholis
longiflora

SPHENOPHOLIS NITIDA, SPHENOPHOLIS FILIFORMIS,
SPHENOPHOLIS INTERMEDIA, SPHENOPHOLIS LONGIFLORA.

33. AVENA L. (à-vē'nà)

Spikelets 2-several-flowered, the rachilla bearded, disarticulating above the glumes and between the florets; **Glumes** about equal, membranaceous or papery, several-nerved, longer than the lower floret, usually exceeding the upper floret; **Lemmas** indurate, except toward the summit, 5-9-nerved, bidentate at the apex, bearing a dorsal bent and twisted awn (this straight and reduced in *Avena sativa*).

Annual or *perennial,* low or moderately tall grasses, with narrow or open usually rather few-flowered panicles of usually large spikelets. Our one species, cultivated oat, is an annual.

In the several varieties of cultivated oat the florets do not disarticulate readily, and the lemmas are usually glabrous with awns straight or wanting, while in *Avena fatua* L., wild oat, from which most of the varieties of cultivated oat are supposed to be derived, the florets disarticulate easily, the awns are bent and twisted, and the lemmas are beset with brown hairs.

A. SATIVA L. (sà-tī'và); CULTIVATED OAT.

Culms 2-4 feet high, erect, tufted, thick but weak stems; **Blades** flat, as much as 19' long and 20 mm. wide, more or less scabrous, especially above and along the margins; **Ligule** membranaceous, almost truncate, less than 5 mm. long, toothed; **Panicle** somewhat narrow and one-sided, erect or nodding, as much as 10' long, its branches ascending, spikelets drooping; **Spikelets** 2-flowered, excluding the awns usually 16-25 mm. long, pedicels thickened just below the spikelet, rachilla of lower floret bearded; **Glumes** broad, acute, about equal, membranaceous, prominently many-nerved (usually 9-11-nerved), commonly 20-25 mm. long and longer than florets; **Lemmas** glabrous, smooth, 2-toothed, awnless, or one or both with a straight dorsal awn as much as 30 mm. long, lower lemma 15-23 mm. long, upper shorter, 5-9-nerved, the awn leaving the midvein from near the middle of the back of lemma; **Palea** nearly as long as its lemma, 2-keeled, ciliate, 2-toothed.

In cultivation over most of the United States. Spring-summer.

AVENA SATIVA, Cultivated Oat

34. AIRA L. (ī′rȧ)
(Aspris Adans.)

Spikelets 2-flowered, the rachilla disarticulating above the glumes, not prolonged; **Glumes** about equal, acute, membranaceous or subscarious; **Lemmas** firm, rounded on the back, tapering into two slender teeth, the callus with a very short tuft of hairs, bearing on the back below the middle a slender, geniculate, twisted, usually exserted awn, this reduced or wanting in the lower floret in one species.

Low, delicate *annuals* with small open or contracted panicles. Species about nine, in southern Europe, three being introduced in the United States, one in Texas.

A. CAPILLARIS Host (kăp-ĭ-lăr′ĭs); *Aspris capillaris* (Host) Hitchc.

Culms 5-12′ tall, rarely taller, tufted, slender; **Blades** 0.5-2′ long, 0.5-1.5 mm. wide, flat; **Sheaths** shorter than the internodes, ciliate; **Ligule** a ring of very short hairs; **Panicles** silvery-shining, 1.5-3′ long, open, the branches commonly less than 1.5′ long, ascending or spreading, the spikelets scattered toward the ends of the capillary branches on scabrous pedicels 3-5 mm. long; **Spikelets** exclusive of the awn 1.5-2.3 mm. long; **Glumes** about equal, exceeding the florets, acute, often abruptly so, sometimes awn-pointed, more or less minutely scabrous; **Lemmas** rather brown, about 1.3 mm. long, lanceolate, scabrous, narrowed above into two pale slender setaceous teeth, a tuft of hairs on the callus; the *lower* with shorter teeth, awnless or rarely awned; the *upper* bearing a geniculate awn from below the middle exceeding the glumes about 1.5-2.5 mm., the awn stouter and brown below the bend; **Palea** slightly shorter than the lemma.

Sandy land, east Texas, Virginia and southward, and on the Pacific coast. (Common from Texarkana to Marshall, Texas.) Spring-summer.

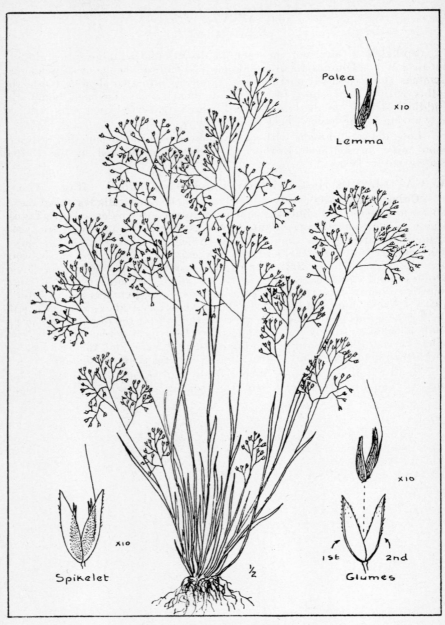

Palea

×10

Lemma

×10

Spikelet

×10

½

1st   2nd

Glumes

AIRA CAPILLARIS

35. HOLCUS L. (hŏl'kŭs)
(Notholcus Nash)

Spikelets 2-flowered, the pedicel disarticulating below the glumes, the rachilla curved and somewhat elongate below the first floret, not prolonged above the second floret; **Glumes** about equal, longer than the two florets; **First Floret** perfect, its lemma awnless; **Second Floret** staminate, its lemma awned on the back.

Perennial grasses, with flat blades and contracted panicles. Two species in the United States, one in Texas.

Velvet-grass has been introduced in various places in the eastern states and also on the Pacific coast where it is abundant. It is sometimes recommended as a meadow grass, but for this purpose it has little value except on moist sandy or sterile soil where other grasses will not thrive. It is an erect, grayish, velvety-pubescent grass 2-3 feet tall, with a contracted pale or purplish panicle 2-6' long, the branches spreading in anthesis.

H. LANATUS L. (là-nā'tŭs) ; *Notholcus lanatus* (L.) Nash; VELVET-GRASS.

Culms 1.5-3 feet tall, tufted, erect or decumbent at the base, simple, softly and densely-grayish pubescent, or glabrous to puberulent below the panicle; **Blades** 1-6' long, 4-12 mm. wide, flat, velvety grayish-green; **Sheaths** shorter or the lower longer than the internodes, velvety grayish-green; **Ligule** 1-2 mm. long, toothed, pubescent; **Panicle** pale or purplish, 2-6' long, oblong to oblong-pyramidal, contracted or open in flower, densely-flowered, the branches mostly in whorls of 1-3, the longer naked at the base, mostly 0.5-1.5' long, erect or appressed, or spreading in flower; **Spikelets** 4-5 mm. long; **Glumes** longer than the florets, pubescent, the hairs longer and stiff on the nerves, the first 1-nerved, acute or obtuse, the second broader, pointed, 3-nerved; **Lemmas** 2 mm. long, shining, the lower perfect, sparsely ciliate on the keel, somewhat obtuse, the upper 2-toothed, and bearing a hooked awn often over 1 mm. long just below the apex. (Drawings with *Danthonia spicata*.)

In moist or dry soil, meadows, fields and waste places, Texas, along the Pacific coast, Illinois to Massachusetts, North Carolina. Here and there over most of the United States, extending into Canada. (Beaumont, Texas.) Spring-summer.

36.   DANTHONIA Lam. & DC. (dăn-thō'nĭ-à)

Spikelets several-flowered, the rachilla readily disarticulating above the glumes and between the florets; **Glumes** about equal, broad and papery, acute, mostly exceeding the uppermost floret; **Lemmas** rounded on the back, obscurely several-nerved, the base with a strong callus, the apex bifid, the lobes acute, usually extending into slender awns, a stout awn arising from between the lobes; **Awn** flat, tightly twisted below, geniculate, exserted, including three nerves of the lemma.

Tufted, low or moderately tall *perennials,* with few-flowered open or spikelike panicles of rather large spikelets.

D. SPICATA (L.) Beauv. (spī-kā'tà).

Culms 1-2 feet tall, tufted, simple, erect, slender, terete, the curly leaves below numerous; **Blades** 1-6' long, the upper short, mostly 1-2 mm. wide, usually involute, often rough toward the apex, pubescent on the upper surface near the base, the lower sparsely-pubescent on both surfaces, especially above; **Sheaths** shorter than the internodes, often pilose at the throat, sometimes sparsely-pubescent below; **Ligule** a ring of short hairs; **Panicle** 1-2' in length, the branches short commonly with 1 or 2 spikelets, the pedicels and branches erect or ascending; **Spikelets** 5-7-flowered, 8-10 mm. long; **Glumes** 8-10 mm. long, the second sometimes slightly shorter, acuminate, 3-5-nerved, sometimes one or two obscure or wanting; **Lemmas** about 4 mm. long, including the triangular teeth about 1 mm. long, broadly oblong, sparsely pilose over the back and margins, 7-nerved, a flat 3-nerved awn extending from the sinus, about 6 mm. long, closely twisted at the base, loosely so above; **Palea** about three-fourths as long as its lemma, obovate, abruptly narrowed into an obtuse apex, the margins ciliate; **Grain** oblong, slightly over 1 mm. long, brown, channeled on one side.

It is said that all the species of this genus in the United States produce *cleistogenes* in the lower sheaths.

In dry soil, eastern Texas to Colorado, South Dakota to Newfoundland, south to North Carolina. (Texarkana, Texas.) Summer-fall.

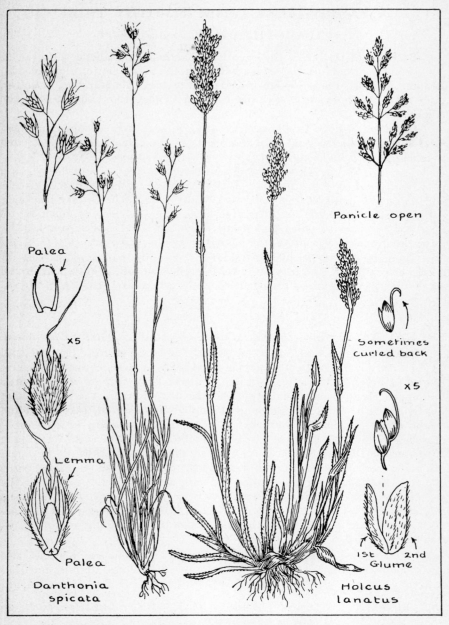

Palea

×5

Lemma

Palea

Danthonia
spicata

Panicle open

Sometimes
curled back

×5

1st   2nd
Glume

Holcus
lanatus

DANTHONIA SPICATA; HOLCUS LANATUS, Velvet-grass

V. AGROSTIDEAE, THE TIMOTHY TRIBE

37. CALAMOVILFA Hack. (kăl-á-mō-vĭl'fá)

Spikelets 1-flowered, the rachilla disarticulating above the glumes, not prolonged behind the palea; **Glumes** unequal, acute, chartaceous; **Lemma** a little longer than the second glume, chartaceous, awnless, glabrous or pubescent, the callus bearded; **Palea** about as long as the lemma.

Perennial, rigid, usually tall grasses, with narrow or open panicles, some species with creeping rhizomes. Species four, confined to the United States and southern Canada, one and perhaps two species in Texas.

Giant reed-grass, often growing to a height of 6-8 feet, and long-leaved reed-grass commonly 2-4 feet tall, both with creeping horizontal rootstocks and pale open panicles, thrive in very sandy land. The former has large panicles, sometimes 2.5 feet long, the spreading branches as much as 16' long, the lemma and palea pubescent, while the latter has a panicle 4-15' long, the branches ascending, the lemma and palea glabrous.

Giant reed-grass is plentiful along the sandy banks of streams of northwestern Texas, and it is likely that long-leaved reed-grass will be found in the vicinity of Texline, Texas. Both are excellent sand binders.

LEMMA and palea pubescent; spikelets 7-9 mm. long. 1. C. gigantea
LEMMA and palea glabrous; spikelets 5-6 mm. long. 2. C. longifolia

1. C. GIGANTEA (Nutt.) Scribn. & Merr. (jī-găn-tē'á) ; GIANT REED-GRASS.

Culms 3-8 feet tall, erect or slightly ascending, rigid, robust and rather woody, with long creeping rootstocks, making excellent sand binders; **Blades** as much as 32' long, 5-18 mm. wide at base, flat or involute near the apex, rigid, long-attenuate; **Sheaths** longer than the internodes; **Ligule** a ring of hairs 1-2 mm. long; **Panicle** long-exserted, 1-2.5 feet long, the lower branches as much as 16' long, the spreading or ascending branches naked at the base, usually in ones along the main axis, each branch with 1-6 branchlets up to 6' long, the spikelets toward the apex, the axils of branches and branchlets pilose; **Spikelets** 7-9 mm. long, light in color; **Glumes** 1-nerved, acute, the first about 6-7 mm. long and the second about 7-8 mm. long; **Lemma** a little longer or shorter than the second glume, *pubescent on the lower half*, the callus copious with long hairs about half as long as the lemma; **Palea** about as long as its lemma, strongly two-keeled, *pubescent*.

In very sandy places, Texas, New Mexico, Arizona and Kansas; also probably in Oklahoma. (Along Canadian River at bridge 20 miles north of Amarillo, Texas.) Summer.

2. C. LONGIFOLIA (Hook.) Scribn. (lŏn-jĭ-fō'lĭ-á) ; LONG-LEAVED REED-GRASS. (*Not yet collected in Texas.*)

Culms 1-4 feet tall, erect, simple, usually stout, firm, from long horizontal rootstocks; **Blades** 4-15' long, 5-9 mm. wide, the upper shorter, flat or involute toward the tip, tough, slightly rough above; **Sheaths** crowded and overlapping, distant above, slightly scabrous, glabrous or pubescent at the throat and margins; **Ligule** a dense ring of hairs 1-2 mm. long; **Panicle** open but comparatively narrow, 4-12' long, pale, the branches usually ascending, rarely spreading, mostly solitary, the lower commonly 4-5′ long; **Spikelets** 5-6 mm. long, rarely 8 mm. long, pale; **Glumes** acuminate, the first about two-thirds as long as the lemma, the second slightly longer or as long as the lemma; **Lemma** acuminate, *glabrous*, the callus hairs copious, about half to two-thirds as long as the lemma; **Palea** about as long as the lemma, *glabrous*.

In sandy places, Colorado to Kansas and Indiana, north to Canada. (As this grass has been collected near Texline, New Mexico, it is likely to be found in the sandy district in Texas south and east of Texline.) Summer.

CALAMOVILFA GIGANTEA, GIANT REED-GRASS

CALAMOVILFA LONGIFOLIA, Long-leaved Reed-grass

38. AGROSTIS L. (à-grŏs'tĭs)

The Bent-grasses

Spikelets 1-flowered, disarticulating above the glumes, the rachilla usually not prolonged; **Glumes** equal or nearly so, acute, acuminate or sometimes awn-pointed, carinate, usually scabrous on the keel and sometimes on the back; **Lemma** obtuse, usually shorter and thinner in texture than the glumes, awnless or dorsally awned, often hairy on the callus; **Palea** usually shorter than the lemma, 2-nerved in only a few species, usually small and nerveless or obsolete.

Annual or usually *perennial,* delicate or moderately tall grasses, with glabrous culms, flat or sometimes involute, scabrous blades, and open or contracted panicles of small spikelets. About 25 species in the United States, 8 in Texas.

All the species of Texas are *perennials* except *A. elliottiana,* an annual and *A. exarata,* perennial and annual. The panicles of many of the species are purplish or reddish-purple or tinged with purple.

Redtop (*A. alba*), commonly 2-4 feet tall, with its green to reddish and purple panicle gives varying tones of green to purple to midsummer fields, especially from New England to the Rocky Mountains. It extends to or within the northernmost borders of Texas. *A. palustris,* with long stolons, has a somewhat open narrow panicle. It is confined to marshes or ditches along or near the coast. Fly-away grass (*A. hiemalis*) is a slender, erect plant, the beautiful nodding purplish panicles being broken off at maturity by the wind and blown over the fields as tumble weeds. *A. verticillata,* 1-2 feet tall, also has beautiful purplish-tinged panicles, but in Texas is confined mostly to wet meadows and along the margins of streams, sometimes forming dense colonies. Thin grass, a slender lax plant, sometimes prostrate, is found in low rather moist places in woodlands in east Texas. *A. elliottiana,* an annual, with a rather narrow open panicle, the branches usually ascending, and *A. retrofracta,* a perennial, with the habit of *A. hiemalis,* though coarser, and an open panicle about as wide as long, both commonly less than 20' tall, have awned lemmas. *A. exarata,* with a perennial or annual base, commonly 1-2 feet tall, sometimes much taller, has a narrow and rather dense panicle 2.5-8' long. It is a very variable plant as to height and aspect.

PALEA AT LEAST HALF AS LONG AS THE LEMMA; PERENNIALS.
  PANICLE OPEN or sometimes contracted after flowering; culms erect or decumbent at the base.
    PANICLE 2-9' long, its branches long and sometimes naked at the base; glumes scabrous on the keel only; rhizomes present.   1. A. alba
    PANICLE 6-8' long, widely spreading, about as wide as long; spikelets 2.5-3 mm. long, the rachilla prolonged; awn of the lemma 3-3.5 mm. long.
                            2. A. retrofracta
  PANICLE CONTRACTED, dense, the branches short; culms decumbent at the base; (*A. palustris* is *stoloniferous*).
    PANICLE 2-5' long, branches erect or spreading in anthesis; glumes strongly scabrous all over.   3. A. verticillata
    PANICLE long, spikelike, its branches short, appressed or ascending; blades short and stiff; glumes acute, scabrous on the upper part of the keel.
                            4. A. palustris
PALEA WANTING; PANICLE DIFFUSELY SPREADING; PERENNIALS.
  CULMS WEAK, usually spreading or prostrate; spikelets 2-2.5 mm. long, woodland species.   5. A. perennans
  CULMS AND blades erect; panicle loose, the capillary branches long, spikelet-bearing toward their ends; spikelets 1.5-2 mm. long; glumes scabrous on the keel.   6. A. hiemalis

PALEA MINUTE; PANICLE USUALLY NARROW, SOMETIMES OPEN; ANNUALS.
  LEMMA AWNLESS or awned; panicle dense, the branches short and appressed; glumes mostly scabrous over the back.   7. A. exarata
  LEMMA AWNED, the awn flexuous, more than twice as long as the spikelet; spikelet 1.5 mm. long; panicle about half as long as the culm, the branches slender and naked below; annual.   8. A. elliottiana

1. A. ALBA L. (ăl'bá); this has been referred to as *A. palustris* Huds., but that is found to be a distinct coastal species; REDTOP.

Culms usually 2-3 sometimes 4 feet tall, erect or erect from a more or less decumbent base, bearing rhizomes; **Blades** 3-7′ long sometimes longer, 2-6 mm. wide, flat, rough, slightly stiff or lax, erect or drooping; **Sheaths** shorter than the internodes; **Ligule** membranaceous, 3-5 mm. long, lacerate; **Panicle** 3-11′ long, exserted, ovate to pyramidal, green, brown or purplish, branches in whorls, the lower 1-4′ long, the longer naked below and the short ones spikelet-bearing to the base, ascending or erect, open in flowering, contracted in fruit; **Spikelets** 2-2.5 mm. long, lanceolate, acute, green or reddish, on scabrous pedicels shorter or longer than the spikelet; **Glumes** about equal, scabrous on the keel; **Lemma** nearly as long as the glumes, obtuse, hyaline, rarely awned near the base; **Palea** more than one-half as long as its lemma, hyaline.

In fields, meadows and along streams throughout most of the United States. Summer.

2. A. RETROFRACTA Willd. (rē-trō-frăk'tà).

Culms 12-20′ tall, erect, with much the habit of *A. hiemalis* but coarser; **Blades** 1.5-2 mm. wide, flat, rough; **Sheaths** smooth; **Ligule** 3-5 mm. long; **Panicles** exserted, 6-8′ long and about as wide, very open, the capillary branches in distant whorls, spreading, *naked at the base;* **Spikelets** 2.5-4 mm. long; **Glumes** subequal, the lower slightly longer, acuminate, scabrous on the keel; **Lemma** slightly over half the length of the glumes, pubescent, the hairs appressed, the callus villous, the dorsal awn attached about one-third the distance below the apex of the lemma, 3-3.5 mm. long, with a bend about 1 mm. from the base of the awn; **Palea** slightly shorter than the lemma, narrow, 2-nerved, rachilla prolonged as a minute bristle.

The above description and the drawings were made from a portion of a branch and information furnished by the Grass Herbarium. This plant has been collected only at Kent, Texas. Spring.

3. A. VERTICILLATA Vill. (vĕr-tĭs-ĭ-lā'tà).

Culms usually 1-2 sometimes 2.5 feet high, erect, but usually decumbent and rooting at the lower nodes, often in dense mats; **Blades** 3-5.5′ long, 3-10 mm. wide, slightly narrowed at base, acuminate, flat, rough above and on margins, sometimes rough below; **Sheaths** shorter than the internodes, loose, sometimes rough; **Ligule** membranaceous, 3-4 mm. long; **Panicles** 2-4.5′ long, 1-2′ wide when open, dense, oblong or slightly pyramidal, branches about 1-5 in half whorls, erect, ascending or spreading, *usually flowering to the base,* 1′ or less long, often interrupted below; **Spikelets** about 1.5 mm. long, usually green but sometimes purple; **Glumes** about equal, hispidulous all over, about 1.5 mm. long, acute, 1-nerved; **Lemma** about 1 mm. long or two-thirds as long as the glumes, 5-nerved, about 5-toothed, oval, truncate, broad, obtuse, hyaline; **Palea** about as long as its lemma, hyaline, obtuse.

Wet meadows and wet places along streams, western Texas to Colorado and California, Mexico. Spring-fall.

4. A. PALUSTRIS Huds. (på-lŭs'trĭs); *A. maritima* Lam.; CREEPING BENT. (*Erroneously referred to Texas.*)

Culms 12-20' tall, tufted, erect or decumbent at the base, finally branching, with long stolons; Blades mostly short and appressed (1.5-3.5' long, 3 mm. wide or less) stiff; Panicle somewhat open but condensed, 1.5-4' long; Spikelets 2-2.5 mm. long, on short hispidulous pedicels enlarged at the apex; Glumes acute, scabrous on the upper part of the keel, especially on the first glume; Lemma about three-fourths as long as the glumes, hyaline, dentriculate at the truncate or rounded apex, scabrous on the upper part of the keel; Palea about half as long as the lemma. (No drawings.)

Marshes along the coast from Newfoundland to Maryland; British Columbia to northern California, occasionally as far south as New Mexico; found especially along ditches. Summer.

5. A. PERENNANS (Walt.) Tuckerm. (pĕr-ĕn'ăns); THIN-GRASS.

Culms 1-2.5 feet tall, simple or branching, slender, weak, lax, erect or decumbent at the base, sometimes prostrate; Blades 4-10' long, 2-6 mm. wide, flat, thin, rough; Sheaths mostly shorter than the internodes; Ligule 3-6 mm. long, membranaceous; Panicles often included at the base, pale-green, diffuse, 4-10' long, oblong-pyramidal, the axis scabrous, the slender scabrous branches ascending, the lower as much as 3' long, 2-10 at each node, distant as much as 2', dividing and *spikelet-bearing at or about the middle,* the branchlets and scabrous pedicels appressed or divergent, the pedicels commonly 1-6 mm. long; Spikelets about 2.5 mm. (2-3) long, acuminate; Glumes subequal, or the first slightly longer, acuminate, 1-nerved, usually very scabrous on the keel; Lemma about three-fourths as long as the first glume, a minute tuft of hairs on each side at base; Palea wanting; Grain about 1.5 mm. long, 0.5 mm. wide, spindle-shaped.

Along streams in woods, eastern Texas, North Carolina, Kentucky, Ohio to Massachusetts. (Tyler, Texas.) Fall.

6. A. HIEMALIS (Walt.) B. S. P. (hī-ē-mā'lĭs); *A. scabra* Willd.; FLY-AWAY-GRASS, ROUGH HAIR-GRASS, TICKLE-GRASS.

Culms 1-2 feet tall, erect, simple or tufted, slender; Blades 2-5' long, 1-3 mm. wide, rough, flat or involute; Sheaths usually longer than the nodes; Ligule membranaceous, 2-4 mm. long; Panicle 4-12' long, usually purplish, exserted when mature, becoming pyramidal, the rough capillary branches in a half whorl which are distant about 1-2.5', ascending or widely spreading or drooping, the lower 4-6' long, divided near or above the middle, *flowering only towards the extremities;* Spikelets 1.5-2 mm. long; Glumes 1-nerved, pointed, the first usually longer; Lemma about two-thirds as long as the first glume or equaling it, obtuse, 5-nerved, awnless or rarely awned; Palea wanting.

In dry or moist soil throughout nearly the whole of North America. Spring-summer.

7. A. EXARATA Trin. (ĕks-à-rā'tà); *A. grandis* Trin.; *A. asperifolia* Trin.

Culms 1-2 or sometimes 3-4 feet tall, varying much as to size and aspect, erect or geniculate at the base, from perennial or annual roots; Blades, those of the culm 2.4-6' long, of the sterile shoots shorter, 3-7 mm.

wide, erect, flat, rough; **Sheaths** shorter than the internodes, or the lower longer, smooth to rough; **Ligule** decurrent, membranaceous, 2-5 mm. long; **Panicle** exserted, pale-green or tinged with purple, erect or slightly nodding, 2.5-8′ long, 10-15 mm. (6-30) thick, often lobed and somewhat interrupted below, dense, the branches commonly 0.5-2′ long, several to a whorl, commonly *spikelet-bearing to the base,* erect; **Spikelets** 2-3.5 mm. long, acute, on scabrous pedicels 1-2 mm. long; **Glumes** nearly equal, or the lower longer, scabrous or short-hispid on the keel, scabrous along the margins; **Lemma** about two-thirds as long as the glumes, acute or sub-obtuse, awnless, or bearing from about the middle of the back a straight or bent exserted awn, thin, toothed, with a very short sparingly-pilose callus; **Palea** wanting or minute (less than 0.5 mm. long).

Moist or rather dry open ground, west Texas, New Mexico, California, and Colorado north. Summer-fall.

8. **A. ELLIOTTIANA** Schult. (ĕl-ĭ-ŭt-ĭ-ā′ná); *A. arachnoides* Ell.

Culms 5-20′ tall, tufted, erect, slender, weak, simple; **Blades** 0.5-2′ long, 1-2 mm. wide, rough; **Sheaths** shorter than the internodes, smooth or slightly rough, striate; **Ligule** membranaceous, about 2 mm. long; **Panicle** 2-5′ long, usually narrow, finally open, lax, the *capillary branches naked below,* erect or ascending or finally drooping, the lower 1-1.5′ long; **Spikelets** 1.5-2 mm. long, linear-lanceolate; **Glumes** about equal, acute, scabrous on the keel and margins; **Lemma** about four-fifths as long as the glumes, acute or 2-toothed, bearing a very finely filiform flexuous barbellate awn 2-4 times its length inserted just below the apex, sometimes wanting; **Palea** wanting.

Dry or wet land; Texas to Florida, South Carolina, Tennessee, Kansas to Illinois, and Kentucky. (Granite Mountains, Marble Falls, Texas.) Spring-summer.

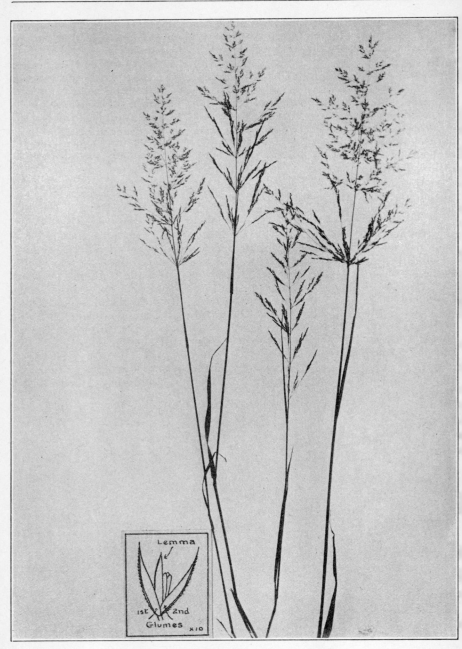

AGROSTIS ALBA, Redtop

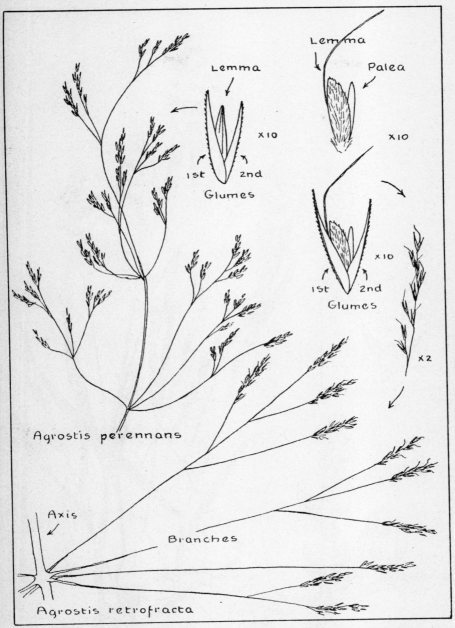

AGROSTIS PERENNANS AND AGROSTIS RETROFRACTA

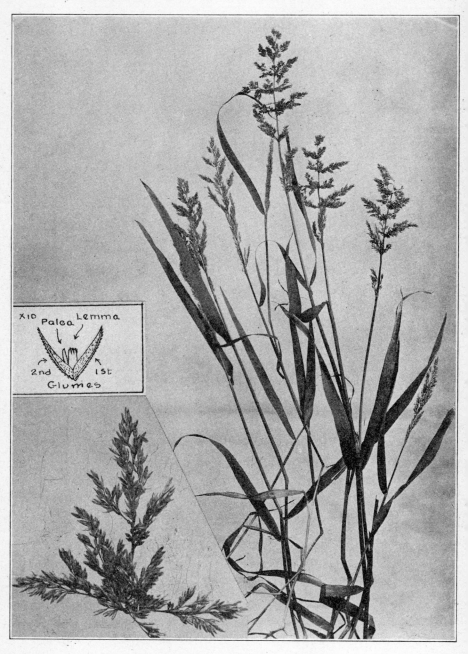

AGROSTIS VERTICILLATA

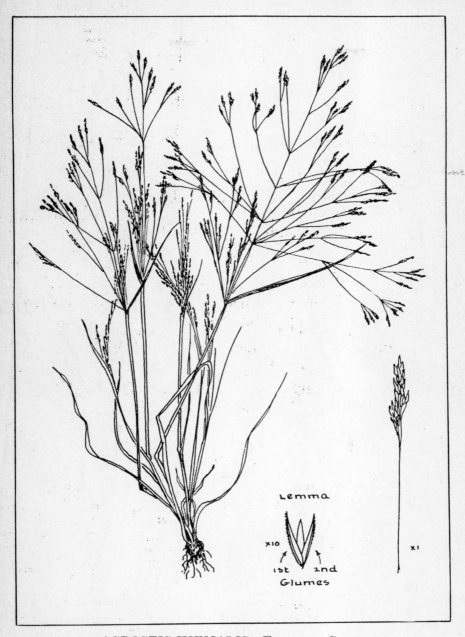

Lemma

x10

1st   2nd
Glumes

x1

AGROSTIS HIEMALIS; Fly-away Grass

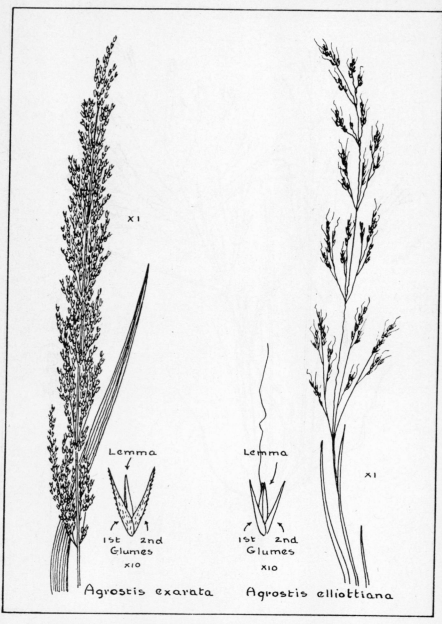

AGROSTIS EXARATA AND AGROSTIS ELLIOTTIANA

39. CINNA L. (sĭn'á)

Spikelets 1-flowered, disarticulating below the glumes, the rachilla forming a stipe below the floret and produced behind the palea as a minute bristle; **Glumes** equal, 1-nerved; **Lemma** similar to the glumes, nearly as long, 3-nerved, bearing minute, short, straight awn just below the apex; **Palea** apparently 1-nerved, 1-keeled.

Tall *perennial* grasses, with flat blades and paniculate inflorescence. Species three, North America and northern Eurasia, two in the United States, one in Texas.

In this genus the palea is apparently 1-nerved, especially so in *C. arundinacea.* This is an exception to the rule that the palea is 2-nerved.

The origin of this apparent single nerve is demonstrated by the fact that in one of the species the nerve may be easily split into two.

C. ARUNDINACEA L. (á-rŭn-dĭ-nā'sē-á) ; Wood Reed-grass, Sweet Wood-grass.

Culms 2-5 feet tall, erect, simple, leafy; **Blades** 6-15' long, 6-14 mm. wide, flat, rather long acuminate, rough or slightly rough; **Sheaths,** upper shorter than the internodes, smooth or rough; **Ligule** membranaceous, 2-5 mm. long; **Panicle** finally exserted, pale green to purple, 6-15' long, rather narrow, somewhat open, or contracted after flowering, the filiform branches erect or drooping, the lower 1.5-4.5' long, the scabrous pedicels enlarged at the apex, about as long as the spikelets; **Spikelets** about 5 mm. long, narrow; **Glumes** unequal, acuminate, scabrous especially on the keel, the first 1-nerved, usually about 1 mm. shorter than the 1 or 3-nerved second; **Lemma** slightly exceeded or equaled by the second glume, minutely scabrous, especially on the keel, usually bearing an awn about 0.5 mm. long from the 2-toothed apex, sometimes awnless; **Palea** nearly as long as its lemma, similar in shape but *1-nerved*, scabrous on the keel.

Along shady streams and in wooded swamps, northeast Texas to Alabama, north to Newfoundland and the Northwest. Summer-fall.

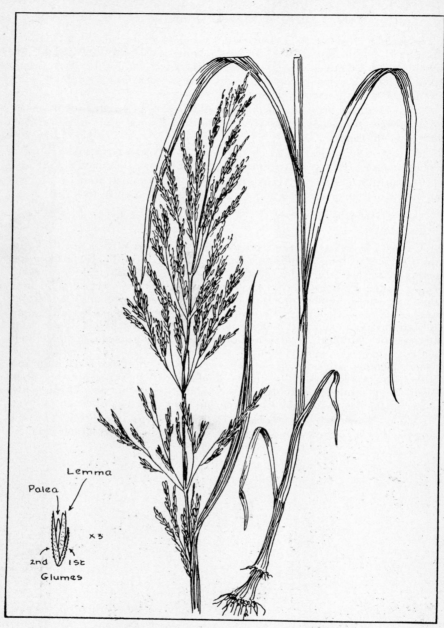

CINNA ARUNDINACEA, Wood Reed-grass

40. LIMNODEA L. H. Dewey (lĭm-nō′dē-à)

Spikelets 1-flowered, disarticulating below the glumes, the rachilla prolonged behind the palea as a short, slender bristle; **Glumes** equal, firm; **Lemma** membranaceous, smooth, nerveless, 2-toothed at the apex, bearing from between the teeth a slender bent awn, twisted at base; **Palea** a little shorter than the lemma.

Species one, a slender *annual* with flat blades and a narrow panicle. It has a range from Texas to Florida. A form with pilose glumes has been named *L. arkansana* var. *pilosa* (Trin.) Scribn. but is included in the species below.

L. ARKANSANA (Nutt.) L. H. Dewey (är-kăn-sā′nà); *Thurberia arkansana* Benth.

Culms 1-1.5, sometimes 3 feet tall, solitary or tufted, slender, erect or geniculate at the base; **Blades** 1-6′ long, 3-5 mm. wide, lance-linear, somewhat flexuous, rough; **Sheaths** mostly shorter than the internodes, pubescent, margins and throat villous, more or less rough; **Ligule** membranaceous, 1-2 mm. long, fringed; **Panicle** 3-6′ long, finally exserted, narrow, erect or nodding, branches erect or appressed, 0.5-2.5′ long; **Spikelets** 3.5-4 mm. long, on pedicels 1-3 mm. long, narrow, oblong; **Glumes** equal, acute, scaberulous or pubescent, with three nerves which can be seen from the inside; **Lemma** about as long as the glumes, the awn two to three times as long as the body of the lemma, the three nerves obscure; **Palea** nearly as long as its lemma, narrow, hyaline.

Dry fields and waste places, Texas to Florida. Spring.

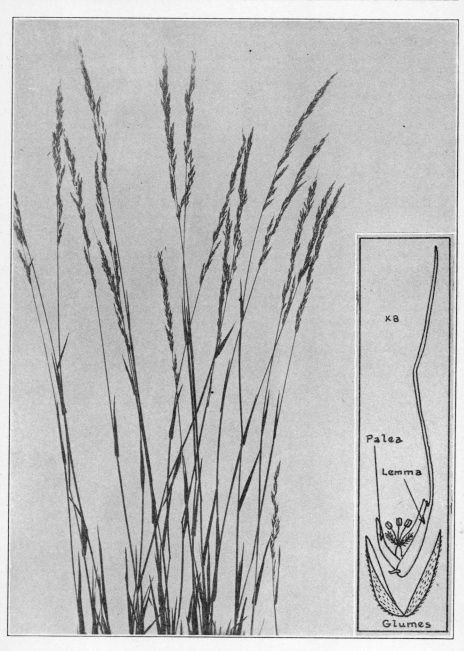

x8

Palea

Lemma

Glumes

LIMNODEA ARKANSANA

41. ALOPECURUS L. (ăl-ō-pē-kū′rŭs)

Spikelets 1-flowered, disarticulating below the glumes, strongly compressed laterally; **Glumes** equal, awnless, usually united at base, ciliate on the keel; **Lemma** about as long as the glume, 5-nerved, obtuse, the margins united at base, bearing from below the middle a slender dorsal awn, this included or exserted two or three times the length of the spikelet; **Palea** wanting.

Low or moderately tall *annual* or *perennial* grasses with flat blades and soft, dense spikelike panicles; one species in Texas.

This grass is a low tufted *annual,* and very much resembles *A. geniculatus* L., a perennial.

A. CAROLINIANUS Walt. (kăr-ō-lĭ-nĭ-ā′nŭs) ; *A. ramosus* Poir.

Culms 6-18′ tall, erect or sometimes geniculate at or near the base, tufted, simple or branching, rather slender; **Blades** 2-4.5′ long, mostly 2-3′, 1-4 mm. wide, flat, rough above; **Sheaths** shorter than the internodes, loose or somewhat inflated, especially the upper; **Ligule** membranaceous, 3-5 mm. long, decurrent; **Panicles** finally exserted, the axillary often included at the base, narrow, spikelike, about 2′ long, 3-5 mm. thick, cylindric, dense, the pedicels enlarged at the apex and turned inward, the main axis, branches and pedicels sparsely pubescent, the branches very short, the spikelets crowded; **Spikelets** 2-2.5 mm. long, flattened, falling from the pedicels entire; **Glumes** equal, slightly united at the base, much flattened, subacute, the keels strongly ciliate, otherwise sparsely hirsute or nearly glabrous; **Lemmas** with a bent awn attached near the base about twice as long as its body.

In low moist ground, eastern and southern Texas. (Texarkana, Goliad and Floresville, Texas.) Early spring.

ALOPECURUS CAROLINIANUS

42. POLYPOGON Desf. (pŏl-ĭ-pō'gŏn)

Spikelets 1-flowered, the pedicel disarticulating a short distance below the glumes leaving a short-pointed callus attached; **Glumes** equal, entire or 2-lobed, awned from the tip or from between the lobes, the awn slender, straight; **Lemma** much shorter than the glumes, hyaline, usually bearing a slender straight awn shorter than the awns of the glumes.

Annual or *perennial* usually decumbent grasses, with flat blades and dense, bristly, spikelike panicles. Species about 10, in the temperate regions of the world, chiefly in the Eastern Hemisphere, three species being introduced into the United States, two in Texas.

Our two species have dense spikelike panicles 1-6' long, the crowded spikelets with long-awned glumes. Annual beard-grass with a soft, bristly, pale-green or yellowish panicle, has numerous long awns concealing the spikelets, and *P. lutosus*, a perennial, with a dull panicle, has shorter awns not concealing the spikelets. Both are plentiful in California, the former being found here and there over much of the United States, sometimes important in low meadows, and the latter has been collected in a few of the southern states including Texas.

PLANTS annual; panicles silky, the awns 2-4 times as long as the glumes, concealing the spikelets.   1. P. monspeliensis
PLANTS perennial; panicle dull, often lobed, the awns about as long as the glumes, not concealing the spikelets.   2. P. lutosus

1. P. MONSPELIENSIS (L.) Desf. (mŏn'spĕl-ĭ-ĕn'sĭs) ; ANNUAL BEARD-GRASS.

Culms usually 8-24' sometimes as much as 35' tall, erect from a decumbent base, sparingly branched, tufted; **Blades** 2-9' commonly 3-5' long, 3-10 mm. wide, some narrowed at the base, acuminate, flat, scabrous especially above; **Sheaths** nearly as long as the internodes, upper slightly inflated, loose, sometimes slightly scabrous; **Ligule** 4-6 mm. long, membranaceous; **Panicle** 1-6' long, sometimes interrupted below, dense and spikelike, oval or cylindric, mostly exserted, soft silky, often of a yellowish shining pale green, the branches short; **Spikelets** about 2 mm. long with awns 2-6 times as long, nearly sessile, crowded, very numerous and nearly concealed by the numerous awns; **Glumes** subequal, about 2 mm. long, hispid, both with awns 4-7 mm. long, from an obtuse, slightly bifid, or entire apex; **Lemmas** much shorter, truncate, erose, hyaline, broad, bearing a delicate awn about 0.5-1 mm. long, inserted just below the apex, or sometimes wanting; **Palea** about two-thirds as long as the lemma, 2-toothed, truncate.

In waste places, especially in low meadows along streams here and there over the United States. Spring to fall.

2. P. LUTOSUS (Poir.) Hitchc. (lū-tō'sŭs) ; *P. littoralis* (With.) J. E. Smith; *Agrostis lutosa* Poir.

Culms 6-32' tall, sometimes taller, erect or decumbent at the base, taking root at the lower nodes; **Blades** 1-6' mostly 2-3.5' long, erect, 3-8 mm. wide, flat; **Sheaths** mostly shorter than the internodes, the upper slightly inflated; **Ligule** membranaceous, strongly-nerved, minutely scabrous, about 2-5 mm. long; **Panicle** commonly finally exserted, 1-6' long, dense, spikelike, more or less lobed or interrupted below; **Spikelet** exclusive of the awns about 2 mm. long, numerous, crowded, narrow **Glumes** about equal, 2-3 mm. long, folded and involute at the tip, more o less scabrous, especially on the midnerve and margins, also puberulen with a straight awn commonly about as long as the glumes, or sometime nearly twice as long, from the sinus of a bifid apex, or below, or whe entire terminal; **Lemma** about three-fourths as long as the glumes, broadl truncate, often erose, thin and hyaline, awnless or with an awn 1-2 mm long; **Palea** nearly as long as its lemma, 2-toothed, hyaline. (For illus tration see photograph of *Polypogon monspeliensis*.)

In wet places, Texas to Louisiana and Alabama, California. (Alpin Texas.) Spring-summer.

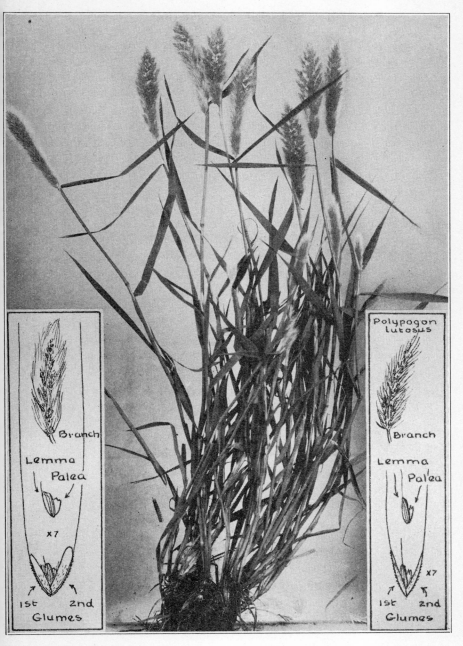

POLYPOGON MONSPELIENSIS; ANNUAL BEARD-GRASS; drawings of
POLYPOGON LUTOSUS.

43.   LYCURUS H. B. K. (lī-kū′rŭs)

Spikelets 1-flowered, the rachilla articulate above the glumes; **Glumes** awned, the first usually 2-awned; **Lemma** narrow, firm, longer than the glume, terminating in a slender awn.

Low *perennial* grasses, with dense spikelike panicle, the spikelets borne in pairs, the lower of the pair sterile, the short branchlets deciduous.   One species in the United States.

L. PHLEOIDES H. B. K. (flē-oi′dēz) ; TEXAS TIMOTHY, WOLFTAIL.

Our only species, Texas timothy, is a tufted, slender grass usually 12-18′ tall, with a dense, narrow, lead-colored, cylindric panicle.   At a distance it somewhat resembles timothy, but the spikelike panicles are smaller and bristly with awns.

Culms 12-27′ tall, usually 12-18′, tufted, erect or ascending, sometimes decumbent at the base with a slightly thickened or bulbous base, freely branching, rather weak; **Blades** 1-3′ long, about 1-3 mm. wide, upper shorter, radical leaves numerous and shorter, flat or folded, rough on the margins and on upper surface toward the apex, the margins and midrib white; **Sheaths** much shorter than the internodes, loose; **Ligule** membranaceous, 3-4 mm. long; **Panicles** commonly 2-4′ long, 3-8 mm. wide, exserted, often an axillary panicle at each node, with peduncles sometimes as long as that of the terminal panicle, dense, spikelike, cylindric, with many very short branchlets; **Spikelets** exclusive of the awns 3.5-5 mm. long, with awns 7-9 mm. long, usually in pairs, sometimes three, on very short branches, the upper perfect and the lower staminate or neuter, falling with the branchlets; **Glumes** about half as long as the lemma, awns unequal, more or less ciliate on the margins, the first oblong, thin, 2-nerved, about 1.5 mm. long, with two or rarely three unequal scabrous awns 2-5 mm. long, the second 1-nerved, 1.5-2 mm. long, terminating in an awn 3-6 mm. long; **Lemma** 3.5-4 mm. long, lanceolate, acuminate, thicker than the glumes, 3-nerved, more or less pubescent, terminating in a scabrous awn 3-4 mm. long; **Palea** lanceolate, 2-toothed, nearly as long as its lemma, thinly pubescent.

Plains and rocky hills, from Mexico through western Texas to Arizona and Colorado.   August to October.

LYCURUS PHLEOIDES; Texas Timothy, Wolftail

44.   PHLEUM L.   (flē'ŭm)

Spikelets 1-flowered, laterally compressed, disarticulating above the glumes; **Glumes** equal, membranaceous, keeled, abruptly mucronate or awned; **Lemma** shorter than the glumes, hyaline, broadly truncate, 3-5-nerved; **Palea** narrow, nearly as long as the lemma.

Annuals or *perennials*, with erect culms, flat blades, and dense, cylindric panicles.   Our only species in Texas is timothy, an erect *perennial* 2-4 feet tall, with a long cylindric spikelike panicle usually 3-5' long, long-exserted on a slender peduncle, the culms swollen at the base.   It is the most important meadow grass in America, and thrives best in the cool humid regions.

P. PRATENSE L. (prā-tĕn'sē).

Culms 16-40' tall, tufted, erect, simple, somewhat swollen at the base; **Blades** 3-13' long, 5-9 mm. wide, flat, scabrous; **Sheaths** often exceeding the internodes; **Ligule** membranaceous, 2-3 mm. long; **Panicle** 1-6' long, spikelike, 5-8 mm. thick, cylindric, obtuse, densely flowered; **Spikelets** excluding the awns 2.5-3 mm. long; **Glumes** ciliate on the keel, the awns less than half their length, usually about 1 mm. long; **Lemma** and **Palea** about equal, thin, half as long as the glumes.

Meadows and waste places, nearly throughout North America. Summer.

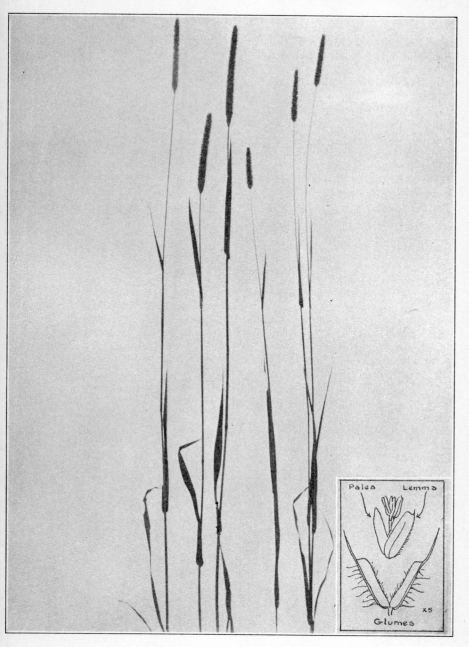

PHLEUM PRATENSE, Timothy

45. GASTRIDIUM Beauv. (găs-trĭd'ĭ-ŭm)

Spikelets 1-flowered, the rachilla disarticulating above the glumes, prolonged behind the palea as a minute bristle; Glumes unequal, somewhat enlarged or swollen at the base; Lemma much shorter than the glumes, hyaline, broad, truncate, awned or awnless; Palea about as long as the lemma.

Annual grasses, with flat blades and pale, shining, spikelike panicles. Species two, in the Mediterranean region; one introduced into the United States.

Our species is distinguished by the long-acuminate glumes and the short hairy lemma with an awn exceeding the glumes. It is a common weed on the Pacific Coast but is rather rare in Texas. It appears to have no economic value.

G. VENTRICOSUM (Gouan) Schinz & Thell. (vĕn-trĭ-kō'sŭm); *G. lendigerum* (L.) Gaud.; *G. australe* Beauv.; NIT-GRASS.

Culms 8-24' tall, erect or decumbent at the base, branching, leafy below, naked above; Blades 1.5-5' long, 2-4 mm. wide, mostly flat; Sheaths shorter than the internodes; Ligule 2-5 mm. long, thin-membranaceous; Panicles exserted or those of the branches included at the base, 1.5-4' long, rarely 6', 5-11 mm. thick, spikelike, densely-flowered, the spikelets on scabrous pedicels 1.5 mm. long or less; Spikelets exclusive of the awn 4-6 mm. long, lanceolate; Glumes long acuminate, scabrous on the keel, the first 3-3.5 mm. long, the second 4-6 mm. long; Lemma about 1.1 mm. long, about one-fourth as long as the second glume, 0.5 mm. wide, truncate, toothed, sparsely hairy, a tuft of short hairs on the callus, the awn exceeding the second glume.

In dry places, Texas, common on the Pacific coast, introduced from Europe. (Alpine, Texas.) Summer.

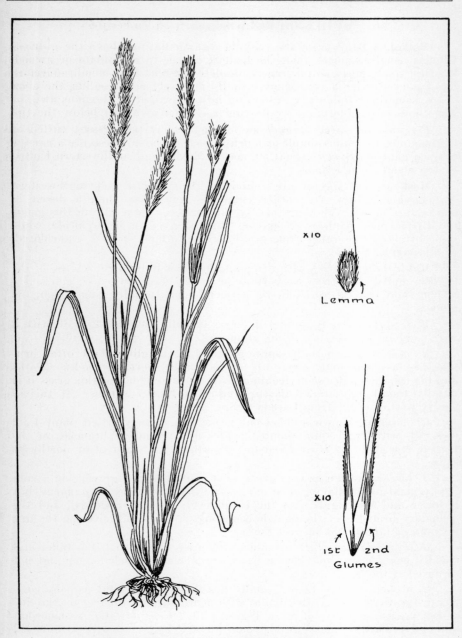

X10

Lemma

X10

1st 2nd
Glumes

GASTRIDIUM VENTRICOSUM, Nit-grass

46.   MUHLENBERGIA Schreb. (mū-lĕn-bẽr′jĭ-à)

Spikelets 1-flowered, the rachilla disarticulating above the glumes; **Glumes** usually shorter than the lemma, obtuse to acuminate or awned, the first sometimes small or rarely obsolete; **Lemma** firm-membranaceous, 3-to-5-nerved, with a very short, usually minutely pilose callus, the apex acute, sometimes bidentate, extending into a straight or flexuous awn, or sometimes only mucronate or bearing a slender awn just below the tip.

Perennial or rarely *annual* low or moderately tall grasses, tufted or rhizomatous, the culms simple or much branched, the inflorescence a narrow or open panicle. Species about 80, mostly Mexico and southwestern United States, about 34 in Texas.

Most of our species are found in the western and southwestern states, where a few are rather common, being less than a dozen in our eastern states. They are mostly fall grasses. As a rule in this genus the diffuse open panicles are purple, usually green in *M. arenicola*, while the contracted ones range from grayish-green to light or dark lead-colored, rarely purple.

Muhlenbergia agrees with *Stipa* and its allies in the firm texture of the lemma; and differs from *Sporobolus* in the 3-nerved awned or mucronate lemma; and from *Agrostis* in the firmer lemma, usually longer than the glumes.

M. texana, the only annual in Texas, usually not over 15′ tall, with a nearly oblong panicle, has ciliate glumes.

M. porteri, known as mesquite grass, is a straggling plant, often in a tangled mass, commonly about 1.5 feet tall, with short internodes, sheaths and blades, the blades soon deciduous. As stock are fond of this grass it is usually found only under the protection of thorny shrubs. It thrives mostly west of a line from Laredo to San Angelo.

M. pungens, known as blow-out grass, is a densely-tufted plant 1.5-2 feet tall, with rigid spiny-pointed blades, the secondary branches of the panicle fascicled. It is confined to very sandy land in west or northwest Texas.

M. torreyi, known as ring grass, as it is often found growing in a ring (the central plants having died out), somewhat resembles *M. pungens,* but is lower and less rigid, with the basal leaves usually recurved, and the secondary branches of the panicle commonly single. It thrives on the dry hillsides of high plains in west Texas.

M. arenicola somewhat resembles ring-grass except that it is taller and usually has a green and longer panicle, the blades much longer and not recurved at the base.

M. arenacea, a low plant, usually less than 10′ tall, and panicles commonly less than 4′ long, the ligules with acute auricles, thrives on the dry sterile mesas or plains of west Texas, while *M. asperifolia,* a somewhat taller plant, with panicles usually more than 4′ long, and without auricled ligules, thrives only in damp places in the valleys of west Texas.

M. involuta, commonly 3-5 feet tall, *M. reverchoni* and *M. rigida* usually about 2.5-3 feet tall, are similar in general appearance. *M. involuta* and *M. reverchoni* have short-awned lemmas while *M. rigida* has long-awned lemmas, the panicle being a darker purple than those of the first two species. *M. rigida* is a rather rare plant on the high mountains of west Texas. *M. involuta,* a new species first collected by the author, has about the same range as *M. reverchoni.* These are found here and there in the hills for about 100 miles north and northwest of San Antonio.

M. expansa and *M. capillaris,* commonly 2.5-3 feet tall, have large open panicles, the former with a short-awned lemma, the latter with a long-awned lemma and glumes often short-awned. Both of these plants are found in eastern Texas.

M. montana may be distinguished by its 3-toothed second glume, the teeth awned. *M. setifolia,* a somewhat taller plant, with involute blades as much as 12' long, has the branches verticillate. Both are west Texas plants.

Our remaining *Muhlenbergias* have mostly contracted panicles, the branches often narrowly ascending in anthesis.

M. schreberi, known as Nimble Will, and *M. repens,* are straggling plants, the former with a panicle 2-6' long, the glumes very minute and lemma with an awn 1-4 mm. long, and the latter with the panicle usually less than an inch long, mostly included at the base, the lemma pointed or with an awn usually less than 0.5 mm. long. *M. schreberi* has a wide range extending into the eastern states where it is a common weed. In Texas it is usually confined to open woods. *M. utilis* and *M. repens* are similar in aspect, both west Texas plants, the former mostly in rather damp soil, the latter forming a dense sod on the Davis Mountains, west Texas.

M. parviglumis, M. monticola, M. pauciflora and *M. metcalfei* are west Texas plants, the first three with long awns and the last with a short awn. *M. metcalfei* was collected in the Guadalupe Mountains by the author, being the first specimen of this species collected in Texas.

M. rigens, known as deer-grass, has a long narrow, densely-flowered pale panicle, the branches short. It is found from western Texas to California. *M. fournieriana* and *M. emersleyi* have nearly oblong purplish panicles, the branches of the former usually less than 2.5' long, of the latter usually less than 4' long. *M. fournieriana* is found in the hills north of San Antonio, extending into western Texas, and *M. emersleyi* in the mountains of west Texas and New Mexico. These three species were formerly placed in the genus *Epicampes.* They are rather tall plants with long narrow blades; the spikelets are very variable. The lemma often bears an awn from just below the tip or from between a bifid apex.

PANICLES OPEN, USUALLY PURPLISH.
   PLANT ANNUAL. Glumes ciliate; plants commonly not over 15' tall; panicles
      nearly oblong, half to two-thirds as long as the plant.   1. M. texana
   PLANTS PERENNIAL. Panicles mostly pyramidal.
      PLANTS weakly ascending from a decumbent base or prostrate, diffusely
         branching throughout.   2. M. porteri
      PLANTS erect, or sometimes spreading; blades mostly less than 2' long
         (1-4' in *M. asperifolius*).
      Plants from creeping rootstocks. Awn commonly shorter than the lemma
         or rarely awnless.
         Secondary branches of the panicle clustered; blades stiff and spiny-
            pointed.   3. M. pungens
         Secondary branches of the panicle usually single, blades neither stiff nor
            spiny.
            Basal blades recurved; plants usually less than 12' tall.   4. M. torreyi
            Basal blades not recurved; lemma with very short awn or awnless.
               Ligule with acute auricles; plants commonly less than 10' tall.
                                                                    5. M. arenacea
               Ligule not auricled; plants commonly 10-16' tall; blades 1-4' long.
                                                                    6. M. asperifolia
      Plants without creeping rootstocks.
         Awn 1-4 mm. long; glumes one-third to three-fourths as long as the
            lemma; pedicels long.

Blades 2-5' long, involute; plants 1-2 feet tall; panicle green, rarely
  somewhat purplish; spikelets 3 mm. long.   7. M. arenicola
Blades much longer, mostly involute; plants taller; panicles purplish;
  spikelets 3.5-4.5 mm. long.
  Plants 2.5-4 feet tall; glumes about three-fourths as long as the
    lemma, subacute or erose; panicle nearly oblong.   8. M. involuta
  Plants 2.5-3 feet tall; panicles narrowly pyramidal.
    Glumes about one-third as long as the lemma.   9. M. reverchoni
    Glumes about half as long as the lemma; awn usually less than
      1 mm. long.   10. M. expansa
Awn 2-6 times as long as the lemma.
  Spikelets 4-4.5 mm. long; blades long and mostly involute, 1-3 mm.
    wide; awn 6-20 mm. long.
    Glumes about one-fourth as long as the lemma, acute or obtuse;
      panicle reddish-purple, the branches erect or narrowly spreading.
                                                   11. M. rigida
    Glumes about half as long as the lemma, often short awned.
                                                   12. M. capillaris
  Spikelets 3-4 mm. long; panicle branches 2-3' long, usually loosely
    appressed, ascending in anthesis.
    Second glume 3-toothed, the teeth awned; plant commonly about 20'
      tall; blades 2-3' long.   13. M. montana
    Second glume not 3-toothed; glumes one-third to half as long as the
      lemma; branches of the panicles mostly verticillate; blades 2-12'
      long, setiform.   14. M. setifolia
PANICLES MORE OR LESS CONTRACTED, NOT DIFFUSE. Blades usually
  flat; culms branching. Perennials.
  PLANTS FROM creeping rootstocks.
    GLUMES not more than one-fourth as long as the lemma, the first very
      minute or wanting; culms long and straggling.   15. M. schreberi
    GLUMES at least half as long as the lemma.
      Glumes half to two-thirds as long as the lemma, usually unequal in
        M. brachyphylla.
        Plants usually erect; glumes broadly ovate.
          Spikelets 1.5-2 mm. long; lemma awnless.   16. M. sobolifera
          Spikelets 2-2.5 mm. long (3-4); lemma awned.
                                              16a. M. sobolifera var. setigera
          Spikelets 3-3.5 mm. long; lemma awned; glumes unequal.
                                                   17. M. brachyphylla
        Plants often straggling or prostrate, slender; panicle slender, reduced,
          usually included at the base; glumes lanceolate; lemma mucronate,
          short-awned or awnless.
          Spikelets 2.8-3 mm. long; glumes about two-thirds as long as the
            lemma.   18. M. repens
          Spikelets 1.5-2 mm. long; glumes about half as long as the lemma.
                                                   19. M. utilis
      Glumes about as long as the lemma, rarely exceeding it; spikelets 2.5-3.5
        mm. long.
        Lemma pubescent at the base.
          Glumes acute or aristate-pointed.
            Lemma awnless.   20. M. mexicana
            Lemma with an awn 5-12 mm. long.   21. M. umbrosa
          Glumes awned; lemma awned.   22. M. lemmoni
        Lemma and callus glabrous, awnless; panicles somewhat glomerate.
                                                   23. M. glabriflora
      Glumes much exceeding the awnless lemma. Glumes awned; panicle dense
        and interrupted.   24. M. racemosa
  PLANTS NOT from creeping rootstocks.
    BLADES short, usually not over 4' long; glumes shorter than the lemma.
      Awn much longer than the lemma. Awn 6-25 mm. long.
        Lemma conspicuously pubescent; glumes nearly as long as the lemma,
          awned.   25. M. polycaulis
        Lemma pubescent at the base.
          Glumes less than one-third as long as the lemma, obtuse, usually erose;
            spikelets 2.3-3 mm. long.   26. M. parviglumis

Glumes half to two-thirds as long as the lemma, acute; spikelets 3-4 mm. long on short stout pedicels; internodes short.
　　　　　　　　　　　　　　　　　　　　　　　　　27. M. monticola
Lemma glabrous, callus prominent and glabrous; glumes half to two-thirds as long as the lemma, acute; spikelets 3-3.5 mm. long.
　　　　　　　　　　　　　　　　　　　　　　　　　.28. M. pauciflora
Awn shorter than the lemma, usually less than 1 mm. long; glumes awned, two-thirds as long as the lemma; panicle usually dense, cylindric, obtuse; spikelets 3 mm. long.　　　　　　　　29. M. wrightii
BLADES much exceeding 4′ long, mostly very long, usually involute or conduplicate.
Glumes two-fifths to half as long as the lemma, awn of lemma 1-5 mm. long; panicles long, loose, the branches erect or narrowly ascending.
Panicle green; spikelets 4-5 mm. long.　　　　　30. M. acuminata
Panicle greenish-purple; spikelets 3.5-4 mm. long.　　31. M. metcalfei
Glumes as long or nearly as long as the lemma (Nos. 32, 33 and 34 formerly placed in genus Epicampes).
Panicle spikelike, narrow, dense, the short branches floriferous from the base or nearly so; lemma acuminate, mucronate or short-awned.
　　　　　　　　　　　　　　　　　　　　　　　　　32. M. rigens
Panicle not spikelike, in anthesis oblong or nearly so; lower sheaths compressed-keeled.
Panicle branches rarely more than 2.5′ long; lemma glabrous or obscurely-pubescent, awnless or with a short awn.
　　　　　　　　　　　　　　　　　　　　　　　　　33. M. fournieriana
Panicle branches rarely over 4′ long; lemma villous below, awnless or with an awn 5-15 mm. long.　　　　　34. M. emersleyi

1. M. TEXANA Buckl. (tĕks-ā′nȧ) ; *M. buckleyana* Scribn.

Culms 8-17′ tall, tufted, slender, spreading, branching below, the internodes glabrous or the lower puberulent; **Blades** 1-2′ long, commonly less than 2 mm. wide, flat or involute, rough; **Sheaths** longer than the internodes, loose, slightly scabrous; **Panicles** 4-8′ long, or those of the branches shorter, half to two-thirds as long as the culms, open, loose, oblong or narrowly pyramidal, purplish or finally pale; the branches 1-2.5′ long, capillary, ascending or spreading, usually solitary and sparingly branching, and spikelet-bearing towards the ends; **Spikelets** mostly 1.8-2 mm. long, narrowly lanceolate; **Glumes** acute or awn-pointed, hyaline, 1-nerved, sparingly pubescent or scabrous on the back, ciliate, about half as long as the spikelet, the second slightly longer; **Lemma** 1.8-2 mm. long, 2-toothed, glabrous or slightly pubescent on the three nerves, midnerve excurrent into a scabrous awn 1.5-2 mm. long; **Palea** nearly as long as the lemma, thin, acute.

Rocky hills, gravelly bars and river banks, western Texas, New Mexico and Mexico. Fall.

2. M. PORTERI Scribn. (pōr′tẽr-ī) ; *M. texana* Thurb. not Buckley; Mesquite Grass, Bush-grass.

Culms 5-25′ tall, sometimes as much as 36′ long, often forming large bunches of tangled culms and leaves, diffusely branching, ascending from a prostrate or geniculate-decumbent base, usually growing among isolated thorny shrubs or bushes; **Blades** 0.8-2.5′ long, about 1.5 mm. wide, flat or involute toward the tip, bristly pointed, slightly rough above, soon deciduous; **Sheaths** shorter than the short internodes, soon spreading; **Ligule** membranaceous, about 2 mm. long, lacerate-ciliate; **Panicles** purplish, mostly 2-4′ long, terminating the numerous branches, commonly included at the base, the scabrous branches mostly 1-2′ long, stiffly ascending or spreading, loosely-flowered, the **scabrous pedicels** commonly 5-8 mm. long; **Spikelets** purplish, narrow, exclusive of the awns 2.5-3.5 mm. long; **Glumes** subequal, linear-lanceolate, half to two-thirds as long as the lemma, 1-nerved, slightly scabrous on the keel, acuminate, acute or more or less erose; **Lemma** 2.5-3.5 mm. long, usually minutely two-toothed, slightly scabrous on the three nerves, sparsely short-pubescent, the scabrous awn 4-10 mm. commonly 4-6 mm. long; **Palea** about equal to its lemma and similar in shape, very sparsely short-pubescent.

Hills, mesas, plains, central Texas west to Arizona and north to Colorado. (Near Dryden, Texas.)   July-August.

3. M. PUNGENS Thurb. (pŭn'jĕns) ; BLOW-OUT GRASS, PURPLE HAIR-GRASS.

Culms 10-24′ tall, densely tufted, often in large clumps, erect from a decumbent branching base, rigid, the nodes and internodes from softly to harshly puberulent or more or less woolly at the base, from strong creeping rootstocks; **Blades** mostly 1-2′ long, about 1.5 mm. wide or less, involute-setaceous or nearly flat at the base, rigidly ascending, not recurved; **Sheaths** longer than the internodes, the lower very short and the upper very long, crowded at the base, puberulent to glabrous, or the lower covered sheaths softly woolly; **Ligule** a very short membrane, densely ciliate with very fine soft hairs, all less than 1 mm. long; **Panicle** purplish, long-exserted, 3-6′, rarely longer, narrowly pyramidal, the slender primary branches mostly 2-2.5′ long, ascending or spreading, usually solitary, rather rigid, naked at the base, branched near the base, the branchlets apparently fascicled or numerous branchlets approximate, spreading, the axis, branches and branchlets harshly puberulent, the scabrous capillary pedicels often 10-20 mm. long, enlarged at the apex; **Spikelets** 3-4.5 mm. long; **Glumes** half to two-thirds as long as the lemma, acuminate, often 2-toothed or awn-pointed, scabrous especially on the keel; **Lemma** scabrous, bristle-pointed or with an awn shorter than the body, usually 1-2 mm. long; **Palea** about as long as the lemma, with two bristle-pointed teeth or short awns.

Sand hills and bad lands, Texas to Utah, and to Colorado and Nebraska.   Summer-fall.

4. M. TORREYI (Kunth) Hitchc. (tŏr'ĭ-ī) ; *M. gracillima* Torr.; RING-GRASS.

Culms 4-12 rarely 20′ tall, densely tufted, erect or decumbent at the base, simple, slender but rigid; **Blades** mostly crowded at the base, recurved, only 2-3 to the culm, erect, mostly 2-36 mm. long, rarely longer, involute-filiform, setaceous, smooth or slightly rough; **Sheaths** longer than the internodes; **Ligule** membranaceous, 4-6 mm. long; **Panicles** 2-9′ commonly 3-6′ long, exserted, finally open, purplish, the slender branches mostly single, usually 1-2.5′ long rarely 3.5′ long, ascending or finally widely spreading, naked below, the branchlets short, solitary and few, commonly 1-3 spikelets to a branchlet, the scabrous capillary pedicels 3-6 mm. long or the terminal longer, enlarged at the apex; **Spikelets** exclusive of the awn 2-3.5 mm. long; **Glumes** unequal, the second slightly longer, half to two-thirds as long as the lemma, acute or awn-pointed, slightly scabrous; **Lemma** scabrous especially toward the apex, a scabrous awn commonly 2-4 mm. long from between the minutely bifid apex; **Palea** about as long as the lemma, usually minutely 2-toothed.   (Two photographs.)

On prairies, mesas, rocky hills and mountains, Texas to Arizona, Colorado and Kansas. (High plains and mountains about 35 miles east of El Paso on the Carlsbad Road.) September-October.

5. **M. ARENACEA** (Buckl.) Hitchc. (ăr-ē-nā'sē-à) ; *Sporobolus arenaceus* Buckl.; *Sporobolus auriculatus* Vasey.

Culms 5-12' commonly about 8' tall, slender but rather rigidly erect or ascending, often scabrous, freely branching below, from long scaly rootstocks; **Blades** 10-30 mm. long, those of the culm sometimes longer, 2 mm. wide or less, flat, soon involute when dry, the cartilaginous margins and both surfaces rough; **Sheaths** longer than the short internodes, or the second one from above shorter, smooth to rough; **Ligule** membranaceous, fimbriate, less than 0.5 mm. long, the acute auricles two or three times as long as the ligule proper; **Panicles** purplish, diffuse, commonly included at the base or finally exserted, 2-4' mostly less than 3' long, open, ovate to pyramidal, thin, the scabrous capillary branches mostly single or in pairs, 1-2.5' long, ascending or spreading or sometimes reflexed, naked at the base, bearing 1-3 spikelets at the end of the branches or short branch-lets, the scabrous pedicels ascending or spreading, commonly 1-4 times as long as the spikelets; **Spikelets** rarely 2-flowered, commonly 2-2.3 mm. long rarely 3 mm. long, lanceolate; **Glumes** 1-nerved, more or less scabrous on the nerve, subequal, about 1 mm. long or scarcely one-half as long as the spikelet, acute or sometimes erose; **Lemma** obtuse, 3-nerved, 2-toothed, the midnerve often extending into a straight awn usually less than 1 mm. long, glabrous, or a few hairs at the base; **Palea** about as long as its lemma.

Plains among the hills and mountains of West Texas to Arizona and south into Mexico. (Mostly west of Del Rio, Sonora, Big Spring.) Summer-fall.

6. **M. ASPERIFOLIA** (Nees & Meyen) Parodi (ăs-pĕr-ĭ-fō'lĭ-à) ; *Sporobolus asperifolius* (Nees & Meyen) Nees; ROUGH-LEAVED DROP-SEED.

Culms 4-24' tall, tufted or in large patches or colonies, erect or ascending from a decumbent base, slender, rather weak, flattened, branching below, from slender creeping rootstocks; **Blades** 0.5-4' long, the upper usually longer, 1-2.5 mm. wide, flat or involute toward the tip, erect or ascending, very rough on the margins and upper surface; **Sheaths,** the upper shorter or about as long as the internodes, the lower short and crowded, flattened; **Ligule** firm, truncate, 0.5-1 mm. long; **Panicles** purplish, 2.5-9' long, usually more than half as wide, often included at the base, ovate to pyramidal, the branches, branchlets and pedicels scabrous, the capillary branches rather stiffly ascending or spreading, solitary or in twos or threes, the lower 2 to 4.5' long, naked at the base, branching nearly to the base, the branchlets mostly 1-2' long, with a few scattered spikelets at the end of the branchlets, the pedicels mostly 10-20 mm. long; **Spikelets** 1.5-2 mm. rarely 2.3 mm. long (sometimes 2-3-flowered; the glumes and lemma vary much as to length); **Glumes** subequal, from one-third to nearly as long as the lemma, acute, often bristly-pointed, thin, scabrous on the keel; **Lemma** acute or subacute, sometimes with a mucro or short-awn, minutely scabrous; **Palea** nearly as long as the lemma, 2-toothed.

In damp soil, west Texas to Mexico, north to Colorado and Missouri (Mosquiz Canyon, Ft. Davis-Alpine Road.) Summer-fall.

7. **M. ARENICOLA** Buckl. (ăr-ĕn-ĭ-kō'lả).

Culms 1-2.5 feet tall, tufted, erect or ascending, branching, slender, rough, glabrous or puberulent at and near the nodes; **Blades** 2-5′ long, those of the culm shorter than those of the sterile shoots, 1 mm. wide or less, involute, not curved, erect, scabrous; **Sheaths** shorter than the internodes, rough to smooth; **Ligule** membranaceous, 4-6 mm. long, decurrent; **Panicle** 6-15′ long, short-exserted or sometimes included at the base, pale-green or sometimes purplish, 6-15′ long, often half as long as the culm, usually narrowly open, sometimes pyramidal, usually somewhat nodding, the axis and branches scabrous, the branches mostly solitary, sometimes subverticillate, naked at the base, slender, rather distant, 2-4′ rarely 6′ long, the branches usually ascending, rarely widely spreading, the branchlets loosely appressed; **Spikelets** exclusive of the awn 3 mm. long, on slender scabrous pedicels usually about as long as the spikelet or the terminal much longer; **Glumes** subequal, half to two-thirds as long as the lemma, acuminate, awn-pointed, scabrous on the nerve, otherwise smooth or scabrous; **Lemma** sparsely scabrous, sparsely ciliate and a few hairs at the base or glabrous, the awn 1-3 mm. long; **Palea** about as long as the lemma.

Plains, mesas and foothills, central Texas west to Arizona. (Abilene and Van Horn, Texas.) Late summer-fall.

8. **M. INVOLUTA** Swallen (ĭn-vō-lū'tả).

Culms 2-5 feet tall, tufted, often densely so, simple, comparatively slender but rigid, minutely strigose below the panicles, growing mostly in isolated tufts; **Blades** 1-14′ long, the upper short, the lower long, about 1 mm. wide when folded, mostly involute, wiry, with a long narrow point, rough; **Sheaths** longer than the internodes, compressed-keeled, the junction of the blades and sheaths obscure, rough; **Ligule** membranaceous, fragile, about 12 mm. long; **Panicle** exserted or slightly included at the base, purple, erect or nodding, 8-18′ long, oblong, when open 2-3′ wide, the axis, branches and pedicels scabrous, the slender branches 2-3.5′ mostly 2′ long, narrowly ascending to narrowly spreading, 1-5 at a node, naked at the base, somewhat distant, the short and almost appressed branchlets with a few spikelets, the pedicels enlarged at the apex, shorter than to as long as the spikelet, terminal as much as 10 mm. long; **Spikelets** exclusive of the awn 3-4.5 mm. long, narrow, lanceolate; **Glumes** three-fourths to nearly as long as the lemma, the second slightly longer than the first, minutely scabrous, entire, erose or toothed at the obtuse apex; **Lemma** 3-nerved, minutely scabrous, acuminate, more or less pubescent at the base at or near the margins, the minutely toothed apex awned from just below the teeth, the awn slender, 1.5-2 mm. long, sometimes longer; **Palea** about as long as the lemma, minutely scabrous toward the apex. (A new species first collected by the author.)

Rocky hillsides and draws, in the hills northeast, north and north-west of San Antonio, Texas. (Bandera, Boerne, Johnson City and north of New Braunfels, Texas.) Fall.

9. **M. REVERCHONI** Vasey & Scribn. (rĕv-ĕr-shō'nī).

Culms 1-3 feet tall, densely tufted, erect or spreading, slender, scabrous below the panicle; **Blades** 2-10′ long, the upper short, mostly involute, 1-1.5 mm. wide when folded, acuminate into long slender points, slightly scabrous; **Sheaths** longer than the internodes, close; **Ligule** membranaceous, 4-6 mm. long, fragile; **Panicle** 6-14′ mostly about 10′ long, oblong-pyramidal, exserted or included at the base, axis scabrous, branches ascending or spreading, 5' or less long, naked at the base, mostly single, the scabrous capillary branchlets 1-2' long, divaricate, with 1-8 spikelets, on capillary divergent pedicels, enlarged at apex, scabrous, 1-3 times as long as the spikelets; **Spikelets** exclusive of awn 3-5 mm. long, narrow, acuminate; **Glumes** commonly half to two-thirds as long as the spikelet, the second slightly longer, 1-nerved, obtuse, erose or toothed, pale; **Lemma** acuminate, pubescent at the base, scabrous, especially toward the apex, straw-colored, with a scabrous awn, straight, 0.5-4.5 mm. long, commonly 2-4 mm. long or awnless; **Palea** about as long as its lemma, scabrous, narrow.

Rocky hillsides western Texas, more common and with a wider range than *M. involuta*. Fall.

10. M. EXPANSA (Poir.) Trin. (ĕks-păn′sà); *M. trichopodes* (Ell.) Chapm.

Culms 2-3.5 feet tall, erect or spreading, often in large dense clumps with a fibrous mass at the base (old shredded sheaths, the tough nerves persisting in this fibrous mass after the balance of the sheath has rotted away); **Blades** 1.5-17' long, the upper short, the lower and basal blades long, 1-2.5 mm. wide, mostly flat or folded somewhat at the base, rather wiry and stiff, erect or the lower spreading, commonly rough near the base; **Sheaths** longer than the internodes, loose, smooth or slightly rough; **Ligule** 2-3 mm. long, firm, wider than the blade; **Panicles** purplish, 4-18' long, finally open and exserted, narrowly pyramidal, nodding, the axis, capillary branches, branchlets and pedicels scabrous, the branches as long as 3.5', ascending or spreading, usually solitary, branching to or near the naked base, the branchlets as much as 2' long, with a few scattered spikelets on pedicels 5-12 mm. long, rarely longer, the pedicels enlarged at the apex; **Spikelets** 3.5-4.5 mm. long, lanceolate, purplish, the glumes soon turning pale; **Glumes** subequal, the first about half as long as the lemma, the second slightly longer, acute or awn-pointed, scabrous on the keel toward the apex; **Lemma** lanceolate, acuminate, with a scabrous awn 0.5-1 mm. rarely 2 mm. long, 3-nerved, the nerves prominent, scabrous especially toward the apex, pubescent at or near the base; **Palea** often slightly longer than the lemma, pointed, scabrous, with appressed hairs between the nerves.

In sandy open pine lands, Texas to Florida, north to North Carolina. (About 4 miles south of Buna, Texas.) Summer-fall.

11. M. RIGIDA (H. B. K.) Kunth (rĭj′ĭ-dà); *M. berlandieri* Trin.

Culms 1.5-3 feet tall, densely tufted, erect, somewhat rigid, simple or branching at the base; **Blades** 1.5-10' long, the upper short, 1.5-3 mm. wide, mostly involute, erect, rather rigid, margins and upper surface rough, nerves prominent; **Sheaths** longer than the internodes with auricles 2-5 mm. long; **Ligule** membranaceous, firm, 3-5 mm. long, wider than the blade, decurrent; **Panicles** dark-purple, narrowly pyramidal, finally exserted, 4-13' long, nearly half as wide, erect or sometimes nodding, the axis scabrous, the capillary branches as much as 5' long, solitary or several to a node, ascending or narrowly spreading, the lower as much as 2' distant, naked below, the few branchlets on the upper half bearing a few spikelets, the pedicels 2-9 mm. long; **Spikelets** exclusive of the awn, 4-4.5 mm. long, lanceolate, purple; **Glumes** about one-fourth as long as the spikelet, 1-nerved or nerveless, acute or obtuse, often erose; **Lemma** scabrous, 2-toothed, a pencil tuft of hairs on each side of the callus, the hairs about 0.5 mm. long, the three nerves prominent, the midnerve produced into a purplish flexuous awn 10-20 mm. long; **Palea** about as long as the lemma, scabrous.

Rocky mountains, western Texas and New Mexico, extending south into Mexico. (On Scenic Drive about 16 miles west of Fort Davis, altitude about 7,000 feet.) Fall.

12. **M. CAPILLARIS** (Lam.) Trin. (kăp-ĭ-lăr′ĭs); LONG-AWNED HAIRGRASS.

Culms 2-4 feet commonly 2-3 feet tall, in small or very large tufts, simple above the base, erect, wiry, smooth or nearly so; **Blades** 4-16′ long, involute and subcylindric, about 1 mm. in diameter, 2-3 mm. when spread out, rigid, pungent pointed; **Sheaths,** the upper long and often sheathing the base of the panicle, the lower short, overlapping; **Ligule** membranaceous, about 4 mm. long; **Panicle** purple, 6-20′ long, exserted or included at the base, ovate-oblong to widely pyramidal, finally diffuse, the axis slightly rough, the lower capillary branches 4-7′ long, mostly in ones or twos, naked at the base, ascending or spreading, the capillary pedicels clavate-thickened at the apex, mostly 15-30 mm. long; **Spikelets** exclusive of the awns about 4 mm. long, lanceolate, acute, purple; **Glumes** unequal, commonly one-half as long as the spikelet, slightly scabrous, the first acute or short-awned, the second awned, the awn sometimes as much as 2 mm. long; **Lemma** exclusive of awn about 4 mm. long, linear-lanceolate, 3-nerved, somewhat scabrous, glabrous except for a tuft of hairs below, scabrous awn 6-18 mm. long; **Palea** about as long as its lemma, acute, narrow.

In dry sandy soil or pine lands, Texas to Oklahoma, east to Florida, north to Missouri and Massachusetts. Fall.

13. **M. MONTANA** (Nutt.) Hitchc. (mŏn-tăn′à); *M. gracilis* of authors, not Kunth; *M. trifida* Hack.

Culms commonly 12-24′ rarely 32′ tall, tufted, rather rigidly erect, unbranched above, from a very short rootstock; **Blades** 2-6′ long, rarely longer, 1-2.5 mm. wide, flat or usually involute above, commonly rough, erect; **Sheaths** longer than the internodes, crowded below, loose; **Ligule** membranaceous, broader than the blades at the base, decurrent, 7-10 mm. long or more, fragile; **Panicles** long-exserted or sheathed below, 2-7′ long, erect or nearly so, the branches usually solitary and rather distant, erect or nearly so, or at anthesis ascending, commonly 2′ long or less, rarely 3.5′, the scabrous branchlets crowded with spikelets on scabrous short pedicels; **Spikelets** exclusive of the awns 3.5-4 mm. long, lanceolate; **Glumes** half to two-thirds as long as the lemma more or less scabrous, the first lanceolate, acuminate, aristate, 1-nerved, the second slightly longer, the three nerves produced into aristate-points or short awns; **Lemma** 3-nerved, the lateral nerves marginal and obscure, more or less pubescent below and ciliate on the margins, tapering into a scabrous flexuous awn (not twisted) 4-13 mm. long; **Palea** slightly shorter than the lemma, pubescent below.

Canyons, mesas and rocky hills 6,500-10,000 feet; west Texas to Mexico and north to Colorado and Montana, Utah, and California. Late summer-fall.

14. **M. SETIFOLIA** Vasey (sĕt-ĭ-fō′lĭ-à).

Culms 20-30′ tall, erect, rather rigid, simple, somewhat scabrous below the nodes, in strongly rooted tufts, rather pale; **Blades** 2.5-12′ long,

1.5 mm. wide or less, involute or conduplicate at the base, very narrow, with filiform tip, setiform, slightly scabrous, often curved, the basal numerous, longer than the upper; **Sheaths** mostly longer than or about as long as the internodes; **Ligule** membranaceous, 4-8 mm. long, decurrent; **Panicles** 4-8' long, usually exserted, erect or somewhat flexuous and nodding, loose, interrupted, somewhat open, nearly oblong, the branches solitary or a few approximate, appressed or ascending, often branched and naked at the base, 2.5-3' long or less; **Spikelets** 4-6 mm. long on rather long, scabrous, capillary pedicels, about twice as long as the spikelet, enlarged at the hispidulous summit; **Glumes** 1-nerved, or the second 3-nerved, one-third to half as long as the lemma, the second usually slightly longer, broad, often mucronate at the acute or erose apex, more or less scabrous; **Lemma** 3-nerved, scabrous toward the apex, the callus glabrous or sparsely pubescent, with a fine flexuous, scabrous awn produced from between two minute teeth, the awn 10-25 mm. long; **Palea** about as long as its lemma, scabrous toward the apex.

Rocky banks and foothills, mountains of western Texas. (Hueco Mountains 15 miles north of Van Horn, Sanderson, Sheffield, Texas.) Fall.

15. M. SCHREBERI Gmel. (shrē'bēr-ī) ; *M. diffusa* Willd.; NIMBLE WILL, SATIN-GRASS.

Culms 12-36' sometimes taller, creeping erect or ascending from a decumbent or prostrate base, often rooting at the nodes, very delicate, slender, diffusely branching; **Blades** 1.5-3.5' long, 1-4 mm. wide, flat, thin, slightly narrowed toward the base, spreading or ascending, rough; **Sheaths** shorter than the internodes, loose; **Ligule** membranaceous, fringed, very short; **Panicle** 2-6' long, finally exserted, slender, somewhat lax, its erect or appressed branches commonly 1-2' long, slender, interrupted, the axillary panicles usually included at the base; **Spikelets** exclusive of the awns about 2 mm. long, narrow, appressed, on short scabrous pedicels commonly 1-2 mm. long; **Glumes** minute, pale, the lower often almost obsolete, the second minute, truncate, less than one-fourth as long as the lemma; **Lemma** exclusive of the awn about 1.9 mm. long, lanceolate, 3-nerved, sparsely hairy below, very scabrous, especially on the nerves and margins, tapering into a slender scabrous straight awn 1-4 mm. long; **Palea** nearly as long as its lemma, acute, lanceolate.

Damp shady places in woods and waste places, Maine to Minnesota and south to Florida and Texas. (Open woods, San Antonio and Angleton, Texas.) Summer-fall.

16. M. SOBOLIFERA (Muhl.) Trin. (sō-bō-lĭf'ēr-à) ; ROCK MUHLEN-BERGIA, ROCK DROPSEED.

Culms 2-3 feet tall, erect or ascending, slender, commonly branching, scabrous below the glabrous nodes, leafy towards the summit, from scaly rootstocks; **Blades** of the culm 4-6' long, 3-6 mm. wide, of the branches 1-3' long, 1-4 mm. wide, narrowed toward the base, flat, rough; **Sheaths** shorter than the internodes or those of the branches crowded and overlapping; **Ligule** a short membrane, truncate; **Panicles** 3-8' long, very slender, finally exserted, those of the branches usually shorter, the slender branches distant their own length below, overlapping above, 0.5-2' long, solitary or an extra shorter branch flowering to the base, appressed or narrowly ascending, the spikelets on short scabrous pedicels; **Spikelets** 1.5-2.5 mm. commonly about 2 mm. long, narrowly lanceolate; **Glumes** subequal, 1-1.7 mm. long, half to three-fourths as long as the lemma, the second usually slightly longer, acute or abruptly cuspidate, scabrous especially on the keel; **Lemma** 3-nerved, obtuse, the midnerve produced into a short point, thinly pubescent on the lower half, scabrous above.

Rocky woods, Texas, Oklahoma, Iowa, Arkansas, Tennessee, Virginia, New Hampshire to Minnesota. Fall.

16a. **M. SOBOLIFERA** var. **SETIGERA** Scribn. (sē-tĭj'ēr-à); SLENDER SATIN-GRASS.

Culms 2-3 feet tall, slender, simple or branching, erect, leafy throughout (branching more freely in the later stages); **Blades** 2-5' (2-7') long, 2-7 mm. wide, flat, narrowed toward the base, acuminate, rough; **Sheaths** mostly shorter than the internodes; **Ligule** short and truncate; **Panicle** 2.5-8' (2.5-16') long, very slender, loosely-flowered, the slender branches appressed, solitary or in pairs, one of the pair shorter, 1-3.5' long; **Spikelets** 2-2.5 mm. (3-4) long on scabrous pedicels 1-2 mm. long; **Glumes** 1-2 mm. long, subequal, two-thirds to as long as the lemma, abruptly acuminate, scabrous, the first very broad; **Lemma** 1.5-2.3 mm. (2.5-3.5 mm.) long, pubescent below, tapering into an awn 2-6 mm. long (2-4 times its length).

In dry rocky woods, Texas and Alabama, Massachusetts to Minnesota. (Dallas, Texas.) Summer-fall.

17. **M. BRACHYPHYLLA** Bush (brăk-ĭ-fĭl'à).

Culms 20' tall more or less, erect or ascending from a decumbent base, leafy, freely branching at the middle nodes, mostly glabrous below the nodes, from scaly rootstocks; **Blades** mostly 1.5-4' long, 2-7 mm. wide, the lower shorter than the upper, flat, rough; **Sheaths** mostly shorter than the internodes; **Ligule** membranaceous, about 1 mm. long; **Panicles** numerous on main culm and branches, 2-4' long more or less, often included at the base, slender, more loosely-flowered than *M. umbrosa*, the slender branches mostly appressed; **Spikelets** exclusive of the awn 3-3.5 mm. long, narrowly lanceolate; **Glumes** subequal, the second about two-thirds as long as the lemma, the first usually slightly shorter, acute, scabrous on the keel; **Lemma** hairy for about one-third the distance from the base, the hairs less than 1 mm. long, glabrous to minutely hispidulous above, 3-nerved; **Awn** 1.5-8 mm. long; **Palea** somewhat shorter than the lemma.

This plant somewhat resembles *M. sobolifera* or a loosely-flowered *M. umbrosa*. It is shown with *M. umbrosa*.

Low woods, Indiana to Nebraska, south to central Texas. (Near Fort Worth.) Late summer-fall.

18. **M. REPENS** (Presl) Hitchc. (rē'pĕns).

Culms 2-20' tall or long, erect or commonly prostrate or straggling, with erect or ascending branches, freely branching, slender, in dense patches or forming a continuous turf, from long rootstocks; **Blades** 6-50 mm. long, those of the main culm as much as 2' long and 2 mm. wide or less, flat toward the base, those of the branches usually shorter, mostly involute and about 0.5 mm. thick, sharp-pointed, often recurved, smooth or minutely scabrous; **Sheaths** commonly longer than the internodes, sometimes shorter, crowded, loose; **Ligule** membranaceous, about 1 mm. long; **Panicles** narrow, erect, 5-50 mm. long, the terminal usually longer than the numerous panicles of the branches, commonly less than 1' long, included at the base, light lead-color, the very short branches appressed or narrowly ascending, the scabrous pedicels 1-3 mm. long; **Spikelets** 2.8-3 mm. long, lanceolate; **Glumes** about two-thirds as long as the spikelet, acute or awn-pointed, rarely obtuse, scabrous toward the tip, 1-nerved, or the first with an extra nerve on each side, pale; **Lemma** slightly longer than the acute palea, sharp-pointed to short-awned, the awn usually less than 0.5 mm. long, 3-nerved, the lateral nerves obscure, scabrous toward the apex.

Dry or moist soil; western Texas to Arizona. (Ft. Davis, Texas.) Fall.

19. M. UTILIS (Torr.) Hitchc. (ū'tĭl-ĭs) ; *Vilfa utilis* Torr.; *Sporobolus utilis* (Torr.) Scribn.; APAREJO GRASS.

Culms commonly 6-12′ sometimes as much as 36′ tall, the short and isolated plants usually somewhat tufted and erect, those of dense colonies or patches usually more or less prostrate, or the taller plants straggling, slender, freely branching from slender rootstocks; **Blades** numerous, stiffly ascending to recurved, 10-40 mm. commonly 10-20 mm. long, mostly involute, when folded about 0.3 mm. thick; **Sheaths** of the culm mostly shorter than the internodes, of the branches mostly longer, smooth or slightly scabrous, the collar white; **Ligule** membranaceous, about 1 mm. long; **Panicle** spikelike, terminal and axillary, 10-30 mm. commonly 10-15 mm. long, interrupted below, included at the base, slender, the short branches appressed, usually with 2-3 spikelets, the spikelets on short pedicels about 1.5 mm. long; **Spikelets** 1.5-2 mm. long, pale; **Glumes** subequal, about half as long as the lemma, acute or subacute, sometimes erose, the first slightly and minutely scabrous toward the apex; **Lemma** lanceolate, acute, with three green nerves or the lateral obsolete, entire or mucronate; **Palea** slightly shorter than the lemma, minutely scabrous on the keels.

In rather moist soil Texas to southern California, south into Mexico. (Comfort, Texas.) Spring.

20. M. MEXICANA (L.) Trin. (mĕks-ĭ-kā'nȧ).

Culms 6-25′ (6-40′) tall, slender, erect or decumbent, sometimes prostrate, plants top-heavy, rooting at the lower nodes, from long scaly rootstocks, glabrous below the nodes; **Blades** 2-6′ long, 2-6 mm. wide, those of the branches smaller, flat, rough; **Sheaths,** the uppermost of the branches crowded and overlapping, the lower usually shorter than the internodes, smooth or slightly rough; **Ligule** a short membrane; **Panicles** numerous, 2-6′ long, contracted, those of the culm and especially those of the branches often included at the base, its branches 1-2′ long, rather spikelike, erect or appressed, rarely ascending, the spikelets appressed, crowded, on short scabrous pedicels; **Spikelets** 2.5-3 mm. or including the short awn sometimes 4 mm. long; **Glumes** subequal, about as long as the lemma, subulate, acuminate or short-awned, scabrous, especially on the keel; **Lemma** acuminate, awnless or short-awned, 3-nerved, scabrous, especially toward the apex, sparsely pilose at the base and very sparsely so a short distance above the base. The glumes and lemma vary much relatively as to length and as to being awnless or short-awned.

In swamps, thickets and borders of fields; Texas to Oklahoma and Colorado, Montana, Nebraska, Tennessee, Canada. Summer-fall.

21. M. UMBROSA Scribn. (ŭm-brō'sȧ) ; *M. sylvatica* Torr.; WOODLAND DROPSEED.

Culms 1-3 feet tall, erect or ascending, freely branching, leafy, minutely strigose below the nodes, from scaly rootstocks resembling *M. mexicana* in habit; **Blades** 2-7′ long, 2-6 mm. wide, flat, rough; **Sheaths** mostly shorter than the internodes, or those of the branches overlapping, smooth or slightly roughened; **Ligule** about 1 mm. long, erose-truncate;

Panicle green, not compactly flowered; exserted or commonly included at the base, linear, numerous, from main culm and branches, 2.5-7′ long, rather lax, the slender branches erect or narrowly ascending, 1-2′ rarely 3′ long; **Spikelets** 2.5-3 mm. long, narrowly lanceolate; **Glumes** equal or the lower slightly shorter, 2-2.5 mm. long, about equal to the scabrous lemma, acuminate, often aristate, or awn-pointed, scabrous; **Lemma** rough, acuminate, the hairs at base about 1 mm. long, appressed, awn slender, 5-12 mm. long; **Palea** about as long as the lemma, acuminate, scabrous on the nerves.

In moist woods and along streams.   Texas, Arizona, Oklahoma, North Carolina, north to South Dakota and New Brunswick.   Summer-fall.

22. M. LEMMONI Scribn. (lĕm′ō-nī).

Culms 1-2 feet tall, usually low, often decumbent, freely branching, leafy throughout, from creeping rootstocks; **Blades** commonly 1.5-4′ long, 1.5-2.5 mm. wide, flat, soon involute, erect, numerous; **Sheaths** longer than the internodes; **Ligule** membranaceous, about 1 mm. long, fringed; **Panicles** 2-6′ long, exserted or included at the base, narrow, interrupted, the branches appressed or narrowly ascending, in ones to threes, unequal, commonly about 1-2′ long, the spikelets crowded on pubescent pedicels about 1 mm. long; **Spikelets** exclusive of the awns 3-3.5 mm. long; **Glumes** equal, acute, prominently keeled, scabrous on the keel, 2.5-3.5 mm. or including the awn sometimes 5 mm. long; **Lemma** excluding the awn 2.5-3 mm. long, strongly 3-nerved, 2-toothed, linear, scabrous toward the apex, pubescent on the lower half, the callus hairs conspicuous, the awn 1-3 mm. long, rarely longer; **Palea** about equal to its lemma, pubescent below the middle.

Mountains, western Texas to Arizona and Mexico.   (Fowlkes Ranch, Black Mountains, Texas.)   Summer-fall.

23. M. GLABRIFLORA Scribn. (glā-brĭ-flō′rā).

Culms 12-25′ tall, slender, erect or decumbent and spreading, freely branching, minutely strigose below the nodes, in habit resembling *M. mexicana;* **Blades** 0.5-3.5′ long, 1-4 mm. wide, flat, rough; **Sheaths** shorter than the internodes; **Ligule** very short; **Panicles** commonly purple, shorter and narrower than in *M. mexicana,* terminal and those of the several branches often included at the base, more or less glomerate, the branches racemose like, 1-2′ long, appressed or ascending; **Spikelets** 2.5-3.5 mm. long, somewhat crowded, on short scabrous pedicels; **Glumes** usually purple, 2-3.5 mm. long, subequal, the second usually slightly longer, acuminate, often awn-pointed, scabrous toward the tip, the length of the glume varying much on the same panicle; **Lemma** awnless, 2.5-3 mm. long, 3-nerved, strongly nerved, scabrous toward the apex, *callus and body glabrous;* **Palea** about equal to the lemma.

Rich woods, Dallas, Texas.   Fall.

24. M. RACEMOSA (Michx.) B. S. P. (rā-sē-mō′sà); *M. glomerata* Trin.; SATIN-GRASS.

Culms 1-3 feet tall, erect, simple or branching, smooth or rough below the panicles and the nodes, from stout, scaly rootstocks; **Blades** 2-5′ long, 2-6 mm. wide, rough; **Sheaths** shorter than the internodes, or those of the branches crowded and overlapping; **Ligule** 1 mm. long, erose-truncate; **Panicle** 2-5′ long, usually exserted, dense and interrupted, erect or slightly nodding, the branches rather distant, overlapping, solitary or one or two short extra branches, appressed or narrowly ascending, commonly 12-25 mm. long, the spikelets densely crowded, subsessile; **Spikelets** 4-6 mm. long; **Glumes** including the awns 4-6 mm. long, acuminate, scabrous on the keel, otherwise smooth to scabrous; **Lemma** half to two-thirds as long as the glumes, acuminate, the three nerves prominent, the midnerve produced into a short point, pubescent toward the base, scabrous above; **Palea** nearly equal to the lemma.

This plant has not been found in Texas, but it has been collected in New Mexico and may appear in western Texas.

In wet places (often in open woods), New Mexico, Oklahoma, Maryland and north. Summer-fall.

25. M. POLYCAULIS Scribn. (pŏl-ĭ-kô′lĭs).

Culms 12-20′ tall, numerous, wiry, decumbent and scaly at the base, from a firm crown; **Blades** mostly less than 2′ long, about 1 mm. wide, mostly flat; **Panicle** narrow, contracted, 1-3′ long, interrupted; **Spikelets** excluding the awn 2.5-3 mm. long; **Glumes** a little shorter than the lemma, tapering into a short slender awn, more or less ciliate on the keel, or scabrous toward the apex; **Lemma** tapering into a delicate awn 5-20 mm. long, conspicuously pilose, especially below. (Drawings on photograph of *M. monticola.*) Shaded ledge and grassy slopes; western Texas to southern Arizona and central Mexico. Fall.

26. M. PARVIGLUMIS Vasey (pär-vĭ-glū′mĭs).

Culms 12-28′ tall, tufted, erect, slender, freely branching throughout with the habit of *M. monticola;* **Blades** 1.5-4′ long, 2 mm. wide or less, erect, flat or closely involute, smooth or slightly rough; **Sheaths** usually shorter than the internodes, or the lower longer, loose, the branches pushing them from the culm, smooth to slightly rough; **Ligule** about 2.5 mm. long, membranaceous, fragile; **Panicles** partly enclosed at the base, erect or slightly nodding, flexuous, greenish-gray, 4-7′ long, the capillary branches solitary or the lower in twos, erect or appressed, subdivided and flowering to the base, the appressed spikelets on short branchlets, the scabrous pedicels 1-3 mm. long; **Spikelets** 2.3-3 mm. long; **Glumes** about equal, 0.5-0.8 mm. long or about one-fourth as long as the spikelet, obtuse or subacute, erose; **Lemma** 2.2-2.9 mm. long, linear-lanceolate, 3-nerved, scabrous on the nerves and toward the apex, 2-toothed, appressed-pubescent on the margin below, the straight slightly scabrous awn 20-25 mm. (20-40) long, from just below the acute bifid apex; **Palea** nearly as long as the lemma, scabrous on the keels.

Rocky hills or mountains, western Texas to Mexico. (Guadalupe Mountains.) Fall.

27. M. MONTICOLA Buckl. (mŏn-tĭ-kō′là).

Culms 6-30′ commonly about 20′ tall, tufted, erect or ascending from a decumbent base, wiry, internodes short, freely branching, rather slender and weak; **Blades** 1-4′ long, the upper longer than the lower, 2 mm. wide or less, flat or involute especially toward the tip, erect, smooth or rough on the upper surface; **Sheaths** shorter than the internodes, the lower spread open by the branches, smooth or slightly rough; **Ligule** membranaceous, 2-3 mm. long, lacerate; **Panicles** numerous, 1.5-8′ long, usually green, exserted or the axillary shorter and included at the base, erect or slightly nodding, rather loose, the branches mostly single, 10-40 mm. long, simple or with short branchlets at the base (appearing to be branches), spikelet-bearing to the base, erect or ascending, the crowded spikelets subsessile or on stout scabrous pedicels 1-4 mm. long; **Spikelets** excluding the awns 3-4 mm. long; **Glumes** subequal or unequal, half to two-thirds the length of the lemma, the second often slightly longer, acute, often minutely toothed, or erose, thin, scabrous on the body and prominent nerve toward the apex; **Lemma** lanceolate, acuminate, the three green nerves prominent, pubescent at the base, scabrous especially toward the base, the scabrous flexuous awn 8-15 mm. rarely 20 mm. long; **Palea** about as long as the lemma, somewhat pubescent toward the base.

Mesas and foothills, western Texas to Arizona. (Marfa road 12 miles west of Alpine, Texas.) Fall.

28. M. PAUCIFLORA Buckl. (pô-sĭ-flō'rà).

Culms 12-20' tall, tufted, erect or spreading, wiry, scabrous, branching, especially toward the base; **Blades** 1.5-5' long, 1 mm. wide or less, the lower short, involute, setaceous; **Sheaths** mostly shorter than the internodes, some of them crowded off by the branches, rough; **Ligule** membranaceous, about 1 mm. long, lacerate, fragile; **Panicles** narrow, 1.5-4.5' long, included at the base or exserted, interrupted below, flexuous, the branches usually solitary, erect or appressed, the longest about 25 mm. long, closely-flowered to the base, the spikelets on scabrous and rather stout pedicels 0.5-1.5 mm. long; **Spikelets** exclusive of the awn 3-3.5 mm. (3-4) long; **Glumes** often awn-pointed, scabrous on the keel, the first 1.1-2 mm. long, the second 2-2.5 mm. long; **Lemma** 3-3.5 mm. long, lanceolate, acuminate, purplish, scabrous on the three nerves, the callus glabrous and prominent, the midnerve produced into a scabrous straight awn 6-13 mm. long; **Palea** about as long as its lemma, scabrous on the keels.

Mountains and rocky hills, western Texas to Arizona and south to Mexico, also north to Colorado. (Guadalupe Mountains.) Fall.

29. M. WRIGHTII Vasey (rīt'ĭ-ī). Not yet collected in Texas.

Culms 1-2.5 commonly about 1.5 feet tall, erect or decumbent at the base, often densely tufted, firm, somewhat flattened, more or less rough, from short rootstocks; **Blades** 3-5' long, 2 mm. wide or less, flat at the base, with filiform involute tips, rigid, rough above; **Sheaths** shorter than the internodes, or the lower overlapping, keeled; **Ligule** 0.5-1.5 mm. long, membranaceous, almost truncate; **Panicles** erect, 2-5' rarely 7' long, obtuse, usually dense and spikelike, cylindric, 2-8 mm. thick, usually dense, or sometimes the branches distant and slender and more or less interrupted, the axis scabrous; the branches mostly 10-20 mm. rarely 35 mm. long, usually appressed or narrowly ascending, spikelike, densely flowered, the spikelets on short scabrous pedicels; **Spikelets** sometimes 2-flowered, 3 mm. long; **Glumes** subequal, ovate but awn-pointed or short awned, two-thirds to as long as the lemma, 1-nerved, scabrous on the nerve toward the apex; **Lemma** awn-pointed or with an awn about 0.5 mm. long, or sometimes 1 mm. long, scabrous toward the apex, sparsely short-pubescent below; **Palea** about as long as the lemma.

This species has not been collected in Texas, but has been collected in Mexico and New Mexico. Mountains, Mexico through New Mexico to Colorado. Summer-fall.

30. M. ACUMINATA Vasey (à-kū-mĭ-nā'tà).

Culms 2-3 feet tall, erect, tufted, rather stout, internodes long, hard and wiry at the base; **Blades** 5-16' long, scarcely 1 mm. wide, folded, 1-1.5

mm. wide, open, very rough; **Sheaths** shorter than the internodes or overlapping below, not broad and papery, closely enclosing the culms, rough,
with erect, firm auricles 4-10 mm. long, rarely longer; **Ligule** about 6 mm.
long, hardened at the base; **Panicle** contracted, narrow, green, 6-12′ long,
about 10 mm. wide, erect or slightly nodding, axis and branches scabrous,
the longer branches mostly less than 2′ long, several at each node, the
shorter spikelet-bearing branches at the base, appressed or erect or
narrowly ascending, spikelets sessile or on short stout pedicels about
1 mm. long, scabrous, enlarged at the apex; **Spikelets** 4-5 mm. long,
narrowly lanceolate; **Glumes** broad, subequal, about half as long as the
lemma, acute or erose-truncate at the apex, scabrous toward the apex;
Lemma scabrous toward the tip, 2-toothed, acuminate or with a scabrous
awn 2-5 mm. long, a few appressed hairs on the callus; **Palea** about equal
to the lemma, scabrous toward the tip.

Rich moist soil, cool slopes, rocky mountains or hills; western Texas,
New Mexico, and south into Mexico. Summer-fall.

31. **M. METCALFEI** Jones (mět-kăf′ē-ī).

Culms 2-4 feet tall, rather rigidly erect, simple, tufted, rough below
the panicle; **Blades** 3-20′ long, the upper short, the lower and those of the
sterile shoots long, about 1 mm. wide when folded, involute, rigidly erect,
smooth or slightly rough; **Sheaths** longer than the internodes, loose; **Ligule**
membranaceous, 2-5 mm. (3-10) long, truncate, firm, fimbriate; **Panicles**
greenish-purple, narrow but usually loose, short-exserted or included at
the base, 4-12′ long, erect or slightly nodding, the axis scabrous, the
branches appressed or narrowly ascending, several at a node, commonly
about 1.5′ long, sometimes as much as 3′ long, the scabrous capillary
pedicels enlarged at the apex, mostly 2-5 mm. long, the spikelets more or
less appressed to the short branchlets; **Spikelets** purple, exclusive of the
awn 3.5-4 mm. long; **Glumes** subequal, two-fifths to half as long as the
lemma, 1-nerved or nerveless, acute to obtuse, often erose, minutely
scabrous toward the apex; **Lemma** lanceolate, scabrous-hispidulous, the
callus glabrous or with a few short hairs, a straight or flexuous awn
mostly 1-5 mm. (5-10) long, from the minutely bifid apex; **Palea** nearly as
long as the lemma, scabrous toward the apex.

Southern New Mexico, Arizona, south through Texas to Mexico.
(Rocky ravine, high point in the Guadalupe Mountains on the Carlsbad-
El Paso Road.) Fall.

32. **M. RIGENS** (Benth.) Hitchc. (rī′jĕns); *Epicampes rigens* Bentham;
DEER-GRASS.

Culms 2-6 feet tall, usually growing in large, dense clumps, rather
coarse, erect or spreading, simple, rigid; **Blades** 4-30′ mostly 5-15′ long,
2-5 mm. wide, usually involute, sometimes flat, rigidly erect or ascending,
rough; **Sheaths** longer than the internodes, the upper very long and the
lower short, loose, smooth or rough; **Ligule** firm, almost truncate, 1-2 mm.
long, wider than the blade; **Panicles** spikelike, exserted or sheathed at the
base, 6-24′ long, 3-8 mm. in diameter, interrupted below, erect or slightly
nodding, densely-flowered, pale, the branches appressed to the scabrous
axis, commonly less than an inch long, the branches and pedicels scabrous,
the pedicels 1-3 mm. long usually about 1 mm.; **Spikelets** 2.5-4 mm. long,
lanceolate, acute, terete; **Glumes** subequal, two-thirds to about as long as
the spikelet, obscurely 1-nerved, commonly scabrous over the back and on
the nerve toward the apex, pale, obtuse or acute, sometimes erose, or

sometimes a mucro from between the lobes of a bifid apex; **Lemma** usually slightly exceeding the glumes, 3-nerved, acute, minutely scabrous, the callus short-pubescent, without an awn or mucro or with a scabrous mucro or short-awn (usually less than 1 mm. long) from between or below the lobes of a bifid apex; **Palea** more than half to nearly as long as the lemma, subacute, minutely scabrous.

Damp rocky canyons and damp meadows, western Texas to California and south to Mexico. (In mountains along Alpine-Ft. Davis road.) Fall.

33. M. FOURNIERIANA Hitchc. (fōōr-nǐ-ěr-ǐ-ā'nà) ; *Epicampes berlandieri* Fourn., not *M. berlandieri* Trin.

Culms 2-6 feet tall, usually in rather large dense tufts, simple, erect, rigid, somewhat flattened, with many sterile branches at the base; **Blades** 2-48' commonly 6-24' long, the upper short, the lower and those of the sterile shoots long, conduplicate toward the base, flat above, when folded 1-2 mm. wide, when flattened 2-5 mm. wide, scabrous to smooth, the margins not rough; **Sheaths** longer than the internodes, junction of sheath and blade obscure, flattened, smooth to rough; **Ligule** membranaceous, firm below, fragile above, decurrent, 10-20 mm. long; **Panicle** pale to purplish, usually exserted, 8-28' long, linear-oblong, when flowering 1-3' wide, interrupted below, the numerous branches usually less than 2.5' long, erect to spreading, usually ascending when in flower, one to several to a node, naked at the very base, the numerous short branchlets crowded with spikelets, the scabrous pedicels usually less than 1 mm. long; **Spikelets** (rarely 2-flowered) 2.5-3 mm. long, pale, often tinged with purple; **Glumes** subequal, the second sometimes slightly longer, and as long as or longer than the lemma, acute or obtuse, entire, erose or mucronate, scabrous on the nerves and body; **Lemma** obtuse, awnless or with a short awn from below a bifid apex, the awn 0.5-1 mm. rarely 3 mm. long, sparsely pubescent below, minutely scabrous, especially on the midnerve and toward the apex; **Palea** shorter to longer than the lemma, acute or obtuse, entire or erose, only slightly scabrous.

There are considerable variations in the comparative length of glumes, lemma and palea.

Along streams, draws, and banks, southern Texas to western Texas. (Hills north of San Antonio, Texas.)   Summer.

34. M. EMERSLEYI Vasey (ē-mērs'lē-ī) ; *M. vaseyana* Scribn.; *Epicampes emersleyi* (Vasey) Hitchc. (includes *Epicampes subpatens* Hitchc.).

Culms 2-4 rarely 6 feet tall, simple, usually in rather large tufts, erect, rigid, scabrous especially below the panicle, or smooth, leafy at the base; **Blades** 3-15' or sometimes 25' long, the upper short, 1-4 mm. wide, conduplicate or flat, harsh, scabrous, especially on the margins and midrib; **Sheaths** longer than the internodes, flattened, usually scabrous, crowded at the base; **Ligule** membranaceous, narrow, as much as 20 mm. long, decurrent, fragile; **Panicle** 8-15' rarely 24' long, usually exserted, contracted, erect or the longer ones nodding, the axis and branches scabrous, the branches in ones to fours, distant, ascending or slightly spreading or appressed, 1-5' rarely 7' long, naked for one-fourth to one-third the distance from the base, the spikelets on scabrous pedicels about half the length of the spikelets; **Spikelets** 2-3.5 mm. mostly 2.5-3 mm. long; **Glumes** equal or the second slightly longer, shorter or longer than the lemma, 1-nerved or an extra one or two dim nerves, acute or obtuse, often erose, scabrous, usually pale; **Lemma** 3-nerved, the lateral often obscure, short-pubescent below, especially along the margins, awnless or the midnerve produced from below the apex into a slender scabrous awn commonly 5-15 mm. rarely only 1-3 mm. or 27 mm. long, or sometimes a part of the spikelets on the same panicle awnless and awned; **Palea** slightly longer or shorter than the lemma, sparsely hairy below.

This plant varies much as to height, length of spikelets, and awns. The plant photographed was much larger than usual.

Hills and mountains, western Texas and New Mexico. (Mosquiz Canyon and Limpia Canyon, near Ft. Davis, and also about 30 miles northeast of San Antonio, Texas.) Summer-fall.

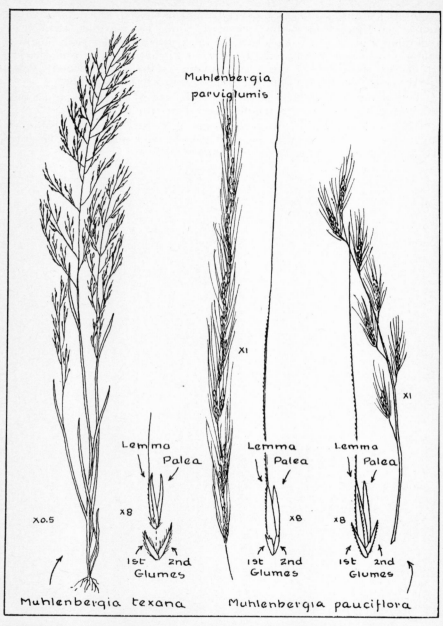

MUHLENBERGIA TEXANA, MUHLENBERGIA PARVIGLUMIS AND MUHLENBERGIA PAUCIFLORA.

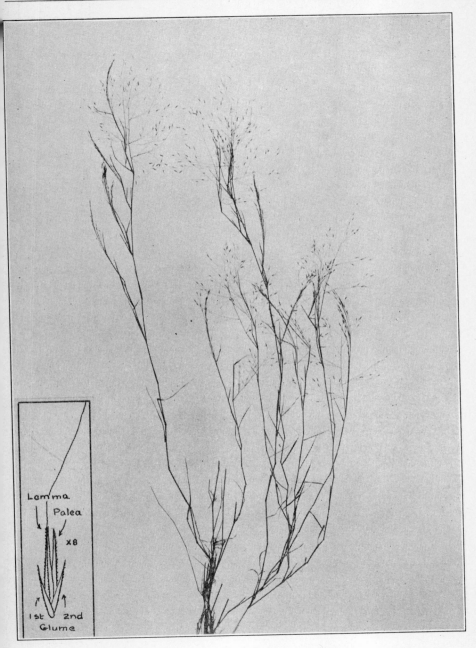

MUHLENBERGIA PORTERI; Large Mesquite-grass

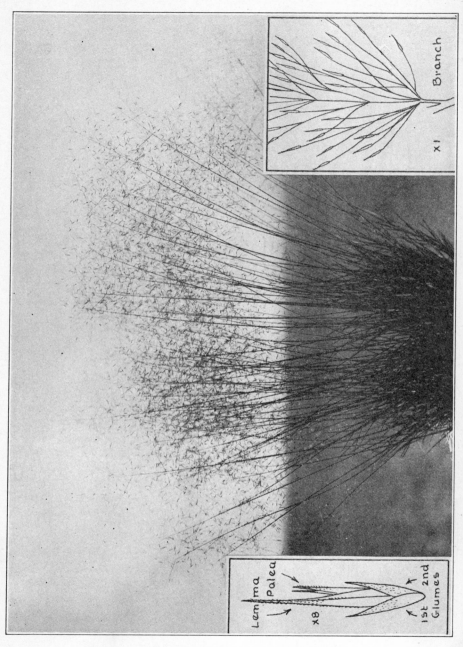

MUHLENBERGIA PUNGENS; Blow-out grass

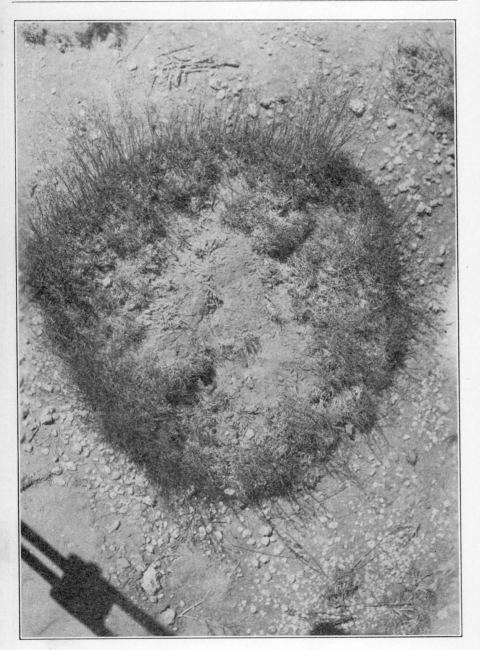

MUHLENBERGIA TORREYI; Ring-grass

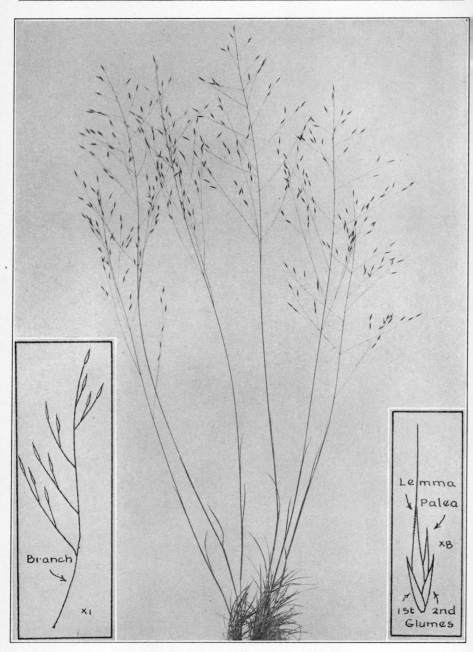

MUHLENBERGIA TORREYI; Ring-grass

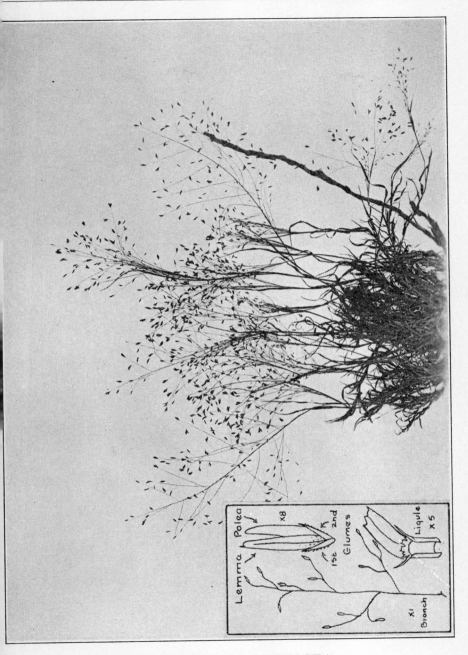

MUHLENBERGIA ARENACEA

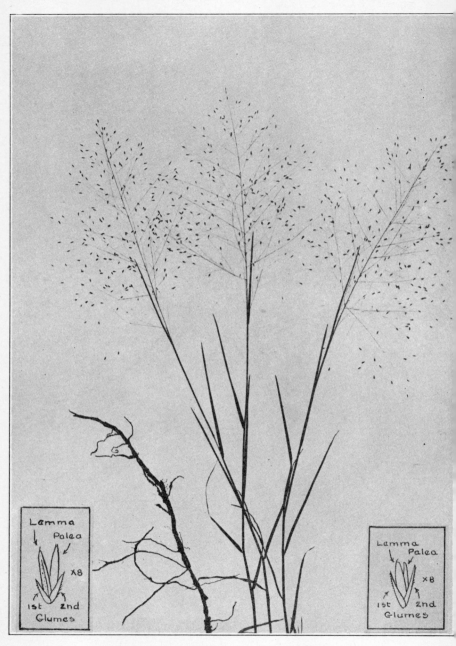

MUHLENBERGIA ASPERIFOLIA

MUHLENBERGIA ARENICOLA

MUHLENBERGIA INVOLUTA

MUHLENBERGIA REVERCHONI

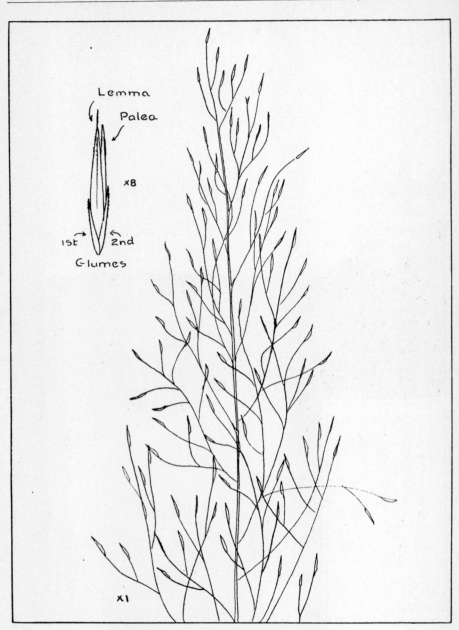

MUHLENBERGIA EXPANSA

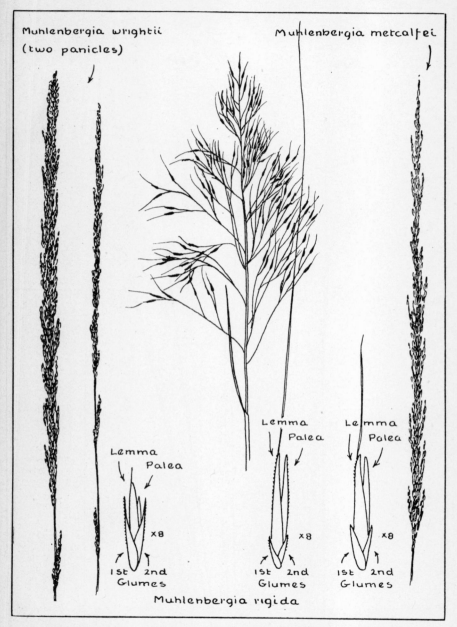

Muhlenbergia wrightii
(two panicles)

Muhlenbergia metcalfei

Lemma
Palea

Lemma
Palea

Lemma
Palea

×8

×8

×8

1st 2nd
Glumes

1st 2nd
Glumes

1st 2nd
Glumes

Muhlenbergia rigida

MUHLENBERGIA WRIGHTII; MUHLENBERGIA RIGIDA;
MUHLENBERGIA METCALFEI

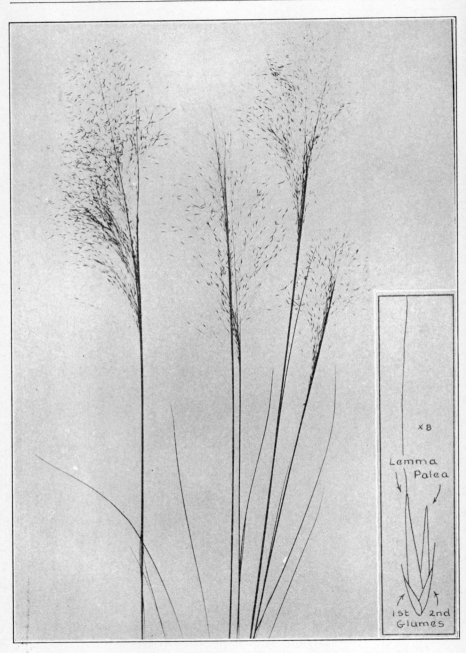

×8

Lemma
Palea

1st   2nd
Glumes

MUHLENBERGIA CAPILLARIS; Long-awned Hair-grass

MUHLENBERGIA MONTANA. Usually the branches of the panicle are appressed or narrowly ascending; the photograph was taken at anthesis, showing the branches ascending.

MUHLENBERGIA SETIFOLIA

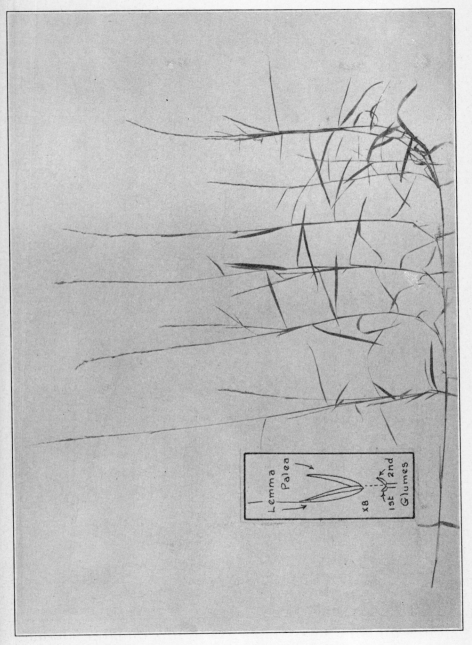

MUHLENBERGIA SCHREBERI; Nimble Will

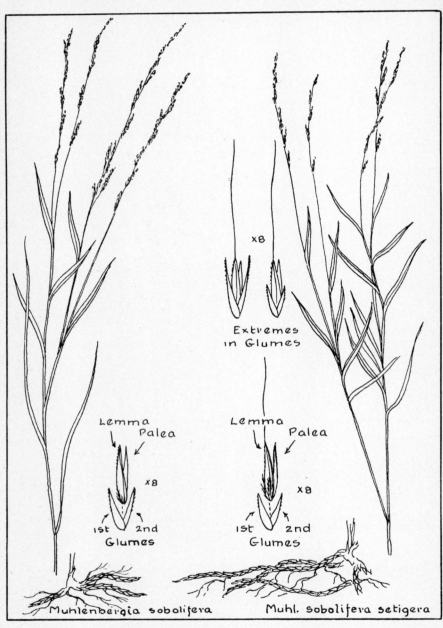

MUHLENBERGIA SOBOLIFERA AND MUHLENBERGIA SOBOLI-
FERA VAR. SETIGERA

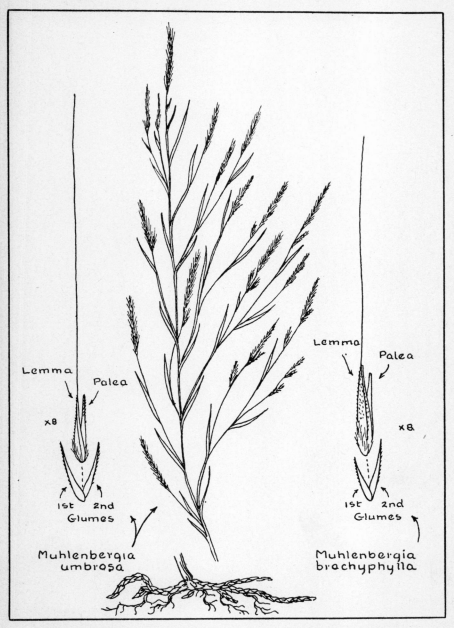

MUHLENBERGIA UMBROSA AND MUHLENBERGIA
BRACHYPHYLLA

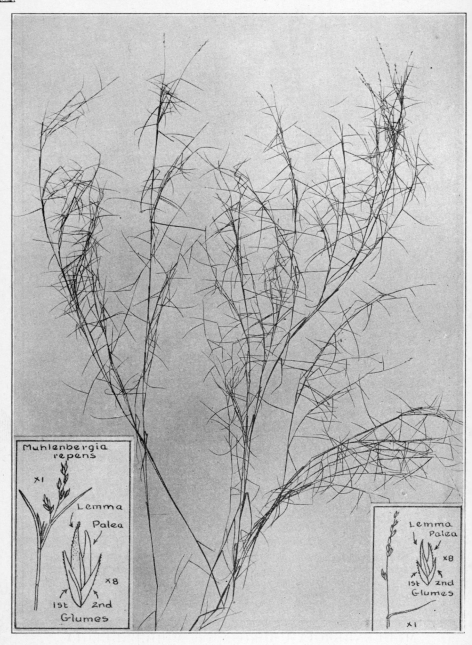

MUHLENBERGIA UTILIS, Aparejo-grass; drawings of M. REPENS to
the left.

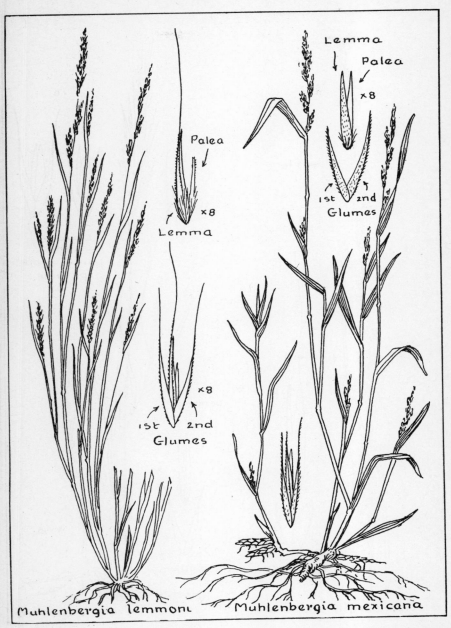

Palea

Lemma

×8

1st 2nd
Glumes

Lemma
Palea

×8

1st 2nd
Glumes

Muhlenbergia lemmoni

Muhlenbergia mexicana

MUHLENBERGIA LEMMONI AND MUHLENBERGIA MEXICANA

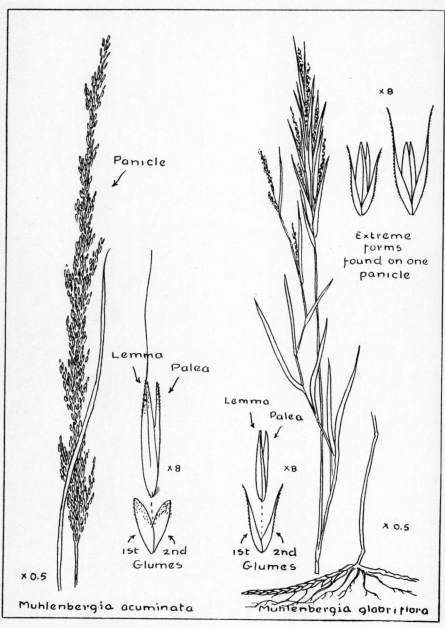

Panicle

Lemma   Palea

×8

1st   2nd
Glumes

×0.5

Muhlenbergia acuminata

×8

Extreme
forms
found on one
panicle

Lemma   Palea

×8

1st   2nd
Glumes

×0.5

Muhlenbergia glabriflora

MUHLENBERGIA ACUMINATA AND MUHLENBERGIA
GLABRIFLORA

Lemma
Palea
×8
1st 2nd
Glumes

Rootstocks
×1

MUHLENBERGIA RACEMOSA, Satin-grass

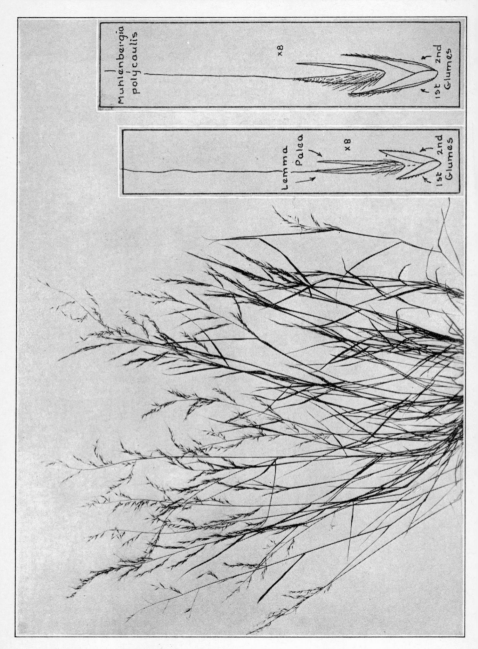

MUHLENBÉRGIA MONTICOLA; drawings of MUHLENBERGIA
POLYCAULIS

MUHLENBERGIA RIGENS; Deer-grass

MUHLENBERGIA FOURNIERIANA

MUHLENBERGIA EMERSLEYI

47. SPOROBOLUS R. Br. (spō-rŏb′ō-lŭs)

Spikelets 1-flowered, the rachilla disarticulating above the glumes; **Glumes** awnless, usually unequal, the second often as long as the spikelet; **Lemma** membranaceous, 1-nerved, awnless; **Palea** usually prominent and as long as the lemma or longer; **Seed** free from the pericarp.

Annual or *perennial* grasses, with small spikelets in open or contracted panicles. About 36 species in the United States.

The fruit is free from the lemma and palea, and falls readily from the spikelet at maturity. Because of this character the species have been called drop-seed grasses. The genus differs from *Muhlenbergia* in having 1-nerved awnless lemmas and from *Agrostis* in having lemmas as long as the glumes or longer and as firm.

We have in Texas about 21 species, 9 with narrow, rather spikelike panicles, and 12 with open panicles. Three are low annuals: *S. microspermus,* with an open panicle, is a west Texas plant; *S. vaginaeflorus* and *S. neglectus,* with narrow usually more or less included panicles, are found here and there in central and southern Texas. Three have creeping rhizomes: *S. texanus* and *S. tharpii* with open panicles, and *S. virginicus* with a narrow panicle. *S. texanus,* a west Texas grass, and *S. virginicus,* confined to the coast and alkaline spots in the interior, are rather low plants, and *S. tharpii,* a taller plant, has been collected on Padre Island.

S. argutus and *S. nealleyi,* usually about a foot tall, have open panicles; the former has a wide range over central and southern Texas, the latter being confined mostly to "gyp" soil in west Texas.

S. flexuosus, commonly 2-3 feet tall, with a long oblong panicle (which often clings to other plants), is confined to very sandy land in west Texas, while *S. cryptandrus,* with the panicle wholly or partly included in the upper sheaths, has a wide range.

S. airoides, 1-3 feet tall, with a loosely-flowered pyramidal panicle, and *S. wrightii,* 3-7 feet tall with a very long, oblong, densely-flowered panicle, both usually in large tussocks, are found here and there from the coast north through western Texas to Colorado. *S. buckleyi,* usually 2-3 feet tall, with a purple nearly oblong panicle, is found in southern Texas and Mexico.

S. poiretii, with a very long slender panicle is common in southwest Texas and extends east into most of the southern states. It is often called smut-grass because it is sometimes affected by a black fungus. When mature the numerous reddish or purplish grains are conspicuous on the pale or dark smutty panicle.

S. giganteus, a stout erect plant with a narrow panicle usually more or less included, is confined to the very sandy land of west and northwest Texas.

S. asper and *S. asper* var. *hookeri,* both either simple or branching, in small or large tufts, vary much as to size of plants and spikelets, the panicles narrow, usually more or less included in the sometimes inflated sheaths. *S. asper* (*S. longifolius* (Torr.) Wood), is usually a stout erect grass, while *S. asper* var. *hookeri* is a rather weak grass, the culms often bent at the nodes. Two forms of *S. asper* var. *hookeri* have been classified as *S. drummondii* (Trin.) Vasey and *S. attenuatus* Nash.

S. contractus, a west Texas grass, and *S. purpurascens,* a sandy land species confined to the Gulf coast and Mexico, are plants usually 2-3 feet tall, the former with a narrow panicle, and the latter with an oblong open panicle.

PANICLE NARROW, SPIKELIKE.
  PLANTS ANNUAL. Culms slender; panicles commonly less than 2′ long, usually more or less included in the sheath.
    Spikelets 3-4.5 mm. long; lemma pubescent.   1. S. vaginaeflorus
    Spikelets 2.5-3 mm. long; lemma glabrous.   2. S. neglectus
  PLANTS PERENNIAL.
    PLANTS tufted; no rootstocks.
      Second glume about as long as the spikelet.
        Plants robust, 3-5 feet tall, erect, panicle long, included below; spikelets 2.6 mm. long.   3. S. giganteus
        Plants slender, mostly 2-3 feet tall.
          Sheaths strongly-pilose at the throat; blades not ciliate or only slightly so at base; panicle long, pale-green; spikelets 2.3 mm. long.   4. S. contractus
          Sheaths glabrous or sparsely-pilose at the throat; blades, at least the lower, ciliate; panicle lead-color or purplish, more or less interrupted; spikelets 3-3.5 mm. long.   5. S. purpurascens
      Second glume shorter than the spikelet.
        Lemma glabrous; panicles often included at the base.
          Plants and inflorescence rather stout, erect.
            Sheaths and blades glabrous or pubescent toward the base; panicle long; spikelets 5-6 mm. long.   6. S. asper
            Sheaths and blades pilose especially the lower; panicle short.   6a. S. asper var. pilosus
          Plants and inflorescence slender.
            Panicles usually short, more or less included; spikelets 3-5 mm. long.   6b. S. asper var. hookeri
            Panicles usually long; spikelets 1.5-2 mm. long; grain reddish.   7. S. poiretii
        Lemma appressed-pubescent, about as long as or much shorter than the acuminate or acute palea; spikelets 4.5-6 mm. long; panicle short.   8. S. clandestinus
    PLANTS with long creeping rootstocks; plants usually about one foot tall; spikelets 2-2.5 mm. long.   9. S. virginicus
PANICLE OPEN, ITS BRANCHES SPREADING, AT LEAST AT MATURITY
  (in *S. cryptandrus* almost entirely included or included at the base).
  PLANTS ANNUAL. Plants 4-12′ tall; spikelets 1-1.5 mm. long; glumes subequal, much shorter than the lemma, often pilose.   10. S. microspermus
  PLANTS PERENNIAL.
    CULMS tufted, no rootstocks; the first glume half as long as the spikelets or less.
      Spikelets 4-5 mm. long; first glume awl-shaped, much narrower than the second; plants 1-3 feet tall.   11. S. heterolepis
      Spikelets 1.5-3 mm. long; glumes ovate to lanceolate.
        Panicle branches verticillate; second glume about as long as the spikelet.
          Spikelets 1.5 mm. long; plants usually less than 12′ tall.   12. S. argutus
          Spikelets 2-3 mm. long; plants 1-3 feet tall.   13. S. gracilis
        Panicle branches scattered, often alternate.
          Sheaths naked or sparingly pubescent at the throat. Spikelets short-pediceled; plants in large tussocks.
            Plants 1-3 feet tall; panicles pyramidal, spikelets comparatively few, 1.5-2 mm. long; glumes nerved.   14. S. airoides
            Plants 3-7 feet tall; panicles oblong, with numerous spikelets; spikelets 2-2.5 mm. long; glumes nerveless.   15. S. wrightii
          Sheaths with a conspicuous tuft of hairs at the throat.
            SHEATHS PUBESCENT; BLADES DIVERGENT; panicle usually less than 3′ long; plants commonly 8-12′ tall.   16. S. nealleyi
            SHEATHS ALMOST OR QUITE GLABROUS; blades not divergent; panicles usually 6-12′ long; plants mostly 2-3 feet tall.
              Panicles usually exserted, nearly oblong, somewhat nodding, the branches spreading, the lower about as long as the upper (panicles easily tangled with other panicles or other plants); spikelets 2 mm. long.   17. S. flexuosus
              Panicles usually mostly included in the sheaths, sometimes open above and spreading, the lower branches longer than the upper; spikelets 2-2.5 mm. long.   18. S. cryptandrus

Panicles exserted at maturity, oblong-pyramidal, the branches
naked below; blades lax, as much as 10 mm. wide; sheaths
ciliate, densely short-pilose at the collar; spikelets 1.5 mm
long.   19. S. buckleyi
CULMS from long running rootstocks; panicles pyramidal, usually erect, the
branches spreading, as much as 7′ long.
Plants 12-18′ tall, sheaths, at least the lower, papillose-hirsute; spikelets
2.5 mm. long, long-pediceled.   20. S. texanus
Plants 3 feet tall; sheaths pilose at the throat; blades 1.5-4 mm. wide;
spikelets 3-4 mm. long, short-pediceled.   21. S. tharpii

1. S. VAGINAEFLORUS (Torr.) Wood (văj-ĭ-nē-flō′rŭs); SOUTHERN
POVERTY-GRASS.

Culms 6-24′ tall, tufted, erect or widely spreading from a decumbent
base, slender, freely branching, exposed internodes often rough, nodes
often reddish, flattened on each side next to the blade; Blades the upper
6-25 mm. long, the lower 1.5-6′ long, mostly about 3′ long, 2 mm. wide or
less, involute toward the tip, erect or ascending, upper surface scabrous
near the base, sometimes sparsely papillose-pilose on the margins and
under surface near the base, the hairs rather stiff and 2-4 mm. long;
Sheaths much shorter than the internodes, wider than the blade, smooth
to slightly rough, sometimes papillose-pilose and pilose at the throat with
hairs 3-4 mm. long; Ligule a ring of minute hairs; Panicles spikelike, commonly less than 1.5′ long, numerous, wholly or partially included in the
usually inflated sheaths, or the terminal, exserted; Spikelets 3.5-4.5 mm.
long on short scabrous pedicels, those of the terminal panicle often larger
than those of the branches; Glumes subequal, the second slightly longer,
nearly as long as the lemma, acute, slightly scabrous on the keel; Lemma
equal to or slightly exceeded by the very acute palea, acuminate, scabrous
toward the apex, sparsely minutely-appressed-pubescent, especially on the
sides; Palea minutely-pubescent especially toward the apex.

In dry sterile soil, Arizona, Texas to Georgia, north to Maine and
South Dakota. (Hills north of San Antonio, Texas.) Summer-fall.

2. S. NEGLECTUS Nash (nĕg-lĕk′tŭs); SMALL RUSH-GRASS.

Culms 2-15′ tall, erect, often decumbent at the base, tufted, freely
branching, usually more slender than *S. vaginaeflorus;* Blades 1-3′ long,
the upper short, the lower longer, sometimes exceeding 3′, 2 mm. wide or
less, flat, attenuate into a slender point, scabrous on the upper surface,
usually sparsely-pilose at the base especially on the margins, sometimes
papillose; Sheaths much shorter than the internodes, inflated, often
sparsely papillose-pilose, especially on the margins; Ligule very short;
Panicles, the terminal 1-2′ long, commonly more or less included in the
upper sheath, the lateral inclosed or nearly so, commonly shorter;
Spikelets 2.5-3 mm. long, on short scabrous pedicels; Glumes acute, more
or less scabrous on the keel, subequal, the lower usually slightly shorter;
Lemma a little longer than the second glume and about equaling the acute
palea, acute, *glabrous.*

In dry sterile or sandy soil, Texas, Missouri, North Dakota, Virginia,
Washington and Arizona. (Austin, Texas.) Summer and fall.

3. S. GIGANTEUS Nash (jī-găn-tē′ŭs); *S. cryptandrus* var. *giganteus*
(Nash) Jones.

Culms 3-5 feet tall, stout, erect, tufted, glaucous, simple or freely
branching; Blades 4-16′ long, 4-11 mm. wide, the upper narrow and 4-5′
long, those of the sterile shoots as much as 22′ long, erect or ascending,

flat, or involute toward the tip, tough, margins rough; **Sheaths** longer than the internodes, the lower internodes short and crowded, throat and collar long-villous, the hairs silky; **Ligule** a ring of dense silky hairs about 1 mm. long; **Panicles** spikelike, included, or from slightly to more than half exserted, as much as 22′ long, the short upper blade often exceeding the panicle, densely-flowered, 5-10 mm. thick, the branches appressed, 1-3′ long, the lower distant about half their length, solitary or a few in a whorl; **Spikelets** 2.5-2.8 mm. long, on pedicels about one-third the length of the spikelet; **Glumes** acute, the first less than half the length of the spikelet, the second exceeding the acute **lemma** which slightly exceeds the acute palea.

Very sandy land or sand dunes, Texas to New Mexico. (Canadian River about 20 miles north of Amarillo; El Paso, Monahans, Texas.)

4. **S. CONTRACTUS** Hitchc. (kŏn-trăk′tŭs); *S. cryptandrus strictus* Scribn.; *S. strictus* (Scribn.) Merr.

Culms 1-4.5 feet commonly 3 feet tall, tufted, erect or spreading, sparingly branching; **Blades** 1.5-11′ long, the upper short and narrow, 1.5-5 mm. wide, mostly flat, slightly rough on the upper surface; **Sheaths**, the upper shorter than the internodes, densely long-villous at the throat and collar, often slightly ciliate; **Ligule** a ring of fine soft hairs nearly 1 mm. long; **Panicles** spikelike, mostly erect, as much as 25′ long, often half included at the base, about 5 mm. in diameter, pale-green and shiny when young, branches 2.5′ long or less, appressed, mostly solitary, branching and spikelet-bearing to the very base, rather densely-flowered; **Spikelets** shining, pale-green, about 2.3 mm. long, on scabrous pedicels usually less than half their length; **Glumes** acute, the first narrow and about half as long as the spikelet, the second slightly shorter than the acute lemma or the second glume; **Lemma** and acute palea about equal, all more or less minutely scabrous on the keels.

Foothills, along streams, western Texas to New Mexico, Nevada, and Colorado. (Foothills and valleys of the Davis Mountains, etc., west Texas.)

5. **S. PURPURASCENS** (Swartz) Hamilt. (pûr-pū-răs′ĕns).

Culms 2-2.5 feet tall, tufted, erect, simple; **Blades** 0.5-6′ long, 2-5 mm. wide, upper one very short, those of the sterile shoots longer, flat, soon involute, erect, slightly rough above, the lower blades appressed-ciliate with long hairs; **Sheaths** shorter than or about as long as the internodes, a few long hairs at the throat; **Ligule** a ciliate ring; **Panicle** slender, 4-5′ long, with branches in whorls of 5-6, less than a half inch long with a few crowded spikelets, green and turning brown with age; **Spikelets** 3-3.5 mm. long, long-pediceled, smooth and shining, light-green to brown or purple; **Glumes** acute, lanceolate, the first about half the length of the spikelet, the second slightly longer; **Lemma** nearly as long as the second glume, hyaline; **Palea** broad, a little shorter than its lemma.

It is found in scattered tufts in loose sandy land, mostly in the shade of oak trees.

Gulf region of the United States and Mexico and in the West Indies. (Leming, Texas.) Fall.

6. **S. ASPER** (Michx.) Kunth (ăs′pĕr); *S. longifolius* (Torr.) Wood; LONG-LEAVED RUSH-GRASS.

Culms 1.5-5 feet tall, erect, tufted, often rather stout and tall, sometimes rough below the nodes, simple or branching; **Blades** 1.5-24′ long,

1.5-5 mm. wide, the upper short and the basal very long, flat, or involute toward long attenuate tip, rough on the margins, hirsute on the upper surface at the base, often pilose above the base; **Sheaths** usually shorter than the internodes, the upper often inflated, more or less pilose or hirsute at the throat and at each end of the collar; **Ligule** a membranaceous line, minutely ciliate; **Panicles** 4-12′ long, terminal, or sometimes one or more axillary panicles, the terminal usually longer than the axillary, mostly 5-10 mm. thick, exserted or included at the base, or the axillary entirely included, in the larger plants the lower branches as much as 3.5′ long, mostly in ones to threes, somewhat distant, erect or sometimes ascending, scabrous; **Spikelets** 4.5-6 mm. long, on scabrous pedicels 1-4 mm. long, appressed; **Glumes** acute, scabrous on the keel, the first about 3 mm. long, the second about 4-4.5 mm. long; **Lemma** usually about 1-2 mm. longer than the second glume, slightly shorter, as long as or longer than the palea, scabrous on the keel; **Palea** scabrous toward the apex.

In dry soil, New England to North Dakota, south to Tennessee, Texas, New Mexico, Colorado and Utah.   (Hills north of San Antonio, Texas.) Summer-fall.

6a. S. ASPER var. PILOSUS (Vasey) Hitchc. (pī-lō′sŭs) ; *S. pilosus* Vasey.

Similar to the species, except: **Blades** and **Sheaths** more or less pilose; **Panicle** usually shorter.

Prairies and rocky hills, western Kansas to Texas. (Del Rio, Texas.)

6b. S. ASPER var. HOOKERI (Trin.) Vasey (hŏŏk′ẽr-ī) ; *S. drummondii* (Trin.) Vasey; *S. asper* var. *drummondii* (Trin.) Vasey; *S. attenuatus* Nash.

Culms 2-4 feet tall, solitary or in large dense tufts, erect or ascending from a decumbent base, slender, often scabrous below the nodes and panicle, simple or branching above; **Blades** 1-20′ rarely 36′ long, 2-5 mm. wide, involute at the long filiform points, scabrous on the margins and toward the tip, glabrous or hirsute (or papillose-hirsute) on the upper surface near the base, often with a few hairs above on the upper surface and beneath toward the base; **Sheaths,** the upper usually much shorter than the internodes, or the lower overlapping, the upper often inflated and more or less inclosing the panicle, glabrous, or pubescent at the throat, otherwise glabrous or sparsely papillose-hirsute; **Ligule** a very short, finely-ciliate membrane; **Panicles** 3-8′ rarely 13′ long, the terminal more or less included or short-exserted, the axillary when present commonly shorter than the terminal and included at the base or entirely included, usually slender, purplish, the slender branches erect or narrowly ascending, as much as 3.5′ long, the main axis, branches and pedicels scabrous, the pedicels shorter than the spikelets; **Spikelets** 3-5 mm. long, at maturity wedge-shaped, purple; **Glumes** acute or acuminate, scabrous on the keel, the first half to two-thirds as long as the lemma, the second two-thirds to three-fourths as long as the lemma, rarely as long as the lemma; **Lemma** narrow, acuminate, scabrous toward the apex; **Palea** usually slightly shorter than or sometimes as long as the lemma, acuminate, scabrous toward the apex.

In dry soil, plains or hills, Missouri, Mississippi, Louisiana, Texas and Oklahoma. Summer.

7. S. POIRETII (Roem. & Schult.) Hitchc. (poi-rĕt'ĭ-ī) ; *S. berteroanus* (Trin.) Hitchc. & Chase; *S. indicus* of earlier floras; *S. angustus* Buckl.; SMUT-GRASS.

Culms 1.5-3.5 feet tall, tufted, rather slender, erect, glabrous and smooth throughout except where noted, the filiform leaves at the base often half as long as the plant; **Blades** 6-21' long, 1.5-3 mm. wide, flat at the base, or involute toward the long-attenuate filiform tip, especially those at the base and sterile shoots; **Sheaths** longer than the internodes, the junction with the blades very obscure, often with a very small tuft of hairs at the throat; **Ligule** a line of very short hairs; **Panicle** 6-14' long, included at the base or long exserted, subcylindric, 3-6 mm. thick, pale-green, *or dark when affected by a black fungus*, the branches commonly less than an inch long, erect or appressed, the spikelets crowded on one side of the short branches or branchlets; **Spikelets** 1.5-2 mm. long, pale-green, on short pedicels less than the length of the spikelets; **Glumes** unequal, minutely fringed, nerveless or the second 1-nerved, thin, the first about one-third the length of the spikelet, the second about two-thirds the length of the spikelet; **Lemma** slightly longer than the broad, obtuse **Palea**, both thin; **Caryposis** soon falling from the lemma and palea, reddish, often adhering to the panicle by the viscid pericarp, a ripe panicle often dotted with the small dark reddish grains.

In meadows and waste places, Texas to Florida, north to Virginia and Missouri, west to California. (Bay City, Texas.) Summer-fall.

8. S. CLANDESTINUS (Spreng.) Hitchc. (klăn-dĕs-tī'nŭs) ; *S. canovirens* Nash.

Culms 1-4.5 feet tall, tufted, erect, simple, leafy, stout to slender; **Blades** 3-15' long, 2-4 mm. wide, attenuate into a long slender involute tip, upper surface and the margins scabrous, often somewhat hairy at the base on the upper surface; **Sheaths** shorter than the internodes, the lower sometimes pilose and papillose; **Ligule** a mere ring, less than 0.5 mm. long; **Panicle** 2-5' long, often included at the base, linear, strict, its branches 1-2' long, appressed; **Spikelets** 4.5-8 mm. long; **Glumes** keeled, unequal, acute, the first about half as long as the acute lemma, the second about one-third longer than the first; **Lemma** acuminate, longer than the second glume, appressed-pubescent toward the base; **Palea** longer than the lemma, acuminate, sometimes long-acuminate (as much as 10 mm. long), appressed-pubescent toward the base.

In dry, mostly sandy soil, Texas to Florida and Missouri to Connecticut. Summer and fall.

9. S. VIRGINICUS (L.) Kunth (vẽr-jĭn'ĭ-kŭs) ; SEA-SHORE RUSH-GRASS.

Culms 6-24' usually 6-12' tall, simple or freely branching, erect, mostly decumbent at base, from extensively creeping rootstocks; **Blades** usually 1-4' sometimes as much as 8' long, 4 mm. or less wide at the base, distichous, acuminate into a long point, involute on the margins, after drying convolute, scabrous above or sparingly hairy, rather rigid; **Sheaths**, upper shorter than the internodes, lower short, crowded, overlapping, sometimes pilose on margins and at throat; **Ligule** a ring of very short hairs; **Panicles** 1-3' long, 4-10 mm. thick, dense and spikelike, light-colored or purplish, the branches short and strict; **Spikelet** about 3 mm. (2-4) long; **Glumes** acute, the first about 2 mm. long, the second about 3 mm. long; **Lemma** slightly shorter than the second glume, acute; **Palea** about equal to its lemma, obtuse.

Salt marshes or sandy soil; Mexico, Texas, and along coast to Florida and Virginia. (Corpus Christi, Texas.) Spring and summer.

10. S. MICROSPERMUS (Lag.) Hitchc. (mī-krō-spēr'mŭs) ; *S. confusus* Vasey; *S. minutissimus* (Steud.) Hitchc.; VASEY'S DROP-SEED.

Culms mostly 4-10' rarely 15' tall, tufted, slender, freely branching below, often growing in colonies or large patches; **Blades** 0.6-2' long, 1.5 mm. wide or less, usually only a few at or near the base of the plant, flat or conduplicate, more or less rough on the margins and upper surface; **Sheaths** shorter or longer than the internodes, loose, smooth or slightly scabrous; **Ligule** membranaceous, thin, 1.2-2 mm. long; **Panicles** 1-8' rarely 10' long, usually more than two-thirds sometimes five-sixths the length of the plant, commonly less than 2' wide, those of the branches usually much shorter, ovate or oblong, often included at the base, open, purplish, loosely-flowered, the capillary branches usually less than 2' long, commonly about equal in length, ascending to spreading, solitary or several to a node, naked at the base, the short branchlets ascending or spreading with a few spikelets at their extremities, the capillary, scabrous, divergent pedicels enlarged at the apex, 5-10 mm. long; **Spikelets** 1-1.5 mm. long, purplish ; **Glumes** subequal, half to four-fifths as long as the spikelet, acute or obtuse, ovate, glabrous or hispidulous and minutely ciliate-fringed ; **Lemma** broad, obtuse, glabrous or slightly scabrous or pubescent toward the apex ; **Palea** nearly equal to and as broad as the lemma, obtuse.

In damp meadows or hillsides, western Texas to Mexico and north to Nebraska, Colorado and Montana. (Below boulders near Baptist Encampment grounds, about 12 miles west of Alpine on Marfa Road.) Summer and fall.

11. S. HETEROLEPIS A. Gray (hĕt-ēr-ŏl'ē-pĭs).

Culms 12-28' tall, densely-tufted, stout, erect, simple; **Blades** 8-20' long, the basal blades about three-fourths as long as the culm, the upper shorter, 2 mm. wide or less, involute-setaceous, the margins and upper part of the midrib rough ; **Sheaths** longer than the internodes, the lower short and the upper long and clinging to the culm, somewhat pilose at the throat, or the lower sparsely pilose at the base ; **Ligule** a ring of short hairs ; **Panicle** long-exserted, 3-10' long, narrowly pyramidal, the branches 1.5-3.5' long, erect or ascending, bearing the dark-colored spikelets toward their tips; **Spikelets** 4-5.5 mm. long; **Glumes**, the first awl-shaped, 2-3 mm. long, about half as long as the broader second, the second usually slightly exceeding the lemma, often awn-pointed ; **Lemma** shorter than or as long as the second glume, obtuse or acute ; **Palea** about equal to the lemma.

In dry soil, eastern Texas to Missouri, Pennsylvania to Connecticut. Summer and fall.

12. S. ARGUTUS (Nees) Kunth (är-gū'tŭs) ; POINTED DROPSEED-GRASS.

Culms 8-18' tall, densely-tufted, erect or ascending from a decumbent base, branching; **Blades** 1-5' usually about 3' long, the upper short, 2-6 mm. wide, flat, scabrous, the white margins scabrous, ciliate near the base with long hairs, a few long hairs on upper surface near base, otherwise glabrous ; **Sheaths** shorter than the internodes; **Ligule** a ring of hairs less than 1 mm. long; **Panicle** exserted, 2-6' commonly 2-3' long, narrowly-pyramidal or ovate, branches 1.5' or less long, verticillate, as many as eight branches at lower node, fewer above, at first appressed, finally widely spreading, flower-bearing on the upper two-thirds; **Spikelets** lead-color, shining, 1.5-1.8 mm. long; **Glumes** the first obtuse, about 0.4 mm. long, the **Second** and **Lemma** subequal, acute.

Dry sandy or gravelly soil, Mexico through Texas to Louisiana and north to Kansas and Colorado. Spring.

13. S. GRACILIS (Trin.) Merr. (grăs′ĭ-lĭs) ; *S. junceus* (Michx.) Kunth; PURPLE DROPSEED-GRASS.

Culms 1-3 feet tall, tufted, erect, simple, slender; **Blades** 1-12′ long, the upper short, the lower and those of the sterile shoots long, sometimes more than 18′, 2-4 mm. wide, flat or folded, erect, the upper surface rough, those of the sterile shoots numerous, narrow, folded; **Sheaths** about as long as, shorter or longer than the internodes; **Ligule** a ring of very short hairs; **Panicle** bronze-brown, exserted, or sometimes included below, 5-9′ long, oblong or oblong-lanceolate, open, branches single and scattered or mostly in whorls, ascending, the lower mostly 1-1.5′ long, the upper shorter, flowering on the upper three-fourths, axis and branches smooth, the pedicels short, much less than the length of the spikelet; **Spikelets** 2.5-3 mm. long, lanceolate, acute, pale-green, purple or reddish-brown; **Glumes** acute, glabrous, the first 1-nerved, 1.5-2 mm. long, varies somewhat, usually about half the length of the spikelet, the second 1-3-nerved, as long as or longer than the lemma; **Lemma** about 2.5 mm. long, slightly shorter than the second glume, acute, similar to the second glume; **Palea** equal to or slightly shorter than the lemma, obtuse.

Dry sandy soil, especially pine barrens of the coastal plain, Texas to Florida, north to Virginia. (In oak woods, Leming, Texas.) Fall.

14. S. AIROIDES (Torr.) Torr. (â-roi′dēz) ; *Alkali saccaton.*

Culms 2-3 feet tall, in tough clumps, erect, simple; **Blades** upper 2-5′, the middle and lower as long as 18′, attenuate into a long slender involute point, 1-3 mm. wide at the base, margins, upper surface and below toward the apex scabrous, few to many hairs at the base on upper surface; **Sheaths** shorter than the internodes, sparsely ciliate or villous at the throat; **Ligule** membranaceous, very short; **Panicle** loosely-flowered, pyramidal, 5-13′ long, exserted or partly included at the base, the branches alternate or somewhat whorled, especially the middle and upper, the lower 3-7′ long, at length spreading, branches and branchlets naked at the base; **Spikelets** 1.5-2 mm. (2-2.5) long, on short pedicels, the lateral about as long as the spikelet; **Glumes** acute, glabrous, nerveless, the first about one-half as long as the second, the second about as long as the lemma; **Lemma** slightly longer than the palea, broadly oval.

Meadows and valleys, especially in alkaline soil, coast of Texas, through west Texas, west and north through New Mexico to Colorado and California. Summer and fall.

15. S. WRIGHTII Munro (rīt′ĭ-ī) ; BUNCH-GRASS OR SACCATON.

Culms usually 2.5-4 feet sometimes as much as 8 feet tall, usually in rather large tufts or bunches, erect or spreading, simple, terete; **Blades** 15-44′ long, upper shorter, 4-8 mm. wide, flat, narrowed toward the base, soon involute, villous above at the base, margins scabrous and toward the apex; **Sheaths** longer than the internodes, closed, sometimes ciliate at the throat; **Ligule** membranaceous, truncate, ciliate; **Panicle** exserted, or included at the base, open, usually 8-15′ sometimes 30′ long, oblong-pyramidal, erect, branches commonly in ones, twos and threes, alternate, ascending or spreading, usually 2-4′ sometimes even 7′ long, spikelets numerous, spikelet-bearing nearly to the base, branchlets 1-2′ or less long; **Spikelets** 2-2.5 mm. long, on short pedicels, usually pale; **Glumes** acute, scarious, the first about one-half as long as the spikelet, the second about three-fourths as long as the spikelet, abruptly narrowed at the apex; **Lemma** and **Palea** subequal, exceeding the glumes.

In adobe soil, along streams or on flats. Rio Grande Valley north to west Texas through New Mexico to Arizona. Summer and fall.

16. S. NEALLEYI Vasey (nē′lē-ī).

Culms 6-12′ rarely 18′ tall, tufted, erect, slender, the larger plants branching, from strong roots; **Blades** 0.5-3.5′ mostly 1-2′ long, about 1 mm. wide, diverging at almost right angles to the culm, rigid, pungent-pointed, involute or flat at the base, slightly scabrous on upper surface and margins; **Sheaths** usually longer than the internodes, pubescent or the upper scabrous, villous at the throat and collar; **Ligule** a ciliate ring less than 0.5 mm. long; **Panicles** less than 3′ long, purple, erect, short-exserted, or partly included at the base, the axillary shorter and mostly included, ovate or linear, the capillary branches ascending, 1′ long or less, commonly solitary, bearing a few spikelets on the outer two-thirds; **Spikelets** purple, about 1.5 mm. long, on scabrous pedicels about as long as or shorter than the spikelets; **Glumes** scabrous on the keels, acute, the first narrow, about half as long as the lemma, the second nearly or about as long as the lemma, lanceolate; **Lemma** lanceolate, acute, scabrous on the keel, equaled by the acute palea.

Dry ground, with large amount of gypsum, Texas to New Mexico and Colorado. (Low prairies west of Monahans, Texas.) Fall.

17. S. FLEXUOSUS (Thurb.) Rydb. (flĕks-ū-ō′sŭs) ; *S. cryptandrus* var. *flexuosus* Thurb.

Culms 2-4 feet tall, tufted, erect or spreading, freely branching, leafy ; **Blades**, the uppermost and those of the branches mostly 3-5′ long and 3-5 mm. wide, the others about a foot long, 4-8 mm. wide, flat, thin, erect or ascending; **Sheaths** about as long as the internodes, the upper inflated and very long, tufts of hairs at the throat and collar; **Ligule** a ring of hairs about 1 mm. long; **Panicle** oblong or narrowly pyramidal, exserted or partly included at the base, the whole panicle as much as 30′ usually 8-15′ long, flexuous, purple, the branches toward the apex 1-3′ long, often spreading or even reflexed, the lower branches of the exposed portion 2-4′ long, usually ascending, making the panicle appear almost oblong, the capillary branches flexuous, mostly solitary, the lowermost distant, naked at the base or hidden in the sheath, branching and spikelet-bearing to the base and as much as 6′ long, the spikelets on short divergent branchlets of short divergent secondary branches, the scabrous capillary pedicels shorter than the spikelet (panicles easily entangled with other panicles or culms); **Spikelets** about 2 mm. long, purple, lanceolate; **Glumes** acute, narrowly lanceolate, very minutely scabrous on the keel, the first nearly half as long as the spikelet, the second about as long as the acute lemma and palea or slightly longer; **Lemma** slightly scabrous on the keel.

Sand dunes or very sandy land, western Texas to Mexico and Arizona. (El Paso and Monahans, Texas.)

18. S. CRYPTANDRUS (Torr.) A. Gray (krĭp-tăn′drŭs).

Culms 1.5-3.5 feet tall, tufted, erect or somewhat spreading, simple or branching below; **Blades** 3-12′ long, the upper short, 3-6 mm. wide, flat, long-acuminate, rough above; **Sheaths,** the lower shorter than the internodes, the upper much longer, inclosing the base of the panicle, margins long-ciliate toward the summit, with a conspicuous tuft or tufts of hairs at the collar; **Ligule** a ring of very short hairs; **Panicles** lead-colored or purplish, 5-14′ long, terminal or sometimes axillary, usually open but included at the base, or sometimes almost the entire panicle included (some 14′ long all included except the tip), the slender branches scattered and single, naked at the base, usually less than 3′ long, the short-pediceled spikelets on short branchlets; **Spikelets** light-green, purplish or lead-color, 2-2.5 mm. long, those hidden in sheaths sometimes *cleistogamous,* usually smaller; **Glumes** unequal, acute, scabrous on the keel, the first one-third to half as long as the lemma, the second broader and nearly equal to the lemma; **Lemma** usually slightly longer than the palea, acute.

The photograph shows the open panicle, the almost included panicle, and one about 14′ long taken from the sheath.

Sandy soil, New England to Montana, south to Texas and Mexico. Spring to fall.

19. S. BUCKLEYI Vasey (bŭk′lē-ī).

Culms 1-4 feet tall, loosely to densely tufted, erect, leafy at the base, rather slender, flattened, especially toward the base; **Blades** 3-19′ long, 3-10 mm. wide, the basal longer and wider, narrowed and conduplicate toward the base, flat above, lax, attenuate, smooth or rough on the margins and upper surface, sparsely-pubescent on the upper surface, especially toward the base; **Sheaths,** the upper shorter than the internodes, the lower crowded and loose, flattened, densely short-pubescent on the collar and at the throat, ciliate on the margins; **Ligule** very short, minutely ciliate; **Panicles** purple or finally pale, 3-18′ commonly 6-12′ long, finally exserted, mostly erect, oblong or oblong-pyramidal, rather lax, the almost capillary branches 2-5′ long, solitary and scattered or sometimes verticillate, ascending or finally spreading, sometimes reflexed, scabrous, bearing short-pedicellate spikelets on the short branchlets on the upper two-thirds, the scabrous pedicels 0.5-1.5 mm. long, the subdivisions sometimes recurved; **Spikelets** purple, about 1.5 mm. long, obovate at maturity; **Glumes** acute, scabrous on the keel, the first about 0.7 mm. long, the second half again or nearly twice as long as the first; **Lemma** longer than the second glume and equaling or exceeding the broader palea, acuminate, scabrous at or near the apex; **Grain** amber-colored, elliptic, about 0.9 mm. long and 0.7 mm. wide, somewhat flattened.

Open ground or open woods, low lands, southern Texas to Mexico. (Pete Heinz farm, six miles from Brownsville on Los Fresnos Road.) Fall.

20. S. TEXANUS Vasey (tĕks-ā′nŭs) ; Texas Dropseed.

Culms 1-2 feet tall, erect or spreading, tufted, rigid, branching, rather slender from long rootstocks; **Blades** 1-6′ long, 2-4 mm. wide, margins and upper surface very scabrous, often a few long hairs above near the base, erect, firm; **Sheaths** longer than the internodes, some rough, the lower papillose-hirsute, sometimes sparsely so, often pilose at the throat; **Ligule** a ring of short hairs; **Panicle** 4-12′ long, about half as long as the culm, usually included at the base, finally diffuse, pyramidal, branches divergent, rigid, slender, 2-7′ long, naked below, mostly alternate and single on a scabrous axis, branchlets usually 1-2′ long, capillary with one or a few long pediceled spikelets on the outer half; **Spikelets** 2.25-2.5 mm. long, linear-lanceolate; **Glumes,** the first about 1 mm. long, the second as long as or a little shorter than the spikelet, scabrous on the nerve; **Lemma** as long as the spikelet, scabrous on the one-nerve; **Palea** nearly as long as its lemma.

West Texas and New Mexico to Colorado, Oklahoma and Kansas. Summer.

21. S. THARPII Hitchc. (thärp′ĭ-ī).

Culms 1-3 feet tall, erect, from horizontal rootstocks; **Blades** 8-12′ long, 1-4 mm. wide, flat at the base, attenuate into a long slender involute tip, ciliate at the base, rough above; **Sheaths** longer than the internodes, long-villous at the throat; **Ligule** very short, minutely ciliate; **Panicle** finally exserted, 15′ long more or less, pyramidal, erect, the axis smooth, the branches stiffly ascending or spreading, 3-7′ long, mostly in ones to threes, usually naked on the lower half, spikelet-bearing on the upper portion of the short branchlets, the branchlets usually less than 1.5′ long; **Spikelets** 3-4 mm. long, appressed, on pedicels shorter than the spikelet; **Glumes** unequal, acute, the first about 1.5 mm. long, the second 3 mm. long or less; **Lemma** slightly exceeding the second glume; **Palea** about 2 mm. long, obtuse.

Very sandy soil, Padre Island, southern Texas. (Collected by B. C. Tharp.)   Fall.

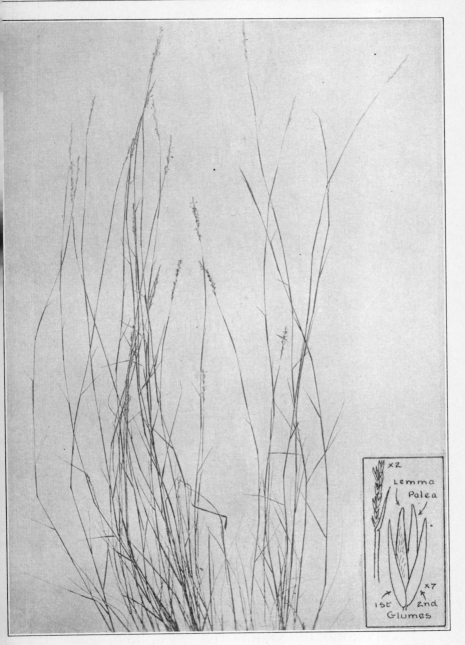

SPOROBOLUS VAGINAEFLORUS; Southern Poverty-grass

SPOROBOLUS NEGLECTUS; SMALL RUSH-GRASS

SPOROBOLUS GIGANTEUS

Lemma
Palea
x7
1st   2nd
Glumes

SPOROBOLUS CONTRACTUS

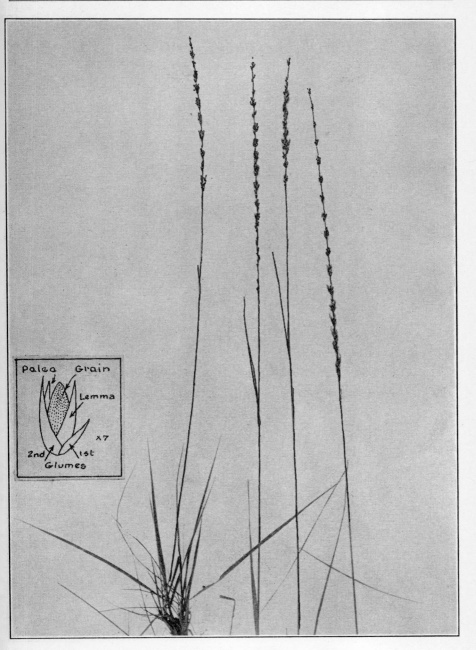

SPOROBOLUS PURPURASCENS

Sporobolus
asper
var. pilosus

Lemma
Palea
×7
1st   2nd
Glumes

SPOROBOLUS ASPER

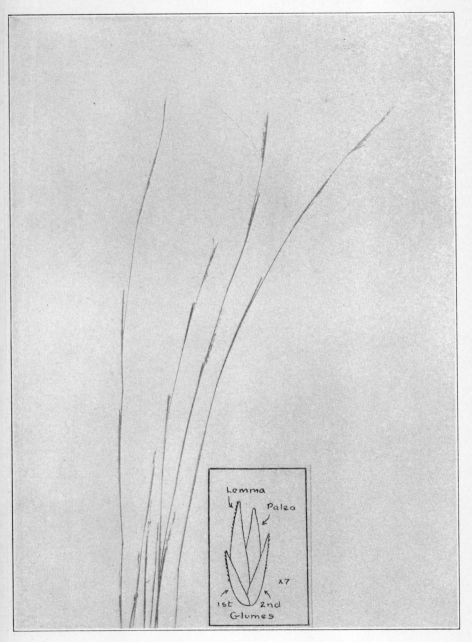

SPOROBOLUS ASPER var. HOOKERI

SPOROBOLUS POIRETII; Smut-grass

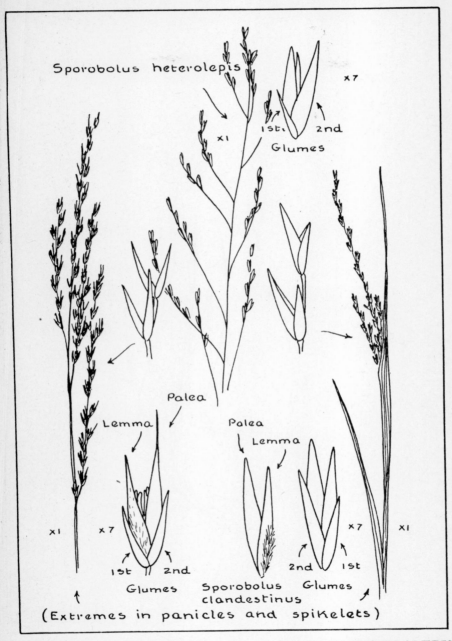

Sporobolus heterolepis

×7

×1

1st. 2nd
Glumes

Palea

Lemma

×1   ×7

1st   2nd
Glumes

Palea

Lemma

×7   ×1

2nd   1st
Sporobolus   Glumes
clandestinus

(Extremes in panicles and spikelets)

SPOROBOLUS CLANDESTINUS AND SPOROBOLUS HETEROLEPIS

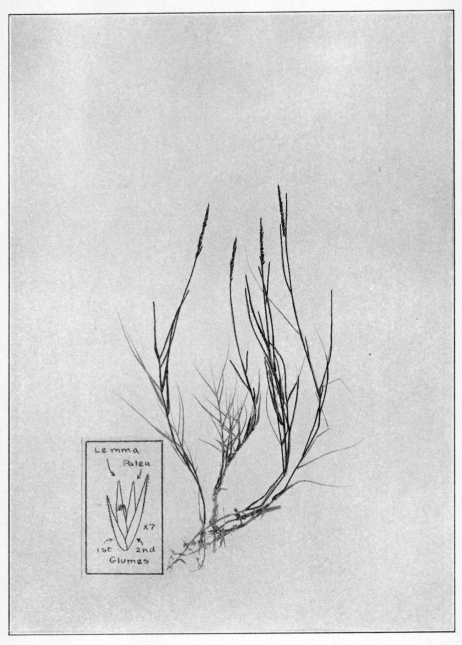

SPOROBOLUS VIRGINICUS; Sea-shore Rush-grass

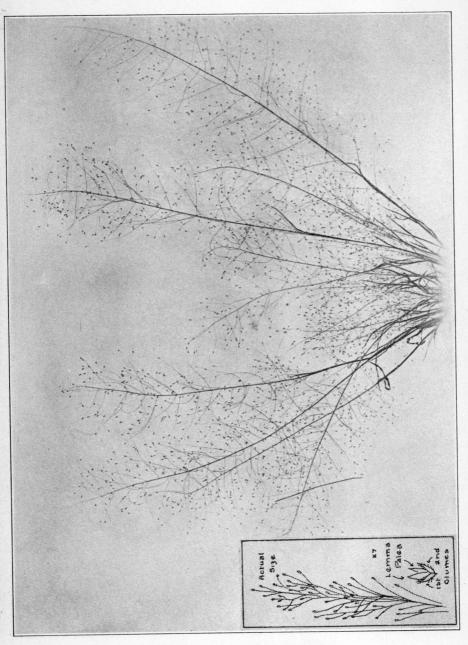

Actual size

K7
Lemma
& Palea

1st and
Glumes

SPOROBOLUS MICROSPERMUS

SPOROBOLUS ARGUTUS; POINTED DROPSEED

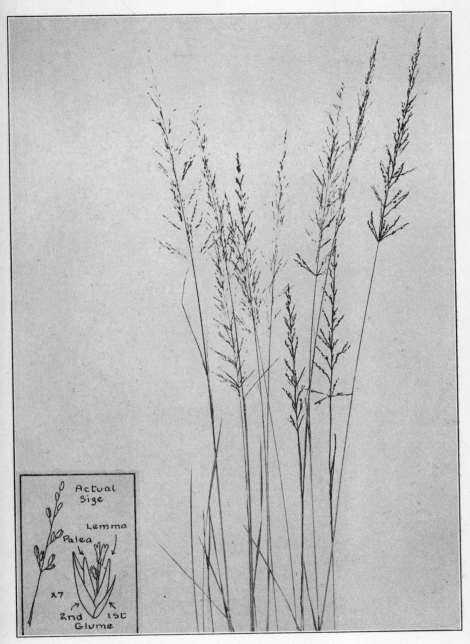

Actual Size

Lemma

Palea

X7

2nd   1st
Glume

SPOROBOLUS GRACILIS; Purple Dropseed

SPOROBOLUS AIROIDES; Alkali Saccaton

SPOROBOLUS WRIGHTII; Bunch-grass or Saccaton

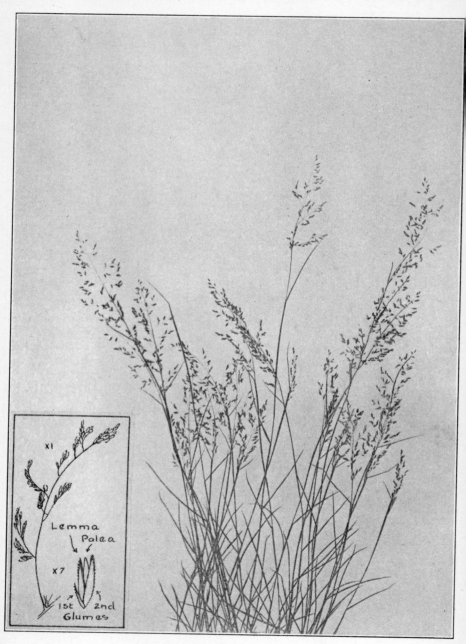

SPOROBOLUS NEALLEYI

Branch
X1

Lemma
Palea

X7

1st 2nd
Glumes

SPOROBOLUS FLEXUOSUS

Tufts of hair at
apex of sheath.

Lemma   Palea

1st   2nd
Glume

SPOROBOLUS CRYPTANDRUS

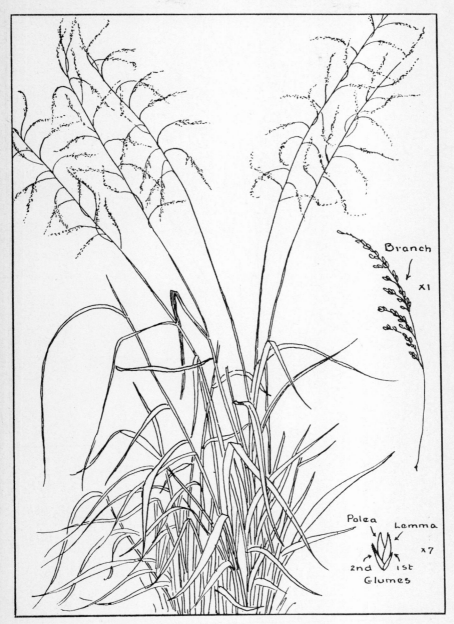

SPOROBOLUS BUCKLEYI

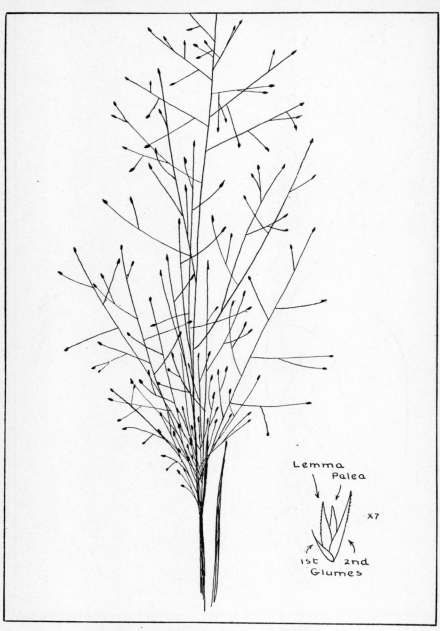

SPOROBOLUS TEXANUS; Texas Dropseed

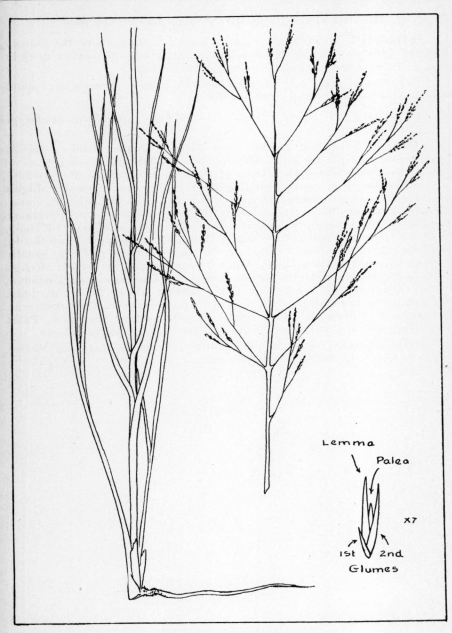

SPOROBOLUS THARPII

48. BLEPHARONEURON Nash (blĕf-à-rō-nū'rŏn)

Spikelets 1-flowered, the rachilla disarticulating above the glumes; **Glumes** subequal, rather broad; **Lemma** 3-nerved, the nerves densely-pilose; **Palea** densely-pilose between the two nerves.

A *perennial* grass with an open, narrow panicle. Species one; southwestern United States and northern Mexico.

B. TRICHOLEPIS (Torr.) Nash (trī-kŏl'ē-pĭs); *Sporobolus tricholepis* (Torr.) Coult.

Culms 1-2 feet tall, tufted, erect, usually simple, slender, slightly compressed, smooth, the culm often purplish; **Blades** 1.5-4' long, those of the sterile shoots longer than those of the blades, 1-2 mm. wide, involute, erect; **Sheaths** close, nearly equaling or exceeding the internodes; **Ligule** membranaceous, truncate, lacerate, decurrent, less than 1 mm. long; **Panicle** dark-purplish to lead-colored, 3-6' long, exserted, ovate, pyramidal to oblong, open, erect, branches mostly alternate, capillary, 1-2' long, spreading, divided and rather loosely-flowered on the upper two-thirds; **Spikelets** 2.5-3 mm. long, lanceolate, on long capillary pedicels, usually 2-3 times as long as the spikelet; **Glumes** nearly equal, the second often as long as the lemma, acute or obtuse, thin, lanceolate, broad, dark-colored, nearly equaling the lemma, 1-nerved; **Lemma** about 2.5-3 mm. long, lanceolate, acute or obtuse, 3-nerved with the midnerve often excurrent, densely-white-pubescent on the nerves except toward the apex; **Palea** lanceolate, acute, about as long as the lemma, more or less pubescent.

Open or rocky soil, at middle altitudes, Texas and northern Mexico, north to Colorado and Utah. Spring-fall.

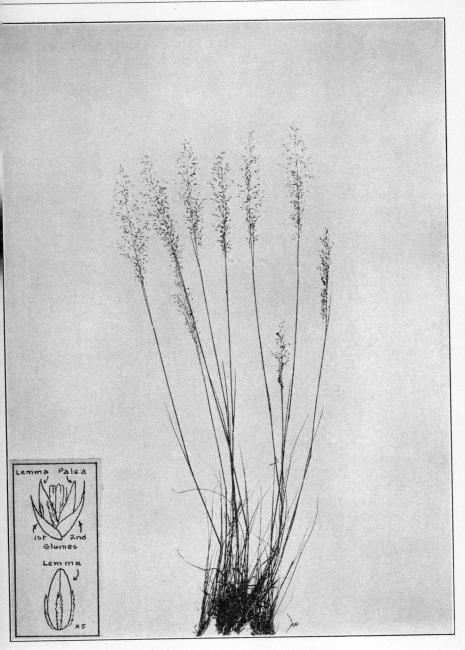

BLEPHARONEURON TRICHOLEPIS

49.   ORYZOPSIS Michx.   (ôr-ĭ-zŏp'sĭs)

Spikelets 1-flowered, disarticulating above the glumes; **Glumes** about equal, obtuse or acuminate; **Lemma** indurate, usually about as long as the glumes, broad, oval or oblong, nearly terete, usually pubescent, with a short, blunt, oblique callus, and a short, deciduous, sometimes bent and twisted awn; **Palea** inclosed by the edges of the lemma.

Perennial, mostly low grasses, with flat or often involute blades and terminal narrow or open panicles.   Species about 20, in the north temperate regions of both hemispheres; 13 species in the United States, one in Texas.

Oryzopsis and *Stipa* are closely related, both with single awns, but the former has broad lemmas and short deciduous scarcely-twisted awns.

O. hymenoides, known as Indian mountain rice, the only species found in Texas, a densely-tufted plant, is conspicuous for its pale diffuse panicle of long pediceled spikelets, the glumes with spreading tips and the lemmas with copious long silky hairs.   It seems to thrive in sandy or rocky soil especially in waste places along roads and railways.

1.   O. HYMENOIDES (Roem. & Schult.) Ricker (hī-měn-oi'dēz) ; *O. mem branacea* (Pursh) Vasey; *Eriocoma cuspidata* Nutt.; INDIAN MOUNTAIN RICE, SILKY-GRASS.

Culms 1-2 feet tall, tufted, erect, rigid, simple except the panicles from the one to three upper sheaths; **Blades** 6-15' long, 2 mm. or less wide, flat or mostly involute, stiff, smooth or somewhat scabrous above, the numerous blades of the sterile shoots long; **Sheaths**, the upper shorter than the internodes, overlapping below, smooth or slightly rough; **Ligule** 3-4 mm. long, membranaceous; **Panicle** 6-12' long, 1-3 panicles from the upper sheaths, and partly included by them, at first green finally pale, diffuse, the many branches widely and stiffly spreading, mostly 2-4' long, the ultimate branches flexuous, the long-pediceled spikelets single at the end of the dichotomous branchlets, all divaricately spreading; **Spikelets** 6-8 mm. long, becoming papery; **Glumes** 3-5-nerved, 6-8 mm. long, broadened below, long-acuminate, the tips somewhat spreading, abruptly pointed, sparsely-minutely-pubescent, thin and papery; **Lemma** exclusive of awn 2.5-3 mm. long, densely-villous with erect hairs about twice its own length; **Awn** about 4-6 mm. long, deciduous.

Sandy land or rocky banks, Texas and Mexico, Kansas, Iowa, Colorado, New Mexico, California and Washington.   Spring.

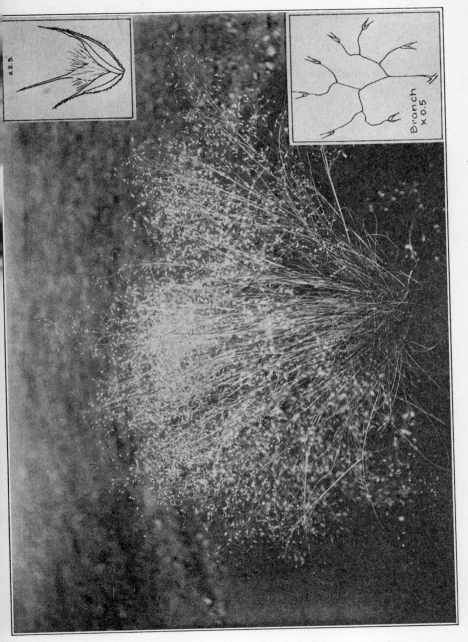

x 2.5

Branch
x 0.5

ORYZOPSIS HYMENOIDES, INDIAN MOUNTAIN RICE, SILKY-GRASS

50.   PIPTOCHAETIUM Presl   (pĭp-tō-kē'tĭ-ŭm)

Spikelets 1-flowered, disarticulating above the glume, the callus of the floret short, acutish, usually bearded; **Glumes** short, equal, broad, ovate, convex on the back, thin, abruptly acuminate; **Fruit** brown or dark-gray, coriaceous, obovate, shorter than the glumes, glabrous or hispid above the callus, often minutely striate, sometimes tuberculate near the summit, the **Lemma** turgid, usually somewhat compressed and keeled on the back, gibbous near the summit back of the awn, the edges not meeting but showing the sulcus of the palea, the summit sometimes expanded into a crown; **Awn** persistent, curved, flexuous or geniculate, often somewhat twisted below; **Palea** narrow, indurate except toward the margins, central keel consisting of two nerves and a narrow channel or sulcus between, the apex of the keel projecting above the summit of the lemmas as a minute point. *Tufted perennials* with narrow usually involute blades and rather narrow few-flowered panicles.

2.   P. FIMBRIATUM (H. B. K.)   Hitchc.   (fĭm-brĭ-ā'tŭm) ; *Oryzopsis fimbriata* (H. B. K.) Hemsl.; *Stipa fimbriata* H. B. K.

Culms 1.2-5 feet tall, tufted, slender, erect, with numerous filiform blades at the base; **Blades**, the upper 2-4' long, flat at the base, about 1 mm. wide, the lower and basal longer, often half as long as the culm, 8-12-16' long or more, involute-setaceous, about 0.5 mm. in diameter, erect or curved; **Sheaths**, upper shorter than the internodes, smooth or slightly rough; **Ligule** membranaceous, 2-3 mm. long, obtuse, wider than the blade; **Panicles** slightly exserted, 4-6' long, open, lax, loose, erect or nodding, the filiform branches 1-3' long, mostly in twos or threes, rather remote, spreading or the lower ones reflexed, bearing a few scattered spikelets near their extremities; **Spikelets** 4-5 mm. long, obovate; **Glumes** slightly exceeding the lemma, about 5 mm. long, the second slightly shorter and narrower, abruptly pointed, 3-5-nerved, papery; **Lemma** 3-4 mm. long, nearly oval or orbicular, obscurely 5-nerved, usually acute at both ends, the dark lemma covered with tawny hairs, bearing a slightly scabrous, flexuous, slender, irregularly twisted **awn** 10-16 mm. long.

Mountains western Texas to California.   (About 12 miles west of Alpine, Texas.)   Fall.

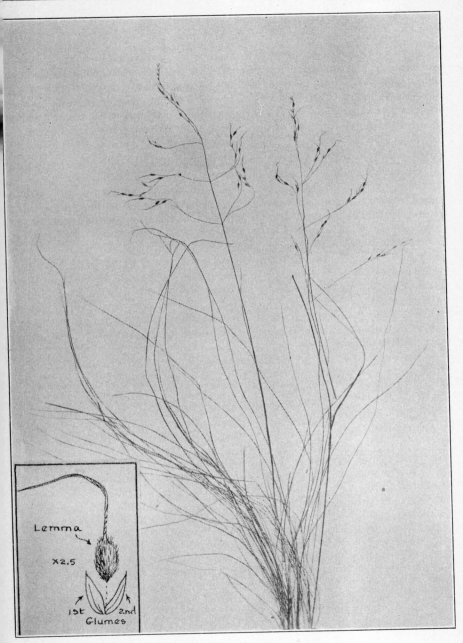

Lemma

×2.5

1st · 2nd
Glumes

PIPTOCHAETIUM FIMBRIATUM

51. STIPA L. (stī′på)

(The Spear-grasses)

Spikelets 1-flowered, disarticulating above the glumes, the articulation oblique leaving a bearded, sharp-pointed callus attached to the base of the floret; **Glumes** membranaceous, often papery, acute, acuminate or even aristate, usually long and narrow; **Lemma** narrow, terete, firm or indurate, strongly convolute, terminating in a usually bent and twisted prominent, persistent awn; **Palea** inclosed in the convolute lemma.

Our species of *Stipa* are *perennials*, but there are a few annuals in Europe and elsewhere. They are tufted, with usually convolute blades and narrow or sometimes open panicles.

The species are known as "spear-grasses", "porcupine-grasses" or "needle-grasses", and are usually found on the drier plains and hills extending into the mountains. It seems that the long-awned grasses are mostly confined to dry land. In America the genus extends from Canada through the western plains and mountains to Chile.

Stipa is distinguished from other allied genera by a simple persistent awn, twisted and bent, several-to-many-times as long as the slender fruit, there being a line of demarcation between the awn and lemma, and a barbed pubescent callus at the base of the fruit. The closely related *Aristida* has a three-awned usually unarticulate lemma, the lateral awns in some species wanting or obsolete, and *Oryzopsis* has broad lemmas and short, deciduous, scarcely twisted single awns.

The awns of *Stipa* are usually hygroscopic; the alternate twisting and untwisting with varying amounts of moisture together with the strongly barbed callus aid in burying the fruit.

S. comata, S. leucotricha, and other species with robust sharp-pointed fruits, may become injurious to stock.

S. robusta, called sleepy-grass, is said to produce narcotic effects upon grazing animals, especially horses.

Cleistogenes have been found in the lower sheaths of *S. leucotricha,* which are shown by the illustrations accompanying the photograph. They have been found also in a few other species.

We have seven species with more or less open panicles: *S. neomexicana* with a plumose or feathery awn 4-8′ long; *S. tenuissima* with the lemma only 3 mm. long, lacking long hairs, and a very slender awn 2-3′ long; *S. eminens* with a villous lemma 5-7 mm. long, the awn 1-2′ long; *S. avenacea,* mostly in the eastern United States, with an awn 1.5-2.5′ long; *S. comata,* mostly a middle western plant with an awn 4-5′ long; *S. pringlei,* a west Texas plant, with an awn 20-30 mm. long; *S. leucotricha,* a Texas-Mexico plant, with a ciliate crown or neck, and a pit in the neck, the awn 2.5-4′ long. The first three plants are mainly confined to the rocky hills and mountains from Mexico through Texas north to Colorado and adjoining states.

All of our other species have narrow panicles. *S. robusta,* with the hairs less copious on the lemma, less than 2 mm. long at the summit, is a robust plant usually 3-5 feet tall, with very long compact panicles, the sheaths being villous at the throat; *S. columbiana,* with the appressed hairs on the lemma rather short, not longer at the apex, has sheaths naked at the throat; *S. lobata,* a rare plant of the Chisos and Guadalupe Mountains, has a 2-lobed lemma.

TERMINAL SEGMENT OF AWN CONSPICUOUSLY PLUMOSE, flexuous, 3-5′ long; glumes 20 mm. long or more. 1. S. neomexicana
TERMINAL SEGMENT OF AWN NOT PLUMOSE; panicles open, loose.
SUMMIT OF mature lemma slightly hispidulous, but lacking long hairs; lemma 2-3 mm. long, the capillary awn 2′ long. 2. S. tenuissima
SUMMIT OF mature lemma with a ciliate crown or neck 0.5-1 mm. long; mature lemma smooth, cylindric, whitish, 10 mm. long, appressed-pubescent below, callus 4 mm. long; awn 2.5-4′ long. 3. S. leucotricha
SUMMIT OF mature lemma not forming a crown or neck; awn scabrous or merely glabrous, rarely appressed-hispid but not plumose.
MATURE lemma pale, sparsely-pubescent to the summit, mostly over 10 mm. long, panicle included at the base, terminal segment of awn curved.
4. S. comata
MATURE lemma dark, 7-10 mm. long; panicles somewhat open; glumes 5-9-nerved.
Lemma glabrous above the base, minutely roughened at apex; callus sharp and slender-tipped. 5. S. avenacea
Lemma sparsely-pubescent to apex; callus rather blunt. 6. S. pringlei
MATURE lemma distinctly pubescent.
Panicles somewhat open but not diffuse, the branches ascending, naked at the base; ligule 3-4 mm. long; awn about 2′ long, the terminal segment flexuous; lemma 5-7 mm. long, villous all over. 7. S. eminens
Panicles narrow, the branches appressed.
Lemma 2-lobed; glumes 3-nerved; lemma 6 mm. long. 8. S. lobata
Lemma not 2-lobed.
Sheaths villous at the throat; callus broad and short, lower nodes of the panicle villous.
Glumes firm, the nerves inconspicuous, plant more than 3 feet tall, mostly robust; panicle large and compact; lemma 6-8 mm. long, villous; awn 20-30 mm. long. 9. S. robusta
Glumes thin and papery; plants usually not over 3.5 feet tall, slender; panicle rather slender and somewhat open.
10. S. viridula
Sheaths not villous at the throat or only slightly so; callus comparatively narrow; nodes of panicle glabrous or nearly so; lemma 6-7 mm. long, densely-appressed-pubescent; hairs at the summit about as long as the others; awn mostly more than 20 mm. long; blades very narrow. 11. S. columbiana

1. S. NEOMEXICANA (Thurb.) Scribn. (nē-ō-mĕks-ĭ-kā′nà) ; *S. pennata* var. *neomexicana* Thurb.

Culms 1-3 feet tall, densely-tufted, erect, simple, from coarse roots; **Blades**, the basal 4-12′ long, the upper short, scarcely 1 mm. wide when unrolled, slender, firm, convolute, scabrous on the upper surface; **Sheaths** longer than the internodes, minutely-pubescent; **Ligule** less than 0.5 mm. long, very short-ciliate; **Panicle**, the axis 1.5-4′ long, narrow, finally exserted, with a few ascending branches, the lowermost 10-30 mm. long, the upper much shorter, with 1-3 pedicellate spikelets, the pedicels more or less pubescent; **Spikelets** pale, more or less shining; **Glumes** lanceolate, narrowed into a slender scarcely-awned point about as long as the body, the total length 30-50 mm., the first a little longer; **Lemma** about 15 mm. long, the sharp densely-villous callus 4-5 mm. long, 5-nerved, at maturity brown, sparsely-pilose, tuberculate at the short slightly-constricted neck, terminating in a readily deciduous **awn** 4-7′ rarely 8′ long, the lower one-fourth straight, strongly twisted, appressed-villous, the middle segment 10-20 mm. long, villous, more or less flexuous, twice-geniculate and slightly twisted, the terminal segment untwisted, flexuous, plumose, the hairs pale or tawny, about 3 mm. long. (Illustrated by artist.)

Mesas, canyons and rocky slopes, western Texas and Colorado to Utah, and Arizona. (Palo Duro Canyon, collected by B. C. Tharp.) Spring.

2. S. TENUISSIMA Trin. (tĕn-ū-ĭs'ĭ-mȧ); WIRY SPEAR-GRASS.

Culms 12-28' tall, in large dense tufts, slender, wiry, erect; Blades 6-12' long or even longer, scarcely 0.5 mm. wide when rolled, wiry, closely-involute tapering into a fine point, more or less scabrous; Sheaths shorter than the internodes, glabrous or minutely-scabrous; Ligule 2-4 mm. long, acute; Panicle 4-10' long, usually included at the base, narrow, soft, nodding, the slender branches appressed, rather loosely-flowered; Spikelets mostly 8-10 mm. long; Glumes 3-nerved near the base, pale or tinged with purple, thin, hyaline, minutely-scabrous on the keel, lance-acuminate, the first usually 5-10 mm. long including the bristle-like point, the bristle sometimes very long, the second about 5 mm. long; Lemma 2-3 mm. long, oblong-elliptic, plump, with minute papillae, the callus 0.5 mm. long, densely-villous, the hairs extending a short distance up on the keel of the body of the lemma, the neck abruptly narrowed, a short crown of hairs at the apex, the capillary flexuous sparsely-minutely-scabrous awn 2-3' long more or less, obscurely geniculate about the middle.   (Illustrated by artist.)

Dry open ground, rocky slopes, dry open woods, in the mountains of western Texas to central Mexico.   Fall.

3. S. LEUCOTRICHA Trin. & Rupr. (lū-kŏt'rĭ-kȧ); SPEAR-GRASS.

Culms commonly 1-2 rarely 3.5 feet tall, usually in small tufts, erect or somewhat decumbent at the base, the nodes pubescent; Blades 2-9' long, 2-6 mm. wide, flat, sometimes involute, scabrous on the upper surface and hispidulous beneath; Sheaths shorter than the internodes, villous at the throat; Ligule membranaceous, short, truncate; Panicle narrow, 4-10' long, often inclosed at the base by the uppermost inflated sheath, nodding, the branches slender, 1-3 at each node, 1.5' long or less, spikelet-bearing on the upper part, 2-4 spikelets to each branch, the pedicels 3-10 mm. long, enlarged at the apex; Spikelets exclusive of the awn about 15 mm. long; Glumes pale-green or purple, about 15 mm. long, acuminate, awn-pointed, somewhat hyaline, the first 3-nerved, the second 5-7-nerved; Lemma including the slender sharp callus and crown about 10 mm. long, the callus about 4 mm. long, the long silky hairs about 3 mm. long, the body of the lemma rounded, oblong, brownish, with appressed hairs below and papillose-roughened above, the smooth neck or crown about 1 mm. long, a pit in the neck below the apex, ciliate with short hairs; Awn 60-100 mm. long, twice bent, the first segment pubescent, twisted, about one-third its length, the second segment about one-sixth to one-fifth its length, the third segment slender and straight; Cleistogamous Spikelets; these are often found at the very base of the culm, in the lower sheath, inclosed by two small scales or a split prophyllum; Spikelets solitary, sessile, excluding the awn about 4-6 mm. long, about 2 mm. wide, irregularly ovate, narrowed above; Glumes wanting; Lemma convolute around the grain, light or brownish color, hardened, more or less pubescent below, crowned with a ring of irregular stiff hairs, awnless or with an awn commonly 2.5-8 mm. long, slightly twisted and slightly scabrous; Grain elliptical, nearly as long as the lemma.   (See illustration by artist with photograph.)

Dry open grass land, Texas to central Mexico.   (Plentiful in every direction from San Antonio, Texas.)   Spring.

4. S. COMATA Trin. & Rupr. (kō-mā'tȧ); NEEDLE-AND-THREAD-GRASS.

Culms 1-3 feet tall, tufted or single, glabrous or sometimes pubescent at the nodes, sparingly branched; Blades 4-8' (4-12) long, uppermost shorter, 1-3 mm. wide, more or less minutely scabrous; **Sheaths** shorter or longer than the internodes, loose, naked at the throat, the uppermost inflated and usually enclosing the base of panicle, smooth or slightly scabrous; **Ligule** 3-4 mm. long, decurrent, those of sterile shoots shorter; **Panicle** exclusive of awns 4-12′ long, usually partly included in the uppermost sheath, the branches slender, scabrous, ascending or appressed, mostly two at a node, the lowest as much as 4′ long, bearing a few spikelets; **Spikelets** exclusive of awns 15-20 mm. long; **Glumes** 15-20 mm. long, subequal, papery, narrowed into a point, 5-nerved; **Lemma** 8-12 mm. long including callus, mostly about 10 mm. long, pale or finally brownish, the callus slender, 3 mm. long, acute, densely-barbed with tawny hairs, the body tapering from just above the callus, villous with short-appressed hairs, sparingly so towards the apex, the joint with the awn distinct; **Awn** about 4-5′ long, indistinctly twice geniculate, scabrous, the first segment straight, twisted, 25 mm. long more or less, the second twisted, about 15 mm. long, the third capillary, merely curved or sinuous.

Plains, prairies and dry hills; west Texas to Minnesota, and west to California; Indiana. Summer.

5. S. AVENACEA L. (ā-věn-ā′sē-à) ; BLACK OAT-GRASS.

Culms 2-3 feet tall, a few culms to a tuft, erect or spreading, simple; **Blades** 8-12′ long, the upper reduced, about 1 mm. wide, flat or involute, sometimes scabrous toward the tip, the upper with a long inflated sheath and short blade; **Sheaths** shorter than the internodes; **Ligule** 2-3 mm. long, firm; **Panicle** 4-7′ long, open, loose, included below, the scabrous distant branches slender, mostly in twos or threes, ascending or finally drooping, usually 20-40 mm. long, bearing 1-2 spikelets, naked below; **Spikelets** 10-15 mm. long; **Glumes** subequal, 12-15 mm. long, acuminate, papery, 5-nerved, the first sometimes obscurely so; **Lemma** dark brown, 9-10 mm. long, the sharp acute callus about 2 mm. long, densely-barbed, the upper hairs, 2-3 mm. long, the body glabrous, papillate-roughened toward the summit, constricted to a very short neck, the crown slightly hispidulous, terminating in a scabrous **awn** 1.5 to 2.5′ long, rarely longer, twice geniculate, the first segment about 20 mm., twisted, the second 10 mm. long, slightly twisted, the third straight. (Illustrated by artist.)

Dry or rocky woods, east Texas to Florida to Massachusetts. (San Jacinto River, collected by B. C. Tharp.) Spring.

6. S. PRINGLEI Scribn. (pr̆ing′lē-ī).

Culms mostly about 39′ tall, tufted, erect, sometimes puberulent about the nodes; **Blades** 4-12′ long, 1-3 mm. wide, flat, or those of the innovations involute, firm, erect, scabrous; **Sheaths** glabrous; **Ligule** about 2 mm. long, decurrent; **Panicles** nodding, 4-6′ long, the axis glabrous, the branches ascending, naked below, few-flowered, the branchlets and pedicels slightly scabrous; **Spikelets** about 10 mm. long; **Glumes** equal, about 10 mm. long, membranaceous, broad, rather abruptly narrowed into a short point, glabrous, the first about 7-nerved; **Lemma** 7-8 mm. long, oblong-elliptic, brown, villous with appressed brownish hairs, the surface also minutely papillate, the callus 1 mm. long, densely-barbed, the abruptly narrowed summit with a dense ring of short brown hairs; **Awn** 20-30 mm. long, obscurely twice geniculate, scabrous, twisted to the second bend. (For drawings see *Stipa eminens*.)

Rocky woods and slopes, Texas to Arizona and Mexico.

7. S. EMINENS Cav. (ĕm'ĭ-nĕns) ; *S. flexuosa* Vasey.

Culms 1.5-3.5 feet tall, tufted, slender, rather wiry, simple; **Blades** mostly 5-14' long, 1-4 mm. wide, involute or the upper flat, smooth or slightly scabrous, glabrous or puberulent on upper surface near the base; **Sheaths,** upper shorter than the internodes, the lower overlapping, glabrous or very short-pubescent at the throat; **Ligule** membranaceous, soon fragile, 3-4 mm. long or sometimes longer, broader than the blade; **Panicles** 4-12' long, usually exserted, erect or nodding, glabrous or densely-pilose at the lower axils, sometimes at the others, the capillary branches scabrous, flexuous, spreading, usually several at a node, the lowermost 2-3' long, bearing toward the apex a few spikelets, the pedicels 1-5 mm. long; **Spikelets** lanceolate, exclusive of the awn 8-11 mm. (12-18) long; **Glumes,** the first longer than the second 8-11 mm. long, 1-nerved or two additional nerves near the base, the second about one-fifth shorter (glumes given by some authors as 12-18 mm. long), 3-5-nerved, both acuminate, membranaceous, scarious; **Lemma** pale or light brown, about 5.5 mm. long, including a densely-barbed callus about 1.5 mm. long, the body broadest about one-third the distance above the callus, villous, the hairs white, narrowed above into an obscure neck; **Awn** 30-55 mm. long, soon deciduous, the first segment 7-10 mm. long, twisted in a righthand spiral, then bent and twisted for about 5-7 mm., the third segment flexuous, not twisted, slightly scabrous; **Palea** about one-third the length of its lemma, obtuse, hyaline; **Stamens** 3, the apex of the anthers bearing a tuft of short hairs.

Rocky hills, Texas to Arizona and south to central Mexico. Always found growing among bushes or shrubs. (A few miles west of Sheffield, Texas.) September.

8. S. LOBATA Swallen (lō-bā'tà).

Culms 14-34' tall, densely-tufted, erect, scaberulous below the panicle; **Blades** as much as 20' long, 1-4 mm. wide at the base, flat or loosely-folded toward the base, long-attenuate to a fine involute tip, scabrous on the upper surface, nearly smooth beneath; **Sheaths** longer than the internodes, or the upper ones shorter, scaberulous, the margins sparsely-pilose; **Ligule** less than 0.5 mm. long; **Panicles** 4-7' long, the branches appressed, rarely more than 2' long, several-flowered; **Spikelets** 9-12 mm. long; **Glumes** subequal, or the first a little longer, acuminate, 9-10 mm. the second sometimes as much as 12 mm. long, both 3-nerved, scabrous; **Lemma** 6 mm. long, brownish, evenly densely-hairy, the hairs 1-2 mm. long, the callus very short and blunt, the summit 2-lobed, the lobes 0.8-1.5 mm. long, awned from between the lobes, the awn 12-16 mm. long, twice bent, the first two segments twisted, appressed hispid, the third segment straight, scabrous.

"This species has been referred to *Stipa scribneri* Vasey, but differs in having shorter, nearly equal glumes, which are prominently scabrous, shorter awns, and shorter, lobed lemmas which are evenly hairy all over. In *S. scribneri* the glumes are unequal, the first about 10 mm., the second 15 mm. long, scaberulous, the awns are 17-20 mm., the lemmas are 7-9 mm. long, the lobes of which are less than 0.5 mm. long, and the hairs at the summit are 2 mm. long, conspicuously longer than those of the body." (This note from description by Jason R. Swallen.)

Rocky hills at medium altitudes, southern Texas and New Mexico. (Chisos and Guadalupe Mountains.)

. S. ROBUSTA (Vasey) Scribn. (rō-bŭs'tà); *S. vaseyi* Scribn.; SLEEPY-
GRASS.

Culms 3-5 feet tall, tufted, erect, robust; Blades as much as 2 feet long
nd 10 mm. wide, flat, or those of the sterile shoots very narrow, 3 mm. wide
nd involute, slightly narrower toward the base, long acuminate, scabrous
n the margins and toward the tip; Sheaths longer than to about as long
s the internodes, glabrous, villous at the throat, with pubescent line across
ne collar; Ligule membranaceous, about 4 mm. long, as short as 1 mm. on
ne sterile shoots; Panicles 8-18' long, half to three-fourths of an inch thick,
ompact, pale-green, more or less interrupted below, the branches appressed,
s much as 5' long exclusive of awns, several at each node, usually one or two
ong and others shorter, 1-3' distant, naked at the base, more or less
ubescent or pilose at the lower nodes; Spikelets exclusive of awns about
0 mm. long; Glumes about 10 mm. long, equal, acuminate to a hyaline soft
oint, rather firm, 3-nerved, or first sometimes 5-nerved, the nerves incon-
picuous; Lemma 6-8 mm. long, at maturity medium dark-brown, the callus
ather blunt, about 0.5 mm. long, densely-barbed with white hairs, the body
arrow-fusiform, narrowed above into an obscure crown or neck, villous all
ver with appressed white hairs, those at the summit as much as 2 mm. long,
Awn about 20-30 mm. long, at first straight, at maturity obscurely twice-
eniculate, twisted to the second bend; Anthers tipped with a minute tuft
f hairs.

Dry plains, hills and mountains; western Texas to Mexico and north
o Colorado. Summer.

0. S. VIRIDULA Trin. (vī-rĭd'ū-là).

This species has not yet been collected in Texas. Differs from S. robusta
n its more slender culms, not over 40' tall; Ligule about 1 mm. long;
Blades not more than 5 mm. wide; in the less dense Panicle of slightly
maller spikelets, the Glumes thinner, the Fruit less turgid.

Dry plains and hills, northern Mexico to Colorado and Kansas.
Summer.

1. S. COLUMBIANA Macoun (kō-lŭm-bĭ-ā'nà); *S. viridula* var. *minor*
Vasey; *S. minor* (Vasey) Scribn.

Culms 1-2 rarely 3.5 feet tall, erect; Blades 4-8' long sometimes
onger, mostly involute especially on the innovations, those of the culms
ometimes flat, 0.5 mm. thick, or wider; Sheaths naked at the throat;
Ligule rather firm, 1-2 mm. long; Panicle often purplish, 2-6' long, narrow,
ompact or rather loose, the branches short and appressed; Spikelets about
10 mm. long; Glumes about 10 mm. long, nearly equal, acuminate or awn-
pointed, glabrous or slightly-scaberulous, 3-nerved, the nerves rather
obscure because of the firm texture; Lemma 6-7 mm. long, the callus short,
barbed, the body densely-appressed-villous, scarcely narrowed at the
summit, the hairs at the summit about the same as the others; Awn mostly
20-25 mm. long, more or less twice geniculate, scabrous or somewhat
scabrous-pubescent to the second bend.

This species is usually smaller and is found at higher altitudes than
S. *viridula* Trin., a plant of New Mexico and north.

Dry plains and open woods, western Texas, New Mexico, north to
Wyoming and Yukon. Summer.

Four Species of Stipa

1st Glumes   2nd Glumes
S. neomexicana

1st Glumes   2nd Glumes
S. avenacea

1st Glumes   2nd Glumes
S. columbiana

1st Glumes   2nd Glumes
S. tenuissima

STIPA NEOMEXICANA; STIPA AVENACEA; STIPA
COLUMBIANA; STIPA TENUISSIMA

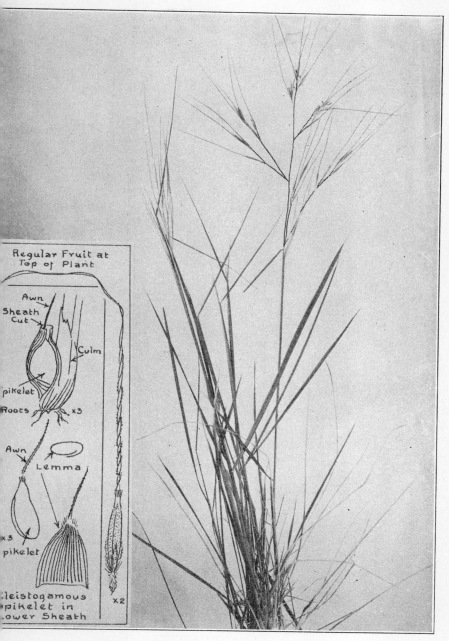

Regular Fruit at
Top of Plant

Awn
Sheath
Cut
Culm
pikelet
Roots x3

Awn
Lemma

x3
pikelet

Cleistogamous
pikelet in
Lower Sheath

x2

STIPA LEUCOTRICHA; SPEAR-GRASS

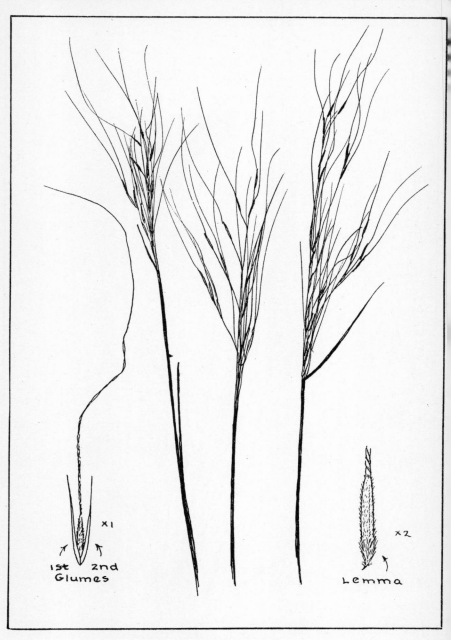

STIPA COMATA

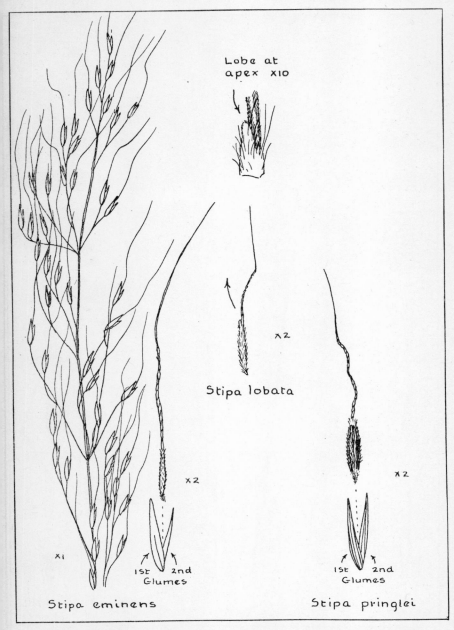

Lobe at
apex x10

x 2

Stipa lobata

x 2

x 2

x1

1st 2nd
Glumes

1st 2nd
Glumes

Stipa eminens

Stipa pringlei

STIPA EMINENS, STIPA LOBATA AND STIPA PRINGLEI

STIPA ROBUSTA, Sleepy-grass; drawings of STIPA VIRIDULA

52. ARISTIDA L. (à-rĭs'tĭ-dà)
(The Needle-grasses)

Spikelets 1-flowered, the rachilla disarticulating obliquely above the glumes; **Glumes** equal or unequal, narrow, acute, acuminate or awn-tipped; **Lemma** indurate, narrow, terete, convolute, with a hard, sharp-pointed, usually minutely-bearded callus at base, terminating above in a usually trifid awn.

Annual or *perennial* mostly low grasses, with narrow frequently convolute blades and narrow or sometimes open panicles. Species about 150, in the warmer regions of the world; 36 species in the United States; especially abundant in the southwestern states; about 24 in Texas.

This genus can usually be distinguished by its 3-awned lemma, hence the name triple-awned or three-awned grass, a closely related genus, *Stipa*, having a 1-awned lemma. It is an important genus in arid or semiarid regions, especially in tropical and subtropical countries.

At maturity the fruit with the three awns is detached and blown about by the wind, and the sharp-pointed callus works its way into the wool of sheep and into the nostrils and eyes of stock, thereby becoming very troublesome.

The genus *Aristida* is divided into three groups—one with the lemma articulate with the column of the awns, the awns nearly equal, and two groups with the lemma not articulate, one with the lateral awns minute, usually less than 1 mm. long or wanting, and the other with the lateral awns more than 1 mm. long, usually well developed.

These plants, when young, commonly have flexuous and purplish panicles, sometimes pale-green. The parts of the spikelets, glumes, lemmas and awns vary much in length, often in the same panicle.

In all of our species the ligules are minutely ciliate, usually not over 0.5 mm. long.

A. tuberculosa (collected in Mississippi and Mexico, and therefore likely to appear in Texas), and *A. desmantha*, both annuals, are the only species described in the group with the lemma articulate with the column of the awns, the former with a twisted column 10-15 mm. long or less, and the latter with a column 2 mm. long.

In the group with the lateral awns minute (less than 1 mm. long) or wanting, we have one species and a variety, *A. schiedeana*, with the awn (column) twisted at the base, and *A. ternipes* var. *minor* with the awn not twisted at the base. Both are perennials and are found in west Texas.

All of our other species belong to the group with the lateral awns more than 1 mm. long.

Including *A. tuberculosa* we have eight annuals: in *A. dichotoma* the central awn is spirally coiled at the base, the straight lateral awns 1-3 mm. long; in *A. oligantha*, known as few-flowered *Aristida*, the nearly equally divergent awns are 1.5-3′ long; in *A. ramosissima*, with the lateral awns usually 2-4 mm. long, and *A. longespica*, with the lateral awns one-third to one-half as long as the central, the central awn has a semicircular bend at the base, spreading or reflexed; in *A. adscensionis* the awns are flat at the base, 10-15 mm. long; and in *A. intermedia*, with terete awns 15-20 mm. long, the awns are about equally divergent, the central awn not sharply curved, the column short or wanting, not twisted.

There are 16 perennials in Texas. *A. barbata* and *A. divaricata*, closely allied species with open panicles, have branches abruptly spreading, the former being distinguished by the hemispheric habit of growth, the implicated branchlets and pedicels flexuous, while in the latter the culms are often prostrate, but do not form hemispheric tufts, the main branches being naked at the base and the pedicels usually appressed along the upper part of the branches, the branches at maturity always divaricately spreading, but very variable as to length, but longer and not so evenly divided throughout the panicle as in *A. barbata;* in *A. pansa* the branches are stiffly ascending or drooping but not abruptly spreading at the base, the nearly equal awns 10-20 mm. long.

The remaining species have narrow panicles, the branches appressed or ascending; *A. spiciformis* has long-awned glumes, the column of the awn of lemma 10 mm. long or more; *A. glauca* has the lemma tapering into a slender somewhat twisted beak 5-6 mm. long, the widely spreading awns 15-25 mm. long; *A. purpurea* and varieties have the lemma beakless or short-beaked, the branches of the rather loose panicle slender and flexuous; *A. wrightii* has a rather stiff and erect panicle at maturity, the branches several-flowered, and sheaths with a hispidulous or villous line across the collar; *A. fendleriana* is a low plant with leaves in a short curly cluster at the base; *A. longiseta,* known as dog-town grass, has awns 60-80 mm. long, and because of a tendency to invade fresh soil is often found in dirt thrown up from the burrows of prairie dogs, hence the name; *A. longiseta* var. *robusta* is stouter and taller, the awns 40-50 mm. long; *A. longiseta* var. *rariflora* has few-flowered panicles, the capillary branches bearing 1-2 spikelets; *A. lanosa* is an erect stout plant with woolly sheaths; *A. purpurascens* is a densely-tufted plant, the long narrow panicles often 8′ long, the first glume often exceeding the second; *A. affinis,* with glumes about 12 mm. long, and *A. virgata,* with glumes about 6 mm. long, both with the central awn horizontally spreading or reflexed by a semicircular bend, have the lateral awns erect, two-thirds to three-fourths as long as the central; *A. arizonica* is a plant growing in the high mountains of west Texas.

LEMMA ARTICULATE WITH THE COLUMN OF THE AWNS.
　　Awns nearly equal; arcuate-contorted at base; culms glabrous; annuals.
　　　Column 2 mm. long or less.　　　　　　　　　　　　　　　1. A. desmantha
　　　Column 10-15 mm. long, twisted.　　　　　　　　　　　　2. A. tuberculosa
LEMMA NOT ARTICULATE.
　　LATERAL AWNS minute (less than 1 mm. long) or wanting; panicle open, branches spreading and naked at the base; perennials.
　　　Awns with a twisted base (column) 5-10 mm. long.　　　　3. A. schiedeana
　　　Awn not twisted.　　　　　　　　　　　　　4. (3a). A. ternipes var. minor
　　LATERAL AWNS more than 1 mm. long, usually well developed.
　　　PLANTS annual.
　　　　Central awn spirally coiled at the base, 3-6 mm. long, the lateral straight, erect, about 1 mm. long.　　　　　　　　　　　　5. A. dichotoma
　　　　Central awn not spirally coiled.
　　　　　Awns mostly 40-80 mm. long, about equal, divergent; first glume 3-7-nerved, often exceeding the second.　　　　　　　6. A. oligantha
　　　　　Awns mostly less than 20 mm. long, often unequal.
　　　　　　Central awn with a semicircular bend at base spreading or reflexed. Lateral awns much reduced; lemma about 20 mm. long.
　　　　　　　　　　　　　　　　　　　　　　　7. A. ramosissima
　　　　　　Lateral awns one-third to half as long as the central; lemma 4-5 mm. long.　　　　　　　　　　　　　　8. A. longespica
　　　　　Central awn not sharply curved, the awns equally divergent.
　　　　　　Awns flat at the base, 10-15 mm. long.　　　　　9. A. adscensionis
　　　　　　Awns terete 15-20 mm. long.　　　　　　　　10. A. intermedia
　　　PLANTS perennial.
　　　　Panicle open, the branches spreading (in *A. pansa* ascending); naked at the base.

Branches of the panicle stiffly and abruptly spreading or reflexed at the base.

Branchlets divaricate and implicate.   11. **A. barbata**

Branchlets appressed.   12. **A. divaricata**

Branches of the panicle stiffly ascending, not abruptly spreading at the base, lateral awns about as long as the central, at least more than half as long; glumes unequal, the first 5-7 mm., the second 7-10 mm. long.   13. **A. pansa**

Panicle narrow, the branches ascending or appressed.

Column 10 **mm.** or more long, twisted; glumes awned; first glume shorter than the second; blades all involute.   14. **A. spiciformis**

Column less than 10 mm. long.

First glume about half as long as the second (as much as two-thirds as long as in *A. glauca*).

LEMMA TAPERING INTO A SLENDER SOMEWHAT twisted beak 5-6 mm. long; awns 15-25 mm. long, widely spreading.
                                                        15. **A. glauca**

LEMMA BEAKLESS OR ONLY SHORT-BEAKED.

BRANCHES OF the rather loose and nodding panicle slender and flexuous.

BRANCHES of the panicle many, usually several-flowered.

First glume 6-8 mm. long; lemma 10 mm. long, awns 30-50 mm. long.   16. **A. purpurea**

First glume 4-5 mm. long; lemma 7-8 mm. long, awns 20 mm. long.   16a. **A. purpurea var. micrantha**

BRANCHES of the panicle few, capillary, bearing 1-2 spikelets.
                                16b. **A. purpurea var. laxiflora**

BRANCHES OF the erect panicle stiff and appressed, or the lowermost sometimes flexuous.

PANICLE mostly more than 6' long, the branches several-flowered; awns about 20 mm. long; sheaths with a villous line across the back of the collar.   17. **A. wrightii**

PANICLE mostly less than 6' long, the branches few-flowered; awns 20-80 mm. long; culms closely-tufted, erect.

Lemma gradually narrowed above, scaberulous on the upper half; leaves mostly in a short cluster at the base of the plant; panicle simple, mostly 1 spikelet to a branch.
                                                        18. **A. fendleriana**

Lemma scarcely narrowed above, scaberulous only at the tip; leaves not conspicuously basal.

Plants 8-12' tall, panicles many-flowered; awns 60-80 mm. long.   19. **A. longiseta**

Plants similar, panicle few-flowered, capillary branches bearing 1-2 spikelets.   19a. **A. longiseta var. rariflora**

Plants taller, stouter, panicle stiffer, longer; awns 40-50 mm. long.   19b. **A. longiseta var. robusta**

First glume more than half as long as the second.

SHEATHS LANATE-PUBESCENT. Awn unequal, the central longer, 12-25 mm. long, recurved.   20. **A. lanosa**

SHEATHS NOT LANATE-PUBESCENT.

COLUMN OF the awn at maturity 3-5 mm. long, distinctly twisted; awns about equal, mostly 10-20 mm. long; blades elongated, flat, the older ones usually curled or flexuous; sheaths glabrous at the throat.   21. **A. arizonica**

COLUMN OF the awn less than 3 mm. long.

AWNS at maturity about equally divergent, horizontally spreading; panicle usually more than 8' long; first glume usually exceeding the second.   22. **A. purpurascens**

AWNS at maturity unequally divergent; central awn horizontally spreading or somewhat reflexed, the lateral erect, two-thirds to three-fourths as long as the central.

Glumes about 12 mm. (6-12) long.   23. **A. affinis**

Glumes about 6 mm. long.   24. **A. virgata**

1. **A. DESMANTHA** Trin. & Rupr. (dĕs-măn'thȧ); WESTERN TRIPLE-AWNED GRASS.

Culms 1-3 rarely 3.5 feet tall, erect or somewhat spreading, branching, especially near the middle; Blades 6-12 rarely 20' long, 1-3.5 mm. wide, flat or folded at the base, involute toward the long filiform tip, scabrous on the upper surface and on the margin, and on the under surface toward the tip; Sheaths shorter than the internodes, glabrous, or the lower pubescent or hispid, or villous at the throat and on the margin; Panicles brownish-yellow or tawny, commonly long-exserted, as much as 10' long, those of the branches shorter, erect, the branches stiffly ascending, the lower as much as 3.5' long and rather distant, in pairs or solitary, naked at the base, bearing one-to-several spikelets at the ends of the branches or short branchlets, the scabrous pedicels 2-10 mm. long, erect, the branches and branchlets very scabrous; Spikelets brownish-yellow; Glumes 1-nerved, slightly unequal, the first about 16 mm. long, including the awn about 4 mm. long, scabrous on the keel, the second about 13 mm. long, including the awn about 2-3 mm. long, scabrous near the apex; Lemma exclusive of the column about 8-10 mm. long, including the densely short-pubescent callus about 2 mm. long, the loosely spiral column about 2 mm. long, glabrous below and scabrous on the back toward the summit; Awns spreading or reflexed, scabrous, 20-25 mm. long, united at their base for about 2 mm., the base curved in a semicircular somewhat contorted bend, the upper part thus deflexed, the lateral awns sometimes shorter.

Open sandy woods or sandy open ground, Texas to Oklahoma, Nebraska and Illinois. (Near Teague, also on the Victoria-Goliad Road, Texas.) Fall.

2. **A. TUBERCULOSA** Nutt. (tū-bĕr-kū-lō'sȧ); SEA-BEACH ARISTIDA. *(Not yet found in Texas.)*

Culms 1-2 feet rarely 3 feet tall, tufted, erect, branching, the internodes mostly naked as the branches crowd the sheaths from the culm; Blades 4-9' long, 2-4 mm. wide, flat at the base, involute above, scabrous on the margins and upper surface, and under surface toward the tip; Sheaths much longer than the internodes to which they belong, sparsely-villous at the throat, or the lower more or less pubescent throughout; Panicles purplish, 4-8' long, those of the branches usually shorter, the scabrous branches stiffly ascending, rather distant, solitary or mostly in pairs, the longer one naked at the base, the shorter one branching near the base and bearing usually two spikelets, the shorter pedicels 3-5 mm. long; Spikelets pale or dark-brown; Glumes gradually narrowed into a rather long awn, about equal, including the awn 25-30 mm. long, the awn sometimes more than half as long as the body of the glume; Lemma including the 4 mm. long bearded sharp callus, about 14 mm. long, and including the 10-15 mm. long twisted beak about 25-30 mm. long, the column of the awns twisted but not united, forming above a semicircular bend, the terminal straight portion of the awns spreading or deflexed 30-45 mm. long.

Open sandy fields, Massachusetts to Georgia and Mississippi, near the coast, and Mexico. Also around the southern end of Lake Michigan and other places in Wisconsin and Illinois. Summer and fall.

3. **A. SCHIEDEANA** Trin. & Rupr. (shē-dē-ā'nȧ).

Culms 1-3.5 feet mostly 1-2 feet tall, tufted, erect or spreading, smooth or slightly rough or puberulent; Blades 4-12' long, 1-3 mm. wide, flat or involute (soon involute on drying), tapering to a fine point, margin and upper surface scabrous; **Sheaths** mostly longer than the internodes, wider than the blades, glabrous and smooth, or minutely scaberulous, or villous at the throat and well-marked collar, or line of minute hairs across the collar; **Panicles** open, exserted, as much as 20' long, pyramidal, nodding or drooping, the branches usually solitary, few, ascending or spreading, drooping, as much as 9' long, branching above the middle, rarely near the base, naked at the base, the main axis and branches scabrous, the branchlets mostly 1-2' long, appressed, with usually 1-3 clusters of 3-5 spikelets, appressed, the angled pedicels mostly 2-4 mm. long, the terminal ones longer; **Spikelets** 15-18 mm. long; **Glumes** 10-15 mm. long, the first usually longer, acuminate, or the second one mucronate from a slightly bifid apex, 1-nerved, or the first with a pair of lateral nerves, scabrous on the back or only on the keel; **Lemma** proper, 8-10 mm. long, gradually narrowed into a scabrous twisted column about 4-7 mm. long, the total length to the bend 10-17 mm., the callus rather obtuse, densely villous; **Central Awn** divergent as much as 45 degrees, straight, 5-10 mm. long, the **lateral awns** obsolete or as much as 1 mm. long, rarely longer, erect. There are considerable variations in the measurements of the parts of the spikelet.

Rocky hills and plains, southwestern United States south to Mexico. (Tippit ranch, Alpine, Texas.) Fall.

4. (3a). A. TERNIPES var. MINOR (Vasey) Hitchc. (tĕr-nī'pēz, mī'nĕr) ; *A. ternipes divergens* (Vasey) Hitchc.; *A. divergens* Vasey; *A. schiedeana* var. *minor* Vasey.

Culms 10-20' tall more or less, erect, often ascending or prostrate, tufted, slender, branching; **Sheaths** mostly longer than the internodes; **Panicles** 2-8' long, usually more than half the length of the plant, pyramidal, but less diffuse than the species, usually included at the base, the shorter branches mostly 1.5-3.5' long, rather stiffly ascending or spreading, sometimes somewhat deflexed, solitary or in twos, often branching at the very base appearing verticillate, and again subdividing and spikelet-bearing beyond the middle; **Spikelets** 10-12 mm. long; **Glumes** 7-9 mm. long, awn-pointed, the first usually slightly shorter than the second, sometimes scabrous on the keel; **Lemma** 9-12 mm. long more or less, narrowed into a laterally compressed somewhat falcate beak or column, scabrous on the edges, the beak as long as or longer than the lemma proper, the callus about 1 mm. long, the solitary arcuate, scabrous, nearly terete **awn** 10-15 mm. long, the **lateral awns** commonly minute or wanting. (One specimen had lateral awns 2-3 mm. long, and a few spikelets with lateral awns half as long as the central.) It is likely that the glumes, lemma, beak and length of awns vary much in this species.

Rocky hills and plains, western Texas to southern California, and southern Mexico to Nicaragua. (El Paso and Limpia Canyon, Texas.) Summer.

5. A. DICHOTOMA Michx. (dī-kŏt'ō-mà) ; POVERTY-GRASS.

Culms 8-16' tall, tufted, slender, erect or ascending from a decumbent base, glabrous or sometimes minutely scaberulous, freely branching; **Blades** 4' long or less, 1-1.5 mm. wide, the lower mostly flat, the upper involute and short, scabrous and strongly nerved on the upper surface; **Sheaths** much shorter than the internodes, loose; **Panicles** terminal and from the upper and middle axils, narrow, almost spikelike, the terminal usually less than 4' long, the lateral panicles smaller, more or less inclosed in the sheath, the axis angled, scaberulous, the branches short and appressed, the lowermost as much as 20 mm. long and bearing a few spikelets, the upper bearing single spikelets; **Spikelets** 7-9 mm. long; **Glumes** 1-nerved, about equal or the first a little shorter, mostly 6-8 mm. long, scabrous on the keel and more or less scaberulous on the back, often toothed and mucronate; **Lemma** 5-6 mm. long, 3-nerved, somewhat compressed above, sparsely-appressed-hispidulous, the callus short, rather blunt, sparingly-pubescent, the column obsolete, the **central awn** spirally 1-2 coiled at the base, horizontally bent or somewhat reflexed, mostly 3-6 mm. long, the **lateral awns** a continuation of the lateral nerves, erect, usually about 1 mm. long.

Dry open ground, central Texas to Georgia and Florida, Maine to eastern Kansas. (Burnet, Texas.) Summer and fall.

6. A. OLIGANTHA Michx. (ŏl-ĭ-găn'thà) ; FEW-FLOWERED ARISTIDA.

Culms 1-2 feet tall, tufted, branched at the base and all the nodes, erect or spreading, slender, smooth or sometimes slightly rough, prophyllum at each branch and at the lowest nodes villous; **Blades** mostly 4-8' long, 1-2 mm. wide, flat or loosely involute, tapering to a fine point, the upper surface rough and sometimes pubescent near the base, sometimes slightly rough; **Sheaths** shorter or longer than the internodes, glabrous or often pilose at the throat, loose; **Panicle** few-flowered, 4-8' long, the axis scabrous, often flexuous and spikelets spreading; **Spikelets** single, borne on pedicels about 1 mm. long, or the lower with supplementary short branches bearing 1 or 2 spikelets arranged along the main axis raceme-like; **Glumes** about equal, 20-30 mm. long, gradually tapering into an awn, often between a bifid apex, the first 3-7-nerved scabrous on the keel, with awn often 3-7 mm. long, the second 1-nerved, minutely scaberulous on the keel, the awn often 10 mm. long or even longer; **Lemma** 3-nerved, scaberulous on the keel, pubescent on the short callus, exclusive of the awns 20-28 mm. long, slender, the **three awns** about equal, divergent, finally horizontally spreading or even reflexed, 40-85 mm. rarely 20 mm. long, the middle a little longer, the glumes, lemma and awns very variable in length.

Dry soil, Texas to Nebraska and New Jersey. August-September.

7. A. RAMOSISSIMA Engelm. (rà-mō-sĭs'ĭ-mà).

Culms 12-20' tall, rarely taller, tufted, slender, wiry, freely branching at the base and all the nodes; **Blades** 2-10' (2-4) long, about 1.2 mm. wide, flat or involute toward the summit, scabrous and strongly nerved on the upper surface; **Sheaths** glabrous, shorter than the internodes; **Panicles** narrow, loose, 3-5' long, the axis scabrous, the spikelets single or sometimes the lower in pairs, distant 10-20 mm., ascending on pedicels mostly 1-2 mm. long; **Spikelets** 16-22 mm. long; **Glumes**, the lower 3-6-nerved, the upper 1-nerved or sometimes 3-nerved, acuminate, unequal, scaberulous on the keels toward the summit, the first 15-17 mm. long, awn-pointed or with a short awn, the second 20-22 mm. long including an awn 3-5 mm. long, the awn often from between two rather long teeth; **Lemma** 13-20 mm. long including the acute short-pilose callus and a short neck, 3-nerved, smooth on the sides, scaberulous on the keel toward the apex, gradually narrowed above into a neck about 5 mm. long, the **central awn** with a semicircular bend, or part of a coil at the base, 15-20 mm. long, the terminal portion spreading or reflexed, the **lateral awns** usually much reduced (rarely obsolete), commonly 2-4 mm. sometimes 6 mm. rarely 10-15 mm. long. (In several panicles there were spikelets with lateral awns 2-6 mm. long, and a few with awns 10-15 mm. long.)

Open sterile soil, east Texas to Louisiana and Oklahoma. (Near Buna, Texas.) Late summer and fall.

8. A. LONGESPICA Poir. (lŏn-jē-spī′kà); *A. gracilis* Ell.

Culms 8-20′ tall, solitary or in small tufts, slender, erect or geniculate at the base, simple or branching at the base or at some of the lower nodes; Blades 1-4′ mostly 1-3′ long, 1.5 mm. wide or less, flat or involute, strongly nerved, scabrous on the upper surface; Sheaths shorter than the internodes; Panicles slender, exserted, the terminal mostly 4-6′ sometimes as much as 8′ long, the axillary panicles often much reduced, the axis minutely scabrous, the appressed spikelets single or as many as six to the short appressed branches, rather distant, especially below; Spikelets 5-6 mm. long; Glumes subequal, the second usually longer, 3.5-6 mm. long, awn-pointed, or the second mucronate from between two short lobes, the first 1-nerved or sometimes 3-nerved, scabrous on the keel; Lemma 4-6 mm. long, 3-nerved, scabrous along the keel, narrowed above, the short callus pilose, the central awn curved at the base, horizontally spreading or somewhat reflexed, 5-15 mm. long, the lateral awns erect, or somewhat divergent, usually one-third to half as long as the central, sometimes only 1 mm. long.

Sterile or sandy soil, east Texas to Florida, north to New Hampshire and Michigan. (Between Buna and Orange, Dallas, Marshall, Texarkana, Milano, Jefferson, Texas.) Fall.

9. A. ADSCENSIONIS L. (ăd-sĕn-sĭ-ō′nĭs); *A. fasciculata* Torr.; *A. dispersa* Trin. & Rupr.; *A. bromoides* H. B. K.

Culms 5-32′ tall, tufted, slender, erect or geniculate at the base, freely branching, especially toward the base; Blades 4-7′ long on the larger plants and 2 mm. wide or less, sometimes flat, on the smaller plants mostly short and involute, smooth or scabrous on the upper surface; Sheaths mostly shorter than the internodes; Panicles narrow, loose, erect or somewhat nodding, 2-8′ usually about 3-6′ long, those of the branches short, the axis usually scabrous above, the branches at first appressed, finally more or less spreading, commonly 1.5′ long or less, mostly solitary or in twos, branching at the very base appearing fascicled, often naked at the base, the spikelets crowded on the short branchlets, the scabrous pedicels mostly 1-2 mm. long; Spikelets 8-10 mm. long; Glumes 1-nerved, unequal, the first 4-7 mm. long, obtuse or acutish, scabrous on the keel, the second 7-10 mm. long, narrowed into a bluntish, notched or acute point, the keel slightly scabrous toward the tip; Lemma about as long as the second glume, 6-10 mm. long, densely-short-villous at the rather obtuse callus, flattened toward the scarcely-beaked summit, scabrous on the upper part of the keel and sometimes on both sides toward the apex; Awns about equal, or the middle slightly longer, 10-16 mm. long, rarely shorter, about equally divergent at an angle of as much as 45 degrees or sometimes horizontal, very scabrous, flat and without torsion at the base, gradually narrowed to a fine terete point.

The author collected in the Hueco Mountains some plants with spikelets 5-7 mm. long, central awn 4-8 mm. long and the lateral 2-5 mm. long.

Dry open ground, often in rocky soil, west Texas to Kansas, west to California, and south into Mexico. (Amarillo, Abilene, Big Spring, Ft. Stockton, Alpine, Limpia Canyon, El Paso.) Summer and fall.

10. A. INTERMEDIA Scribn. & Ball (ĭn-tēr-mē′dĭ-à) ; PLAINS ARISTIDA.

- **Culms** commonly 10-20′ sometimes 30′ tall, tufted, freely branching, especially toward the base, the branches flowering, slender, erect, sometimes from a geniculate base; **Blades** mostly less than 4′ sometimes as much as 10′ long, 1.5-2 mm. wide, flat or involute, scabrous on the upper surface, glabrous to scaberulous beneath; **Sheaths** about as long as the internodes, glabrous or sometimes pilose at the throat and villous at the base; **Panicle** 4-16′ long, those of the branches short, narrow, slender, loosely-flowered, the axis scabrous, the branches appressed, commonly less than an inch long, the lower distant, with one to a few spikelets; **Spikelets** exclusive of the awns 8-10 mm. long, short-pediceled, 1-2 mm. long; **Glumes** about equal, 6-9 mm. long, the second sometimes longer, 1-nerved, scabrous on the keel, narrowed into short awns, sometimes from a bifid or toothed apex, the first glume hispidulous; **Lemma** equaling or exceeding the body of the second glume, 7-9 mm. long, scabrous above, the middle sometimes mottled, minutely-pubescent on the callus with longer hairs at the apex, the **three awns** spreading, the middle one 14-24 mm. long, the lateral ones usually shorter, 11-16 mm. long, all variable.

In sandy soil, Texas and Mississippi to Iowa and Kansas. (San Antonio, Texas.) August-October.

11. A. BARBATA Fourn. (bär-bā′tà) ; *A. havardii* Vasey.

Culms 6-12′ tall, in large dense tufts, rather stiffly radiating in all directions, sparingly branched below, slender; **Blades** mostly 3-4′ long sometimes longer, about 1.5 mm. wide when open and 0.5 mm. thick when closed, involute, erect, rough on the upper surface, scabrous on the margins, glabrous on the under surface or somewhat roughened; **Sheaths** mostly longer than the internodes, glabrous except the hispidulous collar, slightly villous at the throat; **Panicle** about half the length of the culm, usually 4-6′ long, the axis scabrous, the branches 1-1.5′ long, mostly in pairs or with short basal branchlets divaricately spreading, implicate or flexuous, the whole panicle fragile at maturity, breaking away and rolling before the wind, the larger branches only few-flowered; **Spikelets** about 10 mm. long; **Glumes** nearly equal, 10 mm. long, acuminate or awn-pointed, 1-nerved (or the first said to have two additional obscure nerves), the first scabrous on the keel, the second minutely scabrous near the tip; **Lemma** 8-10 mm. long usually a little shorter than the glumes, gradually narrowed into a straight or twisted scaberulous beak, the pubescent callus about 1 mm. long, the three **awns** nearly equal, mostly 15-20 mm. long, somewhat divergent, scaberulous, scarcely curved or warped at the base.

Hills and plains, western Texas to Arizona and central Mexico. (Marathon and Limpia Canyon, Texas.) Summer.

12. A. DIVARICATA Humb. & Bonpl. (dī-văr-ĭ-kā′tà).

Culms 1-3 feet tall, tufted, branching below, simple above, erect or prostrate-spreading, much of the length taken up by the large panicle, retrorsely scabrous; **Blades** 6-12′ long or perhaps shorter, 3 mm. wide or less, flat or convolute, straight, rigid, strongly-nerved and scabrous above; **Sheaths** longer than the internodes, glabrous or slightly scabrous above, pilose at the summit with a few long hairs; **Panicle** large and

liffuse, usually 9-18′ long, as much as half the length of the plant, or sometimes just a few inches long, exserted or sheathed at the base, the branches
spreading or deflexed, naked below, mostly 2-5′ long, the lower sometimes
8′ long, mostly in ones or twos, scabrous on the margins, straight and
rigid, the ultimate branchlets and pedicels appressed, spikelets borne
singly, mostly short-pediceled; **Spikelets** exclusive of awns about 12 mm.
long; **Glumes** subequal, 10-12 mm. long, narrowly linear, membranaceous,
acuminate, purple or tawny, the first 1-nerved or obscurely 3-nerved,
scabrous on the nerve, the second 1-nerved, produced into a short awn
about 1 mm. long; **Lemma** slender, about 10 mm. long, about as long as
the glumes, the pubescent callus about 1 mm. long, the scabrous apex
sometimes slightly twisted forming a beak about 2 mm. long, **awns** unequal
about 10-15 mm. long, straight, terete, scabrous, slightly diverging when
dry, the **lateral** about as long as the body of the lemma, the middle one
usually longer.

Dry plains and hills; west Texas to Kansas and California. (Limpia
Canyon, Texas.) Summer.

13. A. PANSA Woot. & Standl. (păn′sà).

Culms 8-16′ tall, stiffly erect, slender and wiry, minutely scaberulous
or puberulent; **Blades** as much as 6′ long usually less, about 0.5 mm. thick
when rolled, involute, more or less flexuous, scabrous, puberulent on the
upper surface; **Sheaths** minutely puberulent, at least between the nerves,
densely-short-villous at the throat and pubescent on the collar; **Panicle**
narrow, open, rather stiffly upright, 4-8′ long, the axis scaberulous, the
branches stiffly ascending, 1.5-3′ long, single or with a basal shorter
branch, or a single spikelet, the spikelets appressed toward the summit
of the branches; **Spikelets** 8-11 mm. long; **Glumes** unequal, 1-nerved,
acuminate or awn-pointed, the first 5-7 mm. long, minutely scaberulous on
the keel, the second 7-11 mm. long, smooth on the keel; **Lemma** about as
long as the second glume, sometimes a little longer, short-pilose on the
1 mm. long callus, scaberulous above and gradually narrowed into a
scabrous slightly twisted beak of about 2 mm., the whole 7-11 mm. long;
Awns about equal, divergent or finally nearly horizontally spreading,
10-20 mm. long, the bases finally somewhat curved or warped.

This species differs from *A. barbata* in the stiff branches and appressed
pedicels, and from *A. divaricata* in the short branches of the panicle, and
from both in the unequal glumes.

Plains and open ground, western Texas to Arizona. (Marfa, Ft. Stockton, El Paso, Pecos River, Texas.)

14. A. SPICIFORMIS Ell. (spī-sĭ-fôr′mĭs).

Culms 20-40′ tall, tufted, strictly erect, glabrous, sparingly branched;
Blades 12′ long or less, 1-3 mm. wide, erect, flat, or usually inrolled or
tightly involute, scabrous or scabrous-pubescent on the upper surface;
Sheaths, the lower longer than the internodes, glabrous, sometimes slightly
villous at the throat, or the lower sparsely-short-pubescent; **Panicle** erect,
dense and spikelike, oblong, mostly 4-6′ long, the branches short and
appressed, the whole panicle more or less spirally twisted; **Spikelets** excluding the awns 15-35 mm. long; **Glumes** unequal, 1-nerved, abruptly
long-awned, the first about 4 mm. long, scabrous on the keel, the awn
usually 10-12 mm. sometimes only 5 mm. long, the second 8-10 mm. long,
nearly smooth, the awn usually 10-12 mm. sometimes only 7 mm. long;
Lemma, including the sharp densely-short-pubescent 2 mm. long callus,

5-6 mm. long, extending into a slender twisted column 10-30 mm. sometimes only 7 mm. long, **awns** about equal, 20-30 mm. long, divergent or horizontally spreading, more or less curved, or warped at the base.

Pine barrens along the coast, Texas to Florida and South Carolina, Cuba and Porto Rico. (Rio San Pedro, Texas, west of Rio Grande City.) Summer and fall.

15. **A. GLAUCA** (Nees) Walp. (glô′kà) ; *A. reverchoni* Vasey; *A. vaseyi* Woot. & Standl.

Culms 1-2 feet rarely 3 feet tall, tufted, erect, rather rigid; **Blades** commonly 2-4′ long, those of the innovations as much as 10′ long, about 1 mm. wide, involute, mostly curved or flexuous, scabrous on the upper surface; **Sheaths** longer than the internodes, sparsely-villous at the throat, especially on the innovations; **Panicle** mostly 3-6′ or sometimes as much as 12′ long, narrow, erect, the branches stiffly appressed, the lower about 1.5′ long, and somewhat distant; 1-to-several-flowered; **Spikelets** 12-15 mm. long, on short pedicels; **Glumes** unequal, 1-nerved, more or less mucronate or awn-pointed, the first 5-8 mm. long, scabrous on the keel, the second usually about twice as long, sometimes only one and a half times as long, glabrous; **Lemma** 10-12 mm. long, the callus pubescent, 0.5 mm. long, the body glabrous, tapering into a minutely-scabrous, slender, somewhat twisted beak about half the total length of the lemma; **Awns** about equal, scabrous, nearly glabrous at the flat slightly contorted base, divergent or nearly horizontally spreading, 15-25 mm. long.

Dry or rocky hills and plains, Texas to California and south into Mexico. (San Antonio, Texas.) Spring to fall.

16. **A. PURPUREA** Nutt. (pûr-pū′rē-à) ; PURPLE NEEDLE-GRASS.

Culms 1-2.5 feet tall, often densely-tufted, the innovations usually numerous, erect, or the outer culms somewhat decumbent at the base, branched at the base and often at the lower and middle nodes, sometimes rough below the panicle; **Blades** mostly less than 4′ long, 1-1.5 mm. wide, sometimes 10′ long and 2.5 mm. wide on the larger plants, involute, some drying flat, rough on the upper surface, especially towards the apex; **Sheaths** mostly longer than the internodes, the lower often very rough, villous at the throat; **Panicle** finally exserted, usually purplish, 4-10′ long, narrow, loose, lax, nodding, the branches rather distant, as much as 2′ long, often in pairs, one short, the branches and longer pedicels curved or flexuous, capillary, the lower longer and naked for 10-20 mm. at the base; **Spikelets** about 15 mm. long; **Glumes** 1-nerved, acuminate, bearing an awn 1-2 mm. long, this often between two slender irregular teeth, the first 6-8 mm. long, scabrous on the keel, the second about twice as long, glabrous; **Lemma** 9-10 mm. long, the pubescent callus less than 1 mm. long, the body gradually tapering to the scarcely beaked summit, tuberculate-scabrous in lines from below the middle to the summit, the background usually purplish, the raised parts whitish; **Awns** nearly equal, very slender, nearly smooth on the outside of the scarcely contorted base, scabrous above, finally widely spreading, mostly 30-50 mm. long.

Rocky hills and sandy plains, Texas north to Kansas, west to California and south to Mexico. Spring to fall.

16a. **A. PURPUREA** var. **MICRANTHA** Vasey (mī-krăn′thà).

Culms commonly 10-20′ sometimes 28′ tall, tufted, usually densely so, slender, erect, more or less branching, often slightly roughened, glabrous or the lower internodes often puberulent; **Blades** 1-5′ usually less than 4′

long, about 1.5 mm. wide, flat or involute, smooth or minutely scabrous;
Sheaths mostly shorter than the internodes, glabrous or minutely scabrous,
naked or sparsely-pilose at the throat; **Panicle** 4-8′ long, narrow and
loose, purple or finally pale, rather flexuous, the branches curved or
flexuous, capillary, rather short with shorter ones intermixed, 1-to-several-
flowered; **Spikelets** exclusive of awns about 10 mm. long; **Glumes** 1-
nerved, acuminate, the first 4-5 mm. long, scabrous on the keel, the second
about twice as long, glabrous; **Lemma** 7-8 mm. long, the short-villous
callus about 0.5 mm. long, the body glabrous, narrowed into a slightly
scaberulous beak, the three **awns** about equal, about 20 mm. long, slender,
divergent, somewhat contorted at the base. (See *A. purpurea* for drawings.)

Plains and rocky hills, often in sandy land, Texas to northern Mexico.
Spring to fall.

16b. A. PURPUREA var. LAXIFLORA Merr. (lăks-ĭ-flō′rà).

Differs from the species in the few-flowered panicle, the branches
capillary and flexuous, bearing 1 or 2 spikelets.

Dry plains, Texas to Arizona. (Dallas.)

17. A. WRIGHTII Nash (rīt′ĭ-ī); WRIGHT'S TRIPLE-AWNED GRASS.

Culms 1-2 feet or sometimes taller, densely-tufted, erect, smooth to
rough; **Blades** 3-8′ long, those of the innovations longer, 1-2 mm. wide,
involute, the culm blades often drying flat, curved, rough on the upper
surface, smooth or slightly rough below; **Sheaths** smooth or those of
the innovations rough, often villous at the throat, usually minutely hispidulous or villous across the collar; **Panicle** purplish, at first included
and nodding, finally erect and exserted, 4-8′ long, narrow, the rather
distant branches straight, appressed or ascending, the lower sometimes
flexuous, as much as 2.5′ long, usually 2-4 spikelets to a branch; **Spikelets**
about 13 mm. long; **Glumes** unequal, 1-nerved, acuminate or mucronate,
the first 5-7 mm. long, scabrous on the keel, the second about twice as
long, glabrous; **Lemma** 10-12 mm. long, the pubescent callus about 1 mm.
long, body glabrous below, gradually narrowed toward the summit,
scaberulous toward the summit; **Awns** nearly equal, about 20-30 mm. long,
divergent, sometimes nearly horizontally spreading, somewhat contorted
at the base.

In dry sandy soil, or rocky hills, Texas to Mexico and southern California. (San Antonio, Texas.) Spring to fall.

18. A. FENDLERIANA Steud. (fĕnd-lĕr-ĭ-ā′nà); *A. purpurea* var.
fendleri Vasey.

Culms 4-12′ tall, densely-tufted, often in large bunches, rather rigidly
erect, simple, with numerous curly leaves at the base; **Blades,** the basal
as much as 4′ long, those of the culm less than 2′ long, curved or flexuous,
involute, scabrous or nearly smooth beneath; **Sheaths** mostly basal,
smooth to scabrous, a tuft of hairs on each side at the summit; **Panicle**
20-60 mm. long, erect, narrow, nearly simple, the spikelets commonly
solitary or the lower in pairs, the scabrous pedicels short and appressed;
Spikelets 12-17 mm. long; **Glumes** 1-nerved, acute but not awned, unequal,
the first 7-11 mm. long, often scabrous on the keel, the second 12-17 mm.
long; **Lemma,** including the pubescent callus 1.5 mm. long, nearly or as
long as the second glume, gradually narrowed to the summit, glabrous,
scaberulous, usually in lines on the upper half; **Awns** about equal, or the
lateral slightly shorter, 20-50 mm. long, divergent.

Dry plains and hills, western Texas to southern California and north to Kansas, Nebraska and Wyoming and Montana. (Palo Duro Canyon, Randall County, Texas.) Summer and fall.

19. A. LONGISETA Steud. (lŏn-jĭ-sē'tà) ; DOGTOWN-GRASS, LONG-AWNED ARISTIDA.

Culms 8-15' tall, erect, mostly in rather large bunches, freely branching; **Blades** mostly 1.5-4' sometimes 6' long, about 1 mm. wide, curved, scabrous on the upper surface, sometimes minutely so beneath, involute; **Sheaths** more or less crowded toward the base, glabrous, or a few rather long hairs at the throat, those of the innovations strongly villous sometimes with a hispidulous line across the collar; **Panicle** erect but not stiff, axis as much as 5' long, the branches naked at base, usually 1-3, ascending or appressed, or the lower somewhat curved, spikelets 1-3 on each branch, the scabrous flexuous pedicels 10 mm. long more or less, approximately 10-15 spikelets to a culm; **Glumes** 1-nerved, narrowed to an awnless or only mucronate summit, the first 8-12 mm. long, keel scabrous, the second about twice as long, glabrous; **Lemma** 12-15 mm. long, terete, callus densely-short-pilose, about 1 mm. long, the flattened tip glabrous, slightly narrowed above, glabrous or the upper part scaberulous; **Awns** about equal, divergent, finally widely spreading, flat and sometimes slightly contorted at the base, mostly 60-90 mm. long.

Dry sandy soil, Texas and Mexico extending to Nebraska, Montana and Washington. April-August.

19a. A. LONGISETA var. ROBUSTA Merr. (rō-bŭs'tà).

Differs from *A. longiseta* in being taller and more robust, 12-20' tall, the innovations fewer and the **blades** longer, not in conspicuous basal tufts or cushions; **Panicles** longer, stiffer, and the branches stiffly ascending rather than curved or flexuous; **Awns** mostly 40-50 mm. long.

Its greater size, stiffer panicle, and shorter awns give the plant a different aspect, though the technical characters are similar to those of the species.

19b. A. LONGISETA var. RARIFLORA Hitchc. (răr-ĭ-flō'rà).

This form bears the same relation to *A. longiseta* that *A. purpurea* var. *laxiflora* does to *A. purpurea*. The two subspecies have the same aspect, but differ in the spikelet characters. More information is needed on both forms. They may prove to be distinct species. Being scattered here and there through the range of the respective species they are referred to them as subspecies.

20. A. LANOSA Muhl. (lā-nō'sà) ; *A. lanata* Poir.; WOOLLY TRIPLE-AWNED GRASS.

Culms 2-5 feet tall, erect, simple, rather robust, solitary or a few culms to a tuft, glabrous or the short lower internodes lanate-pubescent; **Blades** commonly 12-20' long, 3-5 mm. wide, flat, tapering into a fine point, rough or smooth on the upper surface; **Sheaths** overlapping, the lower short and crowded at the base, at least the lower lanate-pubescent; **Panicles** long-exserted, commonly 1-2 rarely 2.5 feet long, narrow, rather loose, erect or nodding, the branches ascending or appressed, mostly in pairs, or solitary but branching at the very base, one shorter, often 4-6' long, distant at the base as much as 4', lanate-pubescent at the base, spikelet-bearing on the upper two-thirds, the several short branchlets somewhat crowded, with a few spikelets to each branchlet, the branches and branchlets very scabrous; **Spikelets** commonly about 12 mm. (12-19) long; **Glumes** unequal, 1-nerved, acute or awn-pointed, the first exceeding the second, 10-14 mm. (12-14) long, scabrous on the keel and more or less on the back, the second about 10 mm. long, scabrous near the apex on body and keel; **Lemma** commonly about 10 mm. (8-19) long, pubescent on the short callus, scabrous on the keel and sides toward the summit; **Awns** unequal, the central finally horizontally spreading, or even reflexed, from a curved base, 15-25 mm. long, the lateral half to two-thirds as long, erect to horizontally spreading, the base a little contorted.

Dry sandy soil, mostly in woods or thickets, coastal plain, Texas to Florida and Delaware; also Oklahoma and Missouri. (Sandy woods near Teague and Henderson, Texas.) Late summer and fall.

21. A. ARIZONICA Vasey (ăr-ĭ-zŏn′ĭ-kà).

Culms 1-4 feet tall, tufted, erect, slightly roughened below the panicle; **Blades** 4-12′ long, 1-4 mm. wide, flat, narrowed into a fine involute point, or some of them involute throughout, scaberulous on the upper surface, the older ones usually curled and flexuous; **Sheaths** glabrous or sometimes villous at the throat; **Panicle** 4-10′ long, narrow, erect or somewhat nodding, closely-flowered or more or less interrupted at the base, the branches appressed, crowded or rather distant, the lower mostly 2-4′ long, sometimes longer, the axis very scabrous; **Spikelets** appressed and closely set on the branchlets; **Glumes** equal or slightly unequal, awn-pointed or with an awn 1-2 mm. long, 1-nerved, mostly 10-15 mm. long, the first scabrous on the keel and sometimes on the back; **Lemma** 10-15 mm. long, including the more or less twisted beak about 3-5 mm. long, the callus pilose, about 1 mm. long; **Awns** about equal, ascending or somewhat spreading, mostly 10-20 mm. long.

Dry plains, stony hills and open forests, mostly at 4500-8000 feet altitude, western Texas to New Mexico, Arizona and Colorado.

22. A. PURPURASCENS Poir. (pûr-pū-răs′ĕns); Broom-sedge, Arrow-grass.

Culms 15-30′ tall, sometimes taller, in rather large dense tufts, erect or somewhat decumbent at the base, branching below, the lower internodes short and sometimes zigzag, slender; **Blades** mostly 5-8′ sometimes 12′ long, 2 mm. wide or less, flat or involute toward the tip, slightly rough towards the tip and a few hairs on the upper surface near the base; **Sheaths** longer than the internodes, sometimes shorter above, the lower glabrous or sometimes with a few loose hairs, flattened and keeled; **Panicle** 6-12′ long, narrow, exserted, purplish or brownish, rather lax and nodding, the branches mostly less than an inch long, the lower somewhat distant and sometimes 2′ long, the upper crowded, rather laxly appressed, spikelet-bearing to or nearly to the base, many spikelets crowded on each branch, commonly 2-4 to a whorl, the axillary panicles usually much shorter than the terminal; **Spikelets** exclusive of the awns 9-12 mm. long; **Glumes** 8-12 mm. long, the first usually a little longer than the second, awn-pointed, the first 1-nerved, scabrous on the keel, the second 1-nerved or an extra obscure nerve on one side, glabrous or nearly so; **Lemma** 6-8 mm. long, callus 0.5 mm. long, slightly pubescent, scabrous on the keel and at the scarcely beaked summit, otherwise glabrous, sometimes with dark spots; **Awns** subequal, the central usually somewhat longer, finally divergent, spreading or somewhat reflexed, the central 20-30 mm. long, the lateral 17-25 mm. long.

Dry sandy soil, Texas and Missouri, east to Florida and Massachusetts. (20 miles north of Victoria, Texas.)   Fall.

23. **A. AFFINIS** (Schult.) Kunth (ăf-ī′nĭs) ; *A. palustris* (Chapm.) Vasey.

Culms 3-5 feet tall, tufted from a hard thickened base, rather stout, stiffly erect; **Blades** 12′ long or less, 3 mm. wide, flat, becoming loosely involute, the apex fine and involute, scabrous-pubescent on the upper surface; **Sheaths** mostly longer than the internodes, naked at the throat; **Panicle** 20′ long or less, narrow, the branches appressed, rather distant, but mostly overlapping, the lower as much as 4′ long, sometimes naked at the base; **Spikelets** about 10 mm. long; **Glumes** about equal, 6-10 mm. long, awn-pointed, sometimes mucronate, the first with a distinct nerve on one side (thus 2-nerved), scabrous on the keel and more or less on the back, the second 1-nerved, glabrous on the back and keel, usually slightly shorter than the first; **Lemma** 6-8 mm. long, sparsely-pubescent on the callus, glabrous on the body, somewhat scaberulous on the straight beak about 1 mm. long; **Awns** unequal, the central horizontally spreading 15-32 mm. long, the lateral erect, two-thirds to three-fourths as long as the central.

Low pine barrens and flatwoods, eastern Texas to Florida and North Carolina.   (Long-pine belt in Texas.)

24. **A. VIRGATA** Trin. (vēr-gā′tȧ) ; *A. chapmaniana* Nash.

Culms 20-32′ sometimes as much as 39′ tall, tufted, erect, from a rather slender soft base; **Blades** as much as 12′ long, usually not over 3 mm. wide, flat, rather lax, tapering to a fine point, scabrous on the upper surface; **Sheaths** scarcely flattened or keeled; **Panicle** one-third to half the entire length of the plant, slender, erect, though not very stiff, rather loosely-flowered, the branches mostly short and somewhat appressed, mostly 10-20 mm. long, not closely overlapping, bearing several approximate spikelets; **Spikelets**; **Glumes** about equal, 6-7 mm. long, acuminate or awn-tipped, the first 1-nerved, sometimes with a weak nerve on each side, scabrous on the keel and back, the second smooth and glabrous; **Lemma** 4-5 mm. long, often mottled, somewhat laterally compressed, glabrous except the short-pubescent callus and the very short slightly scaberulous beak; **Awns** unequal, the central horizontally spreading or somewhat reflexed, 15-20 mm. long, the lateral erect, about two-thirds as long as the central, the base of the central more robust and glabrous on the under side of the curve.

This species differs from *A. longespica* in being perennial; from *A. purpurascens* in the erect lateral awns.   The fruit is distinguished by its size, glabrous surface, and the smooth robust basal curve of the central awn which is sharply bent, the smaller lateral awns being erect.   (See *A. lanosa* for drawings.)

Moist sandy soil of the coastal plain, New Jersey to Florida, Mississippi and Texas.   (Hardin County, Texas.)

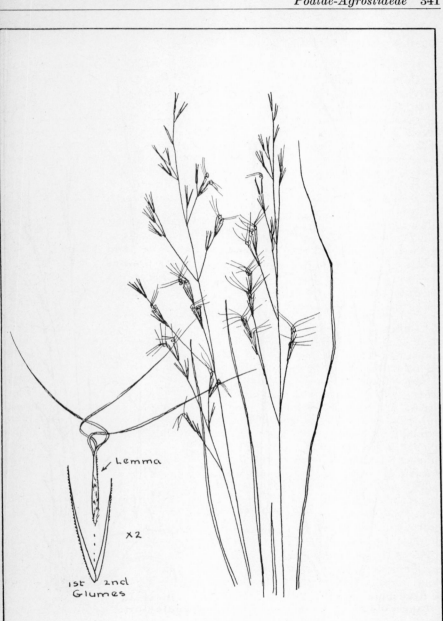

Lemma

×2

1st 2nd
Glumes

ARISTIDA DESMANTHA

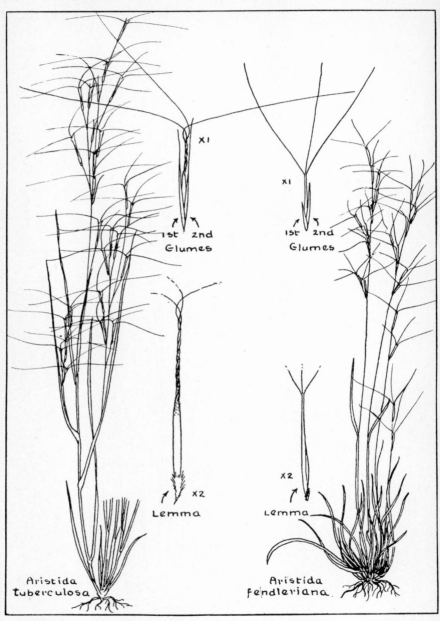

ARISTIDA TUBERCULOSA AND ARISTIDA FENDLERIANA

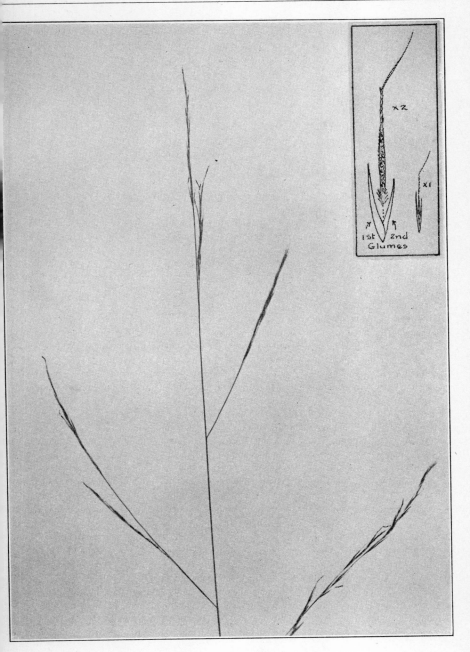

ARISTIDA SCHIEDEANA

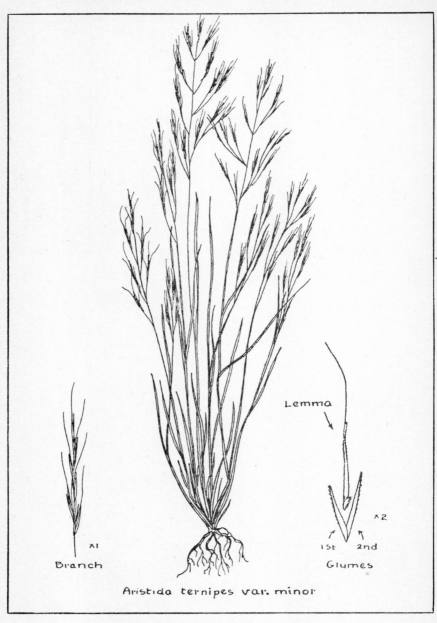

Lemma

Branch

^1

^2

1st   2nd

Glumes

Aristida ternipes var. minor

ARISTIDA TERNIPES VAR. MINOR

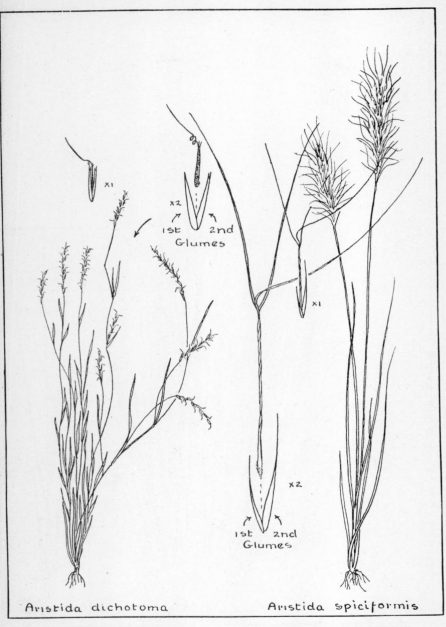

ARISTIDA DICHOTOMA AND ARISTIDA SPICIFORMIS

ARISTIDA OLIGANTHA

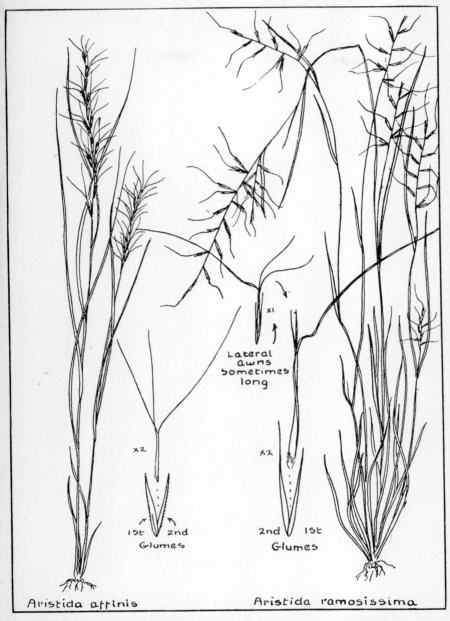

Lateral
awns
sometimes
long

x1

x2

x2

1st   2nd
Glumes

2nd   1st
Glumes

Aristida affinis

Aristida ramosissima

ARISTIDA AFFINIS AND ARISTIDA RAMOSISSIMA

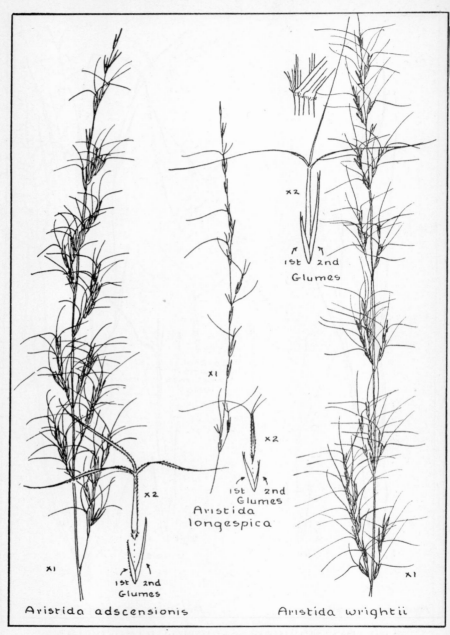

Aristida adscensionis

Aristida longespica

Aristida wrightii

ARISTIDA ADSCENSIONIS, ARISTIDA LONGESPICA AND
ARISTIDA WRIGHTII

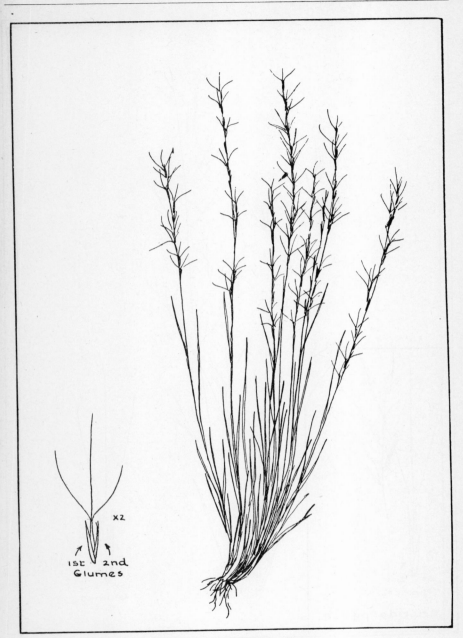

1st 2nd
Glumes

x2

ARISTIDA INTERMEDIA

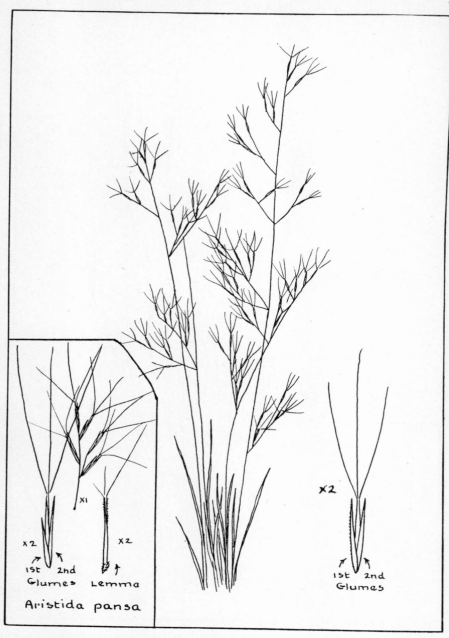

ARISTIDA BARBATA and illustration of ARISTIDA PANSA

ARISTIDA DIVARICATA

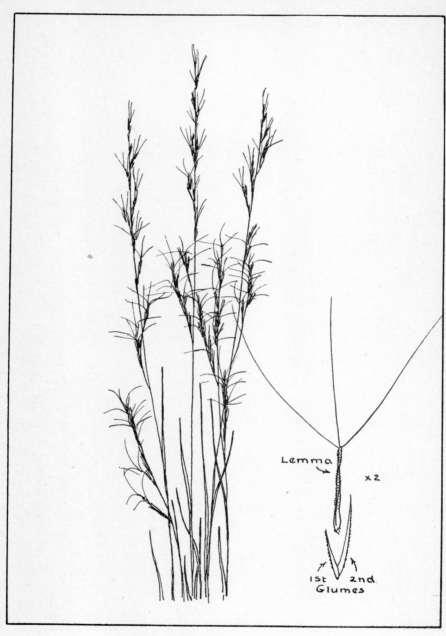

ARISTIDA GLAUCA

ARISTIDA PURPUREA and drawings of ARISTIDA PURPUREA VAR. MICRANTHA

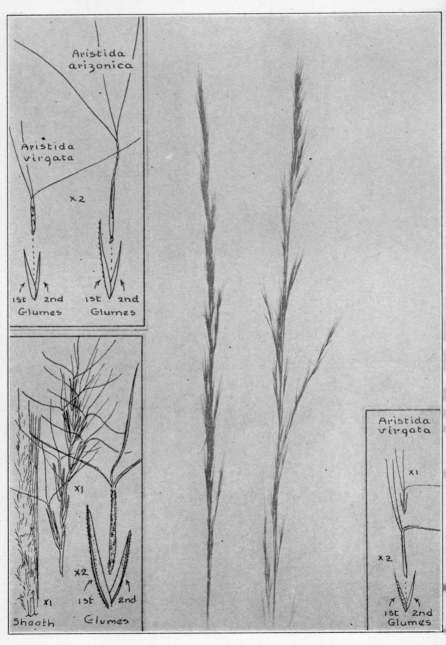

ARISTIDA LANOSA; ARISTIDA ARIZONICA; ARISTIDA VIRGATA

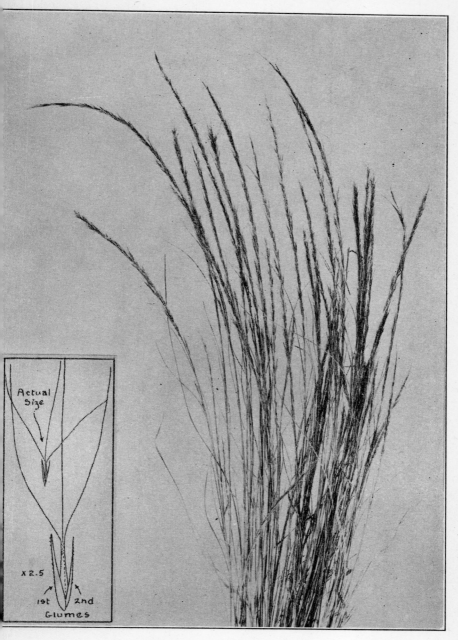

Actual Size

X 2.5

1st 2nd
Glumes

ARISTIDA PURPURASCENS

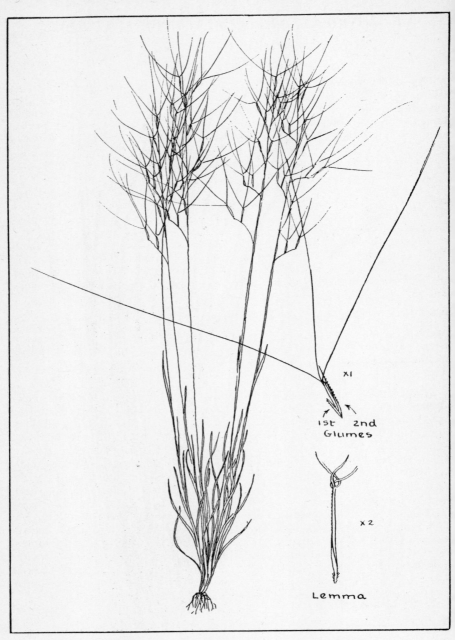

X1

1st   2nd
Glumes

X2

Lemma

ARISTIDA LONGISETA; Dog-town Grass

VI. ZOYSIEAE, THE CURLY-MESQUITE TRIBE

53. TRAGUS Hall. (trā'gŭs)
(*Nazia* Adans.)

Spikelets 1-flowered, in small spikes of 2-5, the spikes subsessile, falling entire, the spikelets sessile on a very short zigzag rachis, the **first glume** small, thin, or wanting, appressed to the rachis, the **second glumes** of the two lower spikelets strongly convex with three thick nerves bearing a row of squarrose stout-hooked prickles along each side, the two second glumes forming the halves of a little bur, the upper 1-3 spikelets reduced and sterile; **Lemmas** and **Palea** thin, the lemma flat, the palea strongly convex.

Low *annual* grasses, with flat blades and terminal inflorescence, the burs of spikes rather closely arranged along an elongate slender axis. Species three, in the tropical regions of both hemispheres; two species introduced in the southern United States, both in Texas.

Tragus racemosus, with 3-5 spikelets in each cluster, the lower about 4 mm. long, is found in open ground from Texas to Arizona, and *T. berteronianus*, with two spikelets in each cluster, the lower 2-3 mm. long, here and there through the southern states to Arizona. They are somewhat weedy grasses of no economic importance.

SPIKELETS 2-3 mm. long, the apex scarcely projecting beyond the spines, the
    bur nearly sessile.   1. T. berteronianus
SPIKELETS 4-4.5 mm. long, the acuminate apex projecting beyond the spines,
    the bur pediceled.   2. T. racemosus

1. T. BERTERONIANUS Schult. (bĕr-tĕr-ō-nĭ-ā'nŭs); *Nazia aliena* (Spreng.) Scribn.; PRICKLE-GRASS.

Culms 2-15′ tall, tufted, erect or ascending or spreading from a decumbent base, slender, branching at the base, taking root at the lower nodes; **Blades** 0.5-3.5′ mostly 1.5-2.5′ long, 4-8 mm. (2-4) wide, flat, slightly rough, the white margins hispid-ciliate; **Sheaths** shorter than the internodes except at the very base, sometimes sparsely-hairy at the throat, hispid-ciliate; **Ligule** a ring of hairs nearly 1 mm. long; **Racemes** commonly 2-4′ long, 4-7 mm. thick, solitary, commonly included more or less at the base, cylindric, dense, with numerous bristle-like clusters nearly sessile on all sides of the terete minutely-pubescent axis, the clusters of burs about 3 mm. long, composed of two approximate spikelets on a very short rachis nearly sessile, its apex scarcely exceeding the spines; **Spikelets**, the lower 2-3 mm. long, the upper usually slightly shorter; **Glumes**, the first minute or wanting, thin, hyaline, glabrous, the second ovatelanceolate, acute, commonly 3-nerved, the convex back beset with hooked spines or prickles; **Lemma** nearly as long as the second glume, lanceolate, 3-nerved, abruptly pointed or awn-pointed, usually thinly pubescent.

On dry hillsides and plains, Texas to Arizona and Mexico. Spring-summer.

2. T. RACEMOSUS (L.) All. (rā-sē-mō'sŭs); *Nazia racemosa* Kuntze.

Differs from *T. berteronianus* in the larger burs with 3-5 spikelets, the lower 4-4.5 mm. long, in the acuminate apex projecting beyond the spines, and in the pediceled burs; plants similar in aspect. (Drawings with the photograph of *T. berteronianus*.)

Waste ground at a few places from Maine to North Carolina; Texas and Arizona. Introduced from Europe.

Tragus
racemosus

×7

×7   Lemma
Palea

Bur   1st   2nd
Glumes

TRAGUS BERTERONIANUS and drawings of **TRAGUS RACEMOSUS**

54. ZOYSIA Willd. (zoĭ′sĭ-à)
(*Osterdamia* Neck.)

Spikelets 1-flowered, laterally compressed, appressed flatwise against the slender rachis, glabrous, disarticulating below the glumes; **First Glume** wanting; **Second Glume** coriaceous, mucronate or short-awned, completely infolding the thin lemma and palea, the palea sometimes obsolete.

Perennial low grasses with creeping rhizomes, short pungently-pointed blades, and terminal spikelike racemes, the spikelets on short appressed pedicels. Species about five, southeastern Asia to New Zealand; perhaps two species in the United States, one in Texas.

It appears that Z. *japonica* Steud. was introduced into the southern states several years ago as a lawn grass under the names of Korean lawn grass and Japanese lawn grass. It seems that our only species in Texas, Z. *tenuifolia*, known as *Mascarene* or velvet-grass, was first introduced into Florida and recently at Brownsville, Texas. It is a very fine-leaved grass, and is said to bloom rarely.

Z. *matrella* (L.) Merr., known as manila-grass, is common in the Philippine Islands and is occasionally cultivated in California.

Z. TENUIFOLIA Willd. (tĕn-ū-ĭ-fō′lĭ-à) ; *Osterdamia tenuifolia* (Willd.) Kuntze; Mascarene-grass, Velvet-grass.

Culms 1-3′ tall more or less, erect, producing comparatively long stolons, a delicate plant with filiform leaves; **Blades** commonly less than 30 mm. long, filiform; **Sheaths** longer than the internodes, crowded toward the base of the plant, loose, villous at the throat; **Spikes** exserted, 15 mm. long more or less, very slender, erect, the solitary alternate spikelets commonly somewhat overlapping, on short appressed pedicels, being 7 spikelets more or less to a spike; **Spikelets** 3-3.5 mm. long including the short scabrous awn; **Glumes**, the first wanting, the second exceeding the lemma and palea, 2-toothed, the awn commonly less than 0.5 mm. long; **Lemma** about 1.7 mm. long, 2-toothed, much thinner than the hardened second glume.

In cultivation as a lawn grass, introduced from Japan into Florida; lately introduced at Brownsville, Texas, by Pete Heinz.

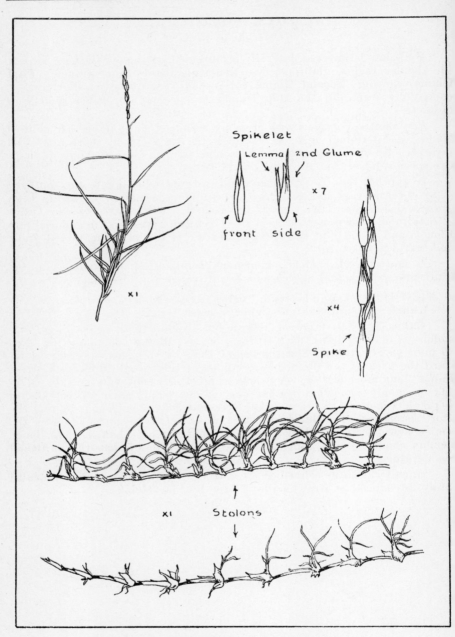

ZOYSIA TENUIFOLIA; Mascarene-grass

55. HILARIA H. B. K. (hī-lă′rĭ-à)

Spikelets sessile, in groups of 3, the groups falling from the axis entire, the central spikelets (next the axis) fertile, 1-flowered, the 2 lateral spikelets staminate, 2-flowered; **Glumes** coriaceous, those of the 3 spikelets forming a false involucre, in some species connate at the base, more or less asymmetric, usually bearing an awn on one side from about the middle; **Lemma** and **Palea** hyaline, about equal in length.

Perennial low grasses, the groups of spikelets appressed to the axis, in terminal spikes.

Four species of this genus inhabit the arid regions of southwestern United States, three in Texas; they are important range grasses. *Hilaria belangeri* (curly mesquite) is stoloniferous, while the other three, placed by some authors in a distinct genus, *Pleuraphis,* have rough scaly rhizomes instead of stolons.

H. jamesii, often known as galleta grass, and *H. mutica,* tobosa grass, commonly about 18′ tall, with spikes 1.5-5′ long, are very similar in aspect. The former has hairs at the base of the clusters 3-5 mm. long and linear-oblong glumes with the nerves parallel, while the latter has hairs at the base of the cluster about 1.5 mm. long and wedge-shaped glumes with the nerves somewhat spreading. In curly mesquite the hairs at the base of the cluster are about 0.5 mm. long, and the glumes have dark spots or glands below. *H. rigida* (Thurb.) Benth., a plant with woolly culms, is found in Arizona and perhaps adjacent states.

Curly mesquite, usually 4-8′ tall, has solid culms terminating in a short solitary spike, the long wiry stolons villous at the nodes, usually producing a new plant at each node. It is one of the most important grazing grasses on the Great Plains of Texas and New Mexico, extending into Mexico. In its range it is found along with buffalo-grass, either in small tufts or patches, or forming a sod, and at a distance resembles that grass. When in blossom it is easily distinguished by its inflorescence, but when not in flower look for the villous nodes of curly mesquite, the nodes of buffalo-grass being glabrous.

As the parts of the spikelets vary much the drawings give only the approximate details.

PLANTS LOW, 4-8′ tall, stoloniferous; spikes short, slender.　　1. H. belangeri
PLANTS USUALLY ABOUT 18′ tall, with scaly rhizomes; spikes long, stout.
　　Glumes oblong-linear, nerves parallel.　　　　　　　　　　2. H. jamesii
　　Glumes wedge-shaped, ciliate, nerves spreading.　　　　　3. H. mutica

1. H. BELANGERI (Steud.) Nash (bē-lăn-gē′rĭ); *H. texana* (Vasey) Nash; *H. cenchroides* H. B. K. var. *texana* Vasey; CURLY MESQUITE, CREEPING MESQUITE.

Culms commonly 4-8′ rarely 12′ tall, erect or decumbent, slender, solid, in dense tufts or forming a firm sod, the short or long stolons with few to many internodes, long-villous at the nodes, producing new plants at many of the nodes; **Blades** usually 2-3′, sometimes 1′ or as much as 6′ long, 2-3 mm. wide, flat or sometimes involute, erect and rather rigid, scabrous above and on the margins, with few to many hairs 0.5-5 mm. long, often papillose-ciliate; **Sheaths** mostly shorter than the internodes, rather distant, tightly sheathing the culm; **Ligule** membranaceous, short, laciniate; **Spike** commonly exserted, 1-1.5′ long, solitary, of 5-10 erect early-deciduous sessile clusters, the hairs at the base of the cluster about 0.5 mm. long; **Spikelets** often purple, finally pale, 5-7 mm. long, spreading above; **Glumes** oblong-linear with parallel nerves and unequal lobes, usually obtuse and with an awn, scabrous and with dark spots below; **Central Spikelet** pistillate, the **Glumes** similar, about equal, separating into two linear-oblong lobes bearing between them a scabrous awn about 1.5 mm. long extending beyond the glume and exceeding the spikelet; **Lemma** linear-acuminate, from a broad oblong base, 3-5-nerved, hyaline; **Lateral Spikelets** staminate, 2-flowered; **Glumes**, the first similar to that of the central spikelet but the awn shorter, the second longer, with shorter lobes and awn; **Lemmas** similar to that of the central spikelet, each subtending a staminate flower.

Dry hills and high prairies and plains, central Texas to Arizona, south into Mexico. Spring-fall.

2. H. JAMESII (Torr.) Benth. (jām′sĭ-ī); *Pleuraphis jamesii* Torr.;
   Galleta-grass.

Culms 8-25′ commonly about 18′ tall, usually in small tufts, branching at the base, erect from creeping rootstocks, strongly rooted, slightly hairy at the nodes, otherwise glabrous and smooth; **Blades** 1-7′ long, 1-3 mm. wide, erect or ascending, rigid, mostly involute, pungent-pointed, very scabrous; **Sheaths,** upper shorter than the internodes, smooth or scabrous, sometimes hairy at the throat; **Ligule** membranaceous, fringed, about 2 mm. long; **Spikes** purplish to pale, usually exserted, 1.5-4′ long, solitary, erect, rather densely-flowered, the hairs at the base of the cluster 3-5 mm. long; **Central Spikelet** pistillate, 6-8 mm. long; **Glumes** exclusive of the awns 4-5 mm. long, awn about as long as the glumes, produced from the midnerve, keeled, margins folded, nerves parallel, cleft nearly to the middle, ciliate, also 3-7 hispid or bristle-like awns 1-3 mm. long; **Lemma** exceeding the empty glumes, 3-nerved, unequally bifid, awn from the midnerve about 1 mm. long, sometimes one or more membranaceous or awnlike projections, margins involute; **Palea** slightly shorter than its lemma, bifid; **Lateral Spikelets** staminate, 2-flowered, 5-7 mm. long; **Glumes** shorter than the lemma, the nerves parallel, the first glume awned, the second emarginate, cuspidate, 3-nerved on the outer and 2-nerved on the inner side; **Lemma** and **Palea** about equal to the glumes, obtuse.

Hills and plains, Texas, New Mexico, to Nevada and Wyoming. Spring-summer.

3. H. MUTICA (Buckl.) Benth. (mū′tĭ-kà); *Pleuraphis mutica* Buckl.;
   Tobosa-grass.

Culms commonly 1-2 sometimes 3 feet tall, tufted, often pubescent at the nodes, erect or ascending from a decumbent base, with many sterile branches below, rootstocks creeping, coarse, woody, scaly; **Blades** 1.5-6′ long, 2-3 mm. wide, flat or involute, more or less scabrous; **Sheaths** overlapping below, distant above, margins sometimes ciliate above, often villous at the throat; **Ligule** membranaceous, fimbriate, about 2 mm. long; **Spikes** purplish to pale, finally exserted, 1.5-3′ long, 5-10 mm. wide, solitary, erect, the hairs at the base of the cluster about 1.5 mm. long; **Spikelets** 4-6 mm. long; **Central Spikelet** pistillate, 5-6.5 mm. long, the **Glumes** slightly shorter than the lemma, similar, usually divided into two irregular shaped lobes, 1-nerved at the base, the nerve splitting above into several awn-like bristles, ciliate on the membranaceous margins; **Lemma** about 5-6.5 mm. long, 3-nerved, bifid, a short awn-like membrane on one side of the apex, linear, obtuse; **Palea** about as long as its lemma; **Lateral Spikelets staminate,** 2-3-flowered, 4-6 mm. long; **Glumes** about 5 mm. long, membranaceous, ciliate, the first fan-shaped, about 7-nerved, thin, with a hairy awn on the edge below the middle next to the middle spikelet, the second awnless, sometimes one of the divergent nerves excurrent as a short awn, only slightly wider at the apex, otherwise similar to the first glume; **Lemmas** nearly as long as the glumes, membranaceous, linear, obtuse or truncate, 3-nerved.

Dry plains or flats, western Texas to Arizona, Colorado and Mexico. Spring-summer.

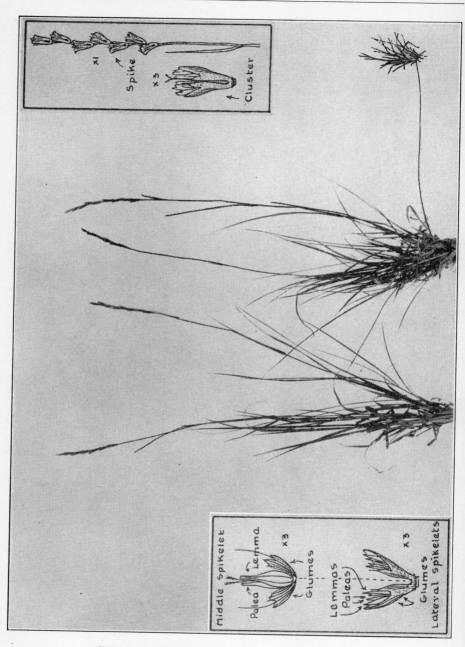

HILARIA BELANGERI, Curly Mesquite

Cluster ×3

Middle Spikelet
Palea — Lemma
Glumes
Lemma
×4 Glume ×4
×3
Lateral Spikelets
Lemma
Glume
×3

HILARIA JAMESII, Galleta-grass

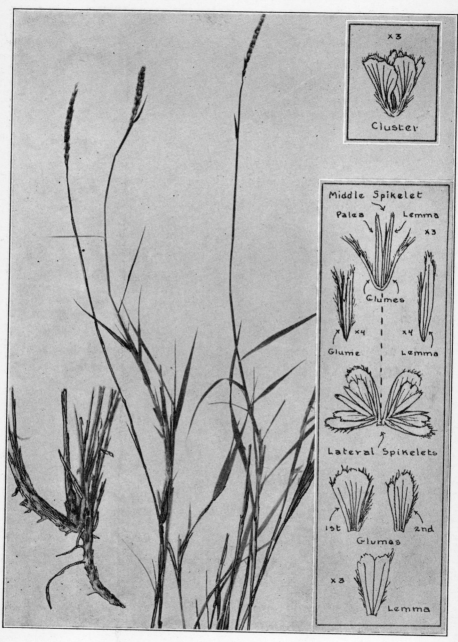

HILARIA MUTICA, Tobosa-grass

VII. CHLORIDEAE, THE GRAMA TRIBE

56. LEPTOCHLOA Beauv. (lĕp-tŏk′lō-à)

Spikelets 2-several-flowered, sessile or short-pediceled, approximate or somewhat distant along one side of a slender rachis, the rachilla disarticulating above the glumes and between the florets; **Glumes** unequal or nearly equal, awnless or mucronate, 1-nerved, usually shorter than the first lemma; **Lemmas** obtuse or acute, sometimes 2-toothed and mucronate or short-awned from between the teeth, 3-nerved, the nerves sometimes pubescent.

Annual or perennial grasses, with flat blades and numerous spikes or racemes scattered along a common axis forming a long or sometimes short panicle. Species probably 20, in the warmer regions; 10 species in the United States, mostly in the southern and southwestern states; 9 in Texas.

Several species of this genus, such as *L. dubia, L. fascicularis* and *L. floribunda,* have linear spikelets somewhat pediceled and less distinctly arranged in one-sided spikes. Some authors recognize this group as a distinct genus *Diplachne* and place it in *Festuceae.*

L. dubia, known as crowfoot, with large panicles, finally drooping, the 5-12 spikes rather heavy, is the only species in Texas with the *lateral nerves glabrous.* By reason of its wide range it varies much as to size and number of spikes, the plants, including the spikes, being much larger in the vicinity of Alpine than at San Antonio, Texas. It thrives on rocky hills and banks.

L. viscida has a short narrow panicle, commonly less than 4′ long, the spikes less than 2′ long, with the lemmas *viscid on the back.* It is found only in extreme western Texas, New Mexico, Arizona, and Mexico.

L. uninervia, commonly growing in damp sandy or brackish soil, has the florets loosely imbricated, the lateral nerves near the margins, while *L. floribunda* has closely imbricated florets with the lateral nerves not close to the margin, the lemmas acute.

L. nealleyi, growing along ditches, and *L. fascicularis,* in shallow water or brackish meadows, have elongated panicles of numerous spikes, the former with a pale-green narrow panicle of short appressed spikes, the latter with longer and heavier spikes ascending or somewhat spreading.

L. filiformis, known as red sprangle-top, a plant of the fields and waste places, has papillose-pilose sheaths, and numerous very slender spikes, the panicles as much as a foot long, the lemmas of the small spikelets awnless.

L. virgata, with numerous slender spikes, the lemmas acute and awnless, or the lower 1 or 2 short-awned, is usually found in sandy land.

L. chloridiformis, heretofore only known from Paraguay and Argentina, is a tall plant somewhat resembling Rhodes grass, but taller and with longer spikes. The author made the only collection of this grass in the United States, having collected it in dark sandy loam a few miles east of San Benito, Texas.

PLANTS PERENNIAL. LEMMAS PUBESCENT OR GLABROUS.
    LATERAL NERVES glabrous; lemmas broad, teeth rounded.   1. L. dubia
    LATERAL NERVES pubescent.
        Lemmas obtuse, mucronate; plants 3-6 feet tall.   2. L. chloridiformis
        Lemmas acute, awnless, or the lower 1 or 2 awned; plants less than 3 feet tall.
                3. L. virgata

PLANTS ANNUAL. LEMMAS USUALLY MORE OR LESS PUBESCENT.
SHEATHS PAPILLOSE-pilose; spikes slender; spikelets small, lemmas about
1.5 mm. long, awnless.
                    4. L. filiformis
SHEATHS NOT pilose; smooth or scabrous.
 LEMMAS awnless or mucronate only.
  Inflorescence very long, narrow, the very numerous spikes commonly erect
   and appressed; lemmas obtuse, 1.75 mm. long.   **5. L. nealleyi**
  Inflorescence not so long, broader, the branches usually ascending; spike-
   lets 3-10-flowered.
   Florets closely imbricated, the lateral nerves of the lemmas not close
    to the margin; lemmas acute.   **6. L. floribunda**
   Florets loosely imbricated (not overlapping more than half their length),
    the lateral nerves marginal, the lemmas obtuse. **7. L. uninervia**
 LEMMAS awned, the awn commonly less than 1 mm. long.
  Panicle large, more than 4′ long, the longer branches commonly as much as
   4′ long; second glume 3 mm. long; lemmas not viscid on the back.
                  8. L. fascicularis
  Panicle smaller, oval, usually less than 4′ long, the longer branches usually
   less than 2′ long; second glume less than 2.5 mm. long; lemmas viscid
   on the back.
                  9. L. viscida

1. L. DUBIA (H. B. K.) Nees (dū′bǐ-à); *Diplachne dubia* (H. B. K.)
Scribn.; TEXAS CROWFOOT or SPRANGLE-TOP.

 Culms 1-3 feet tall, tufted, sometimes branching; **Blades** 2-18′ long,
3-8 mm. wide, the upper short and the basal long, flat or involute, very
rough or rough only on the margin and toward the apex, often pilose on the
upper surface at the base; **Sheaths** shorter or longer than the internodes,
somewhat flattened, nearly smooth to very rough, sometimes pilose at the
throat; **Ligule** a ring of hairs; **Inflorescence** 4-12′ long, finally exserted
and nodding, the axillary included at the base, commonly 5-12, sometimes as many as 20, raceme-like branches 2-5′ long, racemosely arranged
along a scabrous axis, erect or spreading, the rachis scabrous, spikelet-
bearing to the base, the spikelets overlapping, on short pedicels; **Spikelets**
4-8 flowered, 5-8 mm. long, on drying or at maturity the florets spreading;
Glumes 1-nerved, lanceolate-acuminate, scabrous on the nerves, sometimes minutely so on the body, the first 3-4 mm. long, the second 4-5 mm.
long; **Lemmas** 3.5-4 mm. long, oblong, the two-lobed erose apex truncate
or rounded, the three nerves parallel and manifest, the lateral nerves
vanishing short of the apex, the midnerve stopping at the cleft or extending into a mucro, scabrous toward the apex, **Glabrous** or the margins
sparsely pubescent below, or the body below sometimes very sparsely
pubescent.

 Rocky hills and banks, Texas to Florida, Arizona and Oklahoma.
Spring-fall.

2. L. CHLORIDIFORMIS (Hack.) Parodi (klō-rǐ-dǐ-fôr′mǐs); *Diplachne
chloridiformis* Hack.

 Culms 3-6 feet tall, in rather large tufts, the sterile shoots numerous,
spikes and panicle as well as the plant as a whole much resembling Rhodes
grass but usually taller and with longer spikes; **Blades** 7-20′ long,
3-7 mm. wide, flat, narrowed toward the base, smooth or rough especially
toward the tip, often hirsute on the upper surface near the base;
Sheaths longer than the internodes, smooth or rough; **Ligule** a ring
of hairs about 1 mm. long, a row of long hairs just back of it;
Inflorescence finally exserted, consisting of 12-20 spikes, commonly
4-6′ long, arranged along a scabrous axis 1-1.5′ long, somewhat nodding as a
whole, but not widely spreading, the spikes densely-flowered, at first pale-
green or tinged with purple, finally straw-color; **Spikelets** about 4-

flowered, 3.5-4 mm. long, closely imbricated; **Glumes** 1-nerved, keeled, scabrous on the keel, acute, somewhat broad at the base, almost hyaline, the first 1.2 mm. long, the second 2.2 mm. long; **Lemmas,** the lower 2.5-3 mm. long, 3-nerved, the lateral nerves near the margin, scabrous on the midnerve toward the apex, the margins hairy nearly to the apex, the hairs 0.3-0.5 mm. long, the midnerve produced into a scabrous mucro between very short obtuse scabrous teeth; the upper florets similar but progressively smaller upward.

Rio Grande Valley, Paraguay and Argentina. (Dark sandy loam, waste ground, about 3 miles east of San Benito, Texas.) Spring.

3. L. VIRGATA (L.) Beauv. (vẽr-gā′tà).

Culms 1-3 feet tall, tufted, erect, sparingly branched; **Blades** 3-12′ long, about 2-7 mm. (5-15) wide, flat or soon becoming involute, rough below, hirsute above near the base; **Sheaths** usually shorter than the internodes, pilose at the throat, otherwise from glabrous to papillose-hispid; **Ligule** a dense ring of short hairs; **Inflorescence** 4-6′ long, of numerous slender spikes, often more than 15, 1.5-4′ long, erect or ascending, spikelets subsessile, overlapping on a slightly scabrous rachis; **Spikelets** 3-5-flowered, 2.6-4 mm. long; **Glumes** acute, 1-nerved, scabrous on the nerve, subequal, 1.6-2.3 mm. long, the second usually slightly longer; **Lemmas,** the lower 1.7-2.5 mm. long, the upper gradually smaller, awnless, or the lower 1 or 2 with the midnerve excurrent from between a two-lobed apex into an awn as much as half the length of the lemma, rarely as long as the lemma, the upper sometimes with a short awn, the midnerve hispidulous above, the upper portions of the lateral nerves pubescent, the internerves glabrous or sparingly appressed-pubescent.

Southern Texas to Florida near the Coast. Spring and summer.

4. L. FILIFORMIS (Lam.) Beauv. (fĭl-ĭ-fôr′mĭs) ; *Leptochloa mucronata* (Michx.) Kunth; RED SPRANGLE-TOP, SLENDER-GRASS.

Culms 1-3 feet tall, erect, tufted, sparingly branched, smooth, glabrous; **Blades** 3-8′ long, 5-12 mm. (2-6) wide, flat, lax, narrowed at the base, margins and both surfaces scabrous, sparingly papillose-pilose near the base; **Sheaths** shorter than the internodes, mostly papillose-pilose, the lower often almost glabrous; **Ligule** short, lacerate-toothed; **Inflorescence** 4-12′ long, often partially included at the base, slightly pyramidal, spikes numerous, as many as 75, slender, rigid, spreading or ascending, the lower 1.5-5′ long, distant 2-15 mm., axis scabrous; **Spikelets** 2-3 mm. long, 2-4-flowered; **Glumes** membranaceous, with one scabrous nerve, acute, subequal, the first about 1.5-1.8 mm. long, the second 1.7-2 mm. long; **Lemmas** about 1.5 mm. long, two-toothed, broad, obtuse or rounded, ciliate on the nerves and margins.

Fields and sandy river banks, Texas to Florida, north to Virginia and Illinois. Summer.

5. L. NEALLEYI Vasey (nē′lĭ-ī).

Culms 2.5-3 feet tall, in small tufts, erect, slender, somewhat flat-tended; **Blades** 2.5-14′ long, upper short, 3-6 mm. wide, acuminate, rough on both surfaces and margins; **Sheaths** longer than the internodes, upper including the base of the panicle; **Ligule** membranaceous, 1.5 mm. long, fimbriate; **Inflorescence** 6-15′ long, usually partly included at the base, narrow, of 25-27 slender spikes, commonly about 1′ sometimes 2′ long, appressed, erect or ascending, pale-green; **Spikelets**

3-5-flowered, 2-2.5 mm. long, sub-sessile on one side of the rachis; **Glumes** 1-nerved, mostly obtuse (or subacute), scabrous on the nerve; the first about 0.7 mm. long, the second about 1.5 mm. long; **Lemmas** 1.5-1.75 mm. long, 3-nerved, the lateral nerves near the margin, the midnerve sometimes excurrent from between the lobes of a bifid apex, subobtuse, the nerves rather long-pubescent near the apex.

In low lands, usually along ditches, central and southern Texas.

6. L. FLORIBUNDA Doell (flō-rĭ-bŭn′dȧ).

Culms 2-3.5 feet tall, more or less, tufted, erect, rather stout, branching; **Blades** 1.5-13′ long, 1.5-10 mm. wide, flat, slightly rough; **Sheaths** shorter than the internodes, scabrous to smooth; **Ligule** membranaceous, 3 mm. long; **Panicles** erect or slightly nodding, as long as 13′, oblong-linear, densely-flowered, leadish-green, the raceme-like branches 1-3′ long, mostly ascending, the spikelets on scabrous pedicels usually less than 2 mm. long; **Spikelets** 5-7-flowered, 3-4.5 mm. long, ovate-lanceolate, the green nerves prominent; **Glumes** scabrous on the keel, acute, the first about 1.2 mm. long, the second about 2 mm. long; **Lemmas** 2-2.5 mm. long, broadly acute, closely imbricate, overlapping more than two-thirds their length, the lateral nerves not close to the margins, the upper half scabrous especially on the nerves, a few soft hairs at or near the base and sometimes a few on the body of the lemma, the midnerve projected into a mucro from between a minutely two-toothed apex, the lateral nerves barely reaching the margins somewhat below the apex.

Texas, Louisiana, Mississippi, and Indiana; also Brazil. Summer.

7. L. UNINERVIA (Presl) Hitchc. & Chase (ū-nĭ-nûr′vĭ-ȧ) ; *L. imbricata* Thurb.; *Diplachne imbricata* (Thurb.) Scribn.

Culms 1-3 feet tall, densely tufted, erect or geniculate-decumbent at the base, sparingly branching, terete, minutely scabrous just below the panicle; **Blades** 4-16′ long, 2-3 mm. wide, flat or usually involute, radical blades numerous, long-attenuate, very hispid with a white band along the midnerve; **Sheaths** longer than the internodes, open, upper portion sometimes somewhat rough; **Ligule** membranaceous, 3-4 mm. long, decurrent, wider than the blades; **Panicles** exserted or included at the base, narrowly oblong, 4-10′ long, the branches 1-3′ long, solitary or fascicled, ascending or appressed, spikelets equal to the interval or overlapping, arranged along one side of the scabrous angled rachis, the pedicels about 1 mm. long; **Spikelets** 3-10-flowered, linear-oblong, 3.5-8 mm. long, 2 mm. wide or less; **Glumes** ovate, hispidulous on the nerve, the first about 1.6 mm. long, narrow, acute, the second about 2-3 mm. long, obtuse; **Lemmas** loosely imbricate, not overlapping more than half their length; 2.5-3 mm. long, truncate or sometimes narrowly obtuse, oblong, the three nerves parallel, the lateral near the margins, often excurrent into a short point, the midnerve terminating in a short mucro between two short teeth, the lateral nerves pubescent on the lower half and the midnerve pubescent or glabrous at the base.

Ditch or river banks, shell holes on beaches along the Coast; southern and western Texas to California, Colorado, Mississippi and Maine to New Jersey. Spring.

8. L. FASCICULARIS (Lam.) Gray (fȧ-sĭk-ū-lȧr′ĭs) ; *Diplachne fascicularis* (Lam.) Beauv.; SALT MEADOW-GRASS.

Culms 1-4 feet tall, tufted, erect or decumbent at the base, somewhat flattened, branching; **Blades** 18′ long or less, 3-5 mm. wide, flat, soon becoming involute, the midrib and veins on the upper surface white and prominent, long-attentuate, rough; **Sheaths** longer than the internodes, loose, rough toward the summit; **Ligule** membranaceous, 3-4 mm. long; **Inflorescence** exserted or included at the base, as long as 24' usually shorter, as many as 40 raceme-like branches, 4' long or less, mostly in ones or twos, spikelet-bearing to the base, the appressed spikelets overlapping, with pedicels about 1 mm. long; **Spikelets** about 10-flowered, 8-10 mm. long, flattened; **Glumes** 1-nerved, acute or subacute, scabrous on the keel, somewhat scarious, the first 2-2.5 mm. long, the second 3-3.5 mm. long; **Lemmas** exclusive of the awns 3-3.5 mm. long, acutish, narrow, 3-nerved, entire, or the midnerve produced into an awn about 1 mm. long from between a bifid apex, the lateral nerves sometimes excurrent into a short point, the three nerves villous on the lower half, rachilla-joint about 1 mm. long, hairy at the apex.

Brackish meadows or in shallow water, Texas to Florida, and in the Mississippi Valley to Missouri, Illinois and South Dakota. Summer-fall.

9. L. VISCIDA (Scribn.) Beal (vĭs'ĭ-dà); *Diplachne viscida* Scribn.

Culms 5-15' tall, tufted, erect or spreading, geniculate, freely branching (Beal says the plant is covered more or less with acrid viscid glands); **Blades** 0.5-2.5' long, sometimes longer, 2-3 mm. wide, flat or folded, somewhat scabrous; **Sheaths** about equaling the internodes, short and loose, flattened; **Ligule** membranaceous, lacerate, about 1.5 mm. long; **Panicles** usually included at the base, 1-3' long, narrow, rather compact, erect, those from the axils of the numerous leaves short, the angular axis slightly scabrous, the branches slender, appressed or narrowly ascending or somewhat spreading, 10-25 mm. long, bearing a few nearly sessile spikelets; **Spikelets** 3-6-flowered, 3-5 mm. long; **Glumes** acute, scabrous on the keel, the first 1.2-2 mm. long, the second 1.5-2.5 mm. long; **Lemmas** often viscid, 2-2.5 mm. long, elliptic-oblong, obtuse, the two hyaline lobes or teeth somewhat lacerate, the lateral nerves vanishing at the margin in very obscure teeth, the midnerve produced into a short awn usually less than 1 mm. long, all the nerves slightly pubescent below, more or less scabrous towards the apex.

In dry soil, Texas, New Mexico, Arizona; also Mexico. Fall.

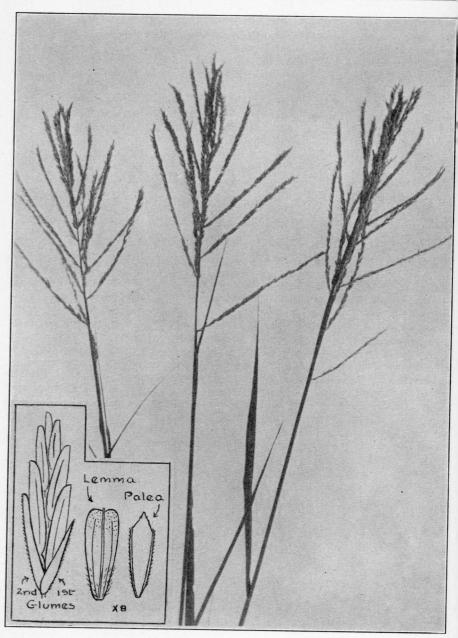

LEPTOCHLOA DUBIA; Texas Crowfoot, Sprangle-top

LEPTOCHLOA CHLORIDIFORMIS

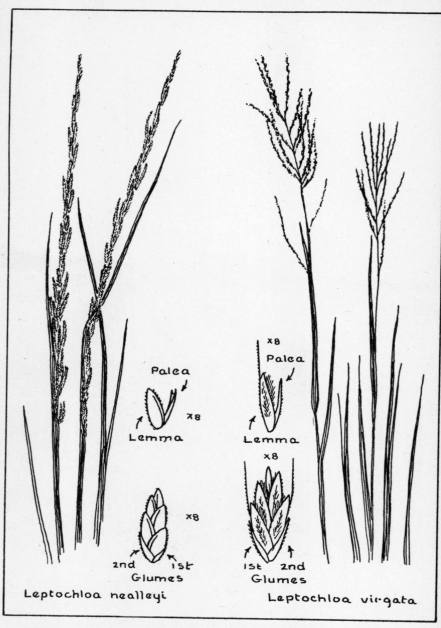

LEPTOCHLOA NEALLEYI AND LEPTOCHLOA VIRGATA

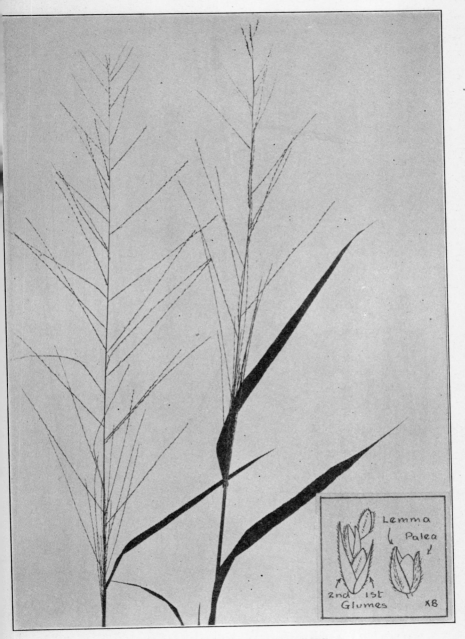

LEPTOCHLOA FILIFORMIS

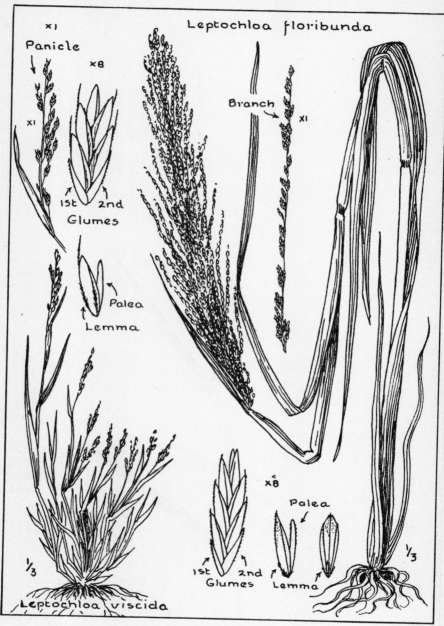

×1
Panicle
×8
Leptochloa floribunda
×1
Branch ×1
1st 2nd
Glumes
Palea
Lemma
×8
Palea
1st 2nd
Glumes Lemma
⅓
Leptochloa viscida
⅓

LEPTOCHLOA VISCIDA and LEPTOCHLOA FLORIBUNDA

LEPTOCHLOA UNINERVIA

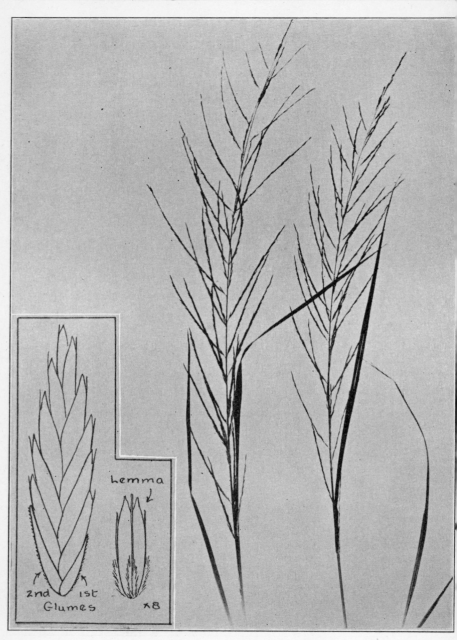

LEPTOCHLOA FASCICULARIS; Salt Meadow-grass

57.   TRICHONEURA Anderss. (trī-kō-nū'rà)

Spikelets few-flowered, the rachilla disarticulating above the glumes, the internodes pilose at the base, disarticulating near their summit, the upper part forming a short callus below the floret; **Glumes** about equal, 1-nerved, long-acuminate, mostly as long as the spikelet or longer; **Lemmas** bidentate, 3-nerved, the lateral nerves near the margin, the midnerve usually excurrent as a short awn, the margins long-ciliate; **Palea** broad, the nerves near the margin.

Annual or perennial grasses with simple panicles, the spikelets short-pediceled along one side of the main branches.

Trichoneura is closely allied to the genus *Leptochloa,* differing in the much larger spikelets, the acuminate or awn-pointed glumes which about equal or exceed the florets, the flattened bearded callus, and the bearded base of the rachilla-joint.   Hackel regards this genus as transitional to *Triodia.*

This is an African and South American genus, *Trichoneura elegans* being a new species and the first plant of this genus collected in North America.   The author first collected this plant in very sandy land just south of Devine, Texas, and later collected it near Refugio and on the sand dunes along the bay about 10 miles south of Corpus Christi, Texas.

It is a tufted annual, 2-5 feet tall, freely branching, and late in the season sends up numerous small culms from the base, often as short as 4', the panicles small and densely-flowered.

T. ELEGANS Swallen (ĕl'ē-găns).

Culms 2-5 feet tall, tufted, erect, branching, hispidulous below the panicle, otherwise glabrous; **Blades** 3-12' long, 3-7 mm. wide, pungently pointed, scabrous; **Sheaths** mostly longer than the internodes, scabrous, minutely papillose, sometimes sparsely pubescent; **Ligule** membranaceous, 2-3 mm. long, almost truncate; **Panicles** ovate, finally exserted, 4-8' long, or those of the branches shorter and often included at the base, about 2' wide at maturity, densely-flowered, the axis hispidulous; **Racemes** 12-20, approximate, narrowly ascending to somewhat spreading, the lower commonly 1.5-3' long, shorter above, spikelet-bearing nearly to the base, the spikelets overlapping, alternate in two rows, the rachis 3-angled, scabrous on the angles; **Spikelets** 4-8-flowered, 8-10 mm. long, on hispidulous pedicels less than 1 mm. long; **Glumes** equaling the florets, sometimes shorter or longer, acuminate, awn-pointed, scabrous; **Lemmas**, the lower about 5 mm. long, the others gradually shorter, 3-nerved, the lateral nerves near the margin, scabrous toward the acute or obtuse 2-lobed apex, awned from between the lobes, the awns not more than 0.5 mm. long, the marginal nerves conspicuously ciliate (on their marginal sides) on the lower half or two-thirds with spreading hairs as much as 1 mm. long, the flattened callus bearded on the margins, the rachilla-joint densely bearded at the base; **Palea** nearly as long as the lemma, acute, two-toothed, scabrous on the back and keels.

White sandy land, Texas.   (Devine, Refugio and the sand dunes below Corpus Christi.)   Fall.

TRICHONEURA ELEGANS

58. TRIPOGON Roth (trī-pō'gŏn)

Spikelets several-flowered, nearly sessile, appressed in two rows along ne side of a slender rachis, the rachilla disarticulating above the glumes nd between the florets; **Glumes** somewhat unequal, acute or acuminate, arrow, 1-nerved; **Lemmas** narrow, 3-nerved, bearing at the base a tuft f long hairs, bifid at the apex, the midnerve extending as a short awn.

Our species is a low tufted *perennial*, with capillary blades and slender ɔlitary spikes, the spikelets somewhat distant.

It is found at several locations in Texas: in Llano County, especially ear the town of Llano; in Mason County about ten miles north of Mason n the Mason-Brady road; and in Gillespie County near the county line n the Llano-Fredericksburg road. It seems to thrive in the cracks, low laces and at the base of granite boulders, rarely distant from the exposed ranite formations. These boulders lie at random, or cover an acre or more, ɔmetimes even entire hills. This grass is not found growing among other ɔck formations, which leads one to believe that it is confined to the granite ɔrmations of the above and perhaps some of the adjoining counties. *Selaginella riddelii Van Eselt.*, a rather rare plant which is shown at the ottom of the photograph, was found growing along with this grass at very location.)

'. SPICATUS (Nees) Ekman (spī-kā'tŭs); *Leptochloa spicata* (Doell) Scribn.; *Diplachne spicata* Doell.

Culms 4-12' commonly 5-8' tall, densely-tufted, erect, very slender, mple, naked above, the leaves numerous at the base; **Blades** 1-3' commonly .5-2' long, the upper short, 1.5 mm. wide or less, flat or involute toward he aristate tip, erect, margins rough, sparsely hispidulous and sparsely ilose on the upper surface; **Sheaths** mostly shorter than the internodes, hort, short-pilose at the throat; **Ligule** a very short ciliate membrane; pikes solitary, 2-4' long, slender, erect, often curved, the sessile appressed pikelets often distant below and somewhat overlapping above; **Spikelets** -12-flowered, 5-8 mm. long, about 1.2 mm. wide, linear-lanceolate, flat; lumes narrow, acute or obtuse, sometimes slightly toothed, the first bout 1.5 mm. long, usually acute, the second about 2.5 mm. long, usually btuse; **Lemmas**, exclusive of the short awn, about 2.5 mm. long, the three erves glabrous, the midnerve excurrent between the lobes of a bifid apex ɪto an awn usually less than 1 mm. long, the lateral nerves stopping short f the obtuse lobes, sometimes slightly pubescent at the base, the rachilla ʲith a tuft of hairs at the nodes; **Palea** apparently stalked at the base, iliate; **Grain** about 1 mm. long, 0.2 mm. wide, oblong, amber color.

Among granite rocks, Mason, Llano and Gillespie counties, Texas, lso northern Mexico, Cuba and South America. Spring and summer.

TRIPOGON SPICATUS

59. ELEUSINE Gaertn. (ĕl-ū-sī′nē)

Spikelets few-to-several-flowered, compressed, sessile or closely im-
ricate, in two rows along one side of a rather broad rachis, the latter not
rolonged beyond the spikelets; **Rachilla** disarticulating above the glumes
nd between the florets; **Glumes** unequal, rather broad, acute, 1-nerved or
he second 3-7-nerved, shorter than the first lemma; **Lemmas** acute with 3
trong green nerves close together forming a keel and an extra nerve on
ach side near the margin, the uppermost somewhat reduced; **Seed** dark
rown, roughened by fine ridges, loosely inclosed in the thin pericarp.

Annual grasses, with two-to-several rather stout spikes, digitate at the
ummit of the culms, sometimes with one or two a short distance below, or
arely with a single terminal spike. Species about six, in the warmer regions
f the Eastern Hemisphere, one a common introduced weed in America.

Goose-grass, usually 6-24′ tall, spreading or prostrate, is a garden or
ommon roadside weed, especially in the warmer parts of America extending
nto many of the northern states.

. INDICA (L.) Gaertn. (ĭn′dĭ-kâ); GOOSE-GRASS, YARD-GRASS.

Culms 6-24′ tall, tufted, coarse, erect or decumbent, and spreading or
rostrate, flattened; **Blades** 3-12′ long, 3-10 mm. wide, flat, margins
cabrous or papillose-ciliate with long hairs near the base; **Sheaths** usually
horter than the internodes above, much overlapping below, flattened,
parsely hirsute or papillose-hirsute at throat and margins at base, or
labrous; **Spikes** 2-7 (2-10) rarely one, stout, whorled or approximate at
he summit, one or two sometimes distant, 1-3.5′ long, axis pubescent or
ilose; **Spikelets** 3-5 mm. long, 3-6-flowered, flattened; **Glumes** acute,
ninutely scabrous on the keel, scarious, the first 1-nerved, narrow, 2-2.5
nm. long, the second 3-7-nerved, broader, about 3 mm. long; **Lemmas**
-4 mm. long, subobtuse, 3-5-nerved at the middle and one nerve extra
ear each margin.

In waste places, throughout North America; common in Texas.
ummer and fall.

ELEUSINE INDICA; Goose-grass, Yard-grass

60. DACTYLOCTENIUM Willd. (dăk-tĭ-lŏk-tē'nĭ-ŭm)

Spikelets 3-5-flowered, compressed, sessile and closely imbricate, in two rows along one side of the rather narrow, flat rachis, the end projecting in a point beyond the spikelets; **Rachilla** disarticulating above the first glume and between the florets; **Glumes** somewhat unequal, broad, 1-nerved, the first persistent upon the rachis, the second mucronate or short-awned below the tip, deciduous; **Lemmas** firm, broad, keeled, acuminate or short-awned, 3-nerved, the lateral nerves indistinct, the upper floret reduced; the **Palea** about as long as the lemma; **Seed** subglobose, rigid or wrinkled, inclosed in a thin, early disappearing pericarp.

Annual or *perennial* grasses, with flat blades and two-to-several short thick spikes, digitate and widely spreading at the summit of the culms. Species three, in the warmer parts of the Eastern Hemisphere, one a common weed in tropical America.

Our one species, crowfoot, a tropical prostrate or spreading annual, often forming mats, and taking root at the nodes, has 2-7 spikes, the rachis prolonged into a long point beyond the uppermost spikelet.

D. AEGYPTIUM (L.) Richt. (ī-jĭp'tĭ-ŭm); CROWFOOT-GRASS, EGYPTIAN-GRASS.

Culms 6-24' tall, tufted, decumbent-ascending or spreading, often extensively creeping and rooting at the nodes; **Blades** 5-10' long, 3-6 mm. wide, flat, smooth or slightly rough, margins papillose-hirsute, especially near the base, both surfaces from glabrous to sparsely pubescent; **Sheaths** shorter than the internodes above, crowded and overlapping below; **Ligule** membranaceous, truncate, about 1 mm. long; **Spikes** 2-7, 0.5-2' long, thick, digitate, ascending or spreading, often curved, villous in axils; **Spikelets** 3-5-flowered, 3-3.5 mm. long, flattened; **Glumes** scabrous on the keel, the first acute, about 1.5 mm. long, persistent, the second a little longer and broader, mucronate or short-awned below the tip, as much as 2-3 mm. long, deciduous; **Lemmas** about 3 mm. long, abruptly pointed or acuminate, or with a short awn usually curved.

In cultivated land and waste places, especially sandy land; in the southern states including Texas, extending northward to Illinois and New York. Summer and fall.

DACTYLOCTENIUM AEGYPTIUM; Crowfoot-grass

61. CYNODON Rich. (sī′nō-dŏn)
(Capriola Adans.)

Spikelets 1-flowered, awnless, sessile in two rows along one side of a slender continuous rachis, the rachilla disarticulating above the glumes and prolonged behind the palea as a slender naked bristle, this sometimes bearing a rudimentary lemma; **Glumes** narrow, acuminate, 1-nerved, about equal, shorter than the floret; **Lemma** strongly compressed, pubescent on the keel, firm in texture, 3-nerved, the lateral nerves close to the margins.

Perennial, usually low grasses, with creeping stolons or rhizomes, short blades, and several slender spikes digitate at the summit of the upright flowering stems. One species in the United States.

Bermuda-grass survives through dry spells, and with its numerous stolons climbing over rocks and banks, spreads over new ground, especially over cultivated fields, thereby propagating readily, and often becoming almost as troublesome as Johnson grass.

From its many stolons arise numerous digitate, one-sided, slender, purple spikes, 3-6 to a culm, with small, dark-purple flowers, rendering a plot of the grass very beautiful.

It is considered the most important grass in the south, being extensively used as a forage and lawn grass, as well as a soil binder. Along walls and other protected places, in its most southern range the grass may be found in blossom during the entire year.

C. DACTYLON (L.) Pers. (dăk′tĭ-lŏn); *Capriola dactylon* (L.) Kuntze; BERMUDA-GRASS, WIRE-GRASS.

Culms 4-12′ tall, sometimes much taller, from long creeping rhizomes, the branching stolons long; **Blades** 1-2.5′ long, 1-4 mm. wide, flat, rigid, scabrous above, smooth or scabrous below, villous at base near ligule; **Ligule** ciliate, or also a few long hairs; **Sheaths** crowded at the base of culm and along stolons, mostly glabrous; **Spikes** 3-8, 1-3′ long, purple, rachis flat; **Spikelets** about 2 mm. long; **Glumes** scabrous on keel, narrow, about 1.5 mm. long, first slightly shorter than the second; **Lemma** broader and longer than glumes, narrowly oval, about 2 mm. long, some sparsely pubescent on keel, lateral nerves near the margin; **Palea** about as long as its lemma; **Stigmas** purple; **Stamens** 3, and rachilla prolonged into bristles.

In fields and waste places in southern states, extending north to Kansas and Maryland. Spring to fall.

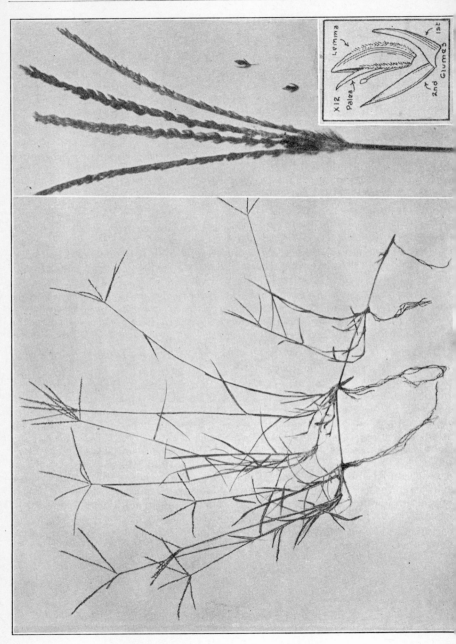

CYNODON DACTYLON; BERMUDA-GRASS

62. WILLKOMMIA Hack. (wĭl-kŏm'ĭ-à)

Spikelets 1-flowered, dorsally compressed, sessile in two rows on one side of a slender rachis and appressed to it, the rachilla somewhat lengthened below and above the second glume, disarticulating just above it, not prolonged above the floret; **Glumes** thin, the first narrow, about two-thirds as long as the second, nerveless, obtuse, the second 1-nerved, subacute; **Lemma** about as long as the second glume, awnless, 3-nerved, the lateral nerves near the margins, the back of the lemma sparingly pubescent between the nerves, the margins densely covered with silky hairs; **Palea** 2-nerved, the nerves densely silky hairy.

Annuals or *perennials*, with several short spikes scattered along a main axis; one species a low, tufted *perennial*. Species four; three in South Africa, one in Texas.

W. TEXANA Hitchc. (tĕks-ā'nà).

Culms 8-16′ tall, tufted, erect, slender; **Blades** from a few millimeters to 3.5′ long, the upper very short, 1-2 mm. wide, flat or soon involute, often sparsely ciliate-hispid on the cartilaginous margins toward the base; **Sheaths** shorter than the internodes, the upper somewhat inflated and often enclosing the base of the panicle; **Panicle** erect, narrow, 2-5′ long, the 3-8 spikes 1-1.5′ long, appressed or nearly so to the axis, densely-flowered; Spikelets 3-3.5 mm. long, oblong, elliptic; **Glumes** and **Lemmas** as described above; **Palea** about as long as the lemma, the silky hairs long.

In alkali spots (hardpan), in prairies and openings in woods, confined to a few localities in Texas. (Near Hempstead, Beeville, and Magnolia Beach.) Spring to fall.

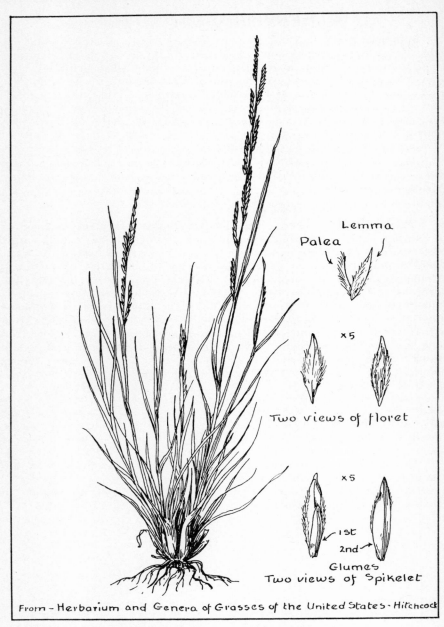

Palea   Lemma

×5

Two views of floret

×5

1st
2nd
Glumes
Two views of Spikelet

From - Herbarium and Genera of Grasses of the United States - Hitchcock

WILLKOMMIA TEXANA

63. SCHEDONNARDUS Steud. (shē-dŏn-är′dŭs)

Spikelets 1-flowered, sessile and somewhat distant, in two rows on one side of a slender continuous 3-angled rachis, appressed to its slightly concave sides, the rachilla disarticulating above the glumes, not prolonged; **Glumes** narrow, stiff, somewhat unequal, acuminate, 1-nerved; **Lemmas** narrow, acuminate, a little longer than the glumes, 3-nerved.

A low, tufted *perennial*, with stiff, slender, divergent spikes arranged rather remotely along a common axis. Species one, on the Great Plains of the United States and in Argentina.

Schedonnardus is a low straggling grass, and at maturity the axis of the plant becomes elongated often to over half the length of the plant, and the scythe-shaped culm turns downward with the tips of the panicle touching the ground. Finally the axis of the panicle breaks away and becomes a tumble weed rolling before the wind.

S. PANICULATUS (Nutt.) Trel. (på-nĭk-ū-lā′tŭs); SCHEDONNARDUS.

Culms 8-25′ tall, tufted, branching at the base, erect or spreading with the tips of the plant turned scythe-shaped toward the ground, slender, rigid, hollow, green or often purple; **Blades** nearly flat becoming conduplicate, 0.5-2.5′ long, 2.5 mm. wide, mostly basal, upper shorter, minutely scabrous on the white margins, when old spirally twisted, otherwise smooth; **Sheaths** loose, flattened, crowded at the base; **Ligule** membranaceous, 3 mm. long, decurrent down the margins of the sheath; **Panicle** from a few inches to 18′ long, with usually 3-13 slender racemose spikes 1-5′ long, distant 0.5 to 2′, alternate on the concave axis, rigid and widely spreading, the rachis hispid; **Spikelets** 3-6 mm. long, narrow; **Glumes** hispid on the nerve, the margins scarious, acuminate or with a short awn, the first including the awn 2-4 mm. long, the awn usually about one-fourth of its entire length, the second including awn 2.5-6 mm. long, the awn being about one-third its entire length; **Lemma** 3-5 mm. long, longer than the body of the second glume, lanceolate, acute, with three green nerves, rounded on the back, minutely hispid on the upper part, slightly pubescent below.

The spikelets on different plants seem to vary much as to length, and even on the same spike the upper are usually shorter.

Open ground, Texas and New Mexico, Montana, North Dakota to Illinois. Spring and summer.

Lemma
Palea

x4

x6

1st 2nd
Glumes

Schedonnardus
paniculatus

SCHEDONNARDUS PANICULATUS

64. SPARTINA Schreb. (spär-tī'nà)

Spikelets 1-flowered, much flattened laterally, sessile and usually closely imbricate, on one side of a continuous rachis, disarticulating below the glumes, the rachilla not produced beyond the floret; **Glumes** keeled, 1-nerved, acute or short-awned, the first shorter, the second often exceeding the lemma; **Lemma** firm, keeled, the lateral nerves obscure, narrowed to a rather obtuse point; **Palea** 2-nerved, keeled and flattened, the keel between or at one side of the nerves.

Stout, erect, often tall *perennials*, with simple rigid culms and usually extensively creeping, firm, scaly rhizomes, long rough blades, and two-to-many appressed or sometimes spreading spikes racemose on the main axis. Eight species in the United States.

Spartina, characteristic plants of the sea sands, marshes and alkaline flats, is represented by five species in Texas. By reason of their long rootstocks they are good sand binders. They are too coarse for forage.

The spikes are usually tinged with purple, and are numerous except in No. 3. In two of our species the spikes are closely appressed forming a narrow cylindrical spikelike panicle. *Spartina alterniflora* var. *glabra* is a rigid erect plant with erect or ascending broad blades. It is common in shallow salt water along the Gulf coast, especially in the shallow inland bays. *Spartina spartinae*, a rigidly erect plant, 2-4 feet tall with narrow conduplicate blades, grows mostly in rather large tough clumps, but where mowed forms a continuous sod. It thrives along the coast from Brownsville, Texas, to Mississippi and Florida, often extending many miles inland and covering extensive areas.

In three of our species the panicles are more or less open, the spikes mostly ascending. *Spartina pectinata*, or slough-grass, an inland grass, is tall and erect with 5-20 erect or ascending light-colored spikes and broad blades. It has been used for waterproof thatch and for the manufacture of paper and twine. *Spartina cynosuroides*, the tallest and most robust of the species, sometimes as much as 9 feet tall and nearly an inch thick at the base, has very broad rough blades and a rather large panicle of ascending or spreading spikes 2-5' long. It is confined to the water's edge and wet marshes. In Texas it has a range from the Houston Ship Channel to the Sabine River. *Spartina patens* var. *juncea* is a slender, wiry, dark grass, 2-3 feet tall, commonly with 4-5 ascending or spreading spikes 1.5-2' long, and narrow involute blades. It is sometimes used to make brooms. It is found growing at the water's edge, but like *S. spartinae*, extends some distance inland and is often associated with that species.

SPIKES NARROWLY ascending to spreading, numerous except in No. 3.
  FIRST glume about as long as the lemma, awn-pointed, keel scabrous; second glume long-awned.   1. S. pectinata
  FIRST glume shorter than the lemma, mostly about half as long; second glume awnless, acute.
    Blades flat, over 12 mm. wide.   2. S. cynosuroides
    Blades involute, less than 5 mm. wide, spikes commonly 4-5.
      3. S. patens var. juncea
SPIKES CLOSELY appressed, numerous, crowded; first glume shorter than the lemma, mostly about half as long; second glume awnless. acute.
  FIRST glume scabrous-hispid on the keel; blades conduplicate, about 2mm. wide, folded.   4. S. spartinae
  FIRST glume not scabrous-hispid on the keel; blades flat, usually 7-12 mm. wide.   5. S. alterniflora var. glabra

1. S. PECTINATA Link (pĕk-tĭ-nā'tå); *S. michauxiana* Hitchc.; TALL MARSH-GRASS, SLOUGH-GRASS.

Culms 3-6 feet tall, erect, simple, stout, from stout rootstocks; **Blades** 8-30' long or even longer, upper shorter, 6-15 mm. wide, flat or involute toward the apex, long-acuminate, tapering to a slender point, margins rough, slightly rough above; **Sheaths** overlapping, crowded below, close; **Ligule** membranaceous, ciliate with soft slender hairs 1-2 mm. long; **Panicle** of about 15 spikes (5-20) 1-2.5' (2-5') long, peduncles of lower spikes as much as 1' long, upper almost sessile, ascending or erect; **Rachis** scabrous on the margin; **Spikelets** including awns 12-15 mm. long; **Glumes** awned-pointed or awned, strongly hispid-scabrous on the keels, the first about 10 mm. long including an awn 1-3 mm. long, about as long as the lemma, the second about 12-15 mm. long including awn 3-5 mm. long, with five nerves so close together as to appear one; **Lemma** 8-10 mm. long strongly keeled, hispid-scabrous on the keel, the midnerve terminating just below the bifid apex.

In swamps, along streams, fresh or brackish water, eastern United States to Colorado and south to New Mexico and Texas. August-October.

2. S. CYNOSUROIDES (L.) Roth (sī-nō-sū-roi'dēz); SALT REED-GRASS.

Culms 4-9 feet tall, erect, simple, robust, often as much as 20 mm. in diameter near the base; **Blades** 1-2.5 feet long, more or less, 12-30 mm. wide, more or less, flat, scabrous, especially on the margin; **Sheaths** overlapping, crowded toward the base; **Ligule** a short membrane, densely ciliate, the hairs 1-2 mm. long; **Panicles** 6-15' long, oblong, purplish, commonly of 20-40 sometimes 50 spikes, often peduncled, ascending or spreading, 2-5' long, the rachis rough on the margins; **Spikelets** 8-14 mm. long, flattened; **Glumes** acute or barely mucronate, scabrous-hispid on the keel, the first about half the length of the second, shorter than the lemma, the second longer than the palea; **Lemma** nearly as long as the palea, the lateral nerves obscure or wanting, scabrous on the upper part of the keel, ciliate on the margin toward the obtuse tip.

Salt and brackish marshes, along the coast, southeast Texas to Florida and Atlantic coast; Galveston Bay and Houston Ship Channel to the Sabine River. (San Jacinto battlefield.) July and August.

3. S. PATENS var. JUNCEA (Michx.) Hitchc. (pā'tĕns jŭn-sē'å); *S. juncea* (Michx.) Willd.; RUSH SALT-GRASS.

Culms 1-3.5 feet tall, usually from a branching and decumbent base, with long slender rootstocks, erect, slender; **Blades** 4-16' long, upper short, 3-4 mm. wide, involute, rather rigid, smooth below, somewhat rough above, dark-green; **Sheaths** overlapping, crowded below; **Ligule** a ring of very short hairs; **Panicle** of 2-8 spikes usually 4-5, sessile or short-peduncled, erect or spreading, 1.5-3' long, usually about 2'; **Spikelets** 6-9 mm. long, oblong-linear, green or purple, crowded; **Glumes** scabrous-hispid on the keel, acute, the first about half as long as the second, linear, mucronate, the second 6-9 mm. long, longer than lemma and palea, linear-lanceolate, with two nerves on one side of the keel; **Lemma** about 5-5.5 mm. long, shorter than the palea, emarginate or two-toothed, somewhat scabrous on the upper part of keel; **Palea** 5-7 mm. long, longer than the lemma.

On salt meadows and sandy beaches, in south Texas extending east along the coast to Florida and north to Canada. Spring to fall.

4. S. SPARTINAE (Trin.) Merr. (spär-tī'nē); *S. junciformis* Engelm. & Gray.

Culms 2-4 feet tall, usually in large tufts, stout, rigid, green but often turning purplish, smooth except just below the panicle; **Blades** sharply pointed, usually 1.5-4' long, lower much longer, about 2 mm. wide when folded, stiff, ascending, conduplicate; **Sheaths** flattened, a little longer than the internodes, often tinged with purple; **Ligule** a ciliate ring of short hairs; **Panicle** spikelike, 5-9' long, about 8-10 mm. thick, with about 26-48 crowded appressed spikes, as much as 2' long below, shorter above, upper often two-fifths inch long, sessile; **Spikelets** about 6-7 mm. long, green to purplish, the stigmas with long styles maturing first, the spikes later thickly covered with yellow stamens; **Glumes** scabrous on the keel, acute, first narrow, 4-6 mm. long, the second 6-7 mm. long; **Lemma** about 6 mm. long, 3-nerved, abruptly acute, scabrous on the keel; **Palea** hyaline, about as long as its lemma, sometimes shorter but usually longer, as much as 7 mm. long. The glumes, lemma, and palea seem to vary much in length.

Common on the flats near the coast, in south Texas mostly from Houston to Brownsville, Texas, to Florida. Spring to fall.

5. S. ALTERNIFLORA var. GLABRA (Muhl.) Fern. (ăl-tĕr-nĭ-flō'rȧ glä'brȧ); SALT MARSH-GRASS.

Culms 2-5 feet, said to grow somewhat taller, stout, 5-10 mm. thick, simple, rigid, smooth, growing in colonies in shallow salt water along the coast; **Blades** numerous, about 12-15, 6-18' long, the upper shorter, 7-11 mm. wide, flat, stiffly ascending, tough, smooth on the margins and the surface toward the apex slightly rough; **Sheaths** longer than the internodes, slightly ciliate on the margins toward the summit, otherwise glabrous and smooth; **Ligule** a ring of fine dense hairs about 2 mm. long; **Panicle** mostly 6-12' long, spikelike exserted, the axis channeled, smooth, with numerous spikes, 20 more or less, 2.5' long or less, appressed, over-lapping, spikelet-bearing to the base, crowded, the rachis extending slightly beyond the spikelets; **Spikelets** 7-10 mm. long, 1.5 mm. wide, flattened, purplish or pale; **Glumes** smooth and glabrous; the first 2-3 mm. long, acute, the second as long as the spikelet, subacute; **Lemma** shorter than the palea, longer than the first glume, obtuse; **Palea** slightly shorter than the second glume, both smooth and glabrous.

Mostly in shallow salt water along the coast, Texas to Florida and north to Virginia. August-October.

Lemma
Palea
x4
1st   2nd
Glumes

Spike
Actual size

SPARTINA PECTINATA; T<small>ALL</small> M<small>ARSH</small>-<small>GRASS</small>, S<small>LOUGH</small>-<small>GRASS</small>

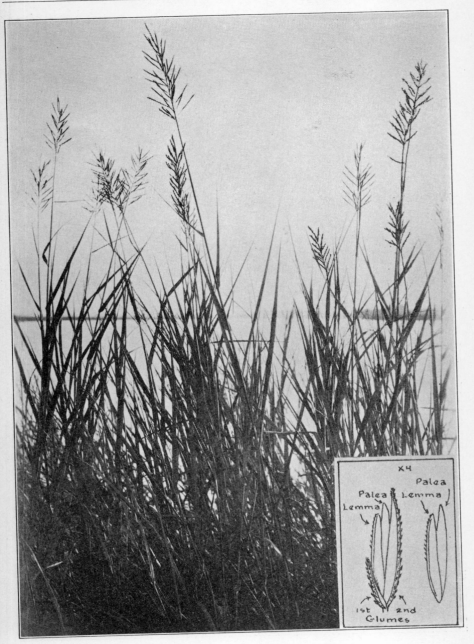

SPARTINA CYNOSUROIDES; Salt Reed-grass

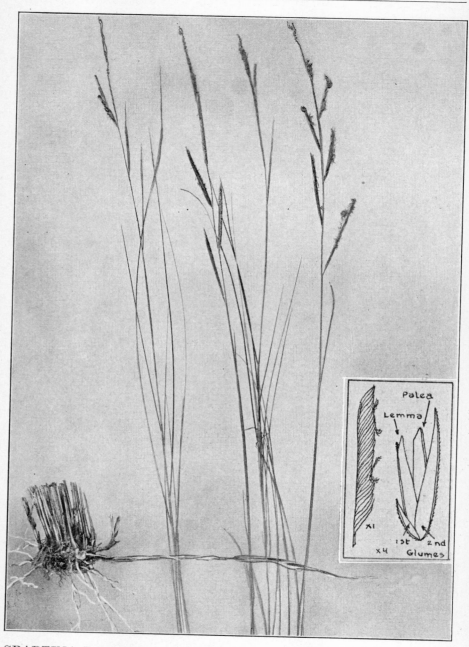

SPARTINA PATENS VAR. JUNCEA; RUSH SALT-GRASS. The drawings
show the first glume too short.

SPARTINA SPARTINAE

SPARTINA ALTERNIFLORA var. GLABRA; Salt Marsh-grass

65. CTENIUM Panzer (tē'nĭ-ŭm)
(Campulosus Desv.)

Spikelets several-flowered but with only one perfect floret, sessile and closely imbricate, on one side of a continuous rachis, the rachilla disarticulating above the glumes; **Glumes** unequal, the first small, hyaline, 1-nerved, the second as long as the lemmas, firm, 3-4-nerved, bearing on the back a strong divergent awn; **Lemmas** rather papery, 3-nerved, villous on the lateral nerves and on the callus, bearing a short straight awn on the back just below the apex, the first and second lemmas empty, the third inclosing a perfect flower, the upper 1-3 empty and successively smaller.

Erect, slender, rather tall *perennials,* with usually solitary, often curved spikes. Species about 12 in the warm regions, three being in the eastern hemisphere and the others in America; two species are found in southeastern United States, one in Texas.

C. AROMATICUM (Walt.) Wood (ăr-ō-măt'ĭ-kŭm); *Campulosus aromaticus* (Walt.) Trin.; TOOTHACHE-GRASS. Not yet collected in Texas.

Plant pungent to the taste; **Culms** 3-4 feet tall, erect, simple, smooth or somewhat scabrous; **Blades** 1-6' long, or the lower longer, 2-4 mm. wide, flat or involute; **Sheaths** shorter than the internodes, rough; **Ligule** 1 mm. long, truncate; **Spike** stout, solitary, 2-5' long, usually curved, about 6 mm. thick, the rachis extended into a point, the spikelets at a right angle to the rachis; **Spikelets** about 6 mm. long; **Glumes,** the first about 1.5 mm. long, the second about 5 mm. long, a row of warty glands on each side of the midnerve, bearing just above the middle a stout horizontal or recurved awn commonly about 4 mm. long; **Lemmas** 4-5 mm. long or the upper shorter, scabrous, villous at the base and on the margin at the middle, awn from below the 2-toothed apex, or the uppermost awnless and glabrous.

In moist soil, pine lands, along the coastal plains from North Carolina to Louisiana, and perhaps southeast Texas. Summer and fall.

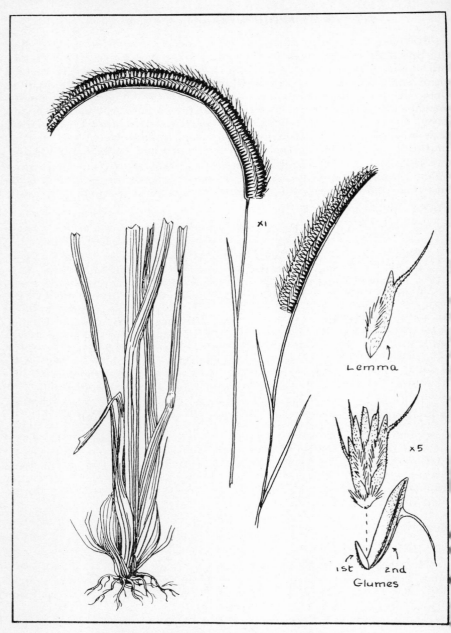

CTENIUM AROMATICUM; Toothache-grass

66. GYMNOPOGON Beauv. (jĭm-nō-pō'gŏn)

Spikelets 1-or rarely 2-or-3-flowered, nearly sessile, appressed and usually remote in two rows along one side of a slender continuous rachis, the rachilla disarticulating above the glumes and prolonged behind the one or more fertile florets as a slender stipe, bearing a rudiment of a floret, this sometimes with one or two slender awns; **Glumes** narrow, acuminate, 1-nerved, usually longer than the floret; **Lemmas** narrow, 3-nerved, the lateral nerves near the margins, the apex minutely bifid, bearing between the teeth a slender awn, or rarely awnless.

Perennial or rarely *annual* grasses, with short, flat, stiff blades, numerous stiff, slender, divergent spikes loosely scattered along the upper culm, or sometimes aggregate toward the summit, the spikes often deflexed at maturity. One or perhaps two species in Texas; *both perennials*.

SPIKES SPIKELET-BEARING the whole length; awn longer than the lemma.
1. G. ambiguus.
SPIKES SPIKELET-BEARING on the upper half; awn shorter than the lemma.
2. G. brevifolius.

1. **G. AMBIGUUS** (Michx.) B. S. P. (ăm-bĭg'ū-ŭs) ; BROAD-LEAVED BEARD-GRASS.

Culms 12-20' tall, erect or decumbent at the base, simple or sometimes sparingly branched, wiry and leafy; **Blades** 1-3.5' long, 5-12 mm. wide, flat, firm, cordate-lanceolate, acute, crowded, spreading, margins rough, the upper surface slightly rough; **Sheaths** overlapping, crowded, a villous ring at the summit, otherwise glabrous; **Ligule** membranaceous, very short; **Inflorescence** purplish, numerous slender spikes finally exserted, 4-7' long, scattered along a rigid axis 3-4' long, erect or ascending, finally spreading, the lower often reflexed, villous in the axis, the rigid rachis spikelet-bearing to the base, rather remote; **Spikelets** 1-flowered, exclusive of the awns 4-6 mm. long; **Glumes** narrow, acuminate, very scabrous, especially on the nerves, awn-pointed; the first about as long as the lemma, the second longer; **Lemma** 3.5-4 mm. long, cylindrical, involute, purplish, villous at the base, sparsely ciliate with stiff hairs on the margins, body scabrous and with a few scattered hairs, bearing a straight scabrous awn from between a bifid apex, 4-8 mm. long, the palea about as long; **Rudiment** a slender stipe about 2 mm. long bearing a rudiment of a floret and an awn 2.5 mm. long.

In sandy soil, New Jersey to Missouri, south to Florida and Texas. Summer and fall.

2. **G. BREVIFOLIUS** Trin. (brĕv-ĭ-fō'lĭ-ŭs) ; SHORT-LEAVED BEARD-GRASS.

This species has not yet been found in Texas, but may extend into eastern Texas. It differs chiefly from *G. ambiguus* by the shorter narrower blades, the spikes only spikelet-bearing above the middle, and the awn shorter than the lemma.

In dry soil, New Jersey to Florida and Mississippi. Summer and fall.

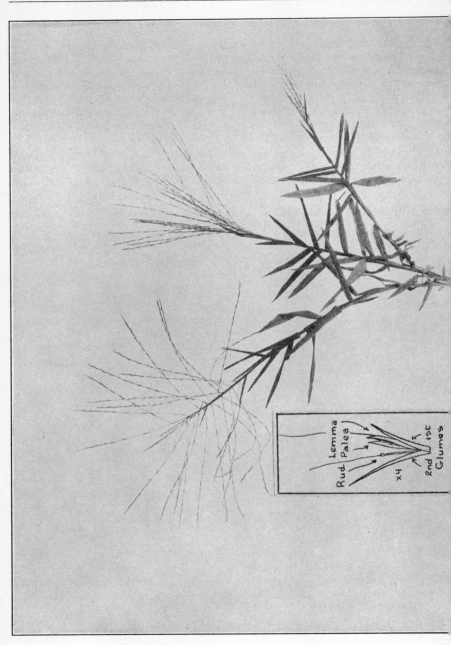

GYMNOPOGON AMBIGUUS

67. CHLORIS Swartz (klō′rĭs)

Spikelets with 1 perfect floret, sessile, in two rows along one side of a ·ntinuous rachis, the rachilla disarticulating above the glumes, produced ·yond the perfect floret and bearing 1-to-several reduced florets con- ·sting of empty lemmas, these often truncate, and, if more than one, the ·aller ones inclosed in the lower, forming a usually club-shaped rudi- ·ent; **Glumes** somewhat unequal, the first shorter, narrow, acute; **Lemma** ·eled, usually broad, 1-5-nerved, often villous on the callus and villous · long-ciliate on the keel or marginal nerves, awned from between the ·ort teeth of a bifid apex, the awn slender or sometimes reduced to a ·ucro, the sterile lemmas awned or awnless.

Perennial or sometimes annual, tufted, grasses, with flat blades and ·o-to-several often showy and feathery spikes aggregate at the summit · the culms. Species about 60 in the warmer regions; 15 in the southern ·nited States; 12 in Texas.

While there are about a dozen species of this grass in Texas they form · unimportant part of the forage of grazing animals. Rhodes grass, the ·ost important of the species, a stoloniferous perennial, is used to some ·tent for forage and occasionally is cut for hay. It is quite troublesome · a weed in the Rio Grande Valley.

Two species have awnless lemmas, but an awned second glume; · *petraea,* limited to very sandy soil, has almost glabrous dark-brown ·mmas, and *C. distichophylla,* a South American species, has brown but ·bescent lemmas. The latter is rare in the United States, having been ·llected only at Bastrop, Texas.

There are four species in Texas in the group with slender spikes, the ·vns usually longer than the lemma.

These species are often known as windmill grass, the inflorescence of ·merous slender spikes breaking away and rolling before the wind as a ·mble-weed. *C. verticillata,* with spikes 2-6′ long, *C. texensis* with spikes ·7′ long, and *C. andropogonoides,* with spikes 2-2.5′ long, are low plants, all ·th a limited range except *C. verticillata.* *C. chloridea,* a tall plant with ·ikes 5-10′ long, is interesting in that it produces awnless underground ·eistogamous spikelets much different from those of the spikes. It is a ·exican plant, and has been collected only twice in the United States, being ·llected recently near Brownsville, Texas, by the author.

There are six species in Texas in the stout-spiked group, three with the ·vn shorter than the lemma—*C. cucullata,* 1-2 feet tall, which is common in ·uthern and western Texas, *C. subdolichostachya,* and *C. latisquamea,* both ·w grasses, and rather rare; and three with the awn longer than the ·mma—*C. virgata,* a weed frequent in west Texas, *C. ciliata,* growing in ·uthwest Texas and in the Rio Grande Valley, and *C. gayana,* Rhodes ·ass. The last three are usually 2-3 feet tall.

The spikes and spikelets and their parts vary much in this genus. The ·ikes are usually tinged with purple, sometimes pale-green. All those in ·exas are perennials except *C. virgata* and *C. verticillata.*

·EMMA AWNLESS OR AWN-POINTED, about 2 mm. long; the second glume
    awned from a broad two-lobed apex.
  Spikes 3-5; lemma dark-brown, the hairs about 0.3 mm. long.   1. C. petraea
  Spikes 8-15; lemma brown, the lower hairs about 1 mm. long.
                                                   2. C. distichophylla

·EMMA AWNED. SPIKES SLENDER OR STOUT.
SPIKES SLENDER, 4-15, interrupted, or naked below, the awn of the lemma
    4-12 mm. long, commonly longer than the lemma.

STERILE lemma narrow, not broadened at the summit.
　Plants 2-4 feet tall; blades elongated, mostly more than 12′ long; awnle;
　　underground **cleistogamous** spikelets present; spikes 5-10′ long; lemn
　　about 6 mm. long; sterile lemma 2 mm. long on a stipe 2 mm. long.
　　　　　　　　　　　　　　　　　　　　　　　　　　　　3. C. chlorid
　Plants less than 15′ tall; blades shorter.
　　Sp.kes 2-2.5′ long; lemma 2.5-3 mm. long, elliptic, acute, about 0.6 m;
　　　wide, the nerves short-pilose.　　　　　　　　　　4. C. andropogonoid
　　Spikes 4-7′ long; lemma about 4 mm. long, the midnerve not pilose, b
　　　hispidulous above.　　　　　　　　　　　　　　　　5. C. texens
STERILE lemma broadened and obliquely truncate at the summit; spikes 2-
　long, in 1-3 whorls; lemma 2.5-3 mm. long, the nerves pilose, the midner
　sparsely so; sterile lemma obliquely truncate; plant annual.
　　　　　　　　　　　　　　　　　　　　　　　　　　　6. C. verticilla
SPIKES STOUT, spikelet-bearing to the base.
　AWN usually shorter than the lemma; spikes 5-20, 1-3′ long; hairs on lemn
　　less than 0.5 mm. long.
　　Lemma 2 mm. long, sparsely short-ciliate; sterile lemma broadly triangula
　　　wider than broad, 5-7-nerved; plant 1-2 feet tall.　　　7. C. cuculla
　　Lemma 2.5 mm. long, in side view elliptic, the three nerves short-pubescen
　　　sterile lemma obovate-cuneate, the apex unequally rounded, 3-nerve
　　　about 0.6 mm. wide as folded; plant low.　　　8. C. subdolichostach}
　　Lemma 2.5 mm. long, short-pubescent on the nerves; sterile lemn
　　　obcuniate or triangular, 1 mm. broad or a little broader, 3-5-nerve
　　　plant low, spikes pale green.　　　　　　　　　9. C. latisquam
　AWN longer than the lemma; spikes 5-20 except in *C. ciliata* 3-5, 2-4′ lon;
　　plant 2-3 feet tall.
　　Lemma 3.5 mm. long, 3-5-nerved, copiously villous on the callus and (
　　　the margins above; **annual.**　　　　　　　　　10. C. virga
　　Lemma 2-3 mm. long, nerves and margins villous the entire length, th
　　　hairs less than 2 mm. long.　　　　　　　　　　11. C. cilia
　　Lemma 3 mm. long, short-villous along the margins; second lemma awne
　　　perfect or staminate; sterile lemma much reduced; plant stoloniferou
　　　　　　　　　　　　　　　　　　　　　　　　　　12. C. gayar

1. **C. PETRAEA** Swartz (pē-trē′à) ; *Eustachys petraea* (Swartz) Desv
C. swartziana Doell.

Culms 1-2.5 feet tall, branching, rather slender, erect or slightl
spreading, in rather small tufts, nodes dark, flattened, the culms more (
less decumbent and often rooting producing distinct stolons; **Blad**
usually 5-6′ long, except the uppermost often as short as 10 mm., 1-4 mn
wide, flat or conduplicate, subobtuse, margins scabrous; **Sheaths** short(
than the internodes, flattened; **Ligule** a ring of very short hairs; **Spik**
3-5, commonly 2-2.5′ long, digitate, nearly erect, slender, dark; **Spikele**
2-flowered, 1.5-2 mm. long; **Glumes** 1-nerved, white, hispid, the first abo
1-1.5 mm. long, acute, incurved, scabrous on the keel, ovate, the secon
oblong, hyaline, the midnerve extending between two acute lobes into
scabrous awn usually about 0.5 mm. long, incurved; **Lemma** about 2 mn
long, irregularly ovate, strongly keeled, mucronate, 3-nerved, dark-brow
short-pubescent on the margins and keel nearly to the apex, the hair
about 0.3 mm. long, the awn short or wanting; **Sterile Lemma** on sho
stipe half included by the fertile lemma, similar to it except smaller an
awnless.

Low sandy land, usually near the coast, Texas to Florida.

2. **C. DISTICHOPHYLLA** Lag. (dĭs-tĭk-ō-fĭl′à) ; *Eustachys distichophyll*
(Lag.) Nees.

Culms 1-2.5 feet tall, tufted, erect or decumbent at the base, leafy
Blades mostly 3-7′ long, 3-6 mm. wide, flat or folded, slightly rough, (
rough on the margins; **Sheaths,** the upper usually shorter than the inte
nodes; **Ligule** a dense ring of hairs less than 0.5 mm. long; **Spikes** rathe

rownish, finally exserted, commonly 8-15, usually 2.5-3.5′ long, closely
ggregate, finally ascending or somewhat spreading or drooping, the
ibsessile spikelets crowded on a scabrous rachis; **Spikelets** 2-flowered,
bout 2.3 mm. long; **Glumes,** the first scarcely 1 mm. long, acute, the
econd about 1.2 mm. long, truncate, a mucro or very short-awn from the
nus of the rounded lobes, minutely scabrous, sometimes sparsely his-
idulous; **Lemmas** awnless, brown, the lower about 2 mm. long, lanceolate,
cute, villous on the margins, the lower hairs about 1 mm. long; **Palea**
bout as long as the lemma, minutely 2-toothed, ciliate, the upper hairs
horter; **Sterile Lemma** about 1.2 mm. long, obovate, mucronate, 5-nerved.
Illustration with photograph of *C. petraea*.)
    This is a South American species, introduced. (Bastrop, Texas,
uly, 1892.)

. C. CHLORIDEA (Presl) Hitchc. (klō-rĭd′ē-à); *C. clandestina* Scribn. &
    Merr.
    Culms 2-4 feet tall, a few culms to a tuft, erect or ascending,
lattened, sparingly branched, very leafy toward the base; **Blades** 2-18′
ong, the upper 2-4′, 3-10 mm. wide, flat, slightly rounded at the base,
nargins and lower surface slightly rough, the upper surface near the
ase sometimes sparsely papillose-pilose, especially those of the sterile
hoots, the blades of the sterile shoots being long and narrow; **Sheaths**
onger than the internodes, flattened, the throat often villous, especially
hose of the sterile shoots; **Ligule** membranaceous, about 1 mm. long,
imbriate; **Spikes** exserted, 7-12, commonly 5-10′ long, slender, erect or
inally spreading, even horizontal or reflexed, aggregate or loosely
scattered along a slightly scabrous axis 2-4′ long, the lower often about 1′
listant, the slender rachis triangular, scabrous, spikelet-bearing to the
ase, but more or less interrupted below, the axils pubescent, often one or
nore spikes included or partly included in 1-3 of the sheaths below;
Spikelets excluding the awns about 6.5 mm. long, lanceolate, appressed to
he rachis; **Glumes** 1-nerved, the first 1.2-1.5 mm. long, narrow, acute, the
second excluding the awn about 2 mm. long, including the awn 3-4.5 mm.
long, obtuse, scabrous on the margins and nerve; **Lemma** exclusive of the
awn about 6 mm. long, narrow, the callus pubescent, the three nerves
slightly scabrous, margins ciliate, an erect scabrous awn 7-12 mm. long
from just below the bifid apex; **Sterile Lemma** about 2 mm. long, on a
stipe 2 mm. long, awn 2-4 mm. long; **Cleistogamous Spikelets** awnless,
about 7.5 mm. long, ovate, wrinkled, the glumes and lemma somewhat
hardened; **Glumes** many-nerved, the first 5-6 mm. long, acuminate, the
second broader, clasping the lemma, acute, 6-7 mm. long, as long as or
slightly longer than the lemma; **Lemma** broad, clasping the palea; **Palea**
slightly shorter than its lemma; **Grain** ovate-oblong, 4-5 mm. long.
    Dry open ground, sandy loam. A Mexican species, Sonora to Oaxaca,
extending into Texas at Brownsville. (About 5 miles from Brownsville
along the Fresno Road.) Fall.

4. C. ANDROPOGONOIDES Fourn. (ăn-drō-pō-gō-noi′dēz); *C. tenuispica*
    Nash.
    Culms 6-15′ tall, densely tufted, flattened, leafy at the base; **Blades**
1-6′ long, the upper short, 1-3 mm. wide, conduplicate, abruptly acute,
rough on the margins and midnerve, very sparsely hirsute on the under
surface or glabrous; **Sheaths** longer than the internodes, flattened, loose;
Ligule a very short ciliate membrane; **Spikes** 8-13, 2-3.5′ long, mostly

about 2′, in one or two whorls or approximate, the axis sometim
10-15 mm. long, ascending or spreading, slender, naked or a few scatter
spikelets below, the axils pubescent; **Spikelets** exclusive of the aw
2.5-3 mm. long; **Glumes** 1-nerved, scabrous on the nerve, awn-pointed, tl
first about two-thirds as long as the spikelet, the second about equal
exceeding the lemma; **Lemma** 2.5-3 mm. long, elliptic in side view, abo
0.6 mm. wide, sparsely pubescent on the three nerves, the scabrous aw
3-6 mm. long; **Sterile Lemma** about half as long as the lemma, 3-nerve
acute, with a scabrous awn 2-4 mm. long; *Rachilla* produced beyond tl
sterile lemma, sometimes with a rudimentary floret. (This and *C. su
dolichostachya* in the same photograph.)

Plains, southern Texas to northern Mexico. (Portland, Texas
Spring and summer.

5. C. TEXENSIS Nash (těks-ĕn′sĭs); *C. nealleyi* Nash.

Culms 1-2 feet tall, tufted, erect or ascending from a decumbent bas
spreading, wiry, leafy at the base; **Blades** 6 mm. to 10′ long, common
2-6′, the upper very short, the basal and lower often long, 3-8 mm. wid
flat or folded, obtuse, about as wide at the apex as at the base, rough
the margins, the midrib below and on the upper surface rough especial
toward the apex; **Sheaths** about as long as the internodes except ove
lapping and crowded at the base, flattened; **Ligule** a ring of hairs 0.5 m
long or less; **Spikes** 5-9, slender, 4-7′ long, villous in the axils, naked
with a few scattered spikelets at the base, crowded above, the rach
scabrous; **Spikelets** 2-flowered, exclusive of the awns 4-5 mm. long, su
sessile, appressed; **Glumes** 1-nerved, acuminate, awn-pointed, the first ha
to two-thirds as long as the spikelet, the second as long or exceeding tl
lemma, awn-pointed or short-awned; **Lemma** about 4 mm. long, lanceolat
narrow, callus pubescent, the lateral nerves near the margins sparse
hispid with appressed hairs above the middle, the internerves rough abov
the midnerve scabrous toward the apex with a scabrous straight aw
5-10 mm. long from the bifid apex; **Sterile Lemma** about 2 mm. long on
stipe about 2 mm. long, with an awn 3-5 mm. long, similar to fertile lemm

In dry soil, Texas. (Angleton, Texas.) Summer and fall.

6. C. VERTICILLATA Nutt. (věr-tĭs-ĭ-lā′tà); WINDMILL-GRASS, BRANC
ING FOXTAIL.

Culms 6-20′ tall, usually a few in a tuft, erect or decumbent, branc
ing at the base, the branches commonly sterile, flattened; **Blades** 2.5-
long, 2-4 mm. wide, the upper shorter, folded, abruptly pointed, marg
and surface rough; **Sheaths** shorter than the internodes, loose, flattene
Ligule membranaceous, fringed, less than 1 mm. long; **Spikes** slend
8-13 (8-21), 2-6′ long, often naked at the base, clustered at the apex of tl
culm, or a few verticillate branches in one or two series on a prolongati
of the axis, the axis usually not over a few mm. long, axils usual
pubescent, the slender rachis scabrous; **Spikelets** exclusive of the aw
2.5-3 mm. long, cuneate-obovate, flattened; **Glumes** 1-nerved, acuminat
awn-pointed, narrow, scabrous on the nerves, the first about 2 mm. lo
and the second about as long as the spikelet; **Lemma** exclusive of the aw
2.5-3 mm. long, 3-nerved, obtuse, the nerves ciliate especially the later
ones, bearing just below the apex a scabrous awn, usually 2-5 mm. lon
sometimes longer; **Sterile Lemma** 1.5-2 mm. long, less than 1 mm. wid
truncate, 3-nerved, bearing just below the apex usually an awn short
than that of the fertile lemma.

Plains, Texas, Louisiana, New Mexico, and north to Kansas; also
aryland and California. Spring-summer.

C. CUCULLATA Bisch. (kū-kŭl-ā'tà).

Culms 9-25' tall, tufted, erect from a decumbent base, rarely branch-
g, flattened; **Blades** 0.7-6' long, 1-3 mm. wide, the upper very short, flat
soon conduplicate, abruptly acute at the apex, rough; **Sheaths** shorter
an the internodes, flattened, margins membranaceous; **Ligule** mem-
anaceous, about 1 mm. long, truncate, ciliate; **Spikes** 7-18, 1-2' long,
ially spreading, purplish, stout, spikelet-bearing to the base, the rachis
abrous; **Spikelets** exclusive of the awns about 2 mm. long, in the form
an equilateral triangle, about as broad as long; **Glumes** scabrous on the
el, 1-nerved, the first acute about half as long as the spikelet, the second
ightly longer and broader, obtuse or abruptly acute; **Lemma** nearly
mm. long, 3-nerved, somewhat flattened, obtuse, in side view elliptic,
ort-villous on the callus, the lateral nerves densely pubescent and the
idnerve sparsely so, the awn usually less than 1 mm. long; **Sterile Lemma**
otruding, 5-7-nerved, the lateral nerves branching once or twice, distant
om the midnerve, each half of the lemma wedge-truncate, as broad as
ng, the apex and margins involute, the awn usually shorter than that of
e lemma.

In sandy soil, central, western and southern Texas to New Mexico.
A frequent weed along the highways.) Spring-fall.

C. SUBDOLICHOSTACHYA Muell. (sŭb-dŏl-ĭ-kō-stăk'ĭ-à) ; *C. brevispica*
Nash.

Culms 4-12' tall, commonly 4-8', tufted, decumbent and often branch-
g at the base, slender; **Blades** 1-4' long, 1-3 mm. wide, scabrous on the
argins and upper surface; **Sheaths** longer than the internodes, flattened,
abrous on the keel; **Ligule** a ring of short hairs; **Spikes** 6-13, stouter
an in *C. andropogonoides*, 1.5-2' long, sometimes longer, finally spreading,
one or two whorls or approximate, spikelet-bearing to the base, densely-
owered; **Spikelets** exclusive of the awn 2.5-3 mm. long; **Glumes** 1-nerved,
nceolate, acute, scabrous on the nerve, the first about half as long and
e second about two-thirds as long as the lemma; **Lemma** about 2.5 mm.
ng, in side view elliptic, the three nerves pubescent, with awn about
mm. long; **Sterile Lemma** about 1.5 mm. long, obovate-cuneate, about
6 mm. wide, 3-nerved, the apex unequally rounded, the awn slightly
orter than that of the fertile lemma. (This species and *C. andropogonoides*
a the same photograph.)

In sandy soil, western and southern Texas. (Corpus Christi, Texas.)
pring-summer.

C. LATISQUAMEA Nash (lăt-ĭs-kwä'mē-à).

Culms 10-28' tall, tufted, erect or decumbent at the base, slender,
king root at the lower nodes, leafy at the base, those of the sterile shoots
ng; **Blades** 1-14', the upper distant and short, 2-3 mm. wide, conduplicate
the base, flat above, abruptly acute, aristate, rough; **Sheaths**, the upper
orter than the internodes, flattened, smooth or rough, glabrous or pilose
a the margins and at the throat; **Ligule** about 1 mm. long, mem-
anaceous, minutely ciliate; **Spikes** pale-green, 8-20, finally long-exserted,
mmonly 2-3' rarely 5' long, ascending or finally spreading, spikelet-bear-
ig to the base, the common axis usually less than 15 mm. long; **Spikelets**
xclusive of the awns 2.5-3.1 mm. long, the sterile lemma conspicuous;

Glumes unequal, the first 1-1.5 mm. long, the second broader, awnless with a very short awn, including the short awn 1.5-3 mm. long, acute, nerved, scabrous on the nerve; **Lemma** 2.2-3 mm. long, 0.8-1 mm. wid folded, in side view narrowly elliptic, pubescent at the base and on th three nerves, sparsely so on the midnerve, the hairs short, the scabrou awn 1-5 mm. long; **Sterile Lemma** 1.2-1.7 mm. long, 1-1.2 mm. wide, folde in side view cuniate or triangular, the apex inrolled and truncate an exceeded by the fertile lemma, when open very broad at the apex, 3-nerved, the lateral nerve near the margins and curved, the scabrous aw 1.5-3 mm. long, a **Second Sterile Lemma** sometimes present, very smal and included in the first.

Sandy river banks and cultivated fields, Texas to Arizona. (Pet Heinz Nursery 8 miles from Brownsville, and Concan, Texas.) Sprin and summer.

10. C. VIRGATA Swartz (vĕr-gā'tà) ; *C. alba* Presl; *C. elegans* H. B. K
FEATHER FINGER-GRASS.

Culms 1-3 feet tall, tufted, erect, often ascending from a decumbe base, branching at the base and lower nodes, sometimes rooting at th lower nodes; **Blades** 3-16' long, 2-7 mm. wide, flat, margins and bot surfaces rough toward the tip, very sparsely long-hairy, papillose at th base; **Sheaths** shorter than the internodes, often a few hairs at the throa **Ligule** membranaceous, about 1 mm. long; **Spikes** included at the base o exserted, 7-16, erect or slightly spreading, sessile, pale-green or purp spikes 2-3.5' long, the rachis slender and scabrous; **Spikelets** 2-flowere exclusive of the awns 2.5-4 mm. long, flattened, the lower fertile, th upper staminate or reduced to a sterile lemma; **Glumes** 1-nerved, slightl scabrous on the keel, lanceolate, membranaceous, the first 1.5-2 mm. lon acute or obtuse, the second 3-3.5 mm. long, awn-pointed; **Lemma** exclusiv of the awn 3.5 mm. long, 3-5-nerved, flattened, wide at the middl narrowed at the apex, the callus and the marginal nerves on the uppe portion long-villous, the hairs extending 2-3 mm. above the apex, shor pubescent below, the apex produced into a slender scabrous awn 2-3 time as long as the body of the lemma; **Palea** about as long as its lemm oblanceolate, abruptly acute, the margins folded inward; **Sterile Lemm** similar in shape but smaller and glabrous, truncate, and with an aw nearly equal to that of the lower lemma; a **Third Floret** sometimes presen

Wet land, plentiful along ditches, west Texas, New Mexico an Arizona. Summer and fall.

11. C. CILIATA Swartz (sĭl-ĭ-ā'tà) ; *C. nashii* Heller; *C. texana* (Vasey Nash.

Culms 10-42' commonly 1-2 feet tall, tufted, erect or ascending fror a decumbent base, leafy at the base; **Blades** 1-12' long, usually 4-8', th upper often much reduced, 1-5 mm. wide, flat or soon involute, attenuat into a long narrow point, rough on the margins and upper surface towar the tip, glabrous or a long tuft of hairs on the upper surface at the base **Sheaths** much shorter than the internodes, or the lower crowded an overlapping, usually long-villous at the throat; **Ligule** membranaceou ciliate, less than 0.5 mm. long; **Spikes** exserted, in a single verticel, 3-ascending or finally spreading, flexuous, 1.5-4.5' long, stout, grayish-green noticeably hairy, the subsessile spikelets crowded, spikelet-bearing to th base, the rachis hispid on the angles; **Spikelets** exclusive of the awn 2.2-3.2 mm. long, 3-4-flowered, the lower fertile, the others sterile or th

cond staminate; **Glumes** 1-nerved, scabrous on the keel, acute or some-
mes awn-pointed and acuminate, the first 1.5-2 mm. long, the second
5-3 mm. long; **Lemmas,** the lower 2-3 mm. oblong, about 1 mm. wide as
old ed, the nerves villous their entire length, those of the lateral nerves
2 mm. long, those of the keel shorter and appressed, the scabrous awn
3 mm. long, commonly shorter than the lemma; **Sterile Lemma** glabrous,
-nerved, about 1.5 mm. long, the margins at the truncate apex scarious,
ot involute, with an awn nearly as long as its lemma, rarely 2 mm. long,
le **Second and third sterile lemmas** awnless, or the second mucronate,
rogressively smaller but otherwise similar.

Sandy land, Rio Grande Valley and southeast Texas. (Near Edna
nd Brownsville, Texas.) Spring and fall.

2. C. GAYANA Kunth (gā-yà′nà); RHODES-GRASS.

Culms 1-5 feet tall, tufted, erect, somewhat flattened, rather stout,
mooth, nodes dark, often with leafy stolons, rather leafy at the base;
lades 2-18′ long or even longer, the upper short, 2-5 mm. wide, flat, soon
ecoming folded when drying, long attenuate, scabrous; **Sheaths** shorter
han the internodes, flattened, smooth except toward the apex, rather
ong-villous at the throat; **Ligule** very short, membranaceous, ciliate, the
airs 3-6 mm. long; **Spikes** 10-20, sessile or subsessile, digitate, 2-4′ long,
isually rather slender; **Spikelets** exclusive of the awns about 3 mm. long,
onsisting of two florets, with one or two rudiments, the second lemma
ometimes empty; **Glumes** lanceolate, scabrous on the nerves, sparingly
uispidulous, the first acute, 1-nerved, 1-1.5 mm. long, the second 2-2.5 mm.
ong exclusive of a short awn, usually 0.5-1 mm. long, 1-nerved, sometimes
2-3-nerved; **Lower Lemma** 2.7-3 mm. long, villous along the margins,
3-nerved, the midnerve prolonged between a bifid apex into an awn one
o one and a half times the length of the body of lemma; **Palea** a little
shorter than its lemma, obovate, acute, 2-keeled; **Second Lemma** fertile
or empty, shorter and with a shorter awn, otherwise similar; **Sterile
Lemmas** included in second, smaller, awnless or short-awned.

In moist soil, south Texas, especially abundant in the Rio Grande
Valley; also to Florida and southern California; introduced from Africa.
Spring-fall.

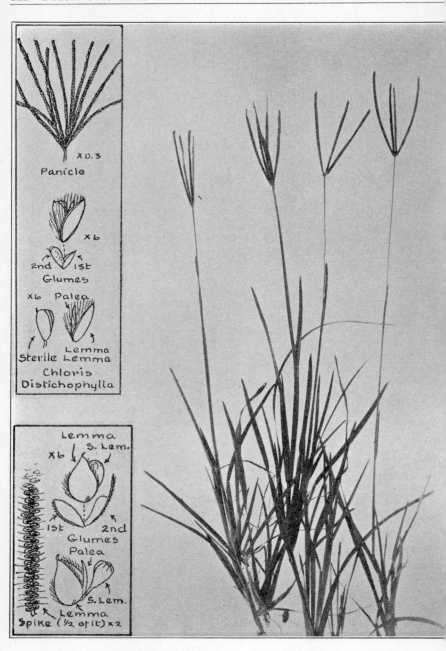

CHLORIS PETRAEA, with drawings illustrating CHLORIS
DISTICHOPHYLLA

CHLORIS CHLORIDEA

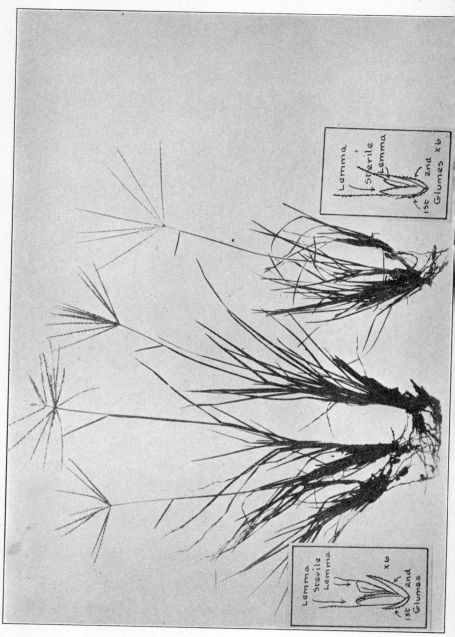

C. SUBDOLICHOSTACHYA and drawings to the left; C. ANDROPO-
GONOIDES, a single culm and drawings to the right.

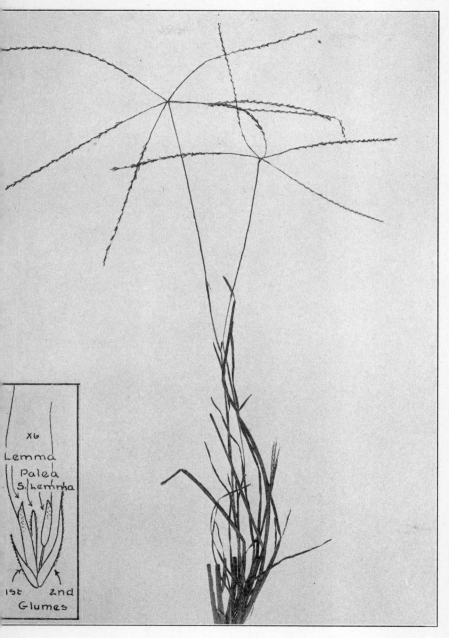

CHLORIS TEXENSIS

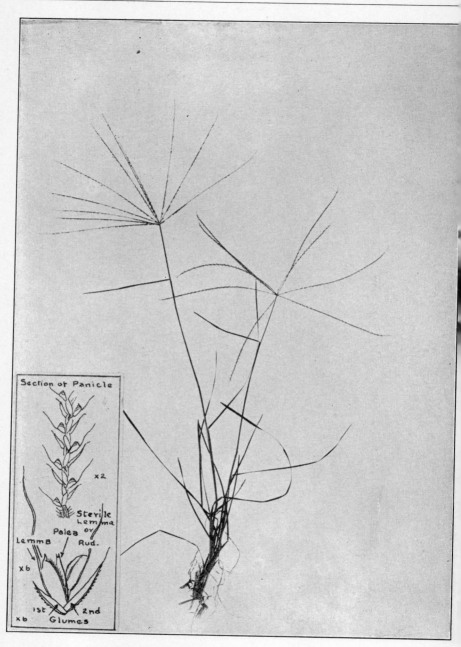

CHLORIS VERTICILLATA; Windmill-grass

CHLORIS CUCULLATA

S. Lemma
Lemma
2nd 1st
Glumes
x6
Sterile Lemma

CHLORIS LATISQUAMEA

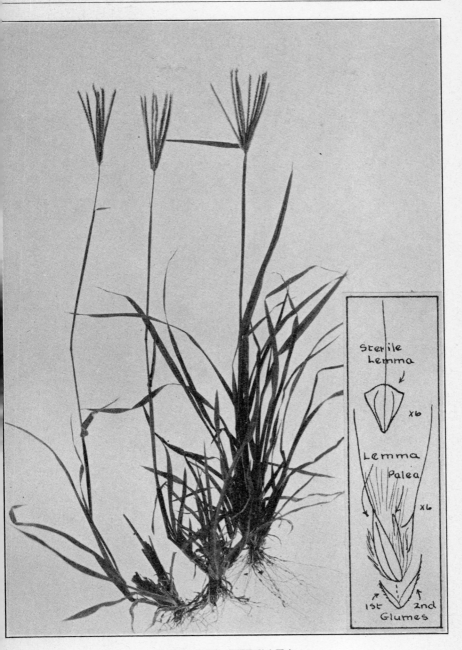

CHLORIS VIRGATA

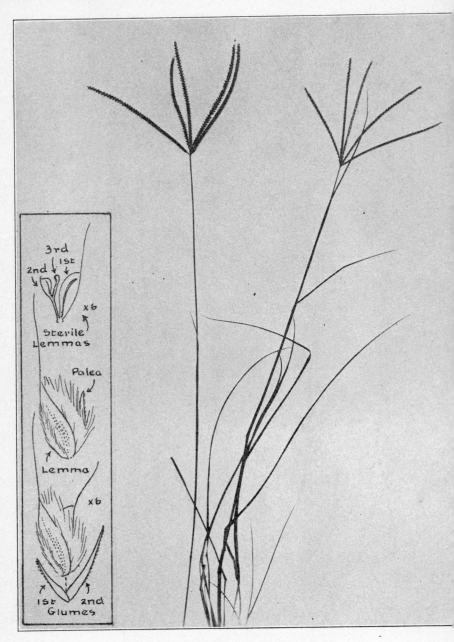

CHLORIS CILIATA

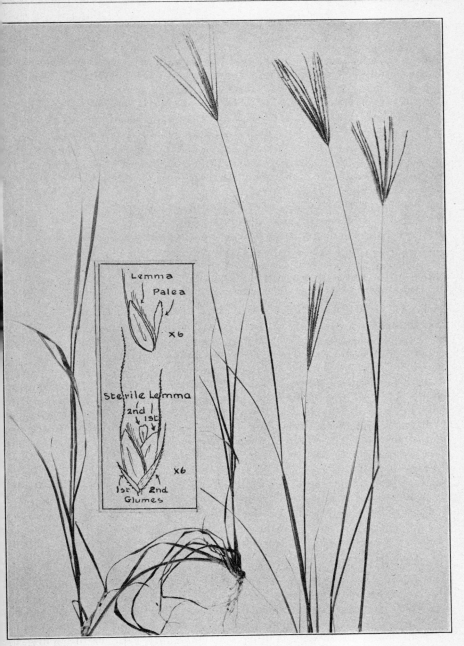

Lemma
Palea
x6

Sterile Lemma
2nd
1st
x6
1st 2nd
Glumes

CHLORIS GAYANA; Rhodes-grass

68. TRICHLORIS Fourn. (trī-klō′rŭs)

Spikelets 1-to-few-flowered, nearly sessile, in two rows along on
side of a continuous slender rachis, the rachilla disarticulating above th
glumes and prolonged behind the uppermost perfect floret, bearing ;
reduced usually awned floret; **Glumes** unequal, acuminate or short-awned
the body shorter than the lower lemma; **Lemmas** narrow, 3-nerved, th
marginal nerves sometimes pubescent, these and the midnerves extendin₁
into awns, the central long and slender, the lateral often much shorter

Erect, slender, tufted *perennials*, with flat blades and numerous erec
or ascending spikes, aggregate but scarcely digitate at the summit of th
culms. Species two or three, in the dry regions of Texas and Mexico an
also in Argentina; two in Texas.

Neither of these species is of agricultural importance, both being con
fined to the arid or semi-arid regions of southern and western Texas, an
southern New Mexico and Arizona, extending south to Mexico.

SPIKES PALE OR WHITISH; spikelets 2-flowered, one perfect floret and
rudiment, both with 3 long awns.   1. T. mendocin
SPIKES USUALLY PURPLISH; spikelets 3-5-flowered, 1 or 2 reduced. th
lateral awns reduced or sometimes wanting.   2. T. pluriflor

1. T. MENDOCINA (Phil.) Kurtz (mĕn-dō-sē′nȧ); *T. fasciculata* Fourn

Culms 2-3.5 feet tall, tufted, erect, often branching below; **Blade**
3-8′ long, 4-6 mm. wide, flat, very scabrous, sparsely to densely papillose
hirsute on the upper surface near the base; **Sheaths** shorter than th
internodes, flattened, very scabrous, upper sheath often including panicl
at the base; **Ligule** a dense ciliate ring about 1 mm. long; **Inflorescence** o
usually 10-20 digitate spikes 3-5′ long, slender, plumose, at the summit o
culm or lateral branch, slender, scabrous; **Spikelets** exclusive of awn
2.5-3 mm. long, the callus pubescent, consisting of one perfect floret an
one reduced, each with three awns; **Glumes** 1-nerved, the first less tha
1 mm. long, narrow, awn-pointed, the second slightly over 1 mm. with aw
1-2 mm. long, obtuse, awn scabrous; **Lemma** 2.5-3 mm. long, hispidulou₁
ciliate, oblong, the three nerves extending into three scabrous awn
10-15 mm. long, the middle about one-third longer than the lateral
Reduced Floret with awns 10-15 mm. long, the lateral somewhat shorter

In dry soil, mountains and valleys; western Texas to Arizona an
northern Mexico. August-September.

2. T. PLURIFLORA Fourn. (plōō-rĭ-flō′rȧ).

Culms 2-4 feet tall, loosely tufted, erect, stout, sometimes branching
Blades 3.5-12′ long, 5-12 mm. wide, flat, usually rough including th
margins, sometimes smooth toward the base; **Sheaths** mostly shorter tha
the internodes, loose and open above; **Ligule** a ring of fine hairs abou
0.5 mm. long; **Inflorescence** purplish, commonly 5-15, rarely more, c
sessile slender spikes, usually 2-5′ long, ascending or slightly spreading
arranged along a hispid rachis about 2′ long, 1-3 at a place, the spikelet
crowded; **Spikelets** exclusive of the awns 4-5 mm. long, 3-5-flowered, th
uppermost sterile; **Glumes** 1-nerved, bristle-pointed, scabrous on th
nerves, the first about 2 mm. long, narrow, the second broader, abou
3.5 mm. long; **Lemmas,** the lower narrowly lanceolate, 3-nerved, abou

3.5 mm. long, ciliate on the margins, scabrous, especially toward the apex, terminating in three hispid awns, the middle about 8 mm. and the lateral about 2 mm. long, or less, the upper lemmas similar but progressively shorter, the awns shorter, the lateral sometimes minute, and the uppermost sterile.   (See photograph of *T. mendocina*.)

In dry sandy soil, western Texas, south to Rio Grande Valley and Mexico, and extending into New Mexico.   Spring to fall.

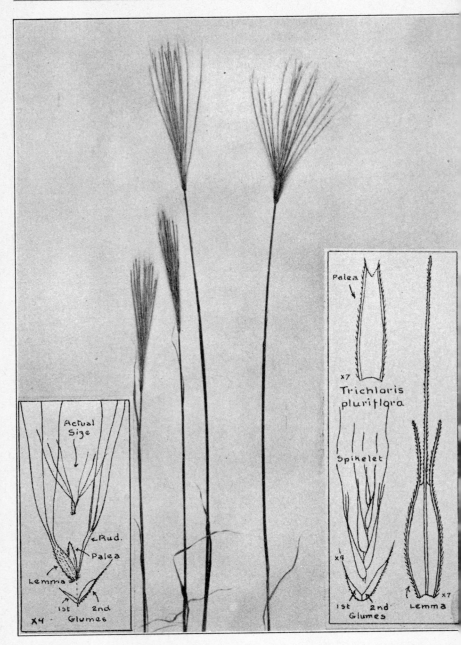

TRICHLORIS MENDOCINA and drawings of TRICHLORIS
PLURIFLORA

69. BOUTELOUA Lag. (bōō-tē-lōō′à)
(The Grama Grasses)

Spikelets 1-flowered with the rudiments of one or more florets above, sessile, in two rows along one side of the rachis; **Glumes** unequal, 1-nerved, acuminate or awn-tipped, the first shorter and narrower; **Lemma** as long as the second glume or a little longer, 3-nerved, the nerves extending into short or often rather long awns, the internerves usually extending into teeth; **Palea** 2-nerved, sometimes 2-awned; **Rudiment** various, usually 3-awned, a second rudimentary floret sometimes present.

Perennial or sometimes annual, low or rather tall grasses, with two-to-several or many spikes racemose on a common axis, or sometimes solitary, the spikelets few-to-many in each spike, rarely solitary, pectinate or more loosely arranged and appressed, the rachis of the spike usually produced beyond the insertion of the spikelets.

Eighteen species found in the United States, about thirteen in Texas, being important grazing grasses in the southwestern states.

Our species fall into two well-marked subdivisions, those in which the spikelets at maturity are crowded and pectinate, the florets falling, leaving the spikes persistent on the axis, and those in which the spikelets are less crowded, ascending rather than pectinate, the spikes falling entire. Blue grama is an example of the first group, and side-oats an example of the second group.

Hairy or black grama, growing mostly in sandy loam or on rocky hills, has about the same range as blue grama. The latter, with buffalo and curly mesquite, constitutes most of what is known in the Middle West as short-grass. Both plants by reason of their wide range are very variable as to size and manner of growth. Hairy grama in the North tends to form sod, and in the South is mostly bunch grass. There are two forms, one 1.5-2.5 feet tall, with large spikes, the other about half as tall with smaller spikes. It is distinguished from blue grama and other species by the prominent prolongation of the rachis beyond the spikelets, and the papillose-hairy glumes and leaf-margins.

Bouteloua breviseta, known as gyp grass, a pale-green wiry plant 10-16′ tall, is an important species growing in gypsum sands, being confined mostly to the calcareous soils on the high mesas along the Rio Grande River and its tributaries. A slightly different form of this species, formerly known as *Bouteloua ramosa* (the spikelets being the same), called by the natives *chino* (*che-no*), is found growing along with *Agave lechuguilla* Torr. on the rocky banks of hills and mountains of the Big Bend country, extending as far north as the Guadalupe Mountains. It has a somewhat different appearance from, and does not always have the thick bloom on the protected internodes of the form known as gyp grass.

Woolly-foot is readily distinguished by its weak and often crooked, geniculate or stoloniferous *woolly* culms, and its lax inflorescence of 3-8 spikes. Its range is mainly west of a line running from Del Rio to Big Spring.

Bouteloua trifida (*B. trinii* Fourn.). commonly 5-10 inches tall, usually with 3-5 spikes, has two forms, the short-awned form with longer and laxer leafage, formerly known as *Bouteloua burkii,* and the long-awned form known as *Bouteloua trifida.* Both are now included in *Bouteloua trifida.*

Side-oats, the tallest of the genus, with several spikelets to each spike, and *Bouteloua uniflora,* with one spikelet to each spike (with a rudiment of a single hispid awn about 4 mm. long), have long, slender, one-sided panicles of numerous short spikes, the only apparent difference in aspect being the size of the spikes. Side-oats by reason of its wide range is very variable as to pubescence and the minuter details of the spikelet. *Bouteloua uniflora* is usually confined to the rocky hills north and northwest of San Antonio, Texas, extending as far west as Crockett county.

Woolly-spiked grass, with 4-6 woolly spikes, commonly 12-15 inches tall, solitary or a few culms to a tuft, the blades mostly basal, is confined mainly to the high plains and gravelly hills or mountains, being plentiful in and near Davis Mountains and extending west to Arizona and south to Mexico.

Large mesquite, commonly 10-20' tall, with 4-10 spikes, is a southwest Texas plant extending south to Mexico. It is plentiful north of Laredo and near Falfurrias.

Bouteloua rigidiseta (*Bouteloua texana*), usually much less than a foot tall, thrives on the dry plains and hills in central and southwest Texas, extending into Mexico. It is plentiful in the vicinity of San Angelo, Texas.

Bouteloua simplex, with a solitary spike, *Bouteloua barbata*, with 3-7 spikes, the latter with two forms, the long-awned and short-awned, both with numerous spikelets, and *Bouteloua aristidoides*, commonly with 10-14 spikes of 2-4 spikelets, are low densely-tufted annuals. *Bouteloua simplex* attains its best development at an altitude of 5000 feet, and has a range from the Pecos River valley and Big Bend country westward to Arizona and Utah, and northward to Colorado Springs, Colorado. The last two species are found commonly with longer culms, often in large prostrate tufts nearly two feet square; both have a range from west Texas to the Pacific slope. In *Bouteloua aristidoides* the spikes fall as a whole, and the sharp base penetrates one's clothing. Because of the injury inflicted by the sharp-pointed spikes which work into their feet and disable them, sheep are kept from places where this plant is plentiful.

In the species of this genus the length of the spikelet, as well as that of its parts, especially the awns, varies much.

All plants perennial except *B. simplex*, *B. barbata* and *B. aristidoides*.

SPIKELETS PECTINATELY arranged at maturity, spikes usually persistent on the main axis.
    SPIKE 1, many-flowered, low tufted annual.   1. B. simplex
    SPIKES normally 2, often 1 or 3, rarely more than 4.
        Stipe of rudiment glabrous or minutely hairy at the apex; rachis prolonged beyond the spikelets as a naked point; second glume strongly papillose-hispid; spikes 3-5, broad.   2. B. hirsuta
        Stipe of rudiment with tuft of hairs at the apex, rachis not prolonged.
            Second glume not strongly papillose-hispid, but scabrous, sometimes sparingly papillose-ciliate on the keel; spikes 1-3, mostly 2, long and narrow.   3. B. gracilis
            Glumes smooth or slightly roughened; culm internodes, when protected, often covered with a thick scaly bloom; plants confined to calcareous soil along the Rio Grande and its tributaries, spikes normally 2, sometimes 1-3.   4. B. breviseta
    SPIKES normally 4 or more.
        Plants low, tufted.
            Plants usually prostrate; annual.   5. B. barbata
            Plants usually erect; rudiment naked at the apex.   6 B. trifida
        Plants taller, culms densely woolly, stoloniferous; spikes loose.   7. B. eriopoda
SPIKELETS NOT pectinately arranged, rather ascending, falling entire.
    SPIKES numerous, usually more than 20, racemose, panicle 4-12' long.
        Spike of one spikelet; rudiment a simple hispid awn about 4 mm. long.
                                    8. B. uniflora
    Spike of more than one spikelet. Spikelets without a second rudiment; plant tall.   9. B. curtipendula

SPIKES 4-6; glumes densely woolly; sheaths not densely woolly; rudiment trifid, long-awned. 10. B. chondrosioides
SPIKES 6-8; panicle racemose, short; plants low, tufted, hairy, rudiments distinctly 2 or more. 11. B. rigidiseta
SPIKES normally 4-10, panicle recemose, 1-6' long; plants taller, more or less papillose-pilose; second floret staminate; rachilla extending beyond its insertion about 1 mm. 12. B. filiformis
SPIKES normally 10-14; plant annual; spikelets closely appressed to the hairy rachis forming a cylindric spike. 13. B. aristidoides

1. B. SIMPLEX Lag. (sĭm'plĕks); *B. procumbens* (Durand) Griffiths; *B. prostrata* Lag.

Culms 4-12' tall, tufted, prostrate or ascending, branching; **Blades** mostly 10-25 mm. (10-35) long, very narrow, involute, puberulent on upper side above the base, otherwise glabrous; **Sheaths** mostly shorter than the internodes, striate; **Ligule** a ring of short hairs; **Spike** solitary, 10-30 mm. long, recurved at maturity; fertile to the end of the rachis, spikelets 20 or more pectinately arranged; **Spikelets** including awns 4-5 mm. long; **Glumes** 1-nerved, acute, lanceolate, keeled, acuminate, pointed, the first smooth, about 2-3 mm. long, the second minutely hispid on the keel 3.5-4.5 mm. long; **Lemmas** broadly oval, with three hispid awns, the central slightly longer, including awns about 4 mm. long, the central expanded with wing-like projections, hairy on the three nerves below; **Palea** 3 mm. long, broadly obovate, rounded above; **Rudiment** consisting of three equal hispid awns, about 4 mm. long, including naked stipe about 1 mm. long which bears a tuft of white hairs at the apex.

Open ground. West Texas to Arizona and Utah, and north to Colorado Springs, Colorado; Maine; Ecuador to Argentina. Summer and fall.

2. B. HIRSUTA Lag. (hĕr-sū'tà); HAIRY GRAMA or BLACK GRAMA.

Culms 6-30' tall, rigid, tufted, simple, erect or often geniculate and branched at the base in the smaller form, striate, sometimes slightly pubescent below, very variable in habit; **Blades** numerous and longer at the base, 2-8', upper 1-4' long, 1-2 mm. wide, flat, slender-pointed, sparsely papillose-hispid on the margins, hirsute on the upper surface near the base, rough except below near the base; **Sheaths**, upper shorter than the internodes, glabrous, or the lower pubescent, sometimes slightly pilose at the throat; **Ligule** a very short ring of hairs; **Panicle** racemose, axis on shorter form 1-2' long, on the longer as much as 6', bearing 1-4 spikes sometimes 5-6, normally two in the North and 3-4 in the South, 15-40 mm. long, with a prominent projection of the rachis beyond the last spikelet for about 5-8 mm.; **Spikelets** pectinate, numerous, including awns 5-6 mm. long; **Glumes** unequal, the first 2-3 mm. long, minutely hispid, narrow, acuminate, the second 4-5 mm. long, acuminate, short-awned, minutely hispid and conspicuously tuberculate-hairy; **Lemma** including awn about 5-6 mm. long, 3-toothed, pubescent, deeply 2-cleft, the lateral lobes acuminate or short-awned, the middle lobe with a hispid awn longer than the lateral teeth, the middle awn often having at its base on each side a tooth; **Palea** oval, broadly pointed, about as long as its lemma; **Rudiment** consisting of 3 equal hispid awns about 6 mm. long and about 2 scales, on a stipe about 2 mm. long, the stipe slightly short-pubescent above, the awns usually extending above the balance of the spikelet.

Rocky hills and plains; Texas and Mexico north to South Dakota, and east along coast to Florida. Summer and fall.

3. **B. GRACILIS** (H. B. K.) Lag. (grăs'ĭ-lĭs); *B. oligostachya* (Nutt.) Torr.; BLUE GRAMA.

Culms 6-24' tall, tufted, erect, sometimes branching at the base, a perennial plant forming a rough sod in the north and usually of much larger growth and in isolated tufts in the south; **Blades** 2-4' long, 2 mm. or less wide, flat, slightly scabrous on margins and toward apex; **Sheaths** shorter than the internodes, striate; **Ligule** very short with few ciliate hairs; **Spikes** 1-4, usually two, very variable in length, 20-50 mm. usually 25-35 mm. long, commonly curved and spreading, no projecting rachis; **Spikelets** pectinate, very numerous, often 60 or more, on short minutely-pubescent pedicels, densely crowded, about 6 mm. long; **Glumes** unequal, awn-pointed, lanceolate, keeled, minutely scabrous, the lower narrow, 3-3.5 mm. long, the upper 5-6 mm. long, sometimes sparingly glandular on the keel and ciliate; **Lemma** including the awn about 6 mm. long, lanceolate, pubescent, 3-awned, the central awn slightly longer, usually 4-lobed, with the lateral awns from the apex of lobes, the central from between two teeth or lobes; **Rudiment** about 5 mm. long consisting of three scabrous nearly equal awns with 2 or 3 scales at their base, on a short pedicel or stipe, having a tuft of white hairs at the base and apex; also another rudiment made up of 1 or 2 pale glumes.

Plains and hills, Texas and Mexico, north to Missouri, Colorado, Wisconsin and North Dakota. Summer.

4. **B. BREVISETA** Vasey (brĕv-ĭ-sē'tà); *B. ramosa* Scribn.; GYP GRASS, CHINO (chē'nō).

Culms 10-17' tall, tufted, erect, rigid, branching from short scaly rootstocks, the internodes when protected often covered with a thick bloom, slightly rough, nodes more or less pubescent; **Blades** 1-3' long, about 2 mm. wide, flat or slightly convolute, rigid, acuminate, ascending, sparingly pubescent on the upper surface, often sparingly papillose-ciliate on the margins; **Sheaths** as long as or shorter than the internodes, rather close, ciliate on the margins, sometimes villous at the throat; **Ligule** a very short ring of hairs; **Spikes** commonly 2, sometimes 1 or 3, 20-35 mm. long, straight or slightly curved, distant approximately their own length, erect or spreading, spikelets 30-70, pectinately arranged; **Spikelets** including awns 4.5-5 mm. long; **Glumes** slightly pubescent at base, acute, scabrous on the keel, the first 2-2.5 mm. long, the second 3-3.5 mm. long; **Lemma** including awns 4.5-5 mm. long, the three nearly equal hispid awns about 1-1.3 mm. long, middle slightly longer and two-toothed (said to have 3 awns and 4 teeth), pubescent; **Palea** awnless; **Rudiment** including awns and stipe about 4 mm. long, stipe about 1 mm. long, villous at the apex, the three hispid awns about equal, and a rudimentary scale; sometimes a second rudiment consisting of a very small scale with one or two teeth or short awns.

Big Bend, Texas, to Roswell, New Mexico. (Sanderson, Shafter, twenty miles north of Van Horn.) Late summer and fall.

5. **B. BARBATA** Lag. (bär-bā'tà); *B. microstachya* (Fourn.) Dewey.

Culms 1-12' rarely 25' tall, erect, geniculate and prostrate, often branching but mostly simple; **Blades** short, 5-50 mm. usually about an inch long, flat, 1-4 mm. wide, divergent; **Sheaths** short, striate, loose; **Ligule** a ring of hairs about 0.8 mm. long; **Spikes** 4-7, rarely 9, 12-20 mm. long, recurved, 10-20 mm. distant, short-pediceled, with 25-32 spikelets; **Spikelets** pectinately arranged, including the awns about 4 mm. long,

Glumes with a short awn between two short teeth, keel hispid, the first 1.5-2 mm. long, the second 2.5-3 mm. long, often purple; **Lemmas** 3.5-4 mm. long with three divergent, hispid, equal awns, about as long as the body of the lemma with two comparatively large lobes between them; **Palea** including awns about 2.5-3 mm. long, two-awned and 4-toothed, the two middle ones sometimes combined into one with a short awn, bearing a few scattered hairs; **Rudiment** about 3-4 mm. long including three divergent, hispid, equal awns about 3 mm. long, on a short-villous stipe, with two or three obovate lobes at base between the awns. (See drawings for long-awned form.)

River valleys, waste places, west Texas to Mexico, west to Arizona, Utah and California. (Big Spring, Eagle Pass, Laredo.) Spring and fall.

6. B. TRIFIDA Thurb. (trī'fĭ-dȧ); *B. trinii* (Fourn.) Griff.; *Chondrosium trinii* Fourn.; *B. burkii* Scribn.

Culms usually 5-10' tall, being very variable in size, tufted, delicate, erect, or in old plants geniculate at the base, crowded on short rootstocks; **Blades** 10-80 mm. long, about 1 mm. wide, flat or involute, divaricate, minutely roughened, very sparsely papillose-pilose, the hairs rather long; **Sheaths** mostly shorter than the internodes, striate, close, smooth or slightly roughened; **Ligule** a ring of short hairs; **Panicle** 1-2.5' long, racemose, bearing mostly 3-5 spikes, 10-20 mm. long, finally curved, with 10-18 spikelets, pectinately arranged, the spikes purple or finally pale; **Spikelets** including awns 6-8 mm. long; **Glumes** about equal, about 3 mm. long, scabrous on the keel, acute, often mucronate or awn-pointed; **Lemma** including awns about 6-7 mm. long, the body 2-2.5 mm. long, bearing three scabrous awns 3-5 mm. long, the body of the lemma pubescent to almost glabrous; **Palea** 2-keeled, not awned, nearly as long as its lemma; **Rudiment** including stipe 6-7 mm. long, consisting of 3 scabrous, equal awns, enlarged at the base, upon a naked stipe about 1-1.5 mm. long.

In dry soil, hills and ravines, central Texas to Mexico and Arizona. Spring and summer.

7. B. ERIOPODA (Torr.) Torr. (ĕr-ĭ-ŏp'ō-dȧ); *Chondrosium eriopodum* Torr.; WOOLLY-FOOT or BLACK GRAMA.

Culms 15-28' long, tufted, rather weak, often much bent, commonly branching, woolly, rigid, often stoloniferous; **Blades** of the culm 1-3' long, those of sterile shoots often 4-6' long, usually 1-2 mm. wide, flat or involute; **Sheaths** shorter than the internodes, the lower often woolly pubescent; **Ligule** a ciliate fringe of hairs; **Panicle** racemose, 4-6' long, with 3-8 commonly 4-5 spikes, 20-35 mm. long, on short hairy peduncles, erect-spreading, each containing 12-20 spikelets pectinately arranged; **Spikelets** 8-10 mm. long; **Glumes** keeled, very unequal, lanceolate, acuminate, smooth except the second glume near the apex, the first about 3 mm. long, the second 6-7 mm. long; **Lemma** 5-6 mm. long, minutely hairy especially below on the three nerves, three-awned, the midnerve prolonged into an awn 1-2 mm. long and lateral nerves prolonged into shorter awns; **Palea** narrower and nearly as long as its lemma, 2-toothed at the apex; **Rudiment** consisting of three equal hispid awns 4-5 mm. long, united at their base by very minute scales and supported upon a slender smooth stipe 2-3 mm. long, hairy-tufted at each end, the entire rudiment including awns 7-10 mm. long.

Dry, gravelly plains and hills, west Texas to Mexico, also New Mexico and Arizona. (On College campus at Alpine, Tex.) Summer and fall.

8. B. UNIFLORA Vasey (ū-nĭ-flō'rȧ).

As the general aspect of this plant is the same as *B. curtipendula,* except the smaller spike, the photograph is dispensed with, and the illustrations of the panicle and spikelets are attached to the photograph of *B. curtipendula.*

The writer collected this grass at several locations, each time on rocky hillsides, on dry sterile soil, sometimes on rocks. In most of the tufts and often in the same panicle were a few spikes with 2 or 3 typical spikelets of *B. curtipendula,* or abortive spikelets, intergrading between the two forms.

Culms commonly 1-2.5 sometimes 3.5 feet tall, tufted, wiry, sparingly branching, erect or spreading, smooth to minutely scabrous, usually more slender than *B. curtipendula,* from slender scaly rootstocks, often stoloniferous; **Blades** 2-12' long, the upper and basal shorter, about 2 mm. wide, flat toward the base, convolute toward the tip, more or less minutely scabrous, glabrous or sparingly papillose-ciliate on the margins at the base; **Sheaths** shorter than the internodes, smooth to minutely scabrous, glabrous to pilose, especially the lower; **Ligule** a ring of short fine hairs; **Panicle** included at the base or finally exserted, 5-12' long, slender, erect or slightly nodding, with 25-35 spreading or reflexed spikes, approximate or distant, the axis channeled and downwardly scabrous, the spike consisting of a solitary spikelet or rarely 2-3 abortive spikelets, or fully developed ones like those of *B. curtipendula,* and a hispid appressed rachis about 4 mm. long; **Spikelets** about 7-8 mm. long; **Glumes** 1-nerved, scabrous on the keel, the first narrow, short and obtuse or longer and acute, 2-3 mm. long, the second broader, 7-8 mm. long, acuminate; **Lemma** 5-6 mm. long, awnless or minutely 3-awned, the central only a little longer, smooth or slightly scabrous toward the apex; **Palea** slightly shorter than the lemma, acuminate, 2-toothed, scabrous above; **Rudiment** consisting of a single hispid awn about 4 mm. long sometimes with two small scales or glumes below.

Rocky banks, north and northwest of San Antonio, Texas, extending to Crockett county, Texas. (Concan, Crockett county, and near Sonora, Texas.) Spring.

9. B. CURTIPENDULA (Michx.) Torr. (kûr-tĭ-pĕn'dū-là); *B. racemosa* Lag.; *Atheropogon curtipendulus* (Michx.) Fourn.; TALL GRAMA GRASS or SIDE-OAT GRAMA.

Culms 1-3 feet tall, tufted, erect, simple, spreading by strong scaly rootstocks; **Blades** numerous, 2-12' long, 4 mm. wide or less, flat or involute, upper surface and margins scabrous, sometimes more or less hairy and sparingly papillose on the margins especially near the base; **Sheaths** usually shorter than the internodes, loose, striate, glabrous or the lower densely papillose-hairy, the throat often pilose and papillose-hispid; **Ligule** ciliate-fringed, very short; **Panicle** racemose, 3-15' long, with angled or flattened axis, spikes numerous, 20-60, 6-15 mm. long, on short flattened puberulent peduncles, approximate or distant; **Spikelets** 5-8 mm. long, green, purplish or brownish, bilateral on a flattened rachis, not pectinate, 5-8 sometimes as few as 3 and as many as 13 spikelets to a spike; **Glumes** unequal, scabrous-keeled, the lower very narrow, 4-5 mm. long, the upper broader, about 7 mm. long; **Lemma** 5-6 mm. long, oblong, smooth or slightly scabrous toward the apex, the 3 nerves extended into 3 short awns; **Palea** about as long as its lemma, acuminate, scabrous above, 2-toothed; **Rudiment** reduced to a minute scale with a delicate scabrous ıwn, and a rudimentary palea consisting of two very delicate awns, or ılmost a full formed lemma with rather long awns.

Dry hills and plains, ranging over most of the United States. Summer ınd fall.

l0. B. CHONDROSIOIDES (H. B. K.) Benth. (kŏn-drō-sĭ-oi'dēz) ; *B. havardii* Vasey; WOOLLY-SPIKED GRAMA.

Culms 10-24' tall, erect, simple, tufted, commonly 1 or 2 culms to a tuft, with numerous crowded leaves at base, few above and short; Blades mostly 1-4' long, those of culm shorter, often 20-30 mm. long, 3 mm. or less wide, flat, firm, rough on margins, sparingly pubescent, more or less papillose-pilose on margins, especially lower ones; Sheaths, upper shorter than the internodes, loose, striate, hairy at the throat; Ligule a ring of hairs; Spikes 4-6, 10-20 mm. long, with 7-12 spikelets on an axis 1.5-2' long, at first purplish later pale, villous, spikes short-pedicellate; Spikelets exclusive of awns about 6 mm. long, pubescent throughout, more or less pectinate before anthesis, but this arrangement lost with final development, all the awns rigid; Glumes densely woolly, acuminate, 1-nerved, keeled, the first narrow and usually shorter than the second, 3-6 mm. long, the second broader, 6-7 mm. long, awn pointed; Lemma 5-6 mm. long, densely-woolly above, the three nerves terminating in three equal awned lobes, strongly ciliate on the margins; Palea as long as its lemma, 2-toothed with awns about 1 mm. long, pubescent above on the nerves and margins; Rudiment consisting of three hispid nearly equal awns about 8-10 mm. long, including stipe 1-1.5 mm. long, the central awn with broad glume-like wings, the lateral often with narrow glume-like wings.

High gravelly hills or plains; Davis Mountains, west Texas to Arizona, also south to Mexico. Summer and fall.

11. B. RIGIDISETA (Steud.) Hitchc. (rĭ-jĭ-dĭ-sē'tà) ; *B. texana* S. Wats.; *Polyodon texanus* (S. Wats.) Nash; *Aegopogon rigidisetus* Steud.; MESQUITE-GRASS.

Culms 4-16' long, erect, tufted, simple, naked dark nodes; Blades narrow, flat or involute, about 1-4' sometimes 7.5' long, 2 mm. wide or less, sparingly pubescent with long papillose hairs on edges, edges slightly scabrous; Sheaths close, striate, with villous throat; Ligule with short-ciliate fringe; Inflorescence racemose, 1.5-2' long, spikes 6-10, longer than interval, each about 10 mm. long, on short pubescent peduncles 1 mm. long; Spikelets including awns 6-8 mm. long, crowded, usually about 3-5 to a spike, not pectinate, callus hairy; Glumes unequal, lanceolate, acuminate, hairy, the first 3-4 mm. long, narrow, awn-pointed, the second about 6 mm. long, short-awned from a bifid apex; Lemmas including awns about 6 mm. long, sparingly hairy on the three nerves, with three equal hispid divergent awns, the middle from a bifid apex; Palea 2-nerved, a little shorter than its lemma, 2-toothed or short-awned, 4-5 mm. long; Rudiments, lower with three hispid awns, equal, about 7 mm. long, united at their base by small glumes, with small palea 2-3 mm. long, upper same except without palea and smaller.

Dry hills and plains, Texas to Mexico. Spring to fall.

12. B. FILIFORMIS (Fourn.) Griffiths (fĭl-ĭ-fôr'mĭs) ; *this species has been referred to as B. humboltiana Kunth and B. bromoides (H. B. K.) Lag.*; LARGE MESQUITE.

Culms 10-21' tall, tufted, branching, erect or geniculate and spreading; Blades narrow, flat, 1-4 mm. usually less than 2 mm. wide, upper-

most leaves about 1′ long, the lower 2-5′ long, papillose-pilose along th
margins, more numerous at base; **Sheaths** shorter than internodes, close
Ligule a ring of short hairs; **Spikes** 5-11, racemose, falling entire
10-18 mm. long on short peduncles, exceeding the intervals; **Spikelet**
4-11, about 8 mm. long including awns, not pectinate; **Glumes** 1-nerved
acuminate, awn-pointed, boat-shaped, minutely scabrous on keel, firs
about 4-5 mm. long, the second about 6-7 mm. long; **Lemmas** 3-awned
about 7 mm. long including short awns, the middle awn about 1 mm.
longer than the lateral; **Palea** about 6 mm. long, 2-toothed; **Rudimen**
with lemma about 8 mm. long including awns, middle about 1-2 mm
longer than the lateral with palea about 5 mm. long, the awns longer than
in lower floret, rachilla about 1-2 mm. long extending above the insertion
of the staminate or sometimes perfect floret.

Dry sandy or rocky soil, southwest Texas to Mexico and Arizona
(Laredo and Falfurrias.) Fall.

13. B. ARISTIDOIDES (H. B. K.) Griseb. (ăr-ĭs-tĭ-doi′dēz); *Triather*
aristidoides (H. B. K.) Nash; NEEDLE GRAMA, SIX-WEEKS GRAMA.

Culms 1-24′ commonly about 12′ tall, tufted, erect, ascending, spread
ing or almost prostrate from a decumbent or geniculate base, simple o
usually freely branching, being very variable as to size and habit; **Blade**
1-3′ long more or less, about 2 mm. wide, flat but involute at the tip, a fev
scattered hairs on the upper surface, slightly scabrous on the margins
Sheaths, the lower one-third to one-half as long as the internodes, th
upper sometimes nearly as long, loose, especially on the branching culms
often with a few hairs at the throat; **Ligule** a membranaceous line usually
short-ciliate; **Panicles,** the terminal usually exserted, the lateral often in
cluded at the base, mostly 2-4′ rarely less than 1′ and as much as 6′ long
spikes racemose, normally 10-14 or in unfavorable conditions reduced t
2-4, mostly 12-20 mm. long, sometimes shorter or longer, on short hairy
peduncles less than 1 mm. long, the peduncles and rachis densely hairy
except toward the tip of rachis merely scabrous; **Spikelets** 2-4 to eacl
spike, the lowermost more or less abortive, loosely arranged, not pectinate
about 2 mm. apart and appressed, consisting of a fertile lemma and a
rudiment, the rudiment usually absent in the lower spikelet; **Glume**
acuminate, 1-nerved, minutely scabrous on the keels, somewhat pubescen
on the back, the first 1.5-3 mm. long, very narrow, the second also narrow
but broader, two to three times as long as the first; **Lemma** 5-7 mm. long
linear-lanceolate, acuminate, pubescent mostly on the three nerves, with
three very short minutely scabrous awns, the middle slightly longer
Palea slightly shorter than the lemma, 2-toothed; **Rudiment** consisting o
three long scabrous awns upon a hairy stipe about 1 mm. long with a
tuft of hairs at the apex, the central awn slightly glumaceous at the base
and about 2 mm. shorter than the lateral, the whole rudiment abou
7-9 mm. long, usually exceeding the lemma about 1-1.5 mm.

This species is as variable as the seasons and conditions of the
capricious climate of its range.

Dry desert mesas and foothills from western Texas to the Pacific
coast. (Shafter, Van Horn, Limpia canyon, El Paso, Texas.) Fall.

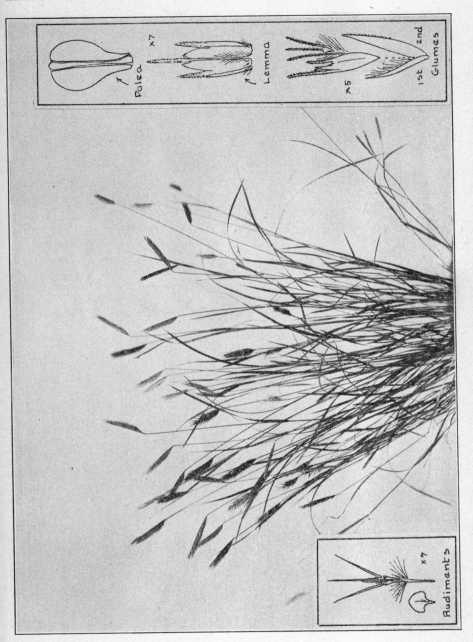

BOUTELOUA SIMPLEX; the first glume is not hairy as shown in the drawing.

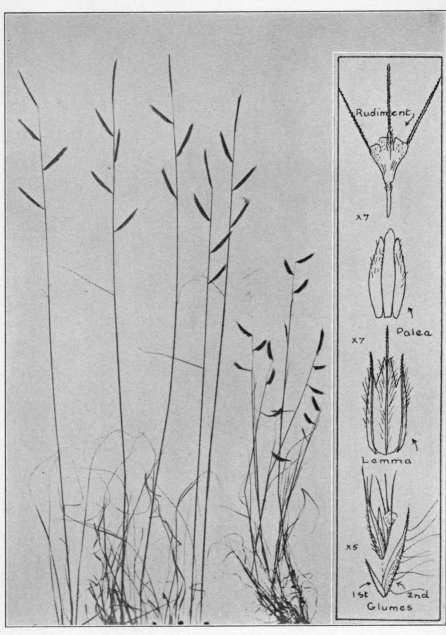

BOUTELOUA HIRSUTA; Hairy Grama. Long and short form

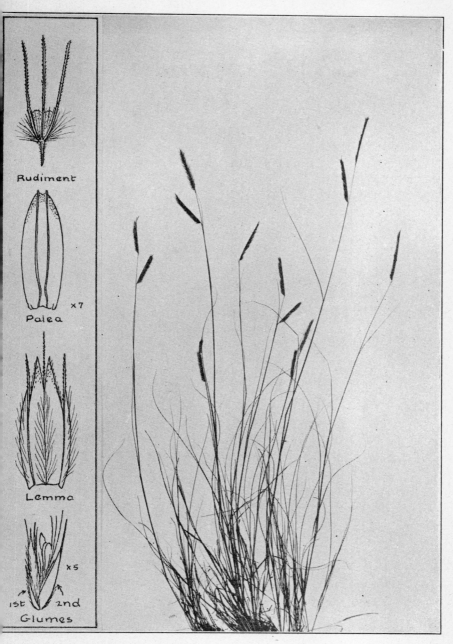

Rudiment

Palea ×7

Lemma

1st 2nd Glumes ×5

BOUTELOUA GRACILIS; BLUE GRAMA

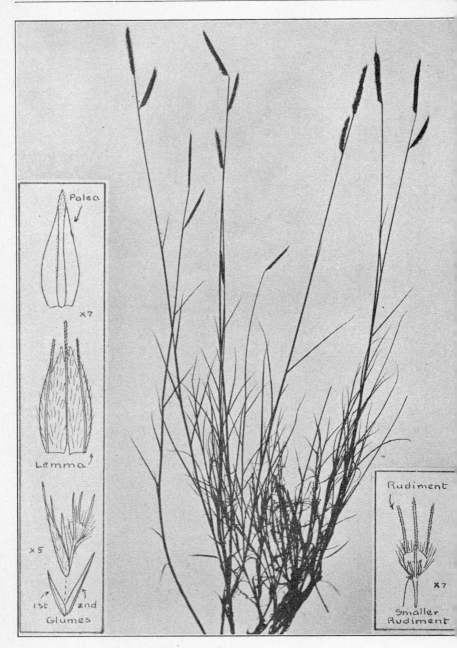

BOUTELOUA BREVISETA; Gyp Grass, Chino

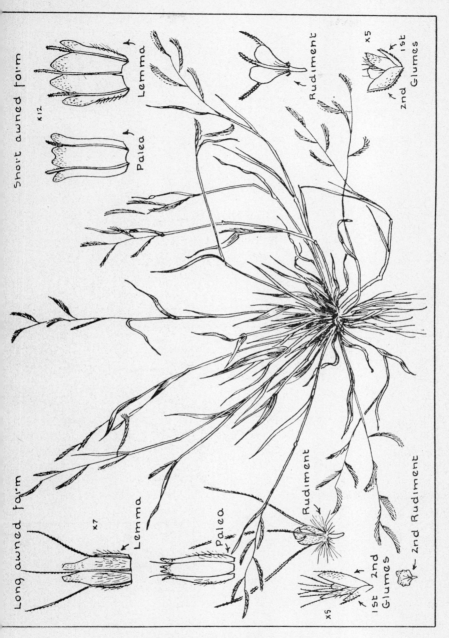

BOUTELOUA BARBATA

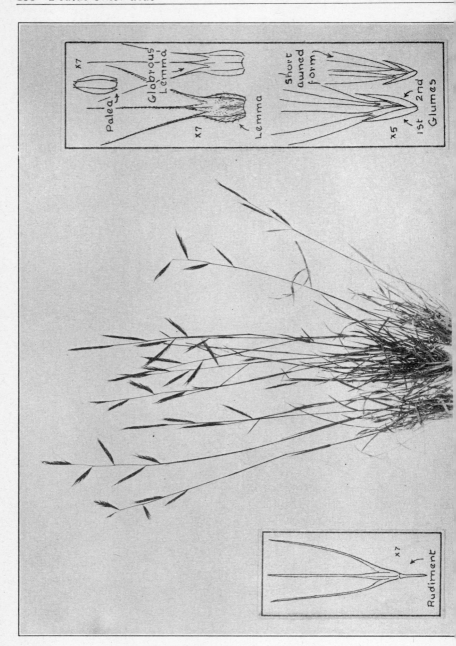

BOUTELOUA TRIFIDA

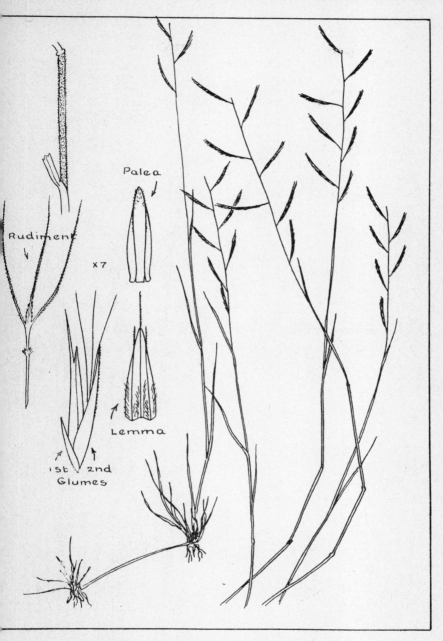

Palea

Rudiment

×7

Lemma

1st 2nd
Glumes

BOUTELOUA ERIOPODA; Woolly-foot

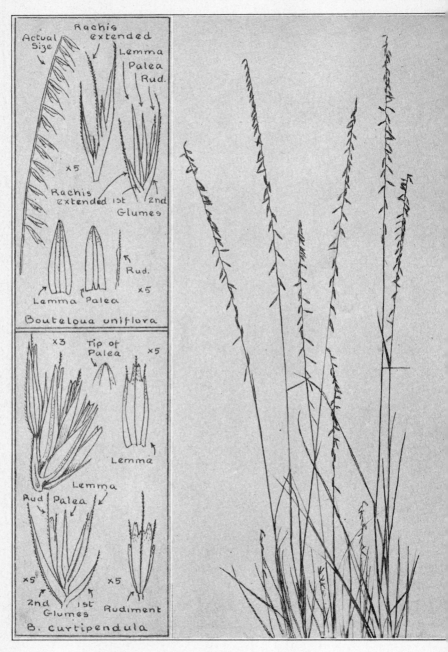

BOUTELOUA CURTIPENDULA; also drawings of
BOUTELOUA UNIFLORA

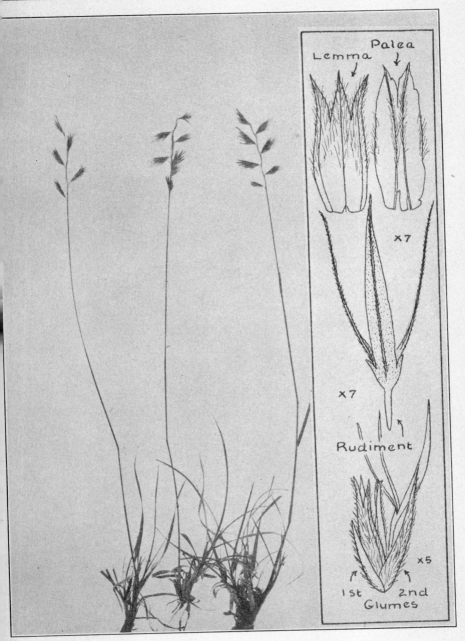

BOUTELOUA CHONDROSIOIDES; WOOLLY SPIKE GRAMA

BOUTELOUA RIGIDISETA; Mesquite-grass

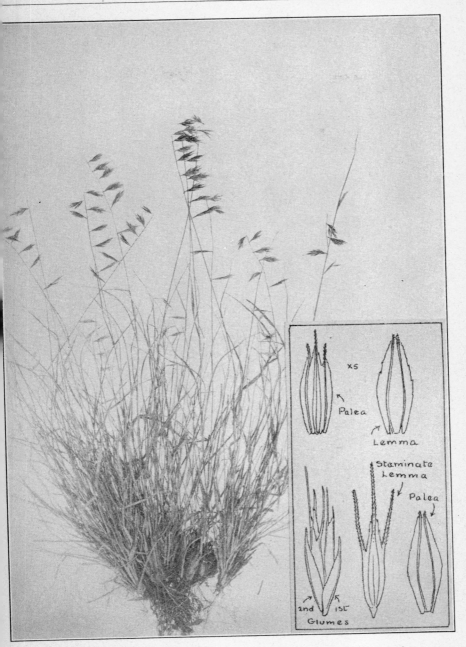

BOUTELOUA FILIFORMIS; LARGE MESQUITE. The scale at the upper left-hand corner should be marked "lemma" and the one to the right "palea".

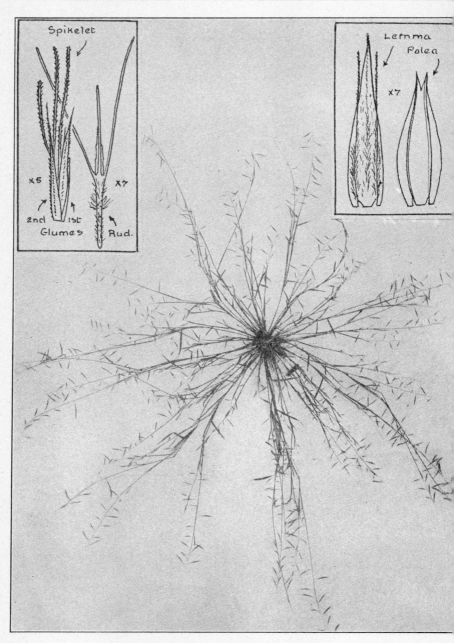

BOUTELOUA ARISTIDOIDES

70. CATHESTECUM Presl (kăth-ĕs-tē′kŭm)

Spikes consisting of 3 spikelets, the upper or central perfect, the 2
lateral staminate or rudimentary, the spike falling entire; **Central Spikelet**
with one perfect floret below and one or more reduced florets above;
Glumes unequal, the first a short, thin, nerveless scale in the central
spikelet, narrow and acuminate in the lateral spikelets, the second about
as long as the lemma, acuminate, all usually villous; **Lemma** 3-nerved or
rarely 5-7-nerved, the nerves extending into awns and the internerves into
teeth; **Palea** 2-nerved, the nerves extending into short awns; **Second and
Third Floret** with a fairly well developed lemma and palea, the fourth
floret, if present, usually reduced.

Low cespitose or stoloniferous *annuals or perennials,* with short blades,
and several or many short deciduous spikes scattered along the main axis.
Species four, on the Mexican plateau, one extending into western Texas.

Cathestecum erectum, a stoloniferous perennial with the aspect of
Bouteloua rigidiseta (*B. texana*) but more delicate, is the only species in the
United States. Before blooming it may be mistaken for curly mesquite, as
it is short and has similar stolons.

It is very variable, there being a short-awned form which is hereafter
described and illustrated, and a long-awned form usually found on separate
plants, but the two forms were found on the same plant in Mexico by
Hitchcock. Griffiths states that in some cases the lower spikelets are much
reduced on the long-awned form, and that it does not appear to be the
lengthening of the awns after anthesis, as with *Bouteloua chondrosioides,*
but a true dimorphic character. It is found from El Paso to the Big Bend
of Texas, where it is rather plentiful.

C. ERECTUM Vasey & Hack. (ē-rĕk′tŭm).

Culms 4-13′ tall, simple or branched, densely tufted, erect or geniculate at the base, with slender stolons sometimes 2 feet long, the arcuate
internodes from a few to 8′ long, rooting at the prominent villous nodes,
the culm nodes puberulent to villous; **Blades,** the basal numerous, commonly 1-2′ sometimes 3.5′ long, the upper much reduced, flat, scabrous on
the margins, commonly sparsely-pilose with rather long hairs, especially
on the upper surface; **Sheaths,** upper shorter than the internodes, pilose
at the throat, and with a few hairs like those of the blades, or glabrous;
Ligule a ring of short soft hairs; **Spikes** 5-8, about 7-8 mm. long, hairy at
the base, distant about their own length, ascending or spreading, arranged
on 1-3 slender usually long peduncles from the upper sheath, the axis at
the apex bifurcate; **Spikelets,** the middle including the awns about 6 mm.
long; **Glumes,** the first as described above, the second of all the spikelets
3-4 mm. long, lanceolate, keeled, mucronate, hairy especially along the keel;
Lower Lemma 3-4 mm. long, the three awns slightly exceeding the four
lobes, more or less hairy especially above; **Palea** nearly equal to its lemma,
with two short awns sparsely hairy, especially above; **Caryopsis** obovate,
1.7 mm. long, 0.7 mm. wide, amber; **Upper Lemmas** similar, but the lobes
broader and deeper, and the awns with comparatively long hairs below,
and somewhat reduced; **Lateral Spikelets** about 4.5 mm. long, the lower
lemma well developed but sterile, the second staminate or neuter, the upper
rudimentary, all the parts somewhat similar to those of the middle spikelet.

Rocky hills and mountains, Big Bend to El Paso, extending to
Arizona and Mexico.

(This grass is plentiful over most of the Big Bend country.) Summer-
fall.

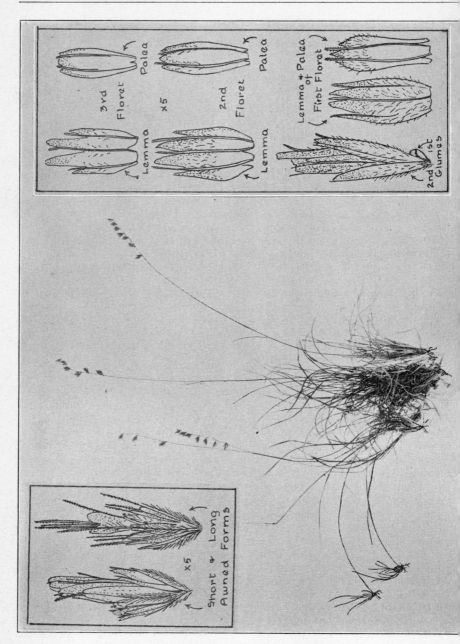

CATHESTECUM ERECTUM

71. MUNROA Torr. (mŭn-rō'à)

Spikelets in pairs or threes on a short rachis; the lower one or two larger, 3-4-flowered, the upper 2-3-flowered, the group (reduced spikes) inclosed in the broad sheaths of short leaves, usually about 3 in a fascicle, forming a cluster or head at the end of the branches; **Rachilla** disarticulating above the glumes and between the florets; **Glumes** of the lower 1 or 2 spikelets equal, 1-nerved, narrow, acute, a little shorter than the lemma, those of the upper spikelet unequal, the first much shorter or obsolete; **Lemmas** 3-nerved, those of the lower spikelet coriaceous, acuminate, the points spreading, the midnerve extended into a mucro, those of the upper spikelet membranaceous; **Palea** narrow, 2-nerved, inclosing the oval dorsally compressed caryopsis.

Low spreading, much branched *annuals*, the short flat pungent leaves in fascicles. It is usually found in open ground or new or sandy soil. One species in the United States with about the range of buffalo grass.

M. SQUARROSA (Nutt.) Torr. (squăr-ō'sà); MUNRO'S GRASS, FALSE BUFFALO-GRASS.

Culms 3-8' tall, tufted, erect, freely branching, spreading, decumbent or widely prostrate, taking root at the nodes, sometimes stoloniferous, the internodes short, 1-2' long, rough, nodes more or less pilose; **Blades** 10-35 mm. long, 1-2 mm. wide, flat, crowded at the nodes and ends of branches, spreading, margins rough and white, pungently-pointed; **Sheaths** crowded at the nodes and ends of branches, pilose at the throat, often ciliate on the margins, loose, soon becoming papery, inflated; **Ligule** a ring of short hairs about 1 mm. long; **Spikes** very short; **Spikelets** in pairs of threes, 2-4-flowered; **Glumes** shorter than the lemmas; **Lemmas** 5-7 mm. long, a tuft of hairs on each side near the middle and usually near the base of the keel, more or less hispidulous all over the back, the midnerve produced into an awn usually 1-1.5 mm. long, the lateral nerves often excurrent as short points; **Palea** nearly as long as its lemma, obtuse.

On dry, usually sandy soil, from Texas north to Montana and South Dakota, extending south into Mexico. Summer and fall.

MUNROA SQUARROSA; MUNRO'S GRASS OR FALSE BUFFALO-GRASS

72. BUCHLOË Engelm. (bū-klō′ē)
(Bulbilis Raf.)

Plants **Unisexal**. **Staminate** spikelets 2-flowered, sessile and closely
bricate, in two rows on one side of a slender rachis forming a short
ike; **Glumes** somewhat unequal, rather broad, 1-nerved, acutish;
•mmas longer than the glumes, 3-nerved, rather obtuse, whitish; **Palea**
long as its lemma, 2-nerved. **Pistillate** spikelets mostly 3 to 5 in a short
ike or head, this falling entire, usually 2 heads to the inflorescence, the
mmon peduncle short and included in the somewhat inflated sheaths of
e upper leaves, the thickened somewhat woody rachis and the 2 or 3
ter (second) glumes appearing like an involucre; **Glumes** very unequal,
e first inside relative to the cluster, thin, 1-nerved, keeled, the nerve
tending into a point or awn, as long as the lemma or reduced in some
the spikelets or wanting, the second glume firm, thick and woody,
nost surrounding the remainder of the spikelet, rounded on the back,
site or yellowish, obscurely nerved, the margins inflexed, thin, ciliate,
e upper part greenish, acuminate, spreading, with one or two teeth at
e sides; **Lemma** firm-membranaceous, 3-nerved, dorsally compressed,
oad below, narrowed into a 3-lobed green summit, the middle lobe much
e larger; **Palea** 2-nerved, broad, obtuse, about as long as the body of the
nma, enveloping the caryopsis.

A low stoloniferous *perennial*, with short curly blades, the staminate
•wers in two or three short spikes on slender erect culms, the pistillate
sessile clusters partly hidden among the leaves. Species one, on the
·eat Plains from Montana to Mexico.

DACTYLOIDES (Nutt.) Engelm. (dăk-tĭ-loi′dēz) ; *Bulbilis dactyloides*
(Nutt.) Raf.; BUFFALO-GRASS.

Buffalo grass is short, commonly 4-8′, in favorable locations 12′ tall,
d is **Dioecious**, i.e., the **Staminate** (male) inflorescence on one plant and
e **Pistillate** (female) on another, or sometimes **Monoecious**, i. e., with the
ıminate and pistillate inflorescence on the same plant or stolon.

Both kinds of plants usually have stolons or runners from a few
ɔhes to a foot or so long, the internodes commonly 2-3′ long, and the
des with tufts of short leaves, often taking root at the nodes and pro-
cing new plants. Each propagates vegetatively its own kind, rarely
th staminate and pistillate. Commonly each kind is found in small or
·ge patches some distance apart.

As buffalo and curly mesquite are both low stoloniferous plants with
rly leaves, some difficulty may be encountered in distinguishing them.
not in flower they can be told by their nodes and internodes, the nodes
the buffalo being glabrous and those of curly mesquite villous, the
:ernodes of buffalo short and those of curly mesquite long. Curly
·squite has a solitary cylindric spike, while buffalo grass, in the stamin-
e plant has 2-3 one-sided approximate spikes, and in the pistillate sessile
ısters partly hidden by the leaves. (See photograph and description of
·ly mesquite.)

As this is the only species of the genus, Hitchcock has very fully de-
·ibed both the staminate and pistillate spikelets, rendering it unnec-
:ary to further describe them. His description, together with the draw-
ɟs and photograph, will give an understanding of the spikelets.

Culms commonly 4-8′ rarely 12′ tall, those of the pistillate plants
ıally shorter, mostly 2-5′, in small tufts, or in densely matted small or

large patches, or forming a continuous sod, slender, erect or decumbent
the base, with stolons a few inches to 2 feet long, the internodes 2-3' lor
or sometimes longer, the nodes glabrous, often with a tuft of short leav
frequently taking root at tho nodes and producing new plants; **Blad**
the basal mostly about 4' rarely 8', those of the culm proper 1-4' and of t
stolons often less than 1' long, in the staminate plants the culms most
exceeding the leaves, and in the pistillate plants the leaves exceeding t
culms, 2 mm. wide or less, flat, acuminate, slightly roughened, the margi
sparingly ciliate or papillose-ciliate; **Sheaths** loose, the throat most
pilose, the upper sheaths in the pistillate plants partly inclosing the flow
clusters; **Ligule** a ring of hairs; **Staminate Plant:** the inflorescence of 2
sessile or subsessile approximate one-sided spikes 14 mm. long or less, wi
about 10 spikelets, each spikelet about 4 mm. long; **Pistillate Plant:** t
spikelets very different from the staminate, each with one flower, and t
parts much indurated and modified.

Great Plains, Montana to Mexico.   Spring to fall.

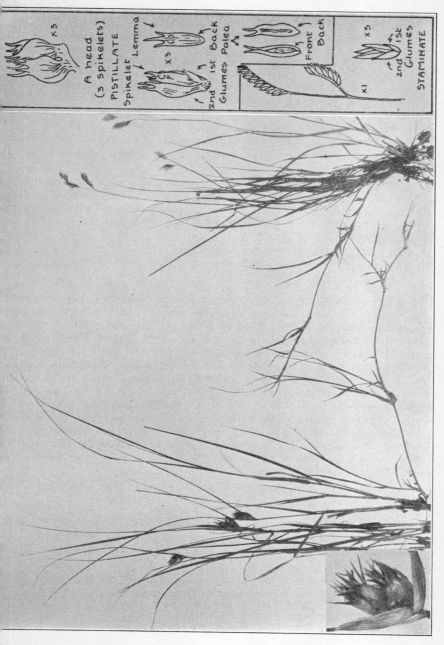

BUCHLOE DACTYLOIDES; BUFFALO-GRASS. Staminate plant to the right; pistillate to the left.

VIII.   PHALARIDEAE, THE CANARY GRASS TRIBE

73.   ANTHOXANTHUM   L.   (ăn-thō-zăn′thŭm)

Spikelets with 1 terminal perfect floret and 2 sterile lemmas, th rachilla disarticulating above the glumes, the sterile lemmas fallin attached to the fertile floret; **Glumes** unequal, acute or mucronate; **Steril** **Lemmas** shorter than the glumes, empty, awned from the back; **Fertil** **Lemma** shorter than the sterile ones, awnless; **Palea** 1-nerved, rounded o the back, inclosed in the lemma.

Sweet-smelling *annual* or *perennial* grasses, with flat blades and spik like panicles.   Species about four, Europe and Asia; two introduced into t United States, both in Texas.

Anthoxanthum odoratum, sweet vernal grass, is sometimes included i meadow mixtures to give fragrance to the hay.   The species is of no fora value but has an aromatic odor due to the presence of coumarin.   Anoth species, *A. aristatum* (*A. puellii* Lec. & Lam.), a low annual, has bee introduced at a few localities.

PLANTS perennial.	1. A. odoratu
PLANTS annual.	2. A. aristatu

1.   A. ODORATUM L.   (ō-dō-rā′tŭm) ; Sweet Vernal-grass.

Culms 1-2 feet tall, tufted, erect, simple or branching, slender; **Blad** 0.5-6′ long, the upper short, 2-6 mm. wide, flat, rough, sparing pubescent; **Sheaths** shorter than the internodes, glabrous to sparing pubescent; **Ligule** membranaceous, 2-4 mm. long, acute; **Panicle** long-e serted, 1-3′ long, bronze-green, spikelike, loosely cylindric, the sho branches erect or ascending or spreading in flower; **Spikelets** crowde about 8 mm. long, linear-oblong; **Glumes** acuminate, glabrous to sparse pubescent, the first 1-nerved, thin, about half as long as the second, t second 3-nerved, firmer than the first; **Sterile Lemmas** exceeding t fertile two-lobed lemma, densely pubescent, the first short-awned below t apex, the second bearing a strong bent exserted awn near the base, t awn more than twice as long as its lemma; **Fertile Lemma** chestn brown, smooth and shining, awnless, truncate; the sterile lemmas f attached to the fertile lemma.

In fields and meadows, throughout nearly the whole of Nor America, especially in the northeastern states.   Spring.

2.   A. ARISTATUM Boiss.   (ăr-ĭs-tā′tŭm) ; Annual Sweet Vernal-gra

Differs from *A. odoratum* in being an *annual*, the plants lower, oft geniculate, and bushy branching; **Panicle** loose and **Spikelets** a litt smaller.

Waste places in several locations from Maine to Iowa; Florida Texas; Oregon and Vancouver Island.   Spring-summer.

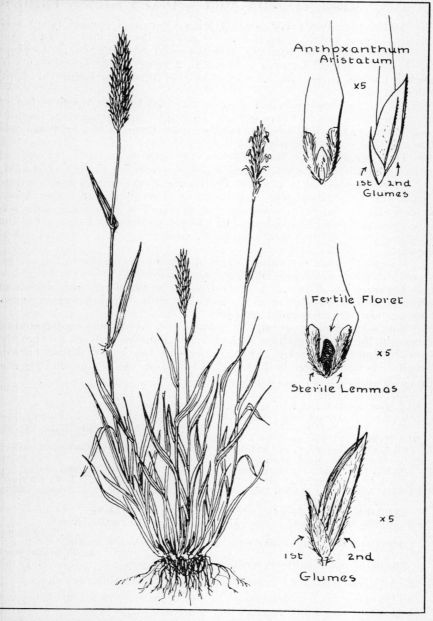

Anthoxanthum Aristatum

x5

1st 2nd
Glumes

Fertile Floret

x5

Sterile Lemmas

x5

1st 2nd
Glumes

NTHOXANTHUM ODORATUM, SWEET VERNAL-GRASS; also drawings
of Spikelet of ANTHOXANTHUM ARISTATUM

74. PHALARIS L. (făl′à-rĭs)

Spikelets laterally compressed, with 1 terminal perfect floret and ?
sterile lemmas below, disarticulating above the glumes, arranged in
usually dense spikelike panicles; **Glumes** equal, boat-shaped, often winged
on the keel; **Sterile Lemmas** reduced to 2 small scales (rarely only 1)
Fertile Lemma coriaceous, shorter than the glumes, inclosing the faintly
2-nerved palea.

Annual or *perennial* erect grasses, with flat blades. Species about 20
in temperate regions of Europe and America. Nine species are found in
the United States, four being introduced from Europe. Six in Texas, three
perennials and three annuals.

These grasses have flat spikelets, the glumes usually winged and
often variegated with white and green nerves, turning papery at maturity

P. brachystachys, a weed on the Pacific Slope, collected only once in
Texas (by the author near Asherton), is very similar in appearance to
P. canariensis, which furnishes the canary seed of commerce, both being
tall leafy plants with ovoid or short-oblong panicles or heads 1-1.5′ long
P. minor, similar in appearance to *P. canariensis,* has a solitary sterile
lemma.

P. arundinacea, reed canary-grass, is a well-known grass in the northern
states, extending south into Oklahoma and some of the other southern states
and perhaps into Texas. A derivative, *P. arundinacea* var. *picta,* with
white striped blades, known as gardener's garters or painted-grass, is some
times grown for ornamental purposes.

Southern canary grass, *P. caroliniana,* sometimes cultivated for
forage in the southern states, has spikelike panicles usually 2-5′ long an
over 10 mm. in diameter, while *P. angusta* has long cylindric panicle
usually less than 10 mm. in diameter, at a distance resembling timothy grass

PLANTS PERENNIAL; PANICLES OVOID, oblong or linear, 1-8′ long; steril
lemmas in pairs.
   GLUMES NOT WINGED; panicles loose, 3-8′ long.
     Blades not striped with white.   1. P. arundinace
     Blades striped with white.   1a. P. arundinacea var. pict
   GLUMES WINGED; panicles 1-6′ long, dense.
     PANICLE linear-oblong, cylindric, less than 10 mm. in diameter; spikele
      3.5-4 mm. long; glumes slightly winged.   2. P. angust
     PANICLE ovoid or linear-oblong, if oblong exceeding 10 mm. thick; spike
      lets 5-6 mm. long; glumes broadly winged.   3. P. carolinian
PLANTS ANNUAL; PANICLES OVOID or short-oblong, 1-1.5′ long. Glume
   broadly winged.
   STERILE lemmas in pairs; fertile lemma 4-6 mm. long.
     Sterile lemmas half to two-thirds as long as the fertile lemma.
                                4. P. canariens
     Sterile lemmas about one-fifth as long as the fertile lemma.
                                5. P. brachystachy
   STERILE lemma solitary; fertile lemma 3 mm. long.   6. P. min

1. P. ARUNDINACEA L. (à-rŭn-dĭ-nā′sē-à) ; REED CANARY-GRASS.

This species is a widely known grass, being very plentiful in the nort
central states and Canada extending southward into some of the souther
states. The author was unable to collect this grass, but collecte
P. arundinacea var. *picta,* a cultivated derivative, which is described unde
the next number. From the drawings, photographs and descriptions give
by several authors this variety is very similar to the species except th
variegated blades and, perhaps, the branching culms.

In moist or wet soil, Maryland to Arizona, north to Canada. May b
found in north or northeast Texas. Spring to fall.

a. P. ARUNDINACEA var. PICTA L. (pĭk′tȧ) ; RIBBON-GRASS, PAINTED-GRASS, GARDENER'S GARTERS.

Culms 2-5 feet tall, flattened, erect, from horizontal rootstocks, growing in large clumps, often with a few leafy branches; Blades with green and white stripes, 1.5-10′ long, mostly 4-7′ long, 3-16 mm. wide, flat, acuminate, narrowed toward the base, usually rough, sometimes very rough; Sheaths longer than the internodes, or the upper shorter, usually smooth; Ligule thin, 2-6 mm. long; Panicles exserted, commonly erect, 3-8′ long, 10-20 mm. thick, contracted except in anthesis, densely-flowered, the axis, branches and pedicels scabrous, the branches 0.5-1.5′ long, appressed or spreading in anthesis, commonly in twos, the pedicels 1-2 mm. long; Spikelets 4-6 mm. long, lanceolate, pale; Glumes not winged, acuminate, equal, 3-nerved, scabrous; Sterile Lemmas less than half as long as the glumes, subulate, hairy; Lemma about three-fourths as long as the glumes, chartaceous, pubescent with rather long appressed hairs.

In cultivation as an ornamental grass, sometimes escaping from cultivation. Spring and summer.

. P. ANGUSTA Nees (ăn-gŭs′tȧ).

Culms 18-42′ tall, erect, somewhat tufted, simple or sparingly branching at the base, slightly scabrous below the panicle; Blades 2-12′ long, -6 mm. wide, the upper short, flat, the plant leafy at the base; Sheaths, upper shorter than the internodes; Ligule membranaceous, obtuse, decurrent down the margins of the sheath, 4-6 mm. long; Panicles finally long-exserted, usually evenly cylindric, 2-6′ long, about 8-10 mm. thick, densely-flowered, the short branches appressed, at a distance resembling timothy heads; Spikelets 3.5-4 mm. long; Glumes equal, about 3.5-4 mm. long, only slightly winged, 3-nerved, scabrous on the keel; Sterile Lemmas less than half as long as the lemma, narrow, hairy at the apex; Lemma 2.5-3 mm. long, acuminate, silky-appressed-pubescent.

In moist soil, Texas, Louisiana, South Carolina and California. Beaumont, Texas.) Spring-summer.

P. CAROLINIANA Walt. (kăr-ō-lĭ-nĭ-ā′nȧ) ; *P. intermedia* Bosc; SOUTHERN CANARY GRASS.

Culms 1-4 feet tall, in rather large tufts, erect, sometimes decumbent at base, simple or branched at base; Blades 2-12′ long, 4-18 mm. wide, upper sometimes about two inches long, in smaller plants much shorter, flat, glaucous; Ligule membranaceous, thin, rounded, 2-6 mm. long; Sheaths shorter than internodes, upper somewhat inflated; Panicle at first included, finally exserted, spikelike, 1-5′ long, usually about 15 mm. wide, oblong, dense, its branches about one-half inch long, crowded with spikelets; Spikelets 5-6 mm. long, flattened, on very short pedicels; Glumes about equal, 5-6 mm. long, winged, flattened, acute, scabrous on the keel, the green nerves prominent; Sterile Lemmas about 1.5 mm. long, about half to two-thirds as long as fertile lemma, narrow, hairy, empty; Lemma ovate-lanceolate, two-thirds as long as spikelet, about 3.5 mm. long, acuminate, pubescent with long appressed silky hairs.

In moist soil, southern United States, California and Mexico. Spring and summer.

P. CANARIENSIS L. (kȧ-nā-rĭ-ĕn′sĭs) ; CANARY-GRASS.

Culms 1-4 feet tall, tufted, erect, simple or branching, more or less roughened, nodes swollen; Blades 3-16′ long, 4-6 mm. (4-12) wide, flat,

strongly scabrous, base of blade rounded; **Sheaths** shorter than the internodes, upper inflated, more or less rough; **Ligule** membranaceous, very
thin, about 4 mm. long; **Panicle** densely spikelike, ovoid or oblong, 20-40
mm. long, 12-15 mm. thick, green turning whitish, crowded branches very
short; **Spikelets** 6-8 mm. (5-8) long, broadly obovate; **Glumes** about equal
white with three prominent green nerves, the keel minutely toothed and
winged above, acute, thin, glabrous or sparingly pubescent; **Sterile**
Lemmas 2-3 mm. long, about two-thirds as long as the fertile lemma, the
first slightly shorter, lanceolate, glabrous or sparingly hairy, with a few
short bristle-like hairs at the acute apex; **Lemma** about 4-5 mm. long, or
about two-thirds length of glumes, acute, appressed-pubescent.

In waste places, Texas to Colorado, Nebraska to Missouri, extending
into Canada. (San Antonio, Texas.) Spring-summer.

5. P. BRACHYSTACHYS Link (brăk-ĭs′tà-kĭs).

Culms 1-3 feet tall, tufted, erect or ascending from a decumbent base
branching toward the base, smooth or rough, nodes somewhat swollen
Blades 2.5-11′ long, 5-12 mm. wide, flat, rounded at the base, rough o
smooth below toward the base; **Sheaths** shorter than the internodes, uppe
inflated, smooth or slightly rough; **Ligule** 3-5 mm. long, membranaceous
fragile, obtuse, decurrent; **Panicle** spikelike, ovoid to oblong-cylindric
1-1.5′ long, 10-13 mm. thick, dense, light-green turning pale; **Spikelet**
6-8 mm. long, obovate; **Glumes** equal, pale with three prominent green
nerves, abruptly acute, the keel winged above, the wing slightly toothen
Sterile Lemmas about one-fifth as long as the fertile lemma (less than
mm. long), ovate, obtuse, a few short hairs at the base, otherwise glabrous
Lemma 4-5 mm. long, lanceolate, pubescent with appressed rather stif
silky hairs.

Dry soil, waste places. Texas and Pacific Slope. (Asherton, Texas.
Spring.

6. P. MINOR Retz. (mĭ′nĕr).

Resembling *P. canariensis;* **Panicle** obovate-oblong, 20-50 mm. long
Spikelets narrow, not so conspicuously striped; **Glumes** 4-6 mm. long, th
wing of the keel narrow, 3-nerved; **Sterile Lemma** solitary, about half a
long as the fertile lemma; **Lemma** lance-ovate, about 3 mm. long, acute
appressed-pubescent. (See drawings on photograph of *P. canariensis.*

Fields and waste places, Texas, Louisiana, New Jersey, Colorado an
Oregon. (Houston.)

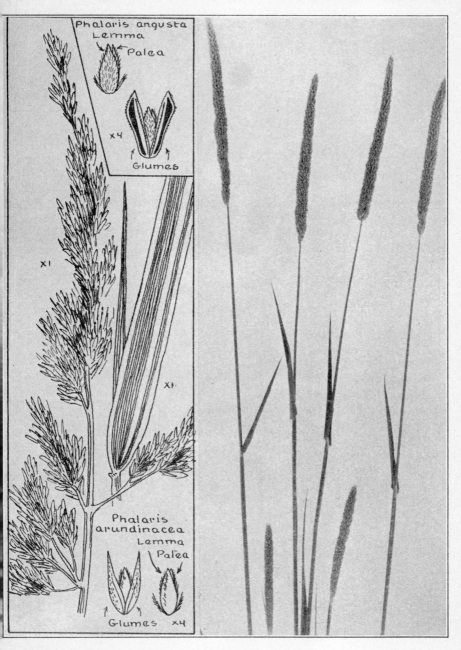

PHALARIS ANGUSTA; PHALARIS ARUNDINACEA VAR. PICTA,
GARDENER'S GARTERS, RIBBON-GRASS, PAINTED-GRASS

PHALARIS CAROLINIANA, Southern Canary-grass

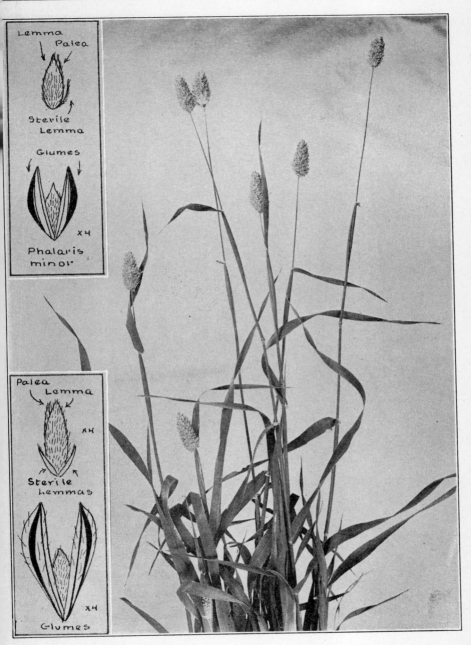

PHALARIS CANARIENSIS, Canary Grass and a drawing of
PHALARIS MINOR

PHALARIS BRACHYSTACHYS

IX. ORYZEAE, THE RICE TRIBE

75. ORYZA L. (ō-rī′zà)

Spikelets 1-flowered, laterally compressed, disarticulating below the glumes; **Glumes** 2, much shorter than the lemma, narrow; **Lemma** rigid, keeled, 3-nerved, sometimes awned; **Palea** similar to the lemma, narrower, keeled, but with no midnerve on the back, 2-nerved close to the margins.

Annual or sometimes perennial swamp grasses, often tall, with flat blades and spikelets in open panicles. One species, an *annual*, cultivated rice, in the warmer parts of North America.

Rice is cultivated in many warm countries, and is one of the important food crops of the world. It thrives in very moist situations, and is grown mostly under irrigation on the lowlands of the south Atlantic, the Mississippi Valley and southeastern Texas. There are many varieties with awned or awnless spikelets. The plant herein described was found near Eagle Lake, Texas, and is one of the awnless varieties. The above descriptions of the genus include all the varieties of the species.

O. SATIVA L. (sā-tī′và); CULTIVATED RICE.

Culms mostly 2-3 feet tall, with about ten culms to a tuft, simple, erect; **Blades** 3-12′ long, about 10 mm. wide, flat, narrowed toward the base, rough, especially on the upper surface and the margin; **Sheaths** mostly longer than the internodes, smooth or rough; **Ligule** membranaceous, 5-10 mm. long; **Panicle** 5-10′ long, narrow, exserted or included at the base, erect or nodding, the leaves often exceeding the panicle, the branches flexuous, mostly 1-3.5′ long, naked at the base, commonly single, the axis, branches and pedicels slightly scabrous; the **Spikelets** single or in pairs on the branches or short branchlets, the pedicels usually less than 1 mm. long; **Spikelets** about 9 mm. long, about 3 mm. wide, somewhat flattened, oblong, rough; **Glumes** about equal, 2.5-3 mm. long, linear-lanceolate, acute, 1-nerved; **Lemma** hispid, especially on the three nerves and toward the apex, closely embracing the palea; **Palea** about equal to the lemma.

In cultivation, southeast Texas, Mississippi Valley and south Atlantic coast. Summer and fall.

ORYZA SATIVA, Cultivated Rice

76. LEERSIA Swartz (lē-ĕr'sĭ-à)
(Homalocenchrus Mieg.)

Spikelets 1-flowered, strongly compressed laterally, disarticulating rom the pedicel; **Glumes** wanting; **Lemma** chartaceous, broad, oblong, ›oat-shaped, usually 5-nerved, the lateral pair of nerves close to the margins, these and the keel often hispid-ciliate, the intermediate nerves ;ometimes faint; **Palea** as long as the lemma, much narrower, usually 3-ıerved, the keel usually hispid-ciliate, the lateral nerves close to the margins, the margins firmly held by the margins of the lemma; **Stamens** ;ix or fewer.

Perennial grasses, usually with creeping rhizomes, with flat scabrous ›lades and open panicles, the spikelets nearly sessile along one side of the ›ranchlets. Species ten, tropical and temperate regions; five species in the ᛁUnited States, all in Texas, mostly swamp grasses.

All of our species have open panicles, commonly rough blades and sheaths, those of *L. oryzoides* being very prickly and adhesive; all have creeping rhizomes and prickly spikelets except *L. monandra*.

L. monandra, a densely tufted grass, thrives in dry open lands or in rich woodlands, mostly near the coast; *L. virginica,* with culms often straggling and entangled, and *L. lenticularis,* with broadly oval spikelets, are usually found in damp open woods, marshes and borders of streams; *L. oryzoides* and *L. hexandra* commonly grow in water along ditches, ponds and streams.

SPIKELETS ORBICULAR, glabrous, 2 mm. long or less; stamen 1.
                     1. L. monandra
SPIKELETS BROADLY oval, bristly, 4-4.5 mm. long; stamens 2.
                     2. L. lenticularis
SPIKELETS OBLONG, their width less than half their length, bristly on the keels.
 PANICLE branches singly disposed, few.
  Panicle branches elongated, each with a long naked base; spikelets 3 mm. long; stamens 2.
                     3. L. virginica
  Panicle branches short, spikelet-bearing to or nearly to the base; spikelet 4-4.5 mm. long; stamens 6.
                     4. L. hexandra
 PANICLE branches, at least the lower whorled, numerous; spikelets 5 mm. long; stamens 3.
                     5. L. oryzoides

1. L. MONANDRA Swartz (mō-năn'drà); *Homalocenchrus monandrus* (Swartz) Kuntze.

Culms 1-2 feet tall, densely tufted, erect, slender; **Blades** usually 4-6' long, 2-5 mm. wide, rather stiffly erect, flat, acuminate, rough; **Sheaths** usually shorter than the internodes; **Ligule** membranaceous, about 3 mm. long; **Panicle** exserted, open, 4-7' long, branches about 4-6, single, spreading, slender, spikelet-bearing towards the ends, as much as 4' long, spikelets arranged along one side of the narrow short branchlets; **Spikelets** about 1.6 mm. (1.5-2) long, 1-1.2 mm. wide, nearly sessile, irregularly ovate, flattened, pale-green; **Glumes** wanting; **Lemma** 5-nerved, sub-indurate, minutely roughened; **Palea** smaller, and almost inclosed by lemma, 3-nerved.

In dry land, open or rich woodlands, along the Gulf coast, Texas to Florida. (Rocky woodlands above Landa Park, New Braunfels, Texas.) Spring.

2. L. LENTICULARIS Michx. (lĕn-tĭk-ū-lā'rĭs); *Homalocenchrus lenticularis* (Michx.) Kuntze; CATCH-FLY GRASS.

Culms 2-4 feet tall, usually simple, often puberulent at, below and above the nodes, from scaly rootstocks; **Blades** 3-12' long, 6-13 mm. wide,

flat, narrowed toward the base, margins rough, surface smooth to rough
Sheaths slightly shorter than the internodes, slightly rough to smooth
often sparsely to densely pubescent at the summit of the sheaths, the
pubescence extending up the midrib of the blade on the under side
Ligule membranaceous, about 1 mm. long, fringed; **Panicle** finally ex
serted, 4-8' long, ovate to pyramidal, its branches lax, naked below, a
first erect, later spreading, commonly 1-3' long, the spikelets closely im
bricate; **Spikelets** about 4-6 mm. long, 3-3.3 mm. wide, flat, broadly oval
Glumes wanting; **Lemma** broad, bristly-ciliate on the keel and margins
Palea bristly-ciliate (aculeate) on the keel, the body of the lemma an
palea glabrous or sparsely hispidulous.

In marshes and wet lands from Virginia to Minnesota, south t
Florida and Texas. (In marsh at Orange, Texas.) Fall.

3. L. VIRGINICA Willd. (vĕr-jĭn'ĭ-kà); *Homalocenchrus virginicu*
    (Willd.) Britton; VIRGINIA CUT-GRASS OR WHITE-GRASS.

Culms 1-3 feet long, sometimes longer, slender, flattened, weak, freel
branching, straggling and much tangled, the swollen nodes pubescen
from a perennial rootstock covered with closely imbricated scales; **Blade**
1-7' mostly 3-5' long, 2-13 mm. wide, flat, narrowed toward the base, thi
easily torn, often sparsely hispid-ciliate on the margins, rough, sometime
hispidulous; **Sheaths** mostly shorter than the internodes, flattened, smoot
to rough; **Ligule** membranaceous, about 2 mm. long; **Panicles** at firs
included, finally long-exserted, 2.5-11' long, the axillary panicles smalle
and usually more or less included and *cleistogamous*, its branches solitary
commonly 1-4' sometimes 6' long, spreading and naked from below th
middle, slender, with a few short-appressed branchlets commonly less tha
1' long; **Spikelets** about 3 mm. long, 1-1.3 mm. wide, flattened, oblong
slightly imbricate, appressed, with short, scabrous pedicels; **Glumes** want
ing; **Lemma** flattened, boat-shaped, curving to one side becoming concav
next to the axis to which it is closely appressed, hispid on the keels an
margins, otherwise hispidulous or smooth; **Palea** hispid on the kee
narrow; **Stamens** 2.

In damp open woods, swamps and along streams. Eastern Unite
States to Florida and Texas. (Along San Antonio River, Brackenridg
Park, San Antonio, Texas.) Fall.

4. L. HEXANDRA Swartz (hĕks-ăn'drà); *Homalocenchrus hexandru*
    (Swartz) Kuntze.

Culms 1-3 feet tall, rather slender and weak, erect or ascending fron
a decumbent base, rooting at the lower nodes, nodes pubescent, other
wise glabrous; **Blades** 1.5-6.5' long, 3-6 mm. wide, flat, erect, narrowe
toward the base, rough; **Sheaths** shorter than the internodes, hispid, th
hairs pointing downward; **Ligule** membranaceous, 3-5 mm. long; **Panicl**
finally exserted, 2-4' long, narrow, erect, the erect or ascending branche
singly disposed, few in number, 12-40 mm. long, spikelet-bearing to o
nearly to the base, pubescent at the axils, the appressed spikelets over
lapping, sessile or on pedicels less than 1 mm. long; **Spikelets** 4-4.5 mm
long, laterally flattened, about 1.2 mm. wide, lanceolate-oblong; **Glume**
wanting; **Lemma** 5-nerved, the lateral pair close to the margins, boat
shaped, the keel and margins bristly-ciliate, the hairs longer toward th
apex, otherwise sparsely hispidulous; **Palea** 3-nerved, the keel bristly
ciliate, the hairs longer toward the apex, the lateral nerves also close t
the margins.

Wet places, in water or along the edges of ditches and ponds. South Atlantic states to Texas, mostly near the coast. Spring-fall.

5. L. ORYZOIDES (L.) Swartz (ō-rĭ-zoi'dēz); *Homalocenchrus oryzoides* (L.) Poll.; RICE CUT-GRASS.

Culms 2-5 feet tall, growing in tufts or colonies in water or mud along the banks of streams and lakes, erect or ascending, mostly from a decumbent base, rooting at the lower nodes, the rootstocks narrow with internodes about an inch long, barbed at the nodes, otherwise glabrous; Blades 3-8' long, 5-15 mm. wide, flat, narrowed toward the base, lanceolate, very rough with recurved prickles on the margins, sometimes a few hairs on upper surface near the base; Sheaths shorter than the internodes, very rough with recurved prickles; Ligule membranaceous, truncate, about 1 mm. long; Panicle finally exserted, 5-8' long, pyramidal, axis scabrous, the lateral panicles included or slightly exserted, branches scabrous, single, or whorled below, naked at the base, 4' long or less, at first erect, finally spreading, the branchlets short, with short scabrous peduncles, with a few appressed imbricated spikelets; Spikelets about 5 mm. long, 1.5 mm. wide, flattened; Glumes wanting; Lemma and Palea about equal, hispidulous, hispid-ciliate on the keels and margins, beset with diminutive prickles toward the apex.

Wet ground or in water. Virginia to Minnesota, south to Florida and Texas. July to October.

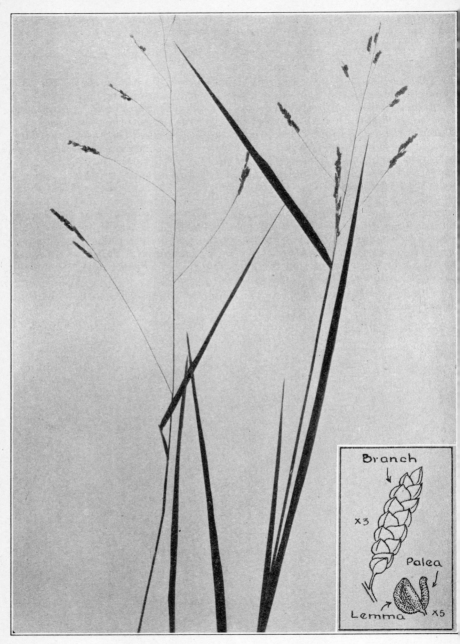

LEERSIA MONANDRA

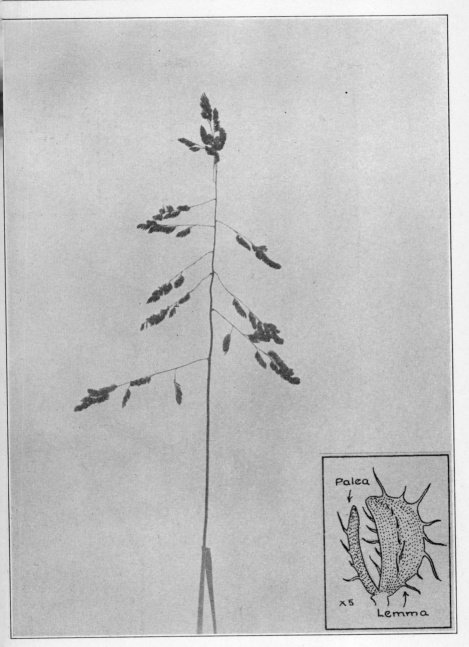

LEERSIA LENTICULARIS

LEERSIA VIRGINICA, Virginia Cut-grass

LEERSIA HEXANDRA

LEERSIA ORYZOIDES, Rice Cut-grass

X. ZIZANIEAE, THE INDIAN-RICE TRIBE

Aquatic or Subaquatic Tribe

77. ZIZANIOPSIS Doell & Aschers. (zĭ-zā-nĭ-ŏp′sĭs)

Spikelets unisexual, 1-flowered, disarticulating from the pedicel, ᵣixed on the same branches of the panicle, the staminate below; **First lume** wanting; **Second Glume** 7-nerved, short-awned in the pistillate ᵣikelets; **Lemma** 3-nerved; **Palea** wanting; **Stamens** six; **Styles** rather ᵣng, united; **Caryopsis** obovate, free, coriaceous, smooth and shining, ᵣeaked with the persistent style.

Robust *perennial* marsh grasses, with stout creeping rhizomes, broad, ᵣat blades, and large open panicles. One species in the United States.

This grass, in large bunches or colonies, grows along the margins of ᵣtreams and ponds, attaining a height of 4-10 feet. It is conspicuous for ᵣs large purple panicles, at first gracefully drooping but finally erect and ᵣpreading.

It is of no economic value except as food or shelter for birds. It is ᵣommon along the San Antonio River, especially at San Antonio, Texas.

Growing along the banks of streams and ponds may be found giant ᵣeed-grass, *Arundo donax*, taller and woody, with erect and very large pale ᵣr purplish densely hairy panicles, the rachilla naked; and also a smaller ᵣeed grass, *Phragmites communis*, with densely hairy, usually purplish, ᵣrooping panicles, the rachilla hairy.

ᵣ. MILIACEA (Michx.) Doell & Aschers. (mĭl-ĭ-ā′sē-à) ; Marsh Millet, Water Millet.

Culms 4-10 feet tall, robust in large clumps, usually in colonies, in the ᵥater or along the margins of streams, ponds and lakes, from long creep-ᵣng rootstocks; **Blades** 1-5 feet long, those of the base 10-40 mm. wide, ᵣlat above, narrowed to a long folded thickened pithy base, the margins ᵥery scabrous with a razor-like edge; **Sheaths**, the lower longer than the ᵣnternodes, flattened, thick and pithy; **Ligule** membranaceous, 6-15 mm. ᵣong; **Panicle** 10-24′ long, finally exserted, purple, pyramidal, at first ᵣodding, finally erect and spreading, its long branches solitary or whorled, ᵣhe lower as long as 12′, naked at the base; **Spikelets** purplish, **Unisexual,** ᵣhe pistillate (female) borne at the end of the branches, and the staminate ᵣmale) below or sometimes mixed with the pistillate; **Glumes**, the first ᵥanting, the second and the **Lemma** about equal, the glume 5-7-nerved, ᵣhe lemma 3-nerved; **Palea** none; **Pistillate Spikelet** exclusive of the awn ᵣ5-6 mm. long, the glume with an awn 2-6 mm. long; **Staminate Spikelet** ᵣ7-8 mm. long, the glume acute, sometimes with a short awn; **Stamens 6.**

In swamps, in water and along the margins of streams, ponds and lakes. Texas to Florida and Virginia, Ohio and Georgia. Spring-summer.

ZIZANIOPSIS MILIACEA, WATER MILLET

78.   ZIZANIA L. (zĭ-zā′nĭ-à)

Spikelets unisexual, 1-flowered, disarticulating from the pedicel; ;aminate **Spikelet** soft, the first glume wanting, the second 5-nerved, embranaceous, linear, acuminate or awn-pointed; **Lemma** about as long , the glume, 3-nerved; **Palea** wanting; **Stamens** 6; **Pistillate Spikelet** rete, angled at maturity; **Glumes** wanting; **Lemma** chartaceous, 3-rved, tapering into a long slender awn; **Palea** 2-nerved, closely clasped , the lemma; **Grain** cylindric, as much as 20 mm. long.

Tall *annual* or *perennial* aquatic grasses, with flat blades and large rminal panicles, the lower branches spreading, bearing the pendulous aminate spikelets, the upper branches ascending, at maturity erect, bear-g appressed pistillate spikelets, the staminate spikelets early deciduous, e pistillate spikelets tardily deciduous.   Four species: one in eastern sia, two in North America, one in Texas.

Indian or wild rice, *Z. aquatica* L. (erroneously determined as , *palustris* L.), growing here and there over the eastern and northern ates, sometimes covering extensive areas, is an erect annual.   It is not nfined to water but thrives in marshes as well.

Z. texana, which seems to be confined to the artificial lake at the head f the San Marcos River and the irrigation ditches and river some distance elow the town of San Marcos, differs from the above mainly in its habit of rowth, being a *floating perennial,* rooting and geniculate at the nodes.   It rows in water from 1-7 feet deep, often in swiftly running currents, the ng blades and culms at first floating on or some distance below the sur-ice of the water as shown by the light streak at the right of the photograph. he culms, sometimes 15 feet long, finally bend upward near the surface of e water, the erect or ascending portion 1-3 feet long, bearing a beautiful anicle similar to that of *Z. aquatica.*   Although this grass was collected me years ago at the above location the material was so scant that its dis-nguishing characteristics were overlooked, and it was classed as *Z. aquatica.* Iowever, the author noticed the difference in habit and called attention this fact, whereupon the plant was given the rank of a species.

The superintendent of the pumping plant at San Marcos informed the uthor that this grass blossoms most of the year, and that the growth is so ixuriant that the irrigation company has great difficulty in keeping the rtificial lake and ditches clean.

. TEXANA Hitchc. (tĕks-ā′nà).

Plants perennial; Monoecious; Culms 3-10 feet long, with thin ransverse sections, simple or freely branching, geniculate, rooting at the odes and floating on or under the water, the culms succulent; **Blades** -60′ long, 8-25 mm. wide, those above the water mostly 6-16′ long and 10re or less roughened, flat, narrowed toward the base, midrib large; **Sheaths** longer than the internodes; **Ligule** membranaceous, 6-10 mm. ong, acute; **Panicles** often somewhat included at the base, 10-15′ long, the ranches slender, 2-4′ long, single or in whorls, the spikelets solitary or in airs, one pedicel of the pair much longer than the other, enlarged at the pex; **Staminate Spikelets** 6-8 mm. long, oblong; **Glumes,** the first want-ng, the second and lemma about equal, acute or awn-pointed; **Palea** want-ng; **Pistillate Spikelets** exclusive of the awns 8-12 mm. long, linear; **Glumes** wanting; **Lemma** exclusive of awns 8-12 mm. long, the scabrous wn 10-20 mm. long; **Palea** nearly equal to the lemma; **Grain** not de-eloped.   (See two photographs.)   In water, often floating, San Marcos River at and below San Marcos, Texas.   Spring to fall.

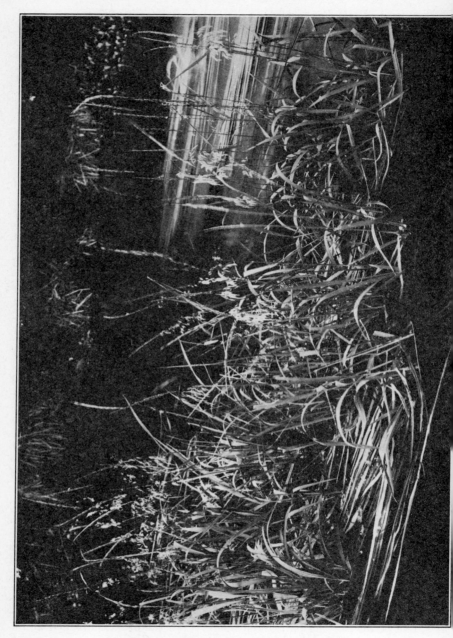

ZIZANIA TEXANA

ZIZANIA TEXANA

XI. PANICEAE, THE MILLET TRIBE

79. ANTHAENANTIA Beauv. (ăn-thē-năn'tĭ-à)

Spikelets obovoid; **First Glume** wanting; **Second Glume** and **Steril Lemma** about equal in length, broad, 5-nerved, villous, the sterile lemm with a small palea and sometimes with a staminate flower; **Fertile Lemm** cartilaginous, boat-shaped, 3-nerved, subacute, chestnut-brown, as long a the glume, the pale margins very narrow, infolding the palea its entir length (lemma and palea called fruit in descriptions).

Perennial erect grass with short creeping rhizomes, narrow, firm, fla blades, the uppermost much reduced, and narrow panicles, the slende branches ascending or appressed. Two species on the coastal plain o southern United States.

The well developed fruits of these two species are plump, being conve on both sides, but the author found many of the fruits undeveloped, bein flat on one side and narrow.

An outstanding characteristic of these two species is the four more o less distinct vertical rows of hairs on the glume and sterile lemma, th hairs longer and more numerous on *A. rufa* than on *A. villosa*.

PANICLE usually purplish. The blades long and nearly linear, the lower mostl
    3-5 mm. wide.   1. A. ruf
PANICLE usually green. The blades shorter, narrowed toward the summit, th
    lower mostly 5-10 mm. wide.   2. A. villos

1. A. RUFA (Ell.) Schult. (rōō'fà).

Culms 1.5-4 feet tall, usually a few culms to a tuft, simple, erect **Blades** from less than an inch to 6.5' long, sometimes those at the base an on the innovations as much as 15' long, 3-7 mm. wide, the upper short an distant, flat, or conduplicate toward the base, almost linear, upper surfac more or less papillose and hairy, especially toward the base; **Sheath** shorter than the internodes, sometimes ciliate at the summit; **Ligule** a rin of hairs less than 1 mm. long; **Panicle** long-exserted, or sometimes include at the base, ovate or linear-oblong, mostly less than 18 mm. wide, 2.5-5 (3-8) long, erect, the branches mostly about 2' long or less, graduall shorter above, the lower often interrupted, erect or ascending, solitary naked at the base, the short branchlets with a few spikelets, single or i pairs, the pedicel enlarged at the summit, one usually shorter than th other of the pair, as long as or longer than the spikelet; the axis, branches pedicels and spikelets commonly purplish; **Spikelets** about 3 mm. (3.5-4 long; **Glumes,** the first wanting, the second and **Sterile Lemma** abou equal, broad, the marginal nerves often faint or wanting, covered witl purplish or white hairs less than 1 mm. long, the hairs usually in fou vertical rows between the nerves; **Fruit** 2.5-3 mm. long, minutely papillose striate, sparsely-ciliate toward and at the apex.

In moist sandy land, especially pine lands, east Texas to Florida anc South Carolina. (Three miles south of Buna, Texas, open pine land, anc about 20 miles north of Victoria in sandy open land.) Fall.

2. A. VILLOSA (Michx.) Beauv. (vĭl-ō'sà).

Culms 1-4.5 feet tall, erect, solitary or in small tufts, slender, leafy at the base; **Blades** 1-11' long, 4-10 mm. wide, the upper reduced and erect, the lower spreading, flat, acuminate, narrowed toward base and tip, scabrous on the margin, sometimes ciliate at the base; **Sheaths** shorter han the internodes, the lowermost crowded and overlapping; **Ligule** a ery short membrane, minutely-ciliate; **Panicle** pale-green, long-exserted, rect, rather narrow, loose, 4-7′ long, 7-18 mm. wide, the few branches ostly solitary, branching nearly to the base, appressed or ascending, sually less than 3′ long, naked at the base, the pedicels much enlarged t the summit; **Spikelets** about 3 mm. (3-4) long, about 1.5 mm. wide, pale-reen, solitary or in pairs, the pedicel of one about as long as spikelet, he other about twice as long; **Glumes,** the first wanting, the second and terile **Lemma** about equal, or the glume somewhat shorter, each more or ess covered with stiff hairs about 0.5 mm. long, mostly confined to four ertical rows along the internerves, the hairs fewer and shorter than in l. *rufa;* **Sterile Palea** about three-fourths as long as the sterile lemma; 'ruit about 2.5 mm. long, 1.3 mm. wide, rather convex on both face and ack.

In pine lands, eastern Texas to Florida. (Open pine lands 3 miles outh of Buna, Texas.) Fall.

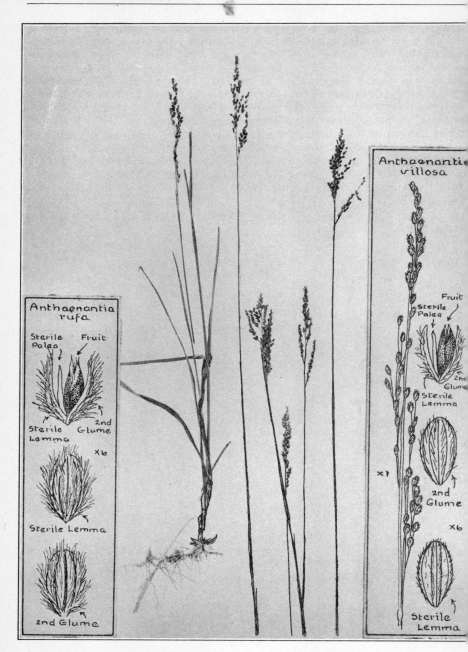

ANTHAENANTIA RUFA and drawings of ANTHAENANTIA
VILLOSA

80. TRICHACHNE Nees (trī-kăk′nē)
(Valota Adans., inadequately published)

Spikelets lanceolate, in pairs, short-pediceled, in two rows along one side of a narrow rachis; **First Glume** minute, glabrous; **Second Glume** and **Sterile Lemma** about as long as the fruit, 3-7-nerved, copiously silky; **Fertile Lemma** cartilaginous, lanceolate, acuminate, usually brown, the flat white hyaline margins broad.

Perennial grasses, the slender racemes erect or ascending, aggregate along the upper part of the main axis forming a white or brownish woolly panicle. Species about 12, in the warmer parts of America and in Australia; 4 species in southern United States, all in Texas.

Trichachne is closely related to *Digitaria* and *Panicum*, differing chiefly from the first in the acuminate fruit and silky spikelets, and from the latter by the cartilaginous fruit, being chartaceous-indurate in *Panicum*.

T. insularis, growing here and there over southern and western Texas, has long-acuminate fruits 4 mm. long, the remaining species having fruits about 3 mm. long; *T. californica*, rather plentiful in central, southern and western Texas, has a slightly obovate fruit, abruptly narrowed into a long slender point; *T. patens*, with an open panicle, the branches being rather loosely-flowered, so far as known limited to southern and western Texas, has an oblong-lanceolate acute fruit; *T. hitchcockii*, a rather rare species collected in southern and western Texas and in Mexico, has a narrowly lanceolate fruit similar to that of *T. patens*.

The first three species have spikelets long-silky, the sterile lemma being glabrous up the middle, and the last with the internerves pubescent up the middle, the hairs less than 1 mm. long.

All of these species have been collected near Mitchell Lake (about 12 miles south of San Antonio) to Natalia, Texas.

BLADES NOT OVER 3′ long; spikelets 2.5-3 mm. long, the hairs less than 1 mm. long; sterile lemma pubescent on the internerves up the middle.
1. T. hitchcockii

BLADES 4-12′ LONG; spikelets silky-villous, the hairs on the spikelet more than 1 mm. long; sterile lemma glabrous up the middle.
HAIRS on the spikelet 2.5-4 mm. long;
  Panicle tawny-white; fruit long-acuminate, 4 mm. long. 2. T. insularis
  Panicle silvery-white; fruit 3 mm. long, slightly obovate, abruptly narrowed to a long slender point. 3. T. californica
HAIRS on the spikelets less than 2 mm. long; panicle open, silky-white, the spikelets rather distant on the ascending or spreading branches; fruit 3 mm. long, oblong-lanceolate. 4. T. patens

1. T. HITCHCOCKII (Chase) Chase (hĭch-kŏk′ĭ-ī); *Valota hitchcockii* Chase.

Culms 1-2.5 feet tall, usually densely-tufted, branching and leafy at or near the base, sometimes a few long hairs at or near the nodes; **Blades** 0.5-2.5′ long, the upper short, 1.5-3.5 mm. wide, flat, glabrous or softly puberulent especially on the upper surface, often very sparsely long-pilose on the margins and upper surface at or near the base; **Sheaths** mostly longer than the internodes, loose, glabrous, puberulent or sparingly pilose, the lower usually softly and densely-pubescent, sometimes sparsely-papillose; **Ligule** membranaceous, fringed or ciliate, less than 1 mm. long; **Panicles** on the larger culms finally long-exserted, erect, the axis 1-6′ mostly less than 3′ long, those of the branches shorter, the 3-8 slender

scabrous branches 1-2′ rarely 3′ long, appressed or finally ascending
rarely spreading, spikelet-bearing or naked toward the base, sometimes
with short branchlets, the spikelets usually in pairs, solitary or in threes
on unequal scabrous pedicels, when in pairs the pedicels of the shorter one
about 2 mm. long, of the other about 3.5 mm. long, and of the third
if present, longer; **Spikelets** 2.5-3 mm. long, nearly 1 mm. wide, lanceolate
silky-pubescent, the hairs usually less than 1 mm. long; **Glumes**, the first
minute usually less than 0.5 mm. long, triangular, the second 5-nerved, the
nerves glabrous or nearly so, the internerves silky-pubescent, usually nearly
equal to the 7-nerved **Sterile Lemma**, which equals or slightly exceeds the
fruit, the nerves glabrous or nearly so, the internerves silky-pubescent
Fruit light to dark-brown, 2-2.5 mm. long, 0.6-0.8 mm. wide, narrowly
lanceolate-acuminate, minutely papillose-striate, often a minute tuft of
stiffish hairs at the apex.

Dry prairies and rocky mountain sides, southwest Texas to Mexico
(South of San Antonio, and 20 miles east of Marathon, Texas.)   Spring
to fall.

2. T. INSULARIS (L.) Nees (ĭn-sū-lâr′ĭs); *Valota insularis* (L.) Chase
    Panicum lanatum Rottb.; *Panicum leucophaeum* H. B. K.; Sour-grass

Culms 2-4 feet tall, tufted, erect or spreading, branching from a
swollen base; **Blades** 3-12′ long, 4-10 mm. (4-20) wide, flat, rough; **Sheaths**
longer than the internodes, glabrous or the lowermost pubescent; **Ligule**
membranaceous, ciliate, decurrent, about 2 mm. long; **Panicle** exserted
4-10′ long, narrow, erect or nodding, silky tawny-white or purplish-tinged
shining, the appressed or ascending branches 1.5-4′ long, often drooping
the spikelets usually in pairs, the pedicels 1-4 mm. long, one longer than
the other, arranged along a narrow 3-angled scabrous rachis; **Spikelets**
about 4 mm. (4-5) long, including the hairs 6-7 mm. long, acuminate
clothed with numerous soft light tawny to purplish hairs 2-4 mm. long
Glumes, the first minute, acute or truncate, the second and **Sterile Lemma**
about equal, acuminate, the second glume 3-nerved, hairy over the back
and along the margins, the sterile lemma 5-7-nerved, often slightly longer
than the second glume, the middle portion being sparsely-hairy and the
margins hairy as on the second glume, the hairs being 2.5-4 mm. long
much exceeding the spikelets, less copious than in *T. californica;* **Fruit**
brown, about 4 mm. long, about 1 mm. wide, lanceolate-acuminate, striate-
roughened.

In dry sandy or rocky soil, southwestern and west Texas, south to
Mexico; also Florida; tropical and subtropical countries.   (South of San
Antonio, and several places in the mountains of west Texas.)   Spring
and fall.

3. T. CALIFORNICA (Benth.) Chase (kăl-ĭ-fôr′nĭ-kà); *T. saccharata*
    (Buckl.) Nash; *Valota saccharata* (Buckl.) Chase; *Panicum sacchara-
    tum* Buckl.; *P. lachnanthum* Torr.

Culms 1-2.5 feet tall, tufted, erect or ascending, rather slender, freely
branching; **Blades** 1.5-9′ commonly 3-5′ long, the upper shorter, 2-5 mm.
wide, flat, soon becoming involute, rough above, glabrous or a few
scattered hairs on the upper surface; **Sheaths** longer than the internodes,
flattened, the upper glabrous or sparingly hairy, or quite hairy at or near
the nodes, the lowermost densely soft-villous, more or less papillose;
Ligule membranaceous, about 4 mm. long, fringed at the apex; **Panicles**
exserted, 4-8′ long, narrow, erect or finally nodding, silvery-white or some-

mes purplish-tinged, with 6-9 appressed or narrowly ascending branches
2' long, the triangular rachis scabrous on the margins, the spikelets
sually in pairs, the pedicels 1-3 mm. long, one shorter than the other;
pikelets 3-4 mm. long, including the hairs 5-6 mm. long, 1.2 mm. wide,
piously silky with silvery-white or purplish-tinged hairs 2.5-3 mm. long,
uch exceeding the spikelet; **Glumes,** the first minute, usually less than
7 mm. long, sometimes obsolete, the second glume 3-nerved, about equal
the fruit, copiously hairy, the **Sterile Lemma** slightly longer than the
cond glume, 5-nerved, almost glabrous along the middle portion and
ng-villous at or near the margins; **Fruit** brown, 2.5-3.5 mm. long, 1 mm.
ide, slightly obovate, abruptly narrowed to the longer scarcely indurate
int, minutely-striate roughened.

Dry soil, well drained sandy or rocky soil, prairies or hillsides, southern
d central Texas, north to Colorado, south to central Mexico, and west to
rizona. (Plentiful over central, western and southwest Texas.) Spring
fall.

T. PATENS Swallen (pā'tĕns). Formerly referred to *T. saccharata*
(Buckl.) Nash.

Culms 1-3 feet tall, tufted, erect or spreading, sometimes geniculate
the lower nodes, branching at or near the base, the upper nodes often
ith a few long hairs, the lowermost almost woolly, otherwise glabrous
the lower internodes sparsely-hairy; **Blades** 1-6' usually 2-4' long, the
pper one very short, 1-4 mm. wide, commonly about 2 mm. wide, flat,
ightly rough, margins rough, often sparsely pilose, especially near the
se; **Sheaths** mostly longer than the internodes, sparsely to rather
ensely papillose-pilose with spreading or retrorse hairs, the lowermost
ensely velvety-pubescent; **Ligule** 2.5-4 mm. long, membranaceous,
inged at the apex; **Panicles** 4-7' long, ovate to ovate-pyramidal, long-
serted, the slender scabrous branches stiffly ascending when young,
reading when mature, usually solitary, 2-3.5' long, comparatively few-
owered; **Spikelets** densely-white, silky, 3-3.5 mm. long, including the
airs 4-5 mm. long (hairs 1.5 mm. long), distant, early deciduous, single
paired, when in pairs, one pedicel 1-2 mm. long, the other 3-7 mm.
ng; **Glumes,** the first minute, commonly not over 0.5 mm. long, acute or
tuse, narrow, the second glume and **Sterile Lemma** about 3 mm. long,
ualing the fruit, the glume narrow, 3-nerved, exposing the fruit, hairy
the nerves and internerves, the **Sterile Lemma** broader, 5-nerved,
vering the fruit, the middle portion glabrous, otherwise villous; **Fruit**
bout 3 mm. long, 0.7-0.8 mm. wide, oblong-lanceolate, acute, minutely
riate-roughened.

Roadsides and fields on dry, well-drained sandy or slightly gravelly
il, south-central and southwestern Texas. (Plentiful south of San
ntonio on the Devine and Frio roads.) Spring and summer

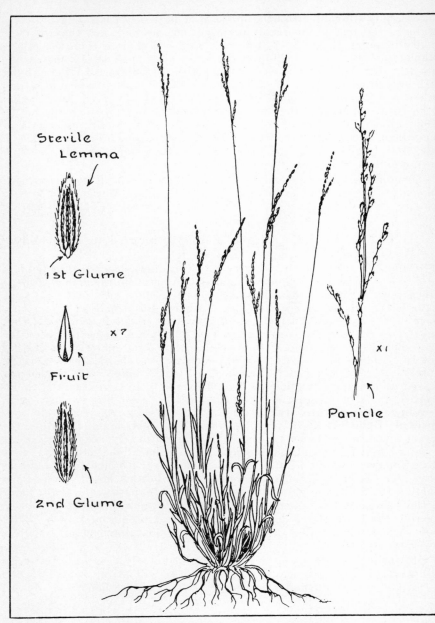

Sterile Lemma

1st Glume

x 7

Fruit

2nd Glume

Panicle

x 1

TRICHACHNE HITCHCOCKII

Sterile
Lemma

1st Glume

×7

2nd Glume

×7

Fruit

TRICHACHNE INSULARIS, Sour-grass

x7

Fruit

Sterile
Lemma

1st Gluma

x7

2nd Gluma

TRICHACHNE CALIFORNICA

TRICHACHNE PATENS

81. DIGITARIA Hall. not Heist. (dĭj-ĭ-tā'rĭ-à)
(Syntherisma Walt.) The Crab-grasses

Spikelets solitary or in twos or threes, subsessile or short-pediceled, alternate in two rows on one side of a three-angled winged or wingless rachis; spikelets lanceolate or elliptic, plano-convex; **First Glume** minute or wanting; **Second Glume** equaling the sterile lemma or shorter; **Fertile Lemma** cartilaginous, the hyaline margins pale.

Annual or sometimes perennial, erect or prostrate grasses, the slender racemes digitate or somewhat scattered, but aggregate along the upper part of the culms. Species about 60, in the warmer parts of the world; 12 in the United States, 6 in Texas.

In *Digitaria, Trichachne* and *Anthaenantia* the fruit is cartilaginous and the lemma with rather prominent hyaline margins, these not inrolled, instead of like the fruit and inrolled margins of *Panicum* and *Paspalum.* In *Digitaria* the spikelets, either glabrous or pubescent, are arranged in slender racemes; in *Anthaenantia* the villous spikelets are arranged in racemes, these panicled. *Trichachne* differs chiefly from *Digitaria* in the silky spikelets and the acuminate fruit.

All of our Texas species are *annuals,* and all except *D. sanguinalis* seem to be confined to sandy land.

D. villosa and *D. filiformis,* erect plants, have the first glume commonly wanting, the first with the racemes usually more than 4' long, the second with the racemes usually less than 4' long. *D. filiformis* is rather rare in Texas.

D. violascens, a Brazilian and West Indies grass, was collected by the author for the first time in the United States near Buna, Texas, appearing a little later in Arkansas.

D. runyoni and *D. texana,* both south Texas plants, are found in sandy land, the first often with a creeping or prostrate culm, many-noded, and with spikelets larger than those of *D. texana.*

FIRST GLUME MINUTE. SECOND GLUME HALF TO TWO-THIRDS AS
    LONG as the spikelet; plants spreading or prostrate at the base; racemes
    5-10, 2-6' long, the rachis winged.   1. D. sanguinalis
FIRST GLUME WANTING OR RUDIMENTARY.
    RACHIS WINGED. Plants about 16' tall, spreading; racemes 1-5, 1-3' long;
      spikelets 1.4 mm. long, the hairs minutely glandular tipped.
                                            2. D. violascens
    RACHIS NOT winged. Second glume pubescent to nearly glabrous.
      RACEMES 5-12, 2-6' long.
        Plants often prostrate, freely branching, many-noded; spikelets 2.5-3.5 mm.
          long.   3. D. runyoni
        Plants erect or decumbent at base; spikelets 2-2.5 mm. long.   4. D. texana
    RACEMES 2-8, 1-5.5' long. Plants erect, simple or sparingly branched at
      the base; spikelets pubescent with glandular tipped hairs.
      Racemes short, 1-4' long; spikelets 1.8 mm. long.   5. D. filiformis
      Racemes exceeding 4' long, rarely shorter; spikelets 2.5 mm. long.
                                            6. D. villosa

1. D. SANGUINALIS (L.) Scop. (săn-gwĭ-nā'lĭs) ; *Syntherisma sangui-nalis* (L.) Dulac.; LARGE CRAB-GRASS.

Culms 1-3 feet tall, erect or prostrate at the base, often rooting at the lower nodes, freely branching, nodes from slightly pubescent to hispid, often slightly rough and puberulent; **Blades** 2-6' long, 4-10 mm. wide, flat, scabrous, often short-pubescent to papillose-hirsute at the base; **Sheaths** shorter than the internodes, loose, the upper sparsely-hispid and lower often densely papillose-hirsute; **Ligule** membranaceous, 2-3 mm. long; **Racemes** 3-13 usually 5-6 rarely 2-3, 2-6′ long, slender, erect or spreading, crowded or approximate, on a short axis, commonly less than 1′ long, at the end of a long peduncle; **Rachis** about 1 mm. wide, flexuous, winged, with spikelets in pairs, one subsessile, the other reaching half its own length above the lower, the pedicel strongly hispidulous, sharply 3-angled; **Spikelets** 2.5-3 mm. long, acute, oblong-lanceolate; **Glumes,** the first minute, glabrous, the second about half to two-thirds as long as the spikelet, 3-5-nerved, pubescent; **Sterile Lemma** 7-nerved, the nerves glabrous or partially hispidulous, the internerves and margins appressed-pubescent (finally erect or spreading), or glabrous or partially pubescent from midnerve to second nerve on each side; **Fruit** cartilaginous with pale hyaline margins, lanceolate, acutely apiculate with age.

Common in waste places and cultivated soil throughout eastern and southern United States. Spring to fall.

2. D. VIOLASCENS Link (vĭ-ō-lăs′ĕns).

Culms 6-24′ tall, tufted, usually geniculate at the base and spreading, branching and leafy below; **Blades** 10-50 mm. long, 2-6 mm. wide, the upper short and narrow, flat, lanceolate, margin cartilaginous, glabrous or a few rather long and stiff hairs on the margins and upper surface near the base; **Sheaths,** the upper shorter than the internodes, the lower crowded, short, glabrous or slightly ciliate at or near the summit and at the throat; **Ligule** membranaceous, 1-1.5 mm. long; **Racemes** 1-5, 1-3′ long, ascending or somewhat spreading, aggregate or scattered, the axis as much as 8 mm. long, the racemes of the branches usually shorter; **Rachis** flattened, winged, scabrous on the margin, about 0.8 mm. wide; **Spikelets** 1.2-1.5 mm. long, about 0.6 mm. wide, usually in pairs, rarely solitary or in threes, the pedicel of one short, less than 1 mm. long, the other about twice as long; **Glumes,** the first wanting, the second about three-fourths as long as the spikelet, 3-nerved, mostly obtuse, the internerves densely silky-hairy, the **Sterile Lemma** as long as or slightly longer than the fruit, 5-nerved, almost glabrous to densely silky-hairy on the internerves, often irregularly hairy, the hairs on both often minutely glandular tipped; **Fruit** slightly shorter and narrower than the spikelet, dark-purple or brown, striate, the flat margins pale. Sandy land, east Texas, Arkansas, Brazil and West Indies. (About 3 miles south of Buna, Texas.) Fall.

3. D. RUNYONI Hitchc. (rŭn′yŭn-ī).

Culms 1-3 feet tall, erect or from a decumbent base, or ascending from a prostrate or creeping base 2-3 feet long, taking root at the nodes, many-noded, nodes pubescent to hirsute; **Blades** 3-5′ long, 3-6 mm. wide, flat, rough, the upper sparingly pilose or glabrous, the lower from densely-pubescent to hirsute on the upper surface at the base or papillose-ciliate; **Sheaths** mostly longer than the internodes, upper glabrous or ciliate, the lower from densely-pubescent to hirsute; **Ligule** membranaceous, 2-3 mm. long; **Racemes** 5-12, 3-6′ long, sometimes naked at the base, the axis about 2′ long, scabrous, the racemes sometimes with branches 1-2′ long, the rachis slender, triangular in cross-section, hispid on the angles, spikelets in twos or threes; **Spikelets** 2.5-3.5 mm. long, lanceolate, narrow, acute; **Glumes,** the first wanting or minute, the second and **Sterile Lemma** about equal, the glume 3-5-nerved, and the sterile lemma 7-nerved, densely-villous on the internerves, the lemma glabrous on the middle internerves, or both nearly glabrous; **Fruit** about as long as the sterile lemma, lanceolate.

Sandy land (and sand dunes) along the coast, southern Texas. (Corpus Christi, Aransas Pass, Padre Island.) Fall.

4. D. TEXANA Hitchc. (tĕks-ā′nȧ).

Differs from *D. runyoni* in being erect, not from a creeping base, not so many-noded, slenderer **racemes**, and **spikelets** 2-2.5 mm. long. (No drawings.) Sandy oak woods and sandy prairies, southern Texas.

5. D. FILIFORMIS (L.) Koel. (fĭl-ĭ-fôr′mĭs); *Syntherisma filiforme* (L.) Nash; SLENDER FINGER-GRASS.

Culms 8-28′ tall sometimes taller, tufted, erect, slender, leafy and branching at and near the base; **Blades** 2-7′ long, 2-4 mm. wide, flat, scabrous on the upper surface, papillose-hirsute on the upper surface at the base, glabrous or sparsely-hirsute on the lower surface; **Sheaths** hirsute or papillose-hirsute, or the upper glabrous; **Racemes** 2-5, usually unequal, 1-4′ long, erect or ascending, slender, the axis of the inflorescence 7-30 mm. long; **Rachis** 3-angled, scabrous on the angles, not winged, flexuous; the spikelets mostly in pairs or threes, the pedicels scabrous, the shorter about 1 mm. long, the second scarcely as long as the spikelet, the third usually slightly longer than the spikelet, appressed; **Spikelets** 1.7-1.8 mm. long, about 0.8 mm. wide, elliptic, acute; **Glumes**, the first wanting, the second 3-nerved, three-fourths to as long as the 7-nerved **Sterile Lemma** which is slightly shorter or equals the fruit, both of them densely- to sparsely-pubescent between the nerves, the hairs glandular tipped; **Fruit** about as long as the spikelet, chestnut-brown, acute, striate.

Sandy or sterile soil, Texas to Florida, Oklahoma, North Carolina, north to New Hampshire and Michigan. Summer and fall.

6. D. VILLOSA (Walt.) Pers. (vĭl-ō′sȧ); *Syntherisma villosum* Walt. SOUTHERN SLENDER FINGER-GRASS.

Culms 2-6 feet tall, tufted, erect, branching below, the nodes pubescent to hirsute; **Blades** 4-18′ long, 3-5 mm. wide, flat, somewhat rough above, the blades from sparsely to densely papillose-hirsute, especially on the upper surface near the base, or the uppermost glabrous; **Sheaths** shorter than the internodes, papillose-hirsute or the uppermost glabrous; **Ligule** membranaceous, about 1 mm. long, ciliate; **Racemes** 2-8 commonly 5-8, with axis 3.5′ long or less, distant as much as 30 mm., erect or ascending, commonly over 4′ often 6-8′ long, slender, much interrupted below, the angles of rachis scabrous, wingless, the clusters rather distant, often not overlapping, in ones to threes, the pedicel of one about as long as the spikelet, the others shorter; **Spikelets** 2.5 mm. long, 0.8 mm. wide, elliptic, acute at both ends; **Glumes**, the first wanting, the second obtuse, 3-nerved, a little shorter than the 7-nerved sterile lemma, both densely matted-villous between the nerves with glandular tipped hairs; **Fruit** slightly exceeding the sterile lemma, deep chestnut-brown, papillose-striate, apiculate.

In sandy soil, southern states north to Oklahoma and Missouri. Summer-fall.

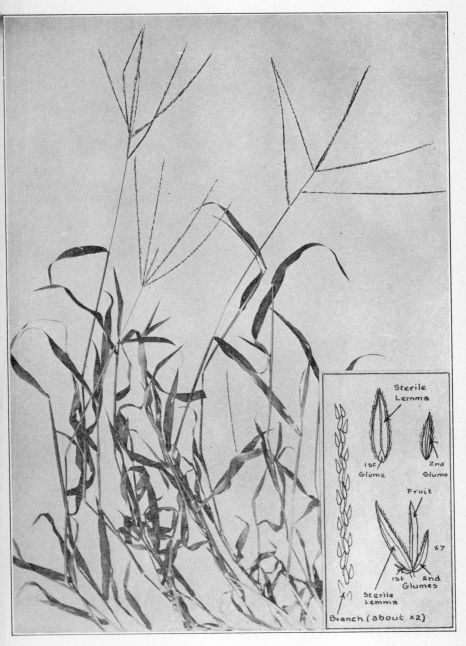

DIGITARIA SANGUINALIS, Large Crab-grass

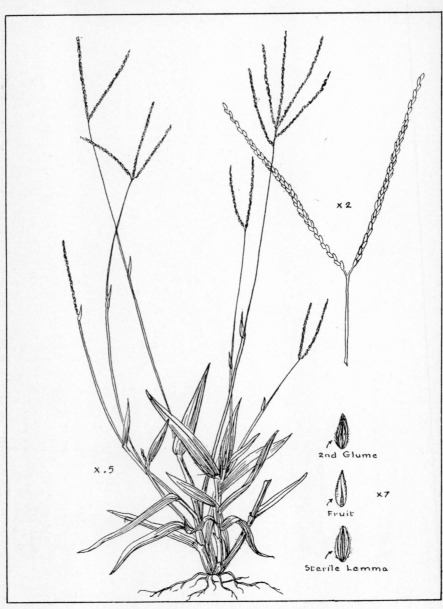

x 2

x .5

2nd Glume

x 7

Fruit

Sterile Lemma

DIGITARIA VIOLASCENS

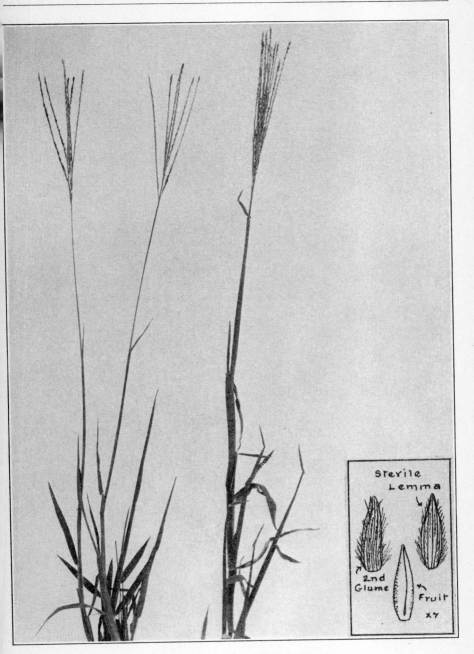

Sterile
Lemma

2nd
Glume

Fruit
x7

DIGITARIA RUNYONI

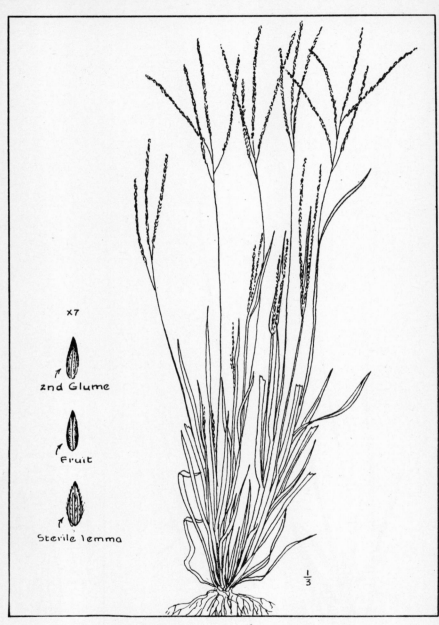

x7

2nd Glume

Fruit

Sterile lemma

$\frac{1}{3}$

DIGITARIA FILIFORMIS

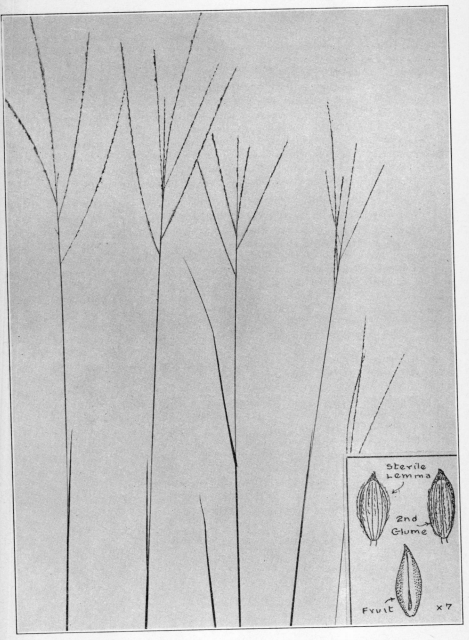

DIGITARIA VILLOSA, Southern Slender Finger-grass

82. LEPTOLOMA Chase (lĕp-tō-lō'mà)

Spikelets on slender pedicels; **First Glume** minute or obsolete; **Second Glume** 3-nerved, nearly as long as the 5-7-nerved **Sterile Lemma,** a more or less prominent stripe of appressed silky hairs down the internerves and margins of each, the sterile lemma empty or inclosing a minute nerveless rudimentary palea; **Fertile Lemma** cartilaginous, elliptic, acute, brown, the delicate hyaline margins inclosing the palea.

Perennial branching grasses, with brittle culms, felty pubescent at base, flat blades, and open or diffuse panicles, these breaking away at maturity becoming tumbleweeds. One species in the United States. It differs chiefly from *Digitaria* in the form of the inflorescence, being an open loose panicle of long-pediceled spikelets rather than an aggregation of slender racemes of rather short-pediceled spikelets.

L. COGNATUM (Schult.) Chase (kŏg-nā'tŭm) ; *Panicum autumnale* Bosc ; *P. divergens* Muhl. ; DIFFUSE CRAB-GRASS, FALL WITCH-GRASS.

Culms 1-2.5 feet tall, tufted, freely branching below, at first erect but finally geniculate, prostrate or spreading, slender, very brittle, glabrous or pubescent toward the base; **Blades** 1.5-4' long, 2-5 mm. wide, flat, rather rigid, margins scabrous, white and often wavy, upper surface rough, the lower glabrous, or with a few hairs on upper surface near the base; **Sheaths** shorter than the internodes, upper glabrous or with a few long hairs, the lower thinly to felty pubescent; **Ligule** membranaceous, about 1 mm. long; **Panicle** 5-12' long, commonly one-third to half as long as the culm, often broader than long, finally exserted and diffuse, axis scabrous, the lower axils sparsely-pilose, the capillary branches long, the lower 4-8' long, at first erect, finally widely spreading at maturity, naked at the base, the short divergent branchlets and pedicels bearing single spikelets at their extremities, the branches, branchlets and long pedicels scabrous, the pedicels 10-35 mm. long; **Spikelets** about 3 mm. long; **Glumes,** the first minute or wanting, thin, glabrous, the second 3-nerved, nearly equal to the 5-7-nerved **Sterile Lemma,** the nerves green and prominent, each with an appressed silky-pubescent stripe down the internerves and on the margins, both ciliate near the apex, the hairs finally becoming loose and spreading or erect; **Fruit** about 2.5 mm. long, acuminate, brown, the hyaline margins inclosing the palea, flat not inrolled.

In dry rocky or sandy soil over much of the United States including Texas. (San Antonio.) Spring to fall.

LEPTOLOMA COGNATUM, Diffuse Crab-grass, Fall Witch-grass

83.   STENOTAPHRUM Trin. (stĕn-ō-tăf′rŭm)

Spikelets embedded in one side of an enlarged and flattened corky rachis disarticulating at maturity, the spikelets remaining attached; **First Glume** small; **Second Glume** and **Sterile Lemma** about equal, the latter with a palea or staminate flower; **Fertile Lemma** chartaceous.

Creeping *stoloniferous perennials*, with short flowering stems, rather broad and short obtuse blades, and terminal and axillary spikes.   Species about five; islands of the Pacific; one in southern United States.

St. Augustine grass is a creeping stoloniferous perennial, the stolons sometimes 2-3 feet long, with short internodes and swollen nodes, a fascicle of leaves or branches at each node, mostly short obtuse blades, the short culms erect or ascending bearing terminal and axillary racemes commonly called spikes 2-4′ long.

It thrives in sandy, alluvial or mucky soil, and is often used as a lawn grass in the coastal cities and towns of the South.   It is easily propagated by setting out cuttings or pieces of stolons bearing shoots.   The objections to its coarse texture is overcome by the fact that it thrives in shady places.

S.   SECUNDATUM (Walt.) Kuntze (sē-kŭn-dā′tŭm); *S. americanum* Schrank; ST. AUGUSTINE GRASS, SHORE-GRASS.

Culms 4-12′ tall, erect or ascending from creeping stolons, the stolons often more than 2 feet long, with short internodes, taking root at the swollen nodes, each node with a fascicle of leaves or branched, sometimes the branches over a foot long, smooth throughout; **Blades** commonly 3-6″ or longer on the upright culms, but only about an inch or two long on the stolons, 4-10 mm. wide, flat or folded on drying, rounded at the apex, usually pale-green; **Sheaths** flattened, loose, slightly ciliate on the margins toward the apex; **Ligule** a ciliate ring of short hairs; **Spikes** terminal and axillary, 2-4′ long, about 4 mm. wide, usually sheathed, the spikelets sunken in one side of a flat, thick, corky rachis, sessile, or with 1 or 2 additional short-pediceled ones in alternate notches of each joint; **Spikelets** about 4 mm. long, lanceolate-ovate; **Glumes** membranaceous, the first small but sometimes nearly half as long as the spikelet, obtuse, nerveless, the second as long as the spikelet, ovate, acute, about 7-nerved; **Sterile Lemma** 5-nerved, somewhat coriaceous, subtending a staminate flower; **Fruit** slightly shorter and more coriaceous than the sterile lemma.

In alluvial or mucky soil, Texas to Florida and North Carolina. (Brownsville, Eagle Pass, Texas.)

STENOTAPHRUM SECUNDATUM, St. Augustine Grass

84. ERIOCHLOA H. B. K. (ĕr-ĭ-ŏk'lō-à)

Spikelets dorsally compressed, more or less pubescent, solitary o
sometimes in pairs, short-pediceled or subsessile, in two rows on one sid
of a narrow usually hairy rachis, the pedicels often clothed with long
stiff hairs, the back of the fertile lemma turned from the rachis; lowe
Rachilla joint thickened, forming a more or less ringlike usually dark
colored callus below the second glume, the **First Glume** reduced to a
minute sheath about this and adnate to it; **Second Glume** and **Steril**
Lemma about equal, acute or acuminate, the lemma usually inclosing a
hyaline palea or sometimes a staminate flower; **Fertile Lemma** indurate
minutely papillose-rugose, mucronate or awned, the awn often readil;
deciduous, the margins slightly inrolled.

Annual or *perennial,* often branching, grasses, with terminal panicle
consisting of several or many spreading or appressed racemes, usually rathe
closely arranged along the main axis.

This genus is distinguished by the dorsally compressed pubescent spike
lets, and the ringlike, usually dark-colored callus just below the secon
glume, the first glume reduced to a minute sheath about this and adnat
to it. Our four species grow in rather large tufts, inhabiting cultivate
land, meadows and waste places. *E. sericea* is an erect plant with blade
usually less than 5 mm. wide, and a long narrow panicle of usually appresse
racemes, the very short pedicels of the spikelets being villous, the hair
more than half the length of the spikelet. The other species have rathe
weak culms, the spreading plants being more or less decumbent at the base
with blades usually more than 5 mm. wide. *E. gracilis,* a west Texas plan
has the pedicels and rachis hispidulous and sparsely-pubescent, the frui
being apiculate, and *E. contracta,* the pedicels and rachis hispidulous, th
fruit with an awn 0.5-1.5 mm. long. Both of these plants often have a fev
hairs at the apex of the pedicels. *E. punctata,* with scabrous pedicels an
rachis, has fruit with an awn 0.5-1.5 mm. long. *E. contracta* is commo
in south Texas, and *E. punctata* in the Rio Grande Valley.

SPIKELETS HAIRY; FRUIT ACUTE, APICULATE OR SHORT-AWNEI
Panicles narrow, with several appressed or spreading racemes; spikele
usually in pairs.
PLANTS PERENNIAL.
PEDICELS very short, villous, the hairs more than half as long as the spik
let; spikelets solitary; fruit acute or apiculate; plant erect; blades 2-
mm. wide. 1. E. serice
PEDICELS and rachis scabrous only; awn of the fruit 0.5-1.5 mm. lon;
plant weak and spreading; blades 3-12 mm. wide. 2. E. puncta
PLANTS ANNUAL. Culms stout, but weak and spreading; blades 5-9 mn
wide; usually a few hairs at the apex of the pedicels.
PEDICELS and rachis hispidulous; fruit with an awn 0.5-1.5 mm. long.
3. E. contract
PEDICELS and rachis pubescent; fruit apiculate.
Spikelet acuminate; fruit shorter than the glume and sterile lemma.
4. E. gracil
Spikelet less acuminate; fruit about as long as the glume and sterile lemm;
4a. E. gracilis var. min

1. E. SERICEA (Scheele) Munro (sē-rĭ-sē'à).

Culms 12-45' tall, rather large tufts with many sterile shoots an
leaves below, slender, simple, erect, pubescent below the panicle and wit
scattered hairs where not covered by sheath, short-villous at nodes
Blades 2.5-12' long, 2-4 mm. wide, flat or convolute, pubescent at th
collar, otherwise more or less minutely pubescent; **Sheaths** mostly shorte

an the internodes, striate, pubescent at apex, otherwise glabrous or a
w scattering hairs; **Ligule** a dense ring of straight hairs; **Panicle** mostly
xserted, 4-8' long, simple, racemose with 4-10 appressed secund racemes,
s much as 30 mm. long at base, shorter above, the lower racemes distant
ore than their own length, upper overlapping, the axis pubescent;
pikelets 3-4.5 mm. long, 1.5 mm. wide, solitary, flattened, elliptical-
blong, the triangular rachis pubescent, the very short pedicels villous,
1e hairs more than half as long as the spikelet; **Glumes,** the first reduced
) a minute sheath folded about the ring-like callus, second glume and
terile Lemma about equal, acute, membranaceous, as long as and in-
losing the rest of the spikelet, oblong-elliptical, 5-nerved, villous; **Fruit**
-3.2 mm. long, 1.2 mm. wide, acute or apiculate, minutely papillose-rugose.

In dry soil, Texas, New Mexico and Oklahoma. Summer.

E. PUNCTATA (L.) Desv. (pŭnk-tā'tà); EVERLASTING GRASS.

Culms 1-3.5 feet tall, flattened, often densely-tufted, erect, or spread-
1g or erect from a decumbent base, finally freely branching, short-
ubescent at nodes and below the panicle; **Blades** 1-12' long, 3-9 mm.
1ostly 4-6 mm. wide, flat; **Sheaths** shorter or longer than the internodes,
hin, loose, collar densely-puberulent, otherwise glabrous; **Ligule** a dense
ing of hairs about 0.7 mm. long; **Panicle** exserted or included at the base,
-6' long, the common axis triangular, short-pubescent with ascending
airs, commonly with 5-19 racemes racemose along the common axis,
ppressed or ascending, overlapping, the lower as much as 2' long, pro-
ressively shorter above, green or purplish, the scabrous rachis triangular,
he spikelets single or in pairs, on unequal short scabrous pedicels;
Spikelets 4-5 mm. long, 1 mm. wide, lanceolate, acuminate; **Glumes,** the
irst reduced to a minute sheath about and adnate to the callus-like ring
elow the second glume, the second and sterile lemma subequal, awn-
pointed or minutely 2-toothed, the **Sterile Lemma** about 0.5 mm. shorter,
acuminate, awn-pointed, both 5-nerved, scabrous toward the apex,
pubescent on the lower half to two-thirds, with appressed silky hairs;
Fruit about 2.5 mm. long and 0.9 mm. wide, obtuse, narrowly oval,
papillose-rugose with a scabrous straight or crooked awn as much as
1.5 mm. long.

On plains and prairies, Texas to Louisiana. Summer-fall.

3. **E. CONTRACTA** Hitchc. (kŏn-trăk'tà).

Culms 1.5-3 feet tall, densely-tufted, decumbent at base, spreading,
freely branching above, pubescent below the panicle, pubescent to
puberulent at the nodes; **Blades** commonly 5-8' long, 5-8 mm. wide, flat,
soon becoming conduplicate when drying, pubescent to glabrous, flaccid;
Sheaths shorter or longer than the internodes, glabrous to short pubescent,
especially near the nodes; **Ligule** a ciliate ring of soft white hairs about
1 mm. long; **Panicle** mostly 3-6' sometimes longer, exserted or partly included, narrow, axis and rachis hispidulous, racemes erect or appressed,
commonly 0.5-1.5' long, as many as 15-20, the spikelets mostly in pairs,
pedicels 1-3 mm. long, hispidulous, often with a few long hairs at the
apex of the pedicels; **Spikelets** 4-4.5 mm. long, acuminate, lanceolate;
Glumes, the first reduced to a minute sheath about the callus below the
second glume; the second glume and **Sterile Lemma** 5-nerved, about equal,
acuminate, lanceolate, pubescent; the **Sterile Lemma** slightly shorter
than the second glume; **Fruit** about 2.2 mm. long, with short scabrous awn

0.5-1.5 mm. long, rounded at the apex, narrowly oval, minutely papillos
rugose.

In cultivated soil, south Texas. Summer.

4. **E. GRACILIS** (Fourn.) Hitchc. (grăs′ĭ-lĭs). This species has been co
fused with *E. acuminata* (Presl) Kunth and *E. polystachya* H. B. I

Culms 2-3 feet tall, tufted, ascending or spreading from a decumbe
base, branched, pubescent below the panicles; **Blades** 4-7′ long, 5-9 m
wide, slightly rough and puberulent on upper surface, margins roug
Sheaths shorter than the internodes; **Ligule** a dense ciliate ring of hai
about 1 mm. long; **Panicle** 4-6′ long, long-exserted; **Racemes** numerou
usually about 12-18, 1-1.5′ long, appressed, ascending or spreading, in on
or twos, main axis, rachis and pedicels pubescent, often a few longer hai
at or near the apex of pedicels; spikelets in pairs, the pedicels 1.5-2 m
long; **Spikelets** 3.5-5 mm. long, ovate-lanceolate, acuminate; **Glumes**, t
first reduced to a minute sheath, the second and **Sterile Lemma** 3-nerve
with appressed hairs covering entire surface, the second glume somewh
more hairy than the slightly shorter sterile lemma; **Fruit** shorter than t
glumes, about 3 mm. long, oblong-elliptical, obtuse, minutely papillos
rugose, minutely pubescent, the apex apiculate.

Cultivated soil, Texas to Kansas and west to California. (Ft. Dav
Texas.) Summer and fall.

4a. E. GRACILIS var. MINOR (Vasey) Hitchc. (mĭ′nĕr).

Mostly smaller than the species and with more crowded less acu
inate **spikelets**; **Fruit** about as long as the **glume** and **sterile lemma** (e
cluding the short point), obtuse, slightly apiculate.

Open ground, Texas. (El Paso.)

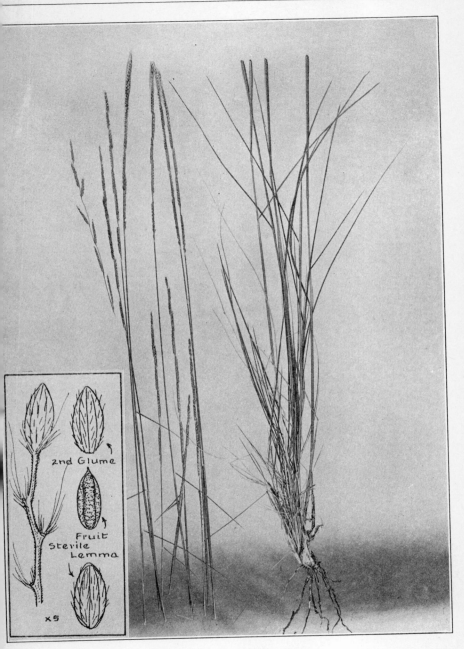

ERIOCHLOA SERICEA

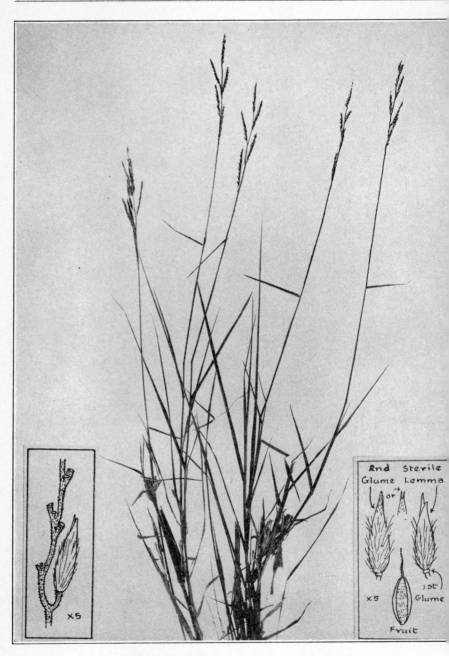

ERIOCHLOA PUNCTATA, Everlasting Grass

ERIOCHLOA CONTRACTA

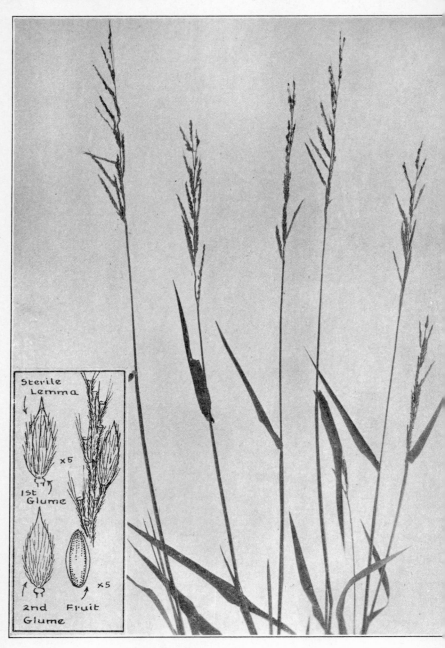

Sterile
Lemma

×5

1st
Glume

2nd
Glume

Fruit

×5

ERIOCHLOA GRACILIS

85. BRACHIARIA (Trin.) Griseb. (brăk-ĭ-ā'rĭ-à)

Spikelets dorsally compressed, solitary, rarely in pairs, subsessile, in ~o rows on one side of a 3-angled sometimes narrowly-winged rachis, the ~st *glume turned toward the axis;* **First Glume** short or nearly as long as ~e spikelet; **Second Glume** and **Sterile Lemma** about equal, 5-7-nerved, ~e lemma inclosing a hyaline palea and sometimes a staminate flower; ~rtile **Lemma** indurate, usually papillose-rugose, the margins inrolled, ~e apex rarely mucronate or bearing a short awn.

Annual or *perennial,* branching and spreading, grasses, with linear ~ades and terminal inflorescence consisting of several spreading or ~pressed racemes along a common axis. Three species in the United ~ates, two in the southern states, both in Texas.

From the species of *Panicum* with spikelets in one-sided spikelike ~cemes this genus differs in having the spikelets in the reverse position ~lative to the rachis, that is, with the first glume toward the rachis.

B. extensa, a decumbent annual, commonly about 2 feet tall, has 2-8 ~cemes about 1.5-2' long, usually ascending or spreading, the spikelets ~abrous; *B. ciliatissima,* a stoloniferous perennial, usually about a foot tall, ~e stolons often over a foot long, has silky pubescent spikelets on short ~ranches of a narrow short panicle. The former is usually found in ~ther low sandy loam, while the latter usually thrives in very sandy ~nd. Both have awnless fruits.

~PIKELETS SILKY PUBESCENT, 3.5-4 mm. long, the pubescence conspicuously
    uneven; plants perennial; panicle narrow, less than 2' long, the racemes
    short.   1. B. ciliatissima
~PIKELETS GLABROUS, 4-4.5 mm. long, flat-beaked beyond the fruit; plants
    annual; panicle more than 4' long, the racemes usually more than 2' long.
                                             2. B. extensa

. **B. CILIATISSIMA** (Buckl.) Chase (sĭl-ĭ-à-tĭs'ĭ-mà) ; *Panicum ciliatis-simum* Buckl.

Flowering Culms 6-24' tall, erect or ascending, sparingly branched, ~ith long leafy stolons, glabrous except the bearded nodes; **Blades** 1-2.8' ~sually about 1.5' long, 3-5 mm. wide, flat, tapering from a rounded base ~o a sharp point, more or less pubescent, sparsely papillose-pilose on the ~nargins near the base; **Sheaths** commonly shorter than the internodes, ~sually densely-pilose; **Ligule** a ring of short hairs; **Panicle** usually long-~xserted, 1-2.5' long, the few branches erect or ascending, usually less than ~n inch long, with a few spikelets alternate in two rows on a slender, ~ngled, puberulent rachis, not regularly arranged as in other species; ~pikelets 3.5-4 mm. long, nearly 2 mm. wide, pointed, distant about half ~heir length; **Glumes**, the first about three-fourths the length of the spike-~et, lanceolate, acuminate, 3-5 obscure nerves, smooth and glabrous except ~a few hairs at the very base, the second and **Sterile Lemma** subequal, ~exceeding the fruit, about 11-nerved (look inside), with a dense row of ~silky hairs on each side running lengthwise midway between the margins ~and the three central nerves, with shorter pubescence on the balance of ~he glume; **Sterile Lemma** inrolled inclosing a hyaline palea about its own ~length 5-7-nerved, with two rows of hairs as on the second glume, but the ~outer surface of same either sparingly short-pubescent or nearly glabrous; **Fruit** 3 mm. long, about 1.5 mm. wide, ellipsoid, apiculate, minutely ~transverse-rugose.

In open sandy soil, Texas to Arkansas. Spring to summer.

2. B. EXTENSA Chase (ĕks-tĕn′sà) ; *B. platyphylla* (Griseb.) Nash.

Culms 20-32′ tall, tufted, at first erect, finally decumbent at the ba
rooting and commonly branched at the lower nodes, the floweri
branches ascending, rather coarse, flattened; **Blades** pale-green, 1.5
long, rarely longer, flat, broad at the base, lanceolate, glabrous except
the rounded margins at the base; **Sheaths** usually overlapping, loo
sparsely-pilose at least along the margins and toward the summit; **Ligᵕ**
a ring of hairs less than 1 mm. long; **Racemes** 2-8, commonly dista
nearly or quite their own length, the common axis flat, exserted or t
lower included at the base, 1.5-2.5′ long, the lowermost sometimes long
ascending or spreading, often curved, rachis villous at the base, abc
2 mm. wide, slightly scabrous on the inturned margins; **Spikelets** 4-
mm. long, about 2 mm. wide, ovate, flattened toward the apex, usua
barely overlapping, glabrous; **Glumes** broad, 3-5-nerved, the first abc
one-third the length of the spikelet, blunt, the second glume and **ster**
lemma equal, exceeding the fruit, 3-5-nerved, with faint transveι
wrinkles between the nerves toward the summit; **Fruit** 2.5-3 mm. loι
1.8 mm. wide, elliptic, turgid, papillose-rugose, roughened.

In low sandy soil, Texas and Louisiana.   Summer-fall.

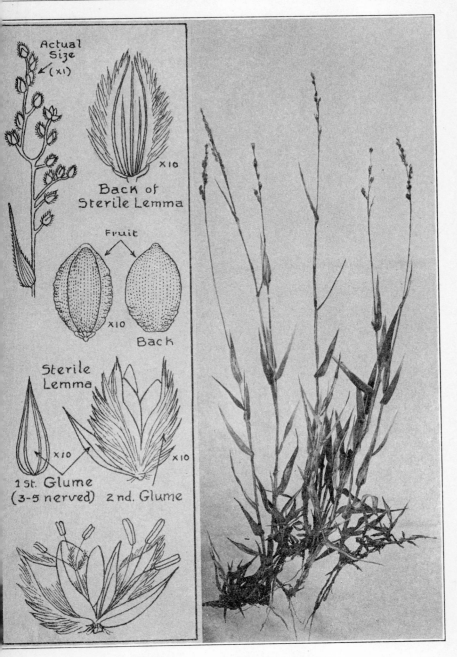

Actual Size ←(×1)

Back of Sterile Lemma ×10

Fruit

×10 Back

Sterile Lemma

×10

1st. Glume (3-5 nerved) ×10 2nd. Glume ×10

BRACHIARIA CILIATISSIMA

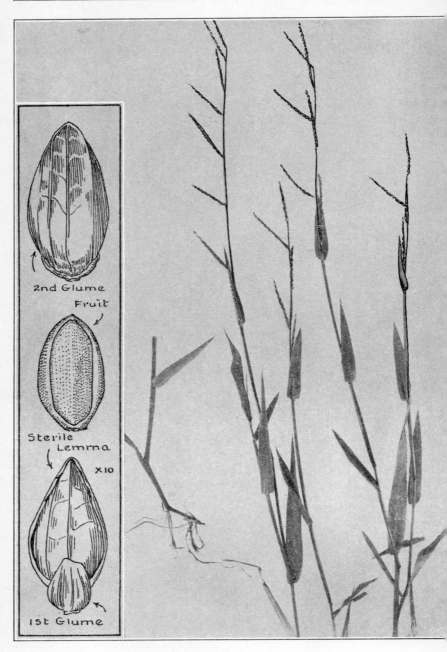

BRACHIARIA EXTENSA

86. AXONOPUS Beauv. (ăks-ŏn'ō-pŭs)
(Anastrophus Schlecht.)

Spikelets depressed biconvex, not turgid, oblong, usually obtuse, ¿litary, sessile and alternate, in two rows on one side of a 3-angled ¿chis, *the back of the fertile lemma turned from the axis;* **First Glume** ¿anting; **Second Glume** and **Sterile Lemma** equal, the lemma without a ¿lea; **Fertile Lemma** and **Palea** indurate, the lemma oblong-elliptic, ¿ually obtuse, the margins slightly inrolled.

Stoloniferous or tufted perennials, rarely annuals, with usually flat or ¿lded, abruptly rounded or somewhat pointed blades, and few or numerous ¿ender spikelike racemes, digitate or racemose along the main axis. Two ¿ecies in the United States confined to near the coast in the southern states.

Our two species, carpet-grass and flat crab-grass are *stoloniferous* ¿erennials with flattened culms and sheaths, obtuse blades, and flowering ¿lms long and filiform. In this genus the first glume is wanting, and the ¿ack of the fruit is turned from the axis. Carpet-grass has pubescent spike- ¿ts about 2 mm. long, and flat crab-grass, glabrous spikelets 4-6 mm. long ¿ith the racemes thicker and longer.

Carpet-grass becomes dominant in alluvial or mucky soil, on open ¿round in the lowlands near the coast from eastern Texas to Florida. It ¿oes not thrive in sandy soil on the uplands. It is often used as a lawn ¿rass. Flat crab-grass is infrequent, but has about the same range as ¿arpet-grass.

¿PIKELETS not over 2.5 mm. long, sparsely pubescent.　　1. A. compressus
¿PIKELETS 4-6 mm. long, glabrous.　　2. A. furcatus

. A. COMPRESSUS (Swartz) Beauv. (kŏm-prĕs'ŭs); *Anastrophus com-pressus* (Swartz) Schlecht.; Carpet-grass or Flat Joint-grass.

Culms 1-2.5 feet tall, slender, flattened, branching, the stolons numer- ¿us and creeping, sometimes as much as 2 feet long, leafy; **Blades** 1-12' ¿ong, those of the stolons as short as 1' and 2-4 mm. wide, the upper culm ¿lades mostly 2-4' long and the basal as much as 12' long and 8 mm. wide, ¿lat or folded at the base, narrowly linear, obtuse, scabrous on the margins ¿oward the apex, sometimes sparsely-ciliate on the margins at the base; **Sheaths** crowded below, flattened, often sparsely-pilose at the throat, ¿therwise glabrous or with a few soft hairs; **Ligule** short-membranaceous, ¿hort-ciliate; **Racemes** terminal and axillary, much exserted on long filiform upper portion of culm, in pairs, or an additional 1-2 below, sub- ¿digitate, 1.5-4' long, slender, the appressed spikelets about equal to the internodes or slightly overlapping, spikelet-bearing to the base, the back of the fertile lemma turned from the rachis; **Spikelets** about 2 mm. long, about 0.8 mm. wide, somewhat flattened, oblong-elliptic, obtuse or sub-acute; **Glumes,** the first wanting, the second (outer one) and the **Sterile Lemma** equal and slightly longer than the fruit, sparsely-pubescent, 5-nerved, or by the suppression of the midnerve 4-nerved, the two lateral nerves on each side close together and near the margins, the sterile lemma depressed along the middle and without a palea; **Fruit** oblong-elliptic, minutely rugose, with a few hairs at the obtuse apex.

Moist soil, fields, roadsides and woods, Texas to Florida and north to Virginia. Common from Bay City east to Orange and some distance north. Summer and fall.

2. A. FURCATUS (Flügge) Hitchc. (fûr-kā'tŭs); *Anastrophus furcat* (Flügge) Nash; FLAT CRAB-GRASS.

Culms 1-3.5 feet tall, erect or spreading, strongly compressed-keele leafy at the base, with long leafy stolons, branching, glabrous or som times pubescent; **Blades** 2-15' long, the upper short, 6-15 mm. wide, fl. or folded at the base, linear, blunt-pointed, glabrous, or ciliate on tl margin, or pubescent; **Sheaths** longer than the internodes, strongly-keele glabrous or pubescent; **Ligule** about 0.5 mm. long, minutely ciliat **Racemes** spikelike, exserted, or those of the axillary peduncles includ. at the base, commonly in pairs, sometimes an additional one a short di tance below, rarely one, ascending, 1.5-5.5' long, the spikelets usual slightly overlapping; **Spikelets** 4-6 mm. long, about 1.6 mm. wid lanceolate, acuminate, not strongly biconvex, glabrous; **Glumes,** the fir wanting, the second and **Sterile Lemma** equal, the second 5-7-nerved, tl midnerve evident; **Fruit** half to two-thirds the length of the second glur and sterile lemma, about 1.5 mm. wide, not strongly biconvex, oblon elliptic or slightly oblong-obovate, obtuse, minutely striate.

In rather moist sandy soil, fields and woods, Texas to Florida ar north to Virginia. (Beaumont and Experimental Station at Angleto. Texas.) Spring to fall.

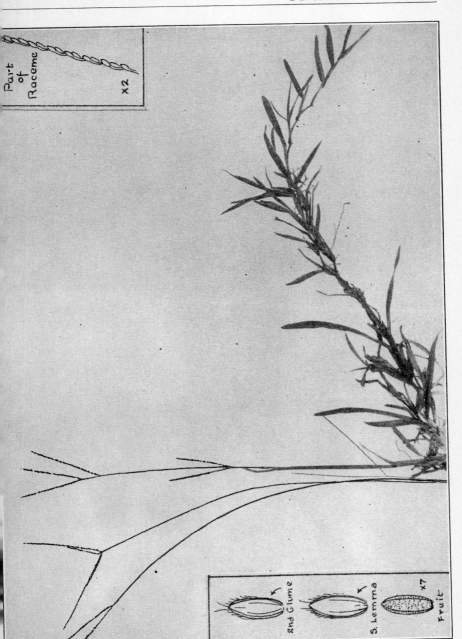

AXONOPUS COMPRESSUS, Carpet-grass

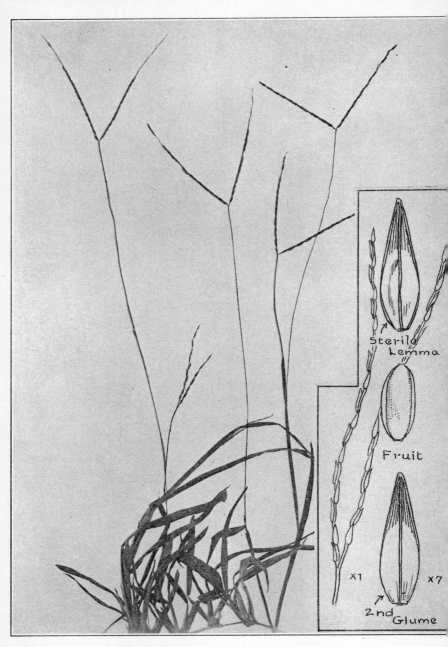

AXONOPUS FURCATUS, Flat Crab-grass

87. PASPALUM L. (păs'pā-lŭm)

Spikelets plano-convex, usually obtuse, subsessile, solitary or in rs, in two rows on one side of a narrow or dilated rachis, *the back of the tile lemma toward it;* **First Glume** usually wanting; **Second Glume** and rile **Lemma** commonly about equal, the former rarely wanting; **Fertile mma** usually obtuse, chartaceous-indurate, the margins inrolled. Mostly rennials, with one to many spikelike racemes, these single or paired at summit of the culms or racemosely arranged along the main axis. Species merous, probably as many as 200, widely distributed in the warmer parts both hemispheres; about 50 species in the United States, mostly in the theastern states. All the Texas species except *P. scrobiculatum* are rennials.

Paspalum differs chiefly from *Panicum,* a closely related genus, by its emose inflorescence and the plano-convex spikelets in which the first me is typically wanting. The first glume is regularly present in one up and in a few other species, occasionally developed in a few others, or many species an occasional spikelet may be found with the first glume reloped. In some species the first glume is developed unequally, being all to almost obsolete on the upper and primary spikelet of a pair and ge on the secondary spikelet.

While the spikelets of the genus are always in two rows on one side of rachis, the species are often described as having spikelets in two, three four rows. They appear to be in three or four rows in a great many cies because the pedicel is actually a branchlet bearing a primary spikelet the summit and a secondary spikelet on a short branchlet or pedicel be-r. When branching and crowded they appear to be in four rows, when so densely crowded and with one of the pair turned toward the center of raceme they appear to be in three rows.

The author, unable to collect all of the species of *Paspalum* in Texas, drawn liberally upon *the North American Species of Paspalum* (Bul. S. Nat. Herb.) by Agnes Chase. The groupings and their order of angement have been used, and many of the illustrations and descriptions ied. In the above work the species of *Paspalum* have been divided into nor groups, the names of which are the plurals of the characteristic cies of the group. *Setacea* is used as the group name for the closely ated species, *P. setaceum, P. debile, P. ciliatifolium,* and others.

Our species are divided into two main subdivisions, those with a iaceous rachis, and those without. In the former there are only three cies and one group, *Dissecta;* in the latter, all the remaining species, in eral groups.

Dissecta (dĭ-sĕk'tà): Plants with foliaceous rachis. Here we have ee straggling plants, *P. dissectum, P. acuminatum* and *P. repens,* all iatic or subaquatic—plants of ditch borders and moist places.

Disticha (dĭs'tĭ-kà): Plants with creeping wiry culms and stolons or zomes, usually with two racemes. Our two species are *P. distichum,* which a wide range and grows in very moist places, and *P. vaginatum* which onfined to the sea coasts and brackish sands.

Livida (lĭv'ĭ-dà): This group has three species with compressed ms and flat blades usually growing in moist meadows or fields. *lividum,* often with long creeping culms, has glabrous spikelets 2-2.5 mm. g, while *P. hartwegianum* has depressed plano-convex spikelets about im. long. *P. pubiflorum,* the spikelets pubescent, and *P. pubiflorum* var.

glabrum, the spikelets glabrous, have turgidly plano-convex spikelets abc 3 mm. long.

Notata (nō-tā′tà) : Plants with compressed culms, leafy at the bas racemes 2; spikelets solitary. *P. notatum* and *P. minus,* with stout hc zontal rhizomes, form a tough sod, while *P. almum,* a recently descril species collected at Beaumont, is a densely-tufted grass.

Setacea (sē-tā′sē-à) : Plants with compressed culms from very sh rhizomes, racemes usually few; ligule with a dense row of long white ha back of it. The first glume is developed in occasional specimens, more f quently so than in most groups of the genus, other than *Decumbentes.* M of the species of this group are poorly defined and appear to intergra Pubescence is extremely variable in amount and position, and the spikel vary in size and shape. We have six species: *P. setaceum, P. debile, stramineum, P. pubescens, P. ciliatifolium,* and *P. rigidifolium.*

Decumbentes (dē-kŭm-bĕn′tēz) : Racemes 1 to several, spikelets pairs, the first glume commonly developed in at least one of the pair, that the primary spikelet (the upper one of the pair) in most species minute obsolete, that of the secondary spikelet (the lower one of the pair) well-veloped, long-pointed and turned to one side of the spikelet. Our t species, usually with 1 raceme, are *P. unispicatum,* with wide flat blades a *P. monostachyum,* with blades narrow and folded at the base, the marg adnate above, and one, *P. langei,* usually with about 5 racemes, the spi lets hairy.

Conjugata (kŏn-jū-gā′tà) : Plants creeping, stoloniferous, with f lax blades, and two slender yellow racemes, usually paired, the spikel ciliate with long hairs. *P. conjugatum,* our only species, is found at ' mouth of the Rio Grande River near Brownsville.

Dilatata (dī-là-tā′tà) : Rather stout, robust plants, in leafy clum blades flat; racemes few to numerous; spikelets in pairs, flat, conspicuou silky-ciliate. *P. dilatatum,* Dallis grass, usually has 3-5 racemes, ascend to drooping, and *P. urvillei* has numerous usually appressed or ascend racemes.

Laevia (lē′vĭ-à) : Culms rather tall, from very short rhizomes, co pressed; racemes few to several; spikelets large, glabrous. *P. laeve, P. lor pilum* and *P. circulare* have spikelets solitary on the racemes, the spikel 3-3.2 mm. long; *P. praecox,* spikelets 2.2-2.8 mm. long, and *P. lentiferu* spikelets 2.7-3.4 mm. long, have spikelets solitary and paired in the sa racemes.

Floridana (flō-rĭ-dā′nà) : Culms robust, simple, blades flat, w heavy racemes of large turgid glabrous spikelets. *P. floridanum* I sheaths and blades hirsute, while *P. floridanum* var. *glabratum* has bla and sheaths glabrous or nearly so.

Virgata (vĕr-gā′tà) : Tall robust plants with sharp-cutting edges the firm blades; panicles with a few to several racemes. Our only speci *P. virgatum,* has spikelets pubescent, especially towards the summit, t fruit brown at maturity. Plants of tropical or subtropical America.

Plicatula (plĭ-kăt′ū-là) : Plants with purplish compressed culms a sheaths; racemes rather heavy; spikelets at first drab turning brown dark olivaceous; fruit dark brown, shining. We have two speci *P. plicatulum,* with turgid obovate spikelets, the sterile lemma wrinkled j within the margin, and *P. scrobiculatum,* our only annual with scrobicu spikelets, the sterile lemma wrinkled.

P. Bifidum (bī′fĭ-dŭm) : Ungrouped, as it is not closely related to any ᵢown species either *Paspalum* or *Panicum*. It has irregular racemes of convex spikelets with 5-7-nerved second glume and sterile lemma.

ACHIS MEMBRANACEOUS OR FOLIACEOUS, INCLOSING THE BASE OF
  the spikelets, green. Spikelets glabrous (minutely pubescent in *P. repens*),
  straggling, branching, mostly aquatic or subaquatic; fruits pale.
RACEMES PERSISTENT on the axis; rachis with a spikelet at the apex;
  second glume developed.
  SPIKELETS 2 mm. long, obovate-oval; racemes 2-4.   1. P. dissectum
  SPIKELETS 3.5 mm. long, pointed; racemes mostly 3-5; blades more than
  8 mm. wide.   2. P. acuminatum
RACEMES FALLING entire from the axis, rachis extending beyond the uppermost spikelet; racemes numerous; spikelets 1.4-2 mm. long, about 0.8 mm.
  wide, whitish.   3. P. repens
ACHIS NOT MEMBRANACEOUS, FOLIACEOUS OR WINGED (slightly
  winged in a few species, but if so, spikelets not silky).
RACEMES 2, CONJUGATE, or nearly so at the summit of the culm, rarely
  a third below.
  SPIKELETS elliptic or narrowly ovate, somewhat pointed. Plants with
  creeping rhizomes or stolons, wiry-compressed.
  Second glume pubescent; midnerve of second glume and sterile lemma
    relatively prominent; spikelets solitary or occasionally in pairs, turgid.
                                                                 5. P. distichum
  Second glume and sterile lemma glabrous; midnerve usually suppressed;
    sterile lemma transversely wrinkled or undulate; spikelets solitary,
    flattened.   4. P. vaginatum
  SPIKELETS suborbicular, broadly ovate or obovate.
  Spikelets concavo-convex, sparsely long-silky around margin; racemes
    yellow, 2, sometimes a third below, rarely more than 5′ long; plants
    stoloniferous.   21. P. conjugatum
  Spikelets plano-convex, not silky-margined. Plants not stoloniferous; leafy
    at the base; culms compressed; racemes 2, sometimes 3 in *P. almum;*
    spikelets green, solitary, in two rows.
    Rhizomes present; stout, forming mats or a tough sod.
    Spikelets 2.5-3.5 mm. long.   9. P. notatum
    Spikelets 2-2.5 mm. long.   10. P. minus
    Rhizomes not present; plants densely-tufted; spikelets 3 mm. long.
                                                                11. P. almum
RACEMES 1 TO MANY, racemose or fascicled on the axis, not conjugate.
  FIRST glume usually developed on at least one of the pair of spikelets.
    Spikelets turgidly biconvex.   33. P. bifidum
    Spikelets plano-convex.
    Culms mostly solitary with stout scaly rhizomes; the first glume often
      obsolete.
      Blades flat; 8-15 mm. wide.   18. P. unispicatum
      Blades folded at the base, margins adnate above, not more than 2 mm.
      wide.   19. P. monostachyum
    Culms more or less tufted, without rhizomes. First glume developed in
      both spikelets; spikelets glandular, speckled, sparsely-pubescent, at
      least on the second glume; spikelet 2.2-2.6 mm. long.   20. P. langei
  FIRST glume normally wanting (rarely developed in occasional spikelet);
    plants from a knotted base or very short rhizomes.
    Racemes terminal and axillary, the axillary sometimes hidden in the
      sheaths; terminal 1-3 rarely 6 racemes; ligule a minute membrane
      with a dense row of hairs back of it.
    Spikelets usually 1.5-1.7 mm. long, or sometimes 1.9 in *P. debile* or
      P. ciliatifolium; blades and sheaths conspicuously pubescent through-
      out.
      Culms slender, erect or suberect; foliage not aggregate at the base;
        blades suberect, usually not more than 5 mm. wide.
                                                                12. P. setaceum
      Culms stouter, mostly spreading; foliage more or less aggregate at
        the base; blades spreading, usually more than 5 mm. wide.
                                                                13. P. debile

Spikelets 2-2.5 mm. long (or 1.8-1.9 in *P. ciliatifolium*).
 Foliage except margins glabrous as a whole, or nearly so (sparsel
   pubescent in exceptional *P. ciliatifolium* and the lower sheat
   usually pubescent in *P. rigidifolium*).
 Blades stiff, usually not more than 6 mm. wide; spikelets mosl
   2.2-2.4 mm. long.   17. P. rigidifoliu
 Blades from lax to rather firm, if firm more than 6 mm. wi
   spikelets mostly 2 mm. long, rounded at the summit; blad
   mostly more than 8 mm. wide.   16. P. ciliatifoliu
 Foliage conspicuously pubescent or sparsely so in exceptio
   specimens of *P. pubescens;* culms erect or nearly so.
 Blades from sparsely to rather densely-pilose, rather thin.
                                                 15. P. pubesce
 Blades puberulent on both surfaces with long hairs intermixed
   the lower surface nearly or quite glabrous except for a f
   long hairs along midrib and margin, usually rather firm.
                                                 14. P. straminei
Racemes terminal on the primary culms or leafy branches, no tr
  axillary racemes. A flower branch, with a leaf reduced to the shea
  sometimes found in *P. laeve* and others, simulates an axillary racen
  racemes 2-to-many.
Spikelets conspicuously silky-ciliate around the margins, the hairs as lo
  as the spikelet or longer, flat, in pairs; plants in stout leafy clum
  blades flat.
 Racemes commonly 3-5; culms geniculate at the base.
                                                 22. P. dilatati
 Racemes commonly 12-18, culms erect.   23. P. urvil
Spikelets not conspicuously ciliate.
 Fruit dark-brown, shining; sterile lemma wrinkled; racemes hea
   commonly 3-10, 1-4′ long, arcuate, spreading.
 Plant perennial; spikelets obovate, turgid; sterile lemma wrinkl
   just within the margin.   31. P. plicatulu
 Plants annual, stout; spikelets suborbicular; sterile lemma loose a
   wrinkled.   32. P. scrobiculati
 Fruit pale to yellowish (brown but not shining in *P. virgatum*).
 PLANTS ROBUST, TALL, MORE THAN 3 FEET. Culms simple
   with a few simple branches.
  BLADES FIRM with sharp cutting edges, flat racemes 10-16, 2
    long; spikelets obovate-obtuse, 2 2 rarely 3 mm. long, pubesce
    at summit.   30. P. virgat
  BLADES RELATIVELY lax, the edges not cutting; racemes rar
    more than 5; spikelets glabrous.
  Sheaths and blades hirsute.   29. P. floridan
  Sheaths and blades glabrous or nearly so.
                                                 29a. P. floridanum var. glabrat
 PLANTS NOT ROBUST, IF MORE THAN 3 FEET TALL culms
   latively slender.
  SPIKELETS SUBORBICULAR, or broadly obovate or broadly ov
    glabrous; plants with short rhizomes. Spikelets depress
    plano-convex or lenticular 2.2-3.4 mm. long.
   SPIKELETS solitary; glume and sterile lemma firm.
    Spikelets orbicular, 3-3.2 mm. long, scarcely one-third as thic
      blades usually equaling the base of the panicle or ov
      topping it.   26. P. circul
    Spikelets longer than broad, more than one-third as thic
      panicle usually much exceeding the blades.
    Sheaths and blades pilose, mostly conspicuously so.
                                                 25. P. longipil
    Sheaths and blades glabrous or nearly so to sparsely-pilo
                                                 24. P. lae
   SPIKELETS solitary and paired in the same raceme (rarely
     solitary or all paired). Lower sheaths strongly compress
     keeled; spikelets suborbicular; glume and sterile lemma th
     the cells visible.
    Spikelets 2.2-2.5 mm. (rarely 2.8) long, foliage not conspicuou
      villous.   27. P. praec

Spikelets 2.7-3.4 mm. long; lower sheaths and blades mostly con-
spicuously villous, at least at the base.   28. P. lentiferum
SPIKELETS ELLIPTIC to oval or obovate; culms decumbent at the
base, rooting at the lower nodes, compressed, branching.
SPIKELETS turgidly plano-convex 3-3.2 mm. long; culms rather
stout.
Spikelets pubescent.   6. P. pubiflorum
Spikelets glabrous.   6a. P. pubiflorum var. glabrum
SPIKELETS depressed plano-convex or slightly concavo-convex.
Spikelet and rachis pale; spikelets pointed, at least the glume
pubescent; spikelets 3 mm. long.   8. P. hartwegianum
Spikelets and usually the rachis stained with lurid purple or
bronze; panicle very slender, flexuous; spikelets 2-2.5 mm.
long, usually minutely apiculate.   7. P. lividum

1. P. DISSECTUM (L.) L. (dĭ-sĕk'tŭm) ; *P. membranaceum* Walt.;
P. walterianum Schult.

Culms 8-24′ tall, ascending, compressed, the nodes usually swollen,
the plant olive-green, creeping, freely branching, rooting at the nodes,
subaquatic; **Blades** 30-60 mm. long, rarely longer, 4-5 mm. wide, flat,
scarcely narrowed at the base, rather abruptly acute, thin; **Sheaths** commonly divergent, often flat and bladelike, the prophyllum visible, soft,
loose; **Ligule** about 2 mm. long, hyaline, lacerate, extending down the
sheath margins; **Inflorescence** terminal and axillary, short-exserted, of
2-4 usually erect racemes, distant half to one-third their own length, on a
slender, narrowly winged axis; **Racemes** usually 20-30 mm. long, the
rachis membranaceous, 2-3 mm. wide, abruptly pointed, and terminating
at the base of the uppermost spikelet, the minutely scabrous margins inflexed, covering the base of the spikelet; **Spikelets** solitary, 2 mm. long,
1.4 mm. wide, obovate, subacute, pale; **Glumes**, the first wanting, the
second and **Sterile Lemma** thin, 3-5-nerved, slightly exceeding the fruit, in
the terminal spikelet usually a little longer, forming a short point; **Fruit**
1.8 mm. long, 1.3 mm. wide, obtuse, minutely papillose-roughened.

On muddy or sandy banks of ponds and ditches or in shallow water,
east Texas to Florida, north to Missouri and New Jersey.   (Houston.)
Late summer and fall.

2. P. ACUMINATUM Raddi (à-kū-mĭ-nā'tŭm).

Culms 12-40′ tall, in clumps of few to several culms, extensively
creeping, erect or ascending from a decumbent base, sparingly branched,
rather fleshy, compressed, the nodes dark-brown, aquatic or subaquatic;
Blades 1.5-5′ long, 5-12 mm. wide, rounded at the base, abruptly acuminate,
flat, soft, ascending; **Sheaths** overlapping toward the summit of the culms,
loose, soft; **Ligule** 2 mm. long, hyaline, slightly erose; **Racemes** 3-5 rarely
2, distant about one-fourth their length, along a narrowly winged rachis,
erect or ascending, 1.5-2.5′ long; **Rachis** membranaceous, 3-3.5 mm. wide,
the margins inflexed over the base of the spikelets, minutely hispidulous,
terminating at the base of the uppermost spikelet; **Spikelets** solitary in
two rows, 3.5 mm. long, 1.6 mm. wide, elliptic; **Glumes**, the first wanting,
the second and **Sterile Lemma** thin, abruptly pointed beyond the fruit;
Fruit 2.9 mm. long, 1.5 mm. wide, obovate-elliptic, faintly 3-5-nerved,
minutely papillose-roughened, the obtuse apex with a minute tuft of short
thick hairs.

In shallow water or wet open ground, Texas to Louisiana, and in
Argentina. (Falfurrias, Texas.)

3. P. REPENS Bergius (rē′pĕns); *P. mucronatum* Muhl.; *P. fluitan*
Kunth; WATER PASPALUM.

Culms submerged, sometimes as much as 6.5 feet long, with tufts o
long roots at the nodes and numerous floating branches, soft and spongy
an aquatic rarely terrestrial plant, the nodes dark, sometimes hispid
Blades 4-8′ long, 12-15 mm. wide, sometimes as much as 11′ long an
25 mm. wide, tapering to both ends, flat, thin, scabrous, often ciliate tc
ward the base, the collar dark-colored, usually strigose; **Sheaths** con
monly overlapping on the branches, those of the floating branches ir
flated, flask-shaped, papery, often purple-spotted, those of the aeria
branches loose, thin, smooth or scabrous above, glabrous to sparsel
papillose-hispid, in all a prominent erect auricle on either side of the sun
mit; **Ligule** rather firm, erose, strigose, extending up the inner margin o
the auricle; **Panicles** short-exserted, usually 4-6′ long, 1.5-4′ wide, som
times as much as 8′ long, of numerous ascending, spreading or recurve
rather lax racemes, solitary or in fascicles of 2 or 3 along a slende
scabrous axis; **Racemes** tardily falling entire, usually 30-50 mm. rarel
90 mm. long, the rachis about 1.5 mm. wide, scabrous, often flexuou
naked at the narrowed base and acuminate tip; **Spikelets** solitary, whitisl
1.4-2 mm. long, about 0.8 mm. wide, elliptic; **Glumes,** the first wantin
the second and **Sterile Lemma** very thin, more or less exceeding the frui
and pointed beyond it, 2-nerved, the nerves near the margins, the mic
nerve suppressed, pubescent with soft spreading hairs to glabrous, th
lemma commonly with a v-shaped pinkish stain at base; **Fruit** 1.4-1.7 mn
long, 0.6 mm. wide, elliptic, smooth and shining.

At maturity the numerous racemes are often curled back, the panic
suggesting an ostrich feather.

Terrestrial plants are usually much dwarfed, the base creeping, roo
ing at the nodes, flowering branches 4-8′ tall.

Most of the specimens from the United States have pubescent, eve
glandular pubescent, spikelets. In those of the Tropics the spikelets ar
either pubescent or glabrous. It has been reported from Arkansas a
causing much trouble by its dense growth in drainage canals.

Floating in sluggish streams or standing water or creeping in we
places, Texas to Florida, north to South Carolina, Indiana and Kansa
(Humble, Houston, Columbia, Texas.) Late summer and fall.

4. P. VAGINATUM Swartz (văj-ĭ-nā′tŭm); SAND KNOT-GRASS.

Flowering Culms 5-24′ tall, the upturned stolons sometimes flowerin
simple or branching, the branches sometimes aggregate, ascending o
erect, usually the greater number on any plant sterile with conspicuousl
distichous stiffly ascending blades, forming dense tufts of stiff foliag
from horizontal rhizomes, pale, glabrous as a whole, the stolons sometim
slender and wiry, sometimes stout and almost succulent, extensively cree
ing, often 3 feet long or more, flattened and often grooved, internode
short, the sheaths short, broad and usually overlapping (or sometim
slightly shorter) sheaths, sometimes bladeless or with short reflexe
blades, often forming extensive colonies; **Blades** distichous, 1-6′ long, 3
mm. (3-8) wide at the base, narrower than the summit of the sheat
tapering from an abruptly narrowed base to an involute tip, usually firr
commonly ascending at a uniform angle, those of the stolons usually sho
and often reflexed; **Sheaths** commonly overlapping, short, broad, loos
usually keeled, the summit with small auricles; **Ligule** membranaceou
about 0.5 mm. long, commonly with a ring of weak hairs back of it, som

imes 5 mm. long; **Racemes** short-exserted, or included at the base, commonly 2 sometimes 3 rarely 1 or as many as 5, conjugate or closely pproximate, at first erect and closely appressed together, finally spreading or reflexed at maturity, often somewhat falcate, commonly 0.6-3′ long; tachis naked at the base, 1-1.5 mm. (1-2.5) wide, triangular, minutely cabrous on the margins; **Spikelets** in two rows, solitary, imbricate, except the lower ones, 3-4.5 mm. (commonly 3.5-4) long, 1.5-1.8 mm. (1.2-1.5) ide, ovate-lanceolate or slightly obovate, acute, pale, stramineous; **lumes,** the first wanting, rarely developed, the second and **Sterile Lemma** qual, thin in texture, 5-nerved, the nerves often obscure, the midnerve f the glume or both usually suppressed, the lateral nerves approximate t the margin, the sterile lemma often transversely undulate, sometimes onspicuously so; **Fruit** 2.5-3 mm. long, about 1.5 mm. wide, narrowly bovate, subacute, slightly concavo-convex.

Sea coasts and brackish sands, often forming a pure stand. Texas) Florida and North Carolina, and southward. (At very mouth of the io Grande River, Galveston, Capano Bay.) Summer and fall.

P. DISTICHUM L. (dĭs′tĭ-kŭm); KNOT-GRASS, JOINT-GRASS.

Culms 1-2 feet tall, erect or ascending, sometimes branched, the long reeping somewhat flattened stolons as much as 2-3 feet long, often orming loose mats or rather close sod, taking root at the nodes, the dark odes often with a few hairs; **Blades** 1.5-5′ usually 2-3′ long, 2-6 mm. wide, at, soon becoming involute, tapering toward the apex, relatively soft, w ciliate hairs at the very base, often puberulent on upper surface; **heaths** usually shorter than the internodes, loose, flattened, pilose at the roat; **Ligule** membranaceous, truncate, lacerate, about 0.5-1 mm. long; **acemes** usually in pairs, rarely 3-4, on short or included peduncles, ually incurved, sometimes reflexed, commonly 1-2.5′ long, the lower ne raised on a short internode of the axis, usually with a few long white airs in the axils, rachis about 1.5 mm. wide, margins minutely scabrous; **pikelets** 2.5-3.5 rarely 4 mm. long, 1.3-1.5 mm. wide, elliptic, acute, pale-reen, flattened, solitary (rarely in pairs at middle of raceme), subsessile, rowded; **Glumes,** the first wanting, occasionally minutely developed, the cond and **Sterile Lemma** equal, 3-5-nerved, the midnerve prominent, the ume minutely appressed-pubescent, sometimes obscurely so; **Fruit** early as long as the spikelet, 1.2 mm. wide, glabrous or with a few short ristly hairs at the apex.

Ditches, creeks and low wet places, often in water. In southern nited States, extending north to New Jersey and west to California and ong coast to Washington, also extending south into Mexico and South merica. Spring and summer.

P. PUBIFLORUM Rupr. (pū-bĭ-flō′rŭm).

Culms 1-3 feet tall, flowering stalks erect or ascending from a dembent base, taking root at the swollen nodes, the internodes of the ecumbent part short, robust, flattened, smooth and glabrous except the rk nodes, the lower pilose and upper sparingly-pubescent or pilose; lades 2-9′ usually 4-6′ long, upper reduced, 6-14 mm. wide, flat, uminate, the margins scabrous, sparsely papillose-pilose on margins at e rounded base, and often appressed-pubescent just above the ligule; eaths mostly shorter than the internodes, loose, the margins brown, the wer sparsely papillose-pilose; **Ligule** membranaceous, 1-3 mm. long; acemes mostly 3-5 (2-8) usually about a half inch apart, lower somewhat distant, 1-4' long, rather thick, erect or horizontally spreading, with tufts of long hairs at the axils; **Rachis** flat, up to 2 mm. wide, green, scabrous on the margins, lowest often naked at the base; **Spikelets** 2.8-3.2 mm. long 2 mm. wide, usually in pairs in two rows, having appearance of four rows plano-convex, turgid, slightly obovate, yellowish-green, crowded; **Glumes** the first wanting, the second and **Sterile Lemma** subequal, 3-5-nerved, the second glume pubescent with spreading hairs, and sterile lemma minutely appressed-pubescent, the margins inclosing the fruit; **Fruit** pale, 3 mm long, 1.9 mm. wide, minutely striate, roughened.

Moist open ground, banks, low woods, along streams and ditches especially in alkaline soil; Texas, Louisiana and Mexico. (San Antonio. Spring to fall.

6a. P. PUBIFLORUM var. **GLABRUM** Vasey (glā′brŭm); *P. geminum* Nash; *P. laeviglume* Scribn.

Plants of the same habit as *P. pubiflorum*, on the average more robust in rich ground the culms sometimes 6.5 feet long, the sheaths less pilose the **blades** a little wider (occasionally 20 mm. wide) and tapering toward the base, the **racemes** commonly longer and oftener more than five **Spikelets** glabrous. In a few specimens the spikelets are obscurely pubescent on the glume. It is a palatable pasture grass and very drought resistent.

Moist low open ground, woods and ditch banks, Texas to Florida north to North Carolina and Kentucky and Kansas. Spring-fall.

7. P. LIVIDUM Trin. (lĭv′ĭ-dŭm); LONG TOM, *"Pull-and-be-damned'*
Culms 1-3 feet tall, solitary or a few culms to a tuft, or in mor favorable locations a thick mass of stolons and culms, simple or bearin a few sterile branches, erect or ascending, the lower part often decumbent often rooting at the nodes, compressed; **Blades** 3-10' long, 2-6 mm. wide usually conduplicate at the base, narrower at the base than the summit of the sheath, often pubescent above near the base, margins ciliate, some what rough near the apex; **Sheaths** loose, keeled, usually overlappin (said to be sometimes pilose, especially near the summit); **Ligule** 1-2 mm long, membranaceous, laciniate; **Racemes** commonly about 4-8, distan about half their own length, on a very slender flexuous axis, 1-2' long thick and densely-flowered, usually ascending and flexuous, rachis abou 2 mm. wide, green to purple, often a few long hairs along the margins an in the axils of racemes; **Spikelets** usually in pairs in two rows, 2-2.5 mm long, 1.3-1.5 mm. wide, obovate; **Glumes**, the first wanting, the secon glume and **Sterile Lemma** equal, often minutely apiculate, yellowish-gree or blotched with livid purple, 3-nerved; **Fruit** slightly smaller, 2-2.3 mm long, about 1.2 mm. wide, elliptic, very minutely striate-roughened.

Low ground along streams and ditches and in moist cultivated field Texas to Mexico. This grass is plentiful at and near Port Lavaca. Sprin and summer.

8. P. HARTWEGIANUM Fourn. (härt-wĕg-ĭ-ā′nŭm); *P. buckleyanu* Vasey.

Culms 2-4 commonly about 3.5 feet tall, solitary or in hard clump ascending from a decumbent base, occasionally creeping, branching fro the lower nodes, flattened; **Blades** 5-14' long, the upper much reduced, 4 mm. wide, the margins very scabrous, often with a few hairs at the bas the midnerve prominent on the lower surface; **Sheaths** overlapping, th ower rather papery, loose; **Ligule** membranaceous, 2-4 mm. long; **Racemes** ommonly 4-7 (3-13), ascending, distant about half their own length, on a lender glabrous axis, pale yellowish-green about 1-3′ long, with a few ong hairs in the axils, rachis 1-1.5 mm. wide, minutely scabrous; **Spikelets** n pairs, imbricate, 2.6-3 mm. long, 1.5 mm. wide, elliptic, apiculate, lightly plano-convex; **Glumes**, the first wanting, the second and **Sterile** ᴧemma equal, 3-5-nerved, softly pubescent, the lemma often sparsely so; ꜰruit about 2.5 mm. long, 1.3 mm. wide, elliptic, minutely striate-·oughened.

Wet prairies, alkaline meadows and along ditches, sometimes in ᴠater. Texas to Mexico. Spring and summer.

ᴑ. P. NOTATUM Flügge (nō-tā′tŭm); Baʜɪᴀ Gʀᴀss.

Culms 6-28′ tall, ascending from stout, woody and comparatively ʜort horizontal rhizomes, the roots on the rhizomes numerous and rather ᴑoarse, the rhizomes covered with the firm persistent bases of old sheaths, ɪmple, flattened, the nodes dark; **Blades** crowded at the base, 1-12′ long, ʜe upper reduced to a mere point, 3-8 mm. wide, flat or folded at the ᴐase, commonly ciliate toward the base; **Sheaths** overlapping, crowded at ʜe base, short, and reaching to a common height, flattened, keeled, ciliate ᴑward the summit, or rarely pubescent throughout; **Ligule** mem-ᴐranaceous, very short, with a dense row of hairs about 1 mm. long back ·f it; **Racemes** 2 rarely 3, subconjugate, commonly 1.5-3′ (1-5′) long, re-ᴄurved-ascending; **Rachis** flat, about 1 mm. wide, flexuous toward the ᴜmmit; **Spikelets** solitary, about 3.2 mm. (2.5-3.8) long, 2.3 mm. (2-2.8) ᴠide, ovate to obovate, green; **Glumes**, the first wanting, the second and ꜱterile **Lemma** equal, green, smooth and shining, firm, thin, 5-nerved, the ɴtermediate often obscure; **Fruit** 3 mm. (2.5-3.5) long, 2.2 mm. (1.8-2.5) ᴠide, oval, margins thick, the back very convex. The spikelets seem to ·ary much in size.

Sandy or clayey soil, open ground. Rare in the United States; intro-ᴅuced; author found it in cultivation at Angleton, Texas, and wild at °ort Arthur, Texas. Fall.

ᴑ. P. MINUS Fourn. (mī′nŭs).

Similar to P. notatum, commonly in denser mats, on the average ᴍaller, the culms rarely more than 12′ tall; **Blades** 2-6′ long; **Sheaths** ɪnd blades commonly ciliate, sometimes conspicuously so; **Racemes** more lender, fewer, rarely 3; **Spikelets** 2-2.5 mm. long, 1.5-1.6 mm. wide, oval, ᴇss shining than those of *P. notatum*. (No drawings.)

Open slopes and savannas from sea level to 5,000 feet, coast of Texas ᴑ Mexico. (Galveston Bay.)

ᴧ. P. ALMUM Chase (ăl′mŭm); Cᴏᴍʙs' Pᴀsᴘᴀʟᴜᴍ.

Culms 12-20′ tall, densely-tufted, ascending to spreading, simple, ꜰlattened, the leaves crowded toward the base; **Blades** 2-6′ long, the upper-ɴost reduced, 2-3 mm. wide, flat, rather firm, long-hirsute on the upper ᴜrface at the base, papillose-hirsute on the lower surface toward the tip, ᴜsually with a few hairs on the upper surface, the margins stiffly ciliate ᴑward the base; **Sheaths**, the lower overlapping, keeled; **Ligule** mem-ᴐranaceous, about 1.5 mm. long, pale; **Racemes** commonly 2 sometimes 3, ᴧpproximate, the common axis 5-20 mm. long, ascending, often somewhat ·ecurved, 2-4′ long; **Rachis** flexuous, 1 mm. wide, with a narrow pale-ᴠinged margin, the margins and midnerve scabrous above, the pedicels

minute, flat; **Spikelets** solitary, scarcely imbricate, 3 mm. long, 2 mm
wide, obovate-elliptic; **Glumes,** the first wanting, the second and **Sterile**
Lemma equal, 5-nerved, the lemma slightly concave and sometimes faintly
fluted; **Fruit** slightly smaller than the spikelet, smooth and shining.   This
grass was first collected by J. F. Combs of Beaumont, Texas.   It is an
excellent forage grass.   (Fine sandy and silty clay soil, near Beaumont
Texas.)   Late summer and fall.

12. P. SETACEUM Michx. (sē-tā′sē-ŭm).

Plants olivaceous; **Culms** 10-28′ tall, tufted, few to several culms
with numerous leafy shoots with long suberect leaves at the base, erect or
suberect or in very large tufts spreading, bearing 1-2 slender peduncles at the
middle and upper nodes; **Blades** 2-7′ commonly 4-5′ long, 2-6 mm. wide
rather firm, erect or nearly so, linear, *densely pilose* on both surfaces and
papillose-ciliate on the margin, the upper sometimes short-pubescent only
Sheaths pilose, the upper often nearly glabrous except on the margin
Ligule a minute membrane, with a dense row of hairs 2-3 mm. long back of
it; **Racemes** on very slender peduncles, solitary or sometimes 2, slender
arching commonly 2-3′ long, the rachis pubescent at the base, sometimes
obscurely so; **Spikelets** in pairs on slender flat pedicels, the lower of the
pair slightly winged at the base, crowded, 1.4-1.7 mm. long, 1-1.3 mm. wide
elliptic-obovate, turgid at maturity, pale; **Glumes** the first wanting, the
second and **Sterile Lemma** equal, barely covering the fruit at maturity, the
glume 3-nerved, the lemma 2-nerved, or the midnerve rarely developed, both
glabrous, or the glume especially more commonly minutely pubescent, with
minutely capitate hairs, often speckled with minute pale brown depressions
Fruit about the size and shape of the spikelet, smooth and shining.

Sandy soil, or rocky banks, mostly in open woods, Texas to Florida and
New York, Coastal Plain.   (Concan, Texas.)   Spring to fall.

13. P. DEBILE Michx. (dĕb′ĭl-ē) ; *P. villosissimum* Nash.

Culms 2-3 feet tall, tufted, weak, ascending or spreading, with numer
ous leafy shoots at base, bearing 1 or 2 slender peduncles at nodes; **Blades**
4-7′ long, about 5-7 mm. wide, acuminate, rounded at the base, papillose
ciliate on the margins, sometimes pilose along midvein below, and above
near the base, otherwise more or less short-pubescent; **Sheaths** shorter
than the internodes, villous at throat and margins, otherwise glabrous to
pubescent; **Ligule** membranaceous, very short, with dense rows of hairs
1-3 mm. long just back of it; **Racemes,** the terminal exserted, usually 2-3
sometimes 4, and axillary racemes mostly 1 or 2 sometimes 3, exserted or
sometimes included at the base, commonly less than 20 mm. distant, 1.5
2.5′ long; **Spikelets** solitary, 1.5-1.8 mm. long, 1.2 mm. wide, elliptic to
slightly obovate, in pairs on short subequal pedicels, the lower slightly
winged at base, rachis winged; **Glumes,** the first wanting, the second and
Sterile Lemma equal, the glume 3-nerved, pubescent with minutely capitate
hairs, the lemma 2-nerved, the midnerve usually not developed, glabrous
to sparsely-pubescent with hairs also capitate, commonly speckled with
small brown spots, often numerous; **Fruit** nearly as long and as wide as
the spikelet, smooth and shining.   *P. setaceum* and *P. debile,* closely related
plants, are both variable and appear to intergrade.   Some of the specimens
from Texas are less villous than usual.

Dry sandy soil, barren and flat woods.   Texas to Mexico, Florida
New York.   Spring and summer.

14. P. STRAMINEUM Nash (strā-mǐn′ē-ŭm) ; *P. bushii* Nash.

Plants yellowish-green; **Culms** 1.5-3.5 feet tall, few to several culms to a tuft, ascending or spreading, slender, flattened, more or less purplish toward the base, nodes appressed-pubescent, especially the lower ones, or glabrous; **Blades** 1-8′ rarely 12′ long, the upper short, 4-13 mm. rarely 20 mm. wide, flat, rounded at the base, puberulent on both surfaces, rarely obscurely so, sparsely-pilose, or conspicuously so on the upper surface, the long hairs intermixed with the short ones, or the lower surface nearly or quite glabrous except for a few hairs along the midrib, the margins commonly papillose-ciliate; **Sheaths** shorter than or about as long as the internodes, flattened, rather broad, pubescent along the margins, especially toward the summit, villous at the throat and sometimes on the collar, or the lower pubescent or puberulent; **Ligule** membranaceous, about 1 mm. long, the white hairs back of it about 2-3 mm. long; **Racemes** 2-3 rarely 4-6, when 3 the terminal reduced, 2.5-5.5′ long, slender, arching, the terminal exserted on a slender peduncle, the axillary on short peduncles, wholly or partly included in the sheaths, or one partly included and the other exserted, often borne in the basal sheaths; **Rachis** about 1 mm. wide, slightly winged, with a few long hairs at the base, the spikelets in pairs, crowded or relatively loose on short pedicels; **Spikelets** 1.9-2.2 mm. long, 1.5-1.9 mm. wide, suborbicular, pale or whitish; **Glumes,** the first wanting (sometimes present on an occasional plant), the second and **Sterile Lemma** about equal, at maturity the summit of the fruit exposed making the glume seem shorter, both 3-nerved, the midnerve of the lemma often suppressed, the glume from sparsely to rather densely-pubescent with minutely capitate hairs, or glabrous, the sterile lemma glabrous or sparsely-pubescent; **Fruit** about the size and shape of the spikelet, pale, shining.

The spikelets seem to vary much as to size and shape; those of the axillary racemes are *cleistogamous.*

Sandy, often in very sandy, soil, in open ground or open woods, Texas to Florida, north to Oklahoma and Vermont; Arizona and northwestern Mexico. Summer and fall.

15. P. PUBESCENS Muhl. (pū-bĕs′ĕns) ; *P. muhlenbergii* Nash.

Plants rather yellowish-green to olivaceous; **Culms** 22-36′ tall, erect or ascending to spreading, in dense tufts, slender, strongly compressed; **Blades** commonly 3-9′ sometimes 12′ long, 2-10 mm. rarely 15 mm. wide, flat, mostly linear, slightly narrowed to the base, scarcely wider than the sheath, or the upper rounded at the base, from sparsely to conspicuously pilose on both surfaces, sometimes minutely puberulent beneath the long hairs on the upper surface; **Sheaths** keeled, pilose toward the summit, at least on the keel and along the margins; **Ligule** a minute membrane with a dense row of white hairs 3-4 mm. long back of it; **Racemes** 1-3, more commonly solitary, mostly arching, 1.5-6′ rarely 7′ long, the peduncles slender, flat, finally elongate, often pilose toward the summit, the axillary 1 or 2 from upper and middle nodes; **Rachis** long-pilose at the base, with spikelets crowded, in pairs, on short pedicels, the lower often winged at the base; **Spikelets** 1.9-2.1 mm. long, 1.7-1.9 mm. wide, suborbicular to broadly obovate; **Glumes,** the first wanting, the second and **Sterile Lemma** subequal, 3-nerved, or the glume rarely 4-5-nerved, or the midnerve of the lemma suppressed, glabrous, the glume rarely sparsely-pubescent; **Fruit** about the size and shape of the spikelet.

The species varies in the amount of pubescence. The spikelets are more uniform in shape and size than in most species of this group.

Dry or moist open ground or open woods, more common in sandy regions, Texas to Florida, north to Oklahoma, Michigan and Vermont. Summer and fall.

16. P. CILIATIFOLIUM Michx. (sĭl-ĭ-ăt-ĭ-fō'lĭ-ŭm). (Includes *P. eggertii* Nash and *P. epile* Nash.)

Culms 16-26′ tall, tufted, erect or spreading, dark-brown or purplish toward the base, slender, the nodes glabrous; **Blades** ascending or spreading, 2-8′ rarely 18′ long, 7-12 mm. rarely 25 mm. wide, flat, rounded to subcordate at the base, or narrowed to the width of the sheath, *typically strongly ciliate*, or papillose-ciliate, along the minutely undulate cartilaginous margins, or sometimes ciliate at the base only, otherwise glabrous, or pilose along the midnerve or minutely pubescent toward the apex, rarely throughout; **Sheaths,** the upper shorter than the internodes, keeled, glabrous or hirsute at the throat, glabrous or sparsely-hirsute on the collar, glabrous or ciliate along the margins, or the lower from puberulent to appressed-pubescent; **Ligule** membranaceous, short, the hairs back of it 1-3 mm. long, commonly produced into an erect auricle 0.5-1 mm. long, on one or both margins; **Racemes** 1-3 rarely 4, the terminal 1-3 peduncles, one long-exserted, the others shorter, the axillary short-exserted or included at the base, slender, the racemes arching, slender, 1.5-4′ commonly 3-4′ long, the slender rachis with a tuft of hairs at the base; **Spikelets** crowded, in pairs, 1.9-2.1 mm. long, 1.5-1.9 mm. wide, elliptic-obovate or suborbicular, strongly plano-convex; **Glumes,** the first wanting, the second slightly shorter than the **sterile lemma,** at maturity exposing the fruit, both 3-nerved, or the midnerve of the lemma suppressed, glabrous, or especially the glume minutely pubescent with obscurely capitate hairs, commonly minutely speckled; **Fruit** about the size and shape of the spikelet, pale, smooth and shining.

This is a polymorphic species. Study of a great amount of material has made it impossible to recognize as distinct the groups segregated by Nash. Pubescence on foliage and spikelets varies in a single plant. Rather stout, somewhat paler seacoast plants, with firmer blades scarcely ciliate, are the form described as *P. eggertii.*

Open ground and woods, mostly sandy land, Texas to Florida, north to New Jersey and Arkansas. (Bellville, Texas.) Spring-fall.

17. P. RIGIDIFOLIUM Nash (rĭj-ĭ-dĭ-fō'lĭ-ŭm).

Culms 10-30′ tall, in tufts, from short scaly rhizomes, slender, relatively stiff, often purplish, erect or somewhat spreading; **Blades** 3-11′ commonly 4-6′ long, 2-5 mm. rarely 8 mm. wide, usually not wider at the base than the summit of the sheath, flat, firm, erect or ascending, linear, the scabrous margins usually sparsely-ciliate toward the base, otherwise glabrous or minutely puberulent on both surfaces; **Sheaths** short and overlapping, the lower usually softly grayish-pubescent, the upper pubescent along the margins, otherwise glabrous; **Ligule** a minute membrane with a dense row of hairs 3-4 mm. long back of it; **Racemes** on very slender peduncles, solitary or 2, straight or arching, 3-6′ long, the **Rachis** with a few long hairs at the base; **Spikelets** in pairs on minute nearly glabrous pedicels, crowded, 2-2.5 mm. commonly 2.2-2.4 mm. long, 1.5-1.8 mm. wide, obovate-elliptic, pale or purplish; **Glumes,** the first wanting, the second and **Sterile Lemma** subequal, scarcely covering the

uit at maturity, 3-nerved, or the glume sometimes 5-nerved, both
labrous or the glume obscurely-pubescent, sometimes minutely speckled;
ruit about the size and shape of the spikelet, pale, shining.

This species is distinguished by its stiff habit and large spikelets.

Sand barrens and high pine lands, Texas to Florida. (Waller county,
exas.) Spring.

8. P. UNISPICATUM (Scribn. & Merr.) Nash (ū-nĭ-spī-kā'tŭm).

Plants rather pale-green, with horizontal scaly rhizomes; **Culms** 20-
6' tall, solitary or a few together, simple or with a single erect leafy
ranch from the lower nodes, terete to subcompressed; **Blades** 4-12' long,
-15 mm. wide, rather stiff, suberect to spreading, the uppermost reduced,
ounded at the base, attenuate at the apex, stiffly papillose-ciliate on the
nargins, very sparsely or rarely rather copiously papillose-hirsute on both
urfaces to scaberulous only, the midnerve deeply impressed, the large
ells of the upper epidermis easily visible under a lens; **Sheaths** mostly
verlapping, papillose-hirsute along the margins, otherwise very sparsely
o to glabrous, commonly with a narrow lacerate membranaceous fringe
n the collar; **Ligule** membranaceous, 2-3 mm. long, with a ring of long
airs back of it; **Racemes** 1 or 2, usually 1, rather stiffly suberect to
lightly arcuate, 2.5-8' long, the nearly straight rachis sometimes with a
ew long stiff hairs at base, otherwise glabrous, the peduncles slender,
ommonly 2 from the upper sheath, the second one often wholly or partly
ncluded (no axillary ones found in other sheaths); **Spikelets** in pairs,
ather crowded, 3-3.5 mm. long (mostly 3.2), about 1.6 mm. wide, elliptic,
omewhat unsymmetrical, especially the lower of the pair, pale, glabrous;
Glumes, the first commonly minute and nerveless on the primary spikelet,
1-nerved, keeled, acuminate and half to three-fourths as long as the spikelet on the secondary, but exceedingly variable in both, sometimes obsolete;
Second and **Sterile Lemma** 5-nerved (occasionally 7-nerved), rather firm
in texture, the glume especially in the lower spikelet a little shorter than
the sterile lemma, the lemma inclosing a palea of nearly equal length,
hyaline in the middle and firm on the 2 keels, and often a well developed
staminate flower, rarely a perfect but infertile one; **Fruit** about 2.8 mm.
long, pale, minutely papillose-striate.

In a single raceme the glumes vary from obsolete to more than half
the length of the spikelet on the primary, and from minute and nerveless
to three-fourths as long as spikelet on the secondary.

Meadows, savannas, open slopes and banks, southern Texas, south
through Mexico. (Kingsville, Texas.)

19. P. MONOSTACHYUM Vasey (mō-nō-stăk'ĭ-ŭm); *P. solitarium* Nash.

Culms 1.5-4 feet tall, with stout horizontal scaly rootstocks, single or
a few culms to a tuft, in open or dense colonies, simple, erect, subterete,
somewhat rigid; **Blades** 12-28' long, the upper sometimes shorter, often
equaling or exceeding the racemes, 1.5-2 mm. wide when folded, the margins
slightly open below and grown together above, erect at the base, the
junction with the sheath obscure, rigid, long-acuminate, villous on upper
surface close to ligule; **Sheaths** longer than or equal to the internodes,
often villous on the slightly auricled summit and margins; **Ligule** membranaceous, about 2 mm. long; **Peduncles** slender, elongate, mostly 1
sometimes 2, the secondary one from the uppermost sheath only, none
inclosed; **Racemes** 1-3, in rather dry sandy situations mostly with 1, and in
rather low moist situations mostly with 2, in either case rarely 3, the lower

distant 20-25 mm., 4-8′ long, slightly arcuate, stiffly erect or ascending the rather slender nearly straight rachis rounded on the back, about 1 mm wide, ciliate on the winged margins, the spikelets in two rows, mostly in pairs, or solitary toward the summit, those in linear rank almost touching each other, on short nearly equal pubescent pedicels; **Spikelets** 3-3.5 mm long, 1.5 mm. wide, subobovate-elliptic, pale, glabrous; **Glumes,** the firs wanting, or sometimes present on the primary spikelet, from minute t two-thirds the length of the spikelet, triangular, the second equal o nearly equal to the fruit, 3-5-nerved; **Sterile Lemma** 3-nerved, equal t the fruit; **Fruit** 2.5-3 mm. long, elliptic, obtuse, pale, minutely papillose striate.

Moist places or flat woods or coastal dunes; Texas to Florida (Texarkana; Harris, Bee, Galveston and Nueces counties.) Fall.

20. P. LANGEI (Fourn.) Nash (lăng′ē-ī).

Plants olivaceous; **Culms** 1-3 feet tall, in small or large tufts, decum bent at the base, ascending, slender, leafy, usually simple, or occasionall; with a single leafy branch, flattened; **Blades** 3-16′ long, 6-15 mm. wide thin, flat, narrowed toward the base or the upper rounder at the base margins scabrous, commonly nearly glabrous, or appressed papillose pubescent on the upper surface with a few long hairs toward the base, o sparsely-pubescent below; **Sheaths** flattened, pubescent along the margin and often on the collar, otherwise glabrous to sparsely papillose-pubescent **Ligule** membranaceous, about 1 mm. long; **Racemes** 2-5, sometimes a many as 7, the slender peduncles 1-3, exserted or partly included from th upper sheaths, the axillary ones usually appearing late and often born in the middle sheaths, partly or wholly included, the racemes flexuou and arched, ascending to spreading, 1.5-4′ long, usually rather distant o a slender channeled axis 3-5′ long, the rachis usually with a few lon; hairs at the base; **Spikelets** in pairs 2-2.6 mm. (2-2.8) long, 1.3-1.4 mm wide, elliptic-obovate, olive-green turning brown at maturity; **Glumes,** th first minute on the primary spikelet, with a ciliate brownish margin, o the secondary usually acuminate and one-fourth to one-third as long a the spikelet, or sometimes alike on both spikelets, the second glume an **Sterile Lemma** 5-nerved, pubescent and more or less speckled with brow glandular spots, the glume slightly shorter than the sterile lemma; **Frui** 2.1-2.3 mm. long, pale, minutely papillose-striate, the summit exposed a maturity.

Moist woods and shaded banks, sometimes in open ground; low altitudes, Texas to Florida. (San Antonio.)

21. P. CONJUGATUM Bergius (kŏn-jū-gā′tŭm) ; Sour-grass.

Plants extensively creeping with long leafy stolons, the flowering culms suberect to ascending, frequently purplish below, commonly form ing a dense cover or colony of tangled culms and stolons; **Culms** 6 fee long or less, rooting at the nodes, the internodes less than an inch to si> inches long, flattened, wiry, nodes glabrous or pubescent, those of th stolons usually conspicuously pilose, the flowering culms commonly 8-24 tall, sometimes taller, simple or sparingly branching; **Blades** 1.5-8′ mostl 3-5′ long, 5-12 mm. wide, those of the stolons short, spreading, slightl narrowed to the base, thin, the white margins scabrous or short-ciliate usually a tuft of rather long stiff hairs at the base close to the ligule otherwise glabrous to sparsely papillose-pubescent on the upper or both surfaces; **Sheaths** usually shorter than the internodes, loose, flattened

1ose of the stolons short and broad, often ciliate toward the summit, commonly with a ring of short or long hairs on the collar; **Ligule** membranaceous, 1-1.5 mm. long; **Racemes** 2, paired or nearly so, sometimes with a third below, rarely axillary, soon turning yellow, widely divaricate, ften curved, slender, 1.5-6′ commonly 3-5′ long; **Rachis** narrowly winged, bout 0.8 mm. wide, densely-pubescent at the base, the hairs rather long nd soft, the spikelets solitary, imbricate, those of each row about 1 mm. istant; **Spikelets** about 1.5 mm. (1.4-1.8) long, 1-1.2 mm. wide, on short lat pedicels, flattened, concavo-convex, ovate, subacute to abruptly piculate; **Glumes**, the first wanting, the second and **Sterile Lemma** equal, ery thin, closely appressed to the fruit, the two nerves marginal, the nidnerves suppressed, the nerves of the glume papillose-ciliate with long ax hairs forming a delicately fringed margin, otherwise glabrous; **Fruit** bout 1.5 mm. long, pale, not strongly indurate.

A tropical weed growing in cultivated and waste ground along litches and roadsides, extending into the most southern parts of the Jnited States, Texas to Florida. (Brownsville, Texas.) Spring and summer.

22. **P. DILATATUM** Poir. (dī-lå-tā′tŭm); DALLIS GRASS, PASPALUM GRASS.

Culms 1-4 feet tall, erect, ascending, or widely spreading from a decumbent base, arising from short knotted rhizomes, rather flattened, nodes swollen, usually dark, the lower sometimes sparsely-pubescent, often bearing leafy shoots at or near the base; **Blades** usually 4-6′ long (uppermost sometimes about 1.5′ the lower sometimes as much as 12′ long), 3-15 mm. wide, flat, narrowed and rounded at the base, midrib large, tufts of long and rather stiff hairs on upper surface near the base, the margins scabrous and ciliate near the base; **Sheaths** shorter than the internodes in the larger plants and longer in the smaller ones, flattened, mostly glabrous above, the lower with rather stiff appressed, short or long, hairs; **Ligule** membranaceous, 1-5 mm. long; **Panicle** erect or nodding, commonly 3-6 (2-11) ascending or drooping racemes, commonly 2-4.5′ long, usually distant 1-2.5′, the rachis about 1.4 mm. wide, with hairs as much as 10 mm. long in the axils; **Spikelets** in two rows, in pairs, with pedicels 1-2 mm. long, overlapping, making it seem to have four rows, 3-3.5 mm. long, 2 mm. wide, ovate, pointed, depressed plano-convex; **Glumes**, the first wanting, the second slightly longer than the sterile lemma, the second glume and sterile lemma pointed beyond the fruit, 5-9-nerved, sparsely covered with silky hairs on the surface, the glume in addition bearing on the marginal internerves a fringe of long white silky hairs, from rather scant to copious and woolly; the **Sterile Lemma** often sparingly ciliate with short hairs; **Fruit** about 2.5 mm. long, broadly elliptic, minutely papillose-striate.

In low ground, from rather dry prairies to marshy meadows, Texas and Arkansas to Florida and Tennessee, north to New Jersey. Spring-fall.

23. **P. URVILLEI** Steud. (ûr-vĭl′ē-ī); *P. vaseyana* Scribn.; *P. virgatum* var. *pubiflorum* Vasey; *P. larranagae* Arech.; VASEY GRASS.

Culms usually 2-4 feet sometimes as much as six feet tall, few to many culms to a tuft, purplish below, stout, erect, simple or branching from middle down, somewhat flattened, nodes dark, glabrous; **Blades** 3-15′ long, sometimes longer, 3-14 mm. wide, the uppermost reduced, flat, ascending, somewhat narrowed from middle down, upper surface long-pilose at the very base, margins slightly scabrous; **Sheaths** keeled toward

the summit, about as long as the internodes, the lower loose, the lower
most sheaths often hirsute, margin often ciliate; **Ligule** usually 3-5 mm
long, membranaceous; **Panicle** 4-9′ long, sometimes longer, erect o
slightly nodding with usually about 10-15 (6-25) slender, flexuous, ascend
ing or slightly nodding racemes, usually 2-3′ long, upper graduall
shorter, the common axis glabrous and angled; **Rachis** flat, winged, nearl
1 mm. wide, edges slightly scabrous, few long hairs at the base, spikele
bearing nearly to the base, one with pedicel about as long as spikelet an
the other shorter, in pairs appearing in four rows; **Spikelets** excluding th
hairs about 2.5 mm. (2-3) long, about 1.5 mm. wide, ovate, abruptl
pointed, depressed plano-convex; **Glumes**, the first wanting, the secon
and **Sterile Lemma** 3-nerved, about equal, extending slightly beyond th
fruit, acute, both with many long silky white hairs along the margins, th
Glume sparsely clothed throughout with appressed silky hairs, the **Steril**
Lemma glabrous or nearly so in the middle, both often with brownis
glands at the base of the hairs; **Fruit** about 1.9 mm. long, elliptic.

Mostly in rather moist soil, in the drier portions of Texas, alon
ditches and streams, in southeastern portion in open fields.   Texas t
Florida and North Carolina, and California.   Spring to fall.

24. P. LAEVE Michx. (lē′vē); *P. angustifolium* Le Conte; *P. austral*
Nash.

Culms 16-40′ tall, erect or ascending, tufted, commonly with nume
ous erect or ascending leafy shoots at the base, simple or rarely wit
concealed or short-exserted raceme-bearing branches in the lower sheath
compressed; **Blades** 2-12′ long, rarely longer, 3-10 mm. rarely 12 mm
wide, the uppermost reduced, usually folded at the base, flat or folde
above, rather firm, erect or nearly so, sometimes glaucous, glabrous t
ciliate or sparsely-pilose on the upper surface, or sometimes toward th
base beneath; **Sheaths** compressed-keeled, usually crowded at the base
glabrous or pilose on the margins or sometimes on the back toward th
summit; **Ligule** brown, 2-3 mm. long; **Racemes** 2-4 commonly 3-4 rarel
6-8, spreading or ascending, 1-4′ long, rarely longer, the common axi
glabrous; **Rachis** about 1 mm. wide, with a tuft of long hairs at the base
Spikelets not crowded, 2.5-3 mm. long, 2-2.5 mm. wide, broadly oval t
suborbicular; **Glumes**, the first wanting, the second and **Sterile Lemm**
equal, toward maturity the tip of the fruit usually exposed, 5-nerved, th
middle of the lemma commonly russet-brownish; **Fruit** nearly the size an
form of the spikelet.

Forms of this exceedingly variable species have been regarded as dis
tinct species or varieties.   The forms have been differentiated as follows
plants with elongated blades and racemes, the blades glabrous or pilose nea
the margins, as *P. angustifolium;* those with the blades (usually short
sparsely-pilose above and sheaths pilose on the margins, as *P. australe;* an
those with short, glabrous leaves mostly crowded toward the base, a
P. laeve proper.   If we try to segregate the specimens into these groups
however, the intermediate specimens are more numerous than those referabl
to definite forms, and the material so segregated appears scarcely mor
homogeneous than does the intermediate material.

Fields, meadows, open woods and waste ground, especially common i
red clay soil, eastern Texas to Florida, north to New Jersey an
Pennsylvania.   (Industry, Beckville, Texarkana, Hempstead.)   Spring
fall.

25. P. LONGIPILUM Nash (lŏn-jĭ-pī'lŭm) ; *P. laeve* var. *pilosum* Scribn.; *P. plenipilum* Nash.

Similar to P. laeve, the **Culms** usually ascending or spreading, the leafy shoots at base mostly fewer, a raceme-bearing branch often borne (usually hidden) in next to the lowest sheath ; **Blades** usually flat, pilose on both surfaces, or glabrous or nearly so beneath, commonly less erect than in *P. laeve;* **Sheaths** pilose with long hairs, often conspicuously so, but sometimes very sparsely so ; **Racemes** 2-6 commonly 2-3, on the average more lax and spreading than in *P. laeve;* **Spikelets** 2.5-2.8 mm. long, rarely to 3 mm. long, 2-2.4 mm. wide ; **Fruit** usually covered at maturity, the sterile lemma often tinged with russet.

This species is fairly distinct from *P. laeve,* but a few specimens grade into the form represented by the type *P. australe.* A few others, with spikelets 2.8-3 mm. long, are scarcely distinguishable from *P. circulare,* but the spikelets are less rounded and the glumes and sterile lemma rather thicker.

Damp mostly sandy soil, savannas, open woods and wet pine barrens, east Texas to Florida, north to Tennessee and New York. (Waller county, Texas.) Summer.

26. P. CIRCULARE Nash (sẽr-kū-lā'rē).

Culms 2-3 rarely 4 feet tall, densely-tufted, usually with conspicuous erect or ascending leafy shoots at the base, compressed, often with branches bearing one leaf and a single raceme more or less concealed in the middle sheaths, rarely with a longer branch from a lower node ; **Blades** 2-12′ rarely 18′ long, 3-12 mm. wide, the uppermost short, flat, erect or suberect, rather thin, scarcely narrowed toward the base, often equaling or exceeding the inflorescence, sometimes reaching only to the base, or the inflorescence short-exserted, glabrous to sparsely-pilose on the upper surface, at least toward the base, or sometimes toward the base on the under surface ; **Sheaths** longer than the internodes, elongated and crowded at the base, flattened, thin, loose, the upper glabrous or nearly so, the lower from sparsely to densely-pilose or glabrous ; **Ligule** membranaceous, brown, 2-3 mm. long ; **Racemes** 2-7 commonly 3-4, mostly *suberect,* or the lower spreading, 2-5.5′ long, the common axis slender, as much as 2′ distant, glabrous ; **Rachis** about 1 mm. wide, long-pilose at the base ; **Spikelets** approximate, 2.8-3.2 mm. long, nearly orbicular ; **Glumes,** the first wanting, the second and **Sterile Lemma** equal, covering the fruit, 5-nerved, rather thin, the cells showing more plainly than in *P. laeve* and *P. longipilum,* the lemma often with an oval brownish spot ; **Fruit** nearly the size and shape of the spikelet.

Fields and meadows and open waste ground, east Texas, Kansas, Mississippi, North Carolina to Connecticut. (Low ground near Hempstead.) Summer-fall.

27. P. PRAECOX Walt. (prē'kŏks).

Culms 20-40′ tall, in small tufts of 1 rarely 2 or 3 flowering culms and, in spring, 1-to-several leafy shoots arising from short scaly rhizomes, these shoots flowering in the late summer and autumn producing few to several short rhizomes with loose overlapping scales, slender, erect, simple, compressed ; **Blades** 4-12′ commonly 6-10′ long, 3-7 mm. wide, the uppermost reduced, folded at the base, flat above, rather firm, ascending, glabrous or sometimes pilose on the upper surface toward the base ; **Sheaths,** the lower overlapping, compressed-keeled, commonly purplish, glabrous, or the lower, especially of the young shoots, silky villous, rarely the others pilose at the summit; **Ligule** brown, 3 mm. long; **Racemes** 2-8 commonly 4-6, narrowly ascending to arcuate-spreading, 20-70 mm. long, the common axis very slender; **Rachis** about 1.5 mm. wide, purplish, pilose at the narrowed base; **Spikelets** solitary or in pairs, commonly both in the same raceme, usually crowded, strongly flattened, 2.2-2.8 mm. long, 2.2-3 mm. wide, suborbicular, glabrous, yellowish-green or purple-tinged; **Glumes,** the first wanting, the second and **Sterile Lemma** equal, 5-nerved (lateral nerve obscure), thin and fragile, under a lens minutely papillose-striate; **Fruit** nearly the size and form of the spikelet, under a lens strongly papillose.

Wet pine barrens, borders of cypress swamps, moist places in flatwoods and wet savannas in the coastal plain, east Texas along the Gulf to Florida, north to North Carolina. (Hempstead.) Spring-fall.

28. P. LENTIFERUM Lam. (lĕn-tĭf'ē-rŭm) ; *P. tardum* Nash; *P. kearneyi* Nash.

Culms erect, as much as 5 feet tall, of the same habit as *P. praecox* but the culms less slender, sometimes robust, the rhizomes on the average more numerous; **Blades** 6-20′ long, 3-10 mm. wide, the uppermost reduced, firm, flat above or folded throughout, pilose, often conspicuously so, on both surfaces, or glabrous beneath, occasionally glabrate on the upper surface except at the base; **Sheaths** usually not so strongly keeled as in *P. praecox,* from densely silky-villous, especially the lower ones, to glabrate; **Ligule** brown, about 3 mm. long; **Racemes** 2-9 commonly 4 or 5, usually spreading at maturity, 1-4′ long; **Rachis** 1.5-1.7 mm. wide, pilose at the narrowed base; **Spikelets** solitary, or more commonly in pairs, usually crowded, 2.7-3.4 mm. long, broadly oval to orbicular, the glume and lemma in color, texture and nerving like those of *P. praecox.*

This variable species intergrades with *P. praecox,* from which it is here delimited by the more robust culms, pilose foliage and larger spikelets, but these three characters are not always found in the same specimens.

Moist pine barrens, borders of flatwoods and cypress swamps, on the coastal plain, Texas, along the Gulf to Florida and north to North Carolina. (Houston.) Summer.

29. P. FLORIDANUM Michx. (flō-rĭ-dā'nŭm).

Culms 2.5-5 rarely 6 feet tall, erect, solitary or a few culms to a tuft, usually stout, simple, compressed, from short stout scaly rootstocks; **Blades** mostly ascending, or spreading at the summit, firm, 5-20′ long, the upper reduced, 4-10 mm. wide, usually folded at the base and flat above, sometimes folded or subinvolute throughout, rough, pilose to densely-hirsute on the upper surface like the sheaths, and usually hirsute or nearly glabrous beneath, more or less papillose; **Sheaths** keeled, overlapping especially below, or the upper shorter than the internodes, strongly nerved, rough, from nearly to quite glabrous to densely rather harshly tawny-hirsute, more or less papillose; **Ligule** firm, 2-3 mm. long; **Racemes** commonly 2-4 rarely solitary or 5 or 6, 1.5-5′ long, suberect or ascending, or the heavy racemes slightly nodding, the common axis slender; **Rachis** usually strongly zigzag, 1-1.5 mm. wide, scabrous, pilose at the base, and sometimes sparsely long-ciliate throughout; **Spikelets** in pairs (one of the pair sometimes rudimentary), crowded, 3.6-4 mm. long, 2.8-3.1 mm. wide, commonly 4 mm. long and 3 mm. wide, oval, pale; **Glumes,** the first wanting, the second and **Sterile Lemma** equal, scarcely covering the fruit at maturity, firm and papery, slightly inflated, irregularly wrinkled, 5-

erved; **Fruit** about 3-3.5 mm. long, 2.5 mm. wide, oval to slightly obovate,
ght brown, minutely papillose-striate.

Low moist sandy land, pine woods, flat woods and low prairies, in
ne coastal plain from Texas to Florida and north to Virginia. (Near
roveton, Fort Worth to Gonzales and east.) Summer and fall.

9a. P. FLORIDANUM var. GLABRATUM Engelm. (glā-brā'tŭm) ;
P. glabratum (Engelm.) Mohr.

Culms 2-3.5 feet tall, solitary or a few culms together, leafy through-
ut, erect or ascending from a decumbent base, the rootstocks stout and
ather short, flattened, sometimes branched and with racemes included or
lightly exserted from one of the middle sheaths; **Blades** 5-9' long, the
pper reduced, 10-12 mm. wide, mostly flat, margins rough, slightly
ough toward the apex, sparsely-hirsute above at the base, otherwise
labrous; **Sheaths** about as long as the internodes, mostly shorter,
attened, smooth, the short lowermost sheaths sometimes pilose, otherwise
labrous; **Ligule** membranaceous, truncate, about 2 mm. long; **Racemes**
nick, 1-5 commonly 2-3, distant mostly 1.5-2', usually 3-4' (3-5.5') long,
ne slender common axis 2-4' long, erect or ascending, or sometimes
lightly nodding, the rachis about 1.5 mm. wide, zigzag, spikelets single
r mostly in pairs, in two rows, one of the pairs sometimes rudimentary,
ometimes an axillary raceme is hidden or slightly exserted in one of the
iddle sheaths; **Spikelets** 3.5-5 mm. long, about 3 mm. wide, almost oval,
ale; **Glumes,** the first wanting, the **Second** and the **Sterile Lemma**
-nerved, about equal, slightly longer than the fruit, obtuse, slightly in-
ated and wrinkled; **Fruit** about 3.2-3.5 mm. long, about 2.6 mm. wide,
val, light-brown, minutely papillose-striate.

Brackish marshes and low sandy land; Texas to Florida and north
 New Jersey and Kansas. Summer and fall.

0. P. VIRGATUM L. (vĕr-gā'tŭm).

Culms 3-5 feet tall, in large dense clumps, robust, purplish below,
mple, erect or the outer curved at the base, subcompressed; **Blades** 12-
0' long, 10-25 mm. rarely 30 mm. wide, the uppermost much reduced, flat,
scending-recurved, slightly rounded at the base, long-hirsute at the very
ase on the upper surface, and often on the margins toward the base, the
argins surrulate; **Sheaths** overlapping, elongate, usually papillose-
irsute along the margins and on the collar, occasionally on the keel to-
ard the summit, rarely pilose throughout, the lower spongy and
icculent, reticulate in drying; **Ligule** 1.5-2 mm. long; **Panicle** slightly
odding, 5-16' commonly 6-10' long, 3-29 commonly 10-16 ascending to
rooping thick racemes, the lower 2-6', rarely 8' long, the upper gradually
horter, the common axis angled, occasionally scabrous on the angles;
achis purplish, 1-1.5 mm. wide, with copious long hairs at the base, the
argins very scabrous and commonly with scattered long quill-like hairs;
pikelets in pairs on angled pedicels, crowded, 2.2 mm. rarely 3 mm. long,
.8-2.3 mm. wide, obovate, grayish, drying yellowish to rusty or purplish-
rown; **Glumes,** the first wanting, the second and **Sterile Lemma** equal,
ather loose, 5-nerved, one or both often minutely apiculate, the glume
ubescent with silky hairs along the margins, at least toward the summit,
ne sterile palea occasionally developed; **Fruit** 2-2.2 mm. long, chestnut-
rown at maturity, papillose-striate.

Most of the specimens from continental North America have spikelets
.5-3 mm. long, commonly puberulent to finely pubescent.

Open mostly moist or swampy ground, southern Texas, Mexico, and the West Indies to Brazil, at rather low altitudes. (Brownsville.)

31. P. PLICATULUM Michx. (plī-kăt'ū-lŭm).

Culms 1.5-3 feet tall, tufted with numerous leafy shoots at the base ascending, or erect from a slightly decumbent base, simple or branched below, the lower nodes sometimes appressed-pubescent; **Blades** 3-18' long 3-8 mm. wide, folded at base, flat or folded above, the uppermost much reduced, often papillose-pilose on upper surface toward the base, some times hirsute on both surfaces, margins scabrous; **Sheaths** flattened shorter than the internodes, sometimes longer, the lower crowded, rather papery, glabrous or papillose-pilose along the margins and keel or rarely hirsute throughout; **Ligule** membranaceous, brown, 2-3 mm. long **Racemes** commonly 3-8 (2-19), 1-4' long, spreading, the common axis slender, rachis about 1 mm. wide, sparingly pilose at the base; **Spikelet** about 2.5 mm. (2.1-3) long, 1.4-2 mm. wide, in pairs (one of the pairs sometimes undeveloped), obovate-oval, turning brown at maturity **Glumes,** the first wanting, the second and **Sterile Lemma** equal, thin, 5 nerved, glabrous or the glume often appressed-pubescent, the lemma at maturity with short transverse wrinkles next to the slightly raised margins, rarely sparsely appressed-pubescent; **Fruit** nearly as large and same shape as spikelet, dark-brown and shining.

Open ground or wet wood borders mostly in moist sandy or clay soil Texas east to Georgia and Florida. Spring and fall.

32. P. SCROBICULATUM L. (skrō-bĭk-ū-lā'tŭm).

Annual; glabrous as a whole; **Culms** 1.5-3 feet tall, rather succulent branching, ascending; **Blades** 6-15' long, 5-12 mm. wide, flat; **Sheaths** flattened, often overlapping; **Ligule** membranaceous, brown, about 2 mm long; **Racemes** mostly 3-5, 2-3.5' long, ascending, the rachis 2-3 mm. wide firm; **Spikelets** solitary, crowded, 3 mm. long, obovate, turgid; **Glume** and **Sterile Lemma** equal, 7-nerved, the latter loose and more or less wrinkled (scrobiculate). (No drawings.)

Cultivated in Asia and Africa, sparingly introduced in Texas (Abilene); also ballast, Camden, N. J.

33. P. BIFIDUM (Bertol.) Nash (bī'fĭ-dŭm); erroneously referred to *P. racemosum* Lam. by Beal.

Culms 1.5-4 feet tall, forming small colonies, from numerous short rhizomes, erect, slender, simple, compressed, nodes glabrous or minutely pubescent; **Blades** 4-20' long, 3-14 mm. wide, the upper commonly obsolete flat, ascending, tapering to a base as narrow as the summit of the sheath the junction obscure, from conspicuously villous on both surfaces to glabrous except the upper surface toward the base; **Sheaths** narrow, the lower commonly free from the culm, from villous to nearly glabrous **Ligule** about 2 mm. long; **Racemes** 2-6 rarely 8 commonly 3 or 4, at first erect, spreading toward maturity, 1.5-6' long, distant on a slender flat rachis; **Rachis** very slender, subflexuous, with copious long hairs at the base; **Spikelets** in pairs, *distant to irregularly approximate* on slender stiff angled pedicels, elliptic-obovate, turgidly *biconvex* 3.3-4 mm. long, 2.2-2.5 mm. wide, olivaceous to russet-brown and commonly blotched with purple umes, the first developed into a minute thin scale or wanting in the same ceme (rarely wholly wanting in an entire inflorescence), second shorter an the fruit, *strongly 7-nerved*; **Sterile Lemma** barely equaling the fruit slightly shorter, *5-nerved*; **Fruit** strongly indurate, stramineous, very scurely papillose-striate.

Sandy pine and oak woods, occasionally in hammocks, nowhere common, on the coastal plain from Texas to South Carolina and Oklahoma. Valler county, Dallas county, Texas.)

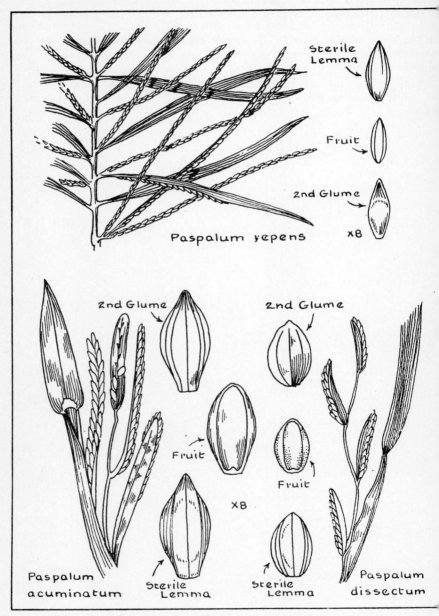

Paspalum repens

Paspalum acuminatum

Paspalum dissectum

PASPALUM REPENS, PASPALUM ACUMINATUM,
PASPALUM DISSECTUM

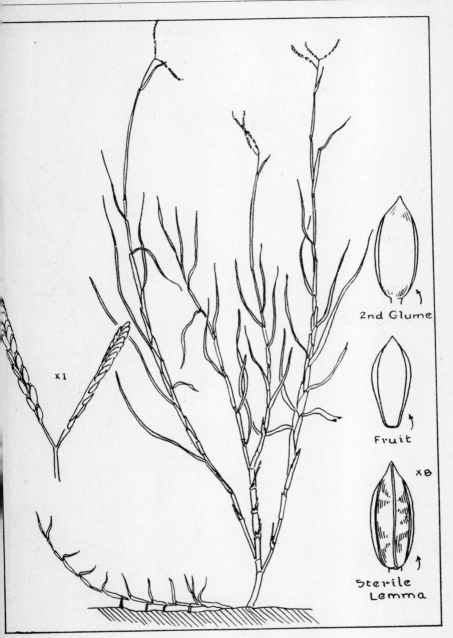

2nd Glume

Fruit

x8

Sterile
Lemma

x1

PASPALUM VAGINATUM

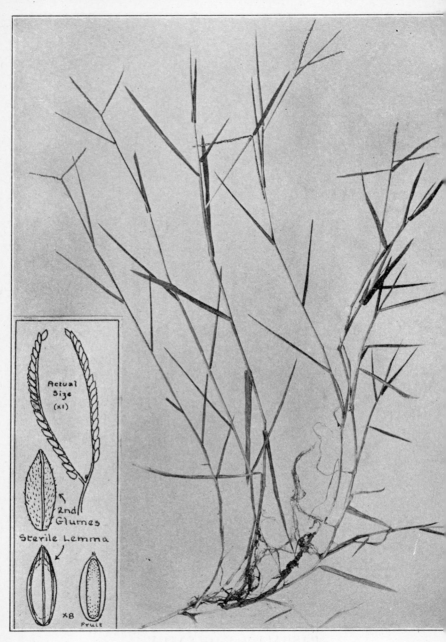

PASPALUM DISTICHUM

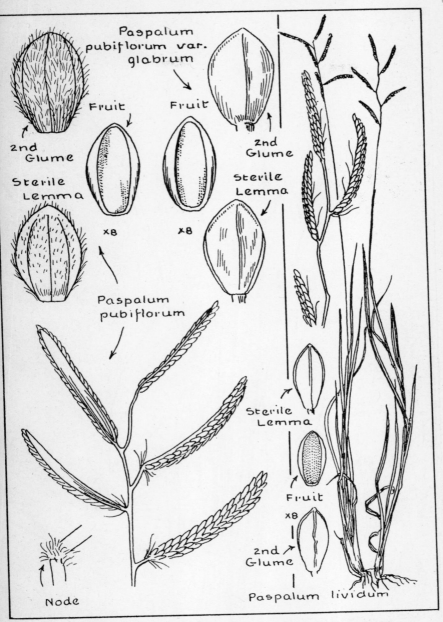

PASPALUM PUBIFLORUM, PASPALUM PUBIFLORUM VAR.
GLABRUM, PASPALUM LIVIDUM

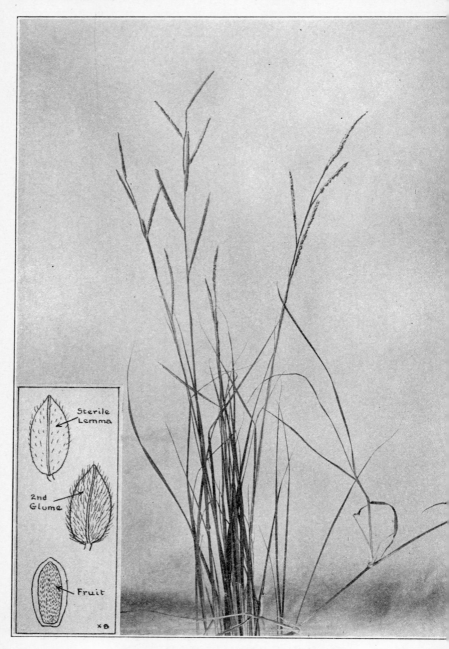

PASPALUM HARTWEGIANUM

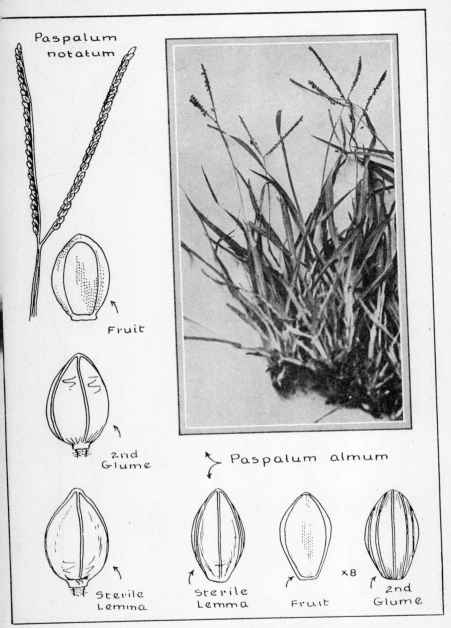

Paspalum notatum

Fruit

2nd Glume

Sterile Lemma

Paspalum almum

Sterile Lemma

Fruit

×8

2nd Glume

PASPALUM NOTATUM, PASPALUM ALMUM, Combs-grass

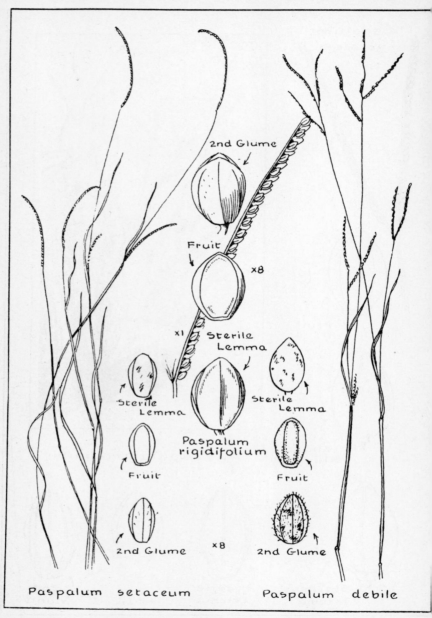

2nd Glume

Fruit ×8

×1 Sterile
Lemma

Sterile
Lemma

Sterile
Lemma

Paspalum
rigidifolium

Fruit

Fruit

2nd Glume ×8 2nd Glume

Paspalum setaceum

Paspalum debile

PASPALUM SETACEUM, PASPALUM DEBILE, PASPALUM
RIGIDIFOLIUM

2nd Glume
x8

Fruit

Sterile
Lemma

PASPALUM STRAMINIUM

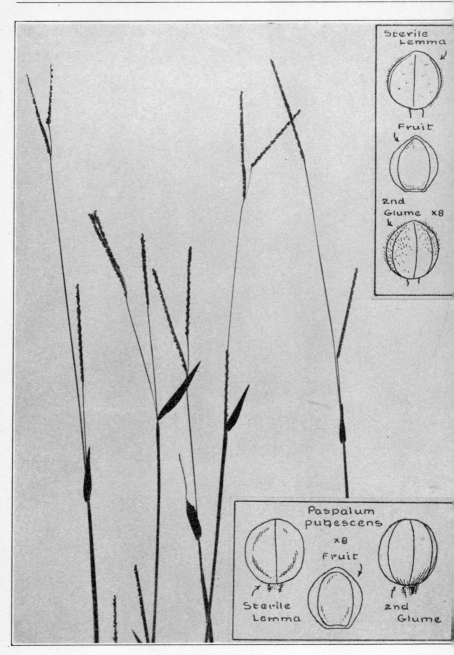

PASPALUM CILIATIFOLIUM, also drawings of PASPALUM
PUBESCENS

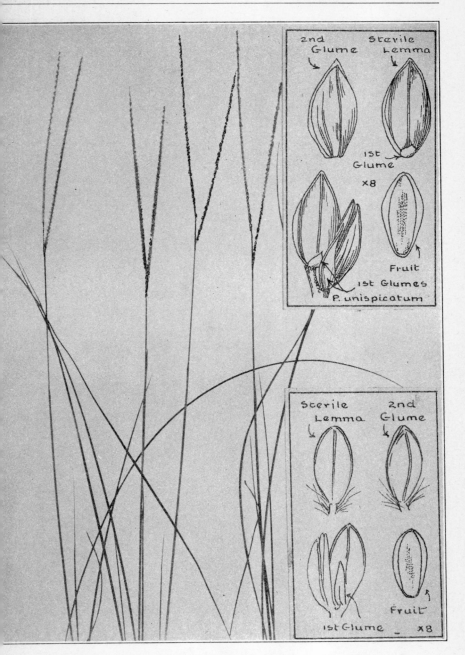

PASPALUM MONOSTACHYUM, also drawings of PASPALUM
UNISPICATUM

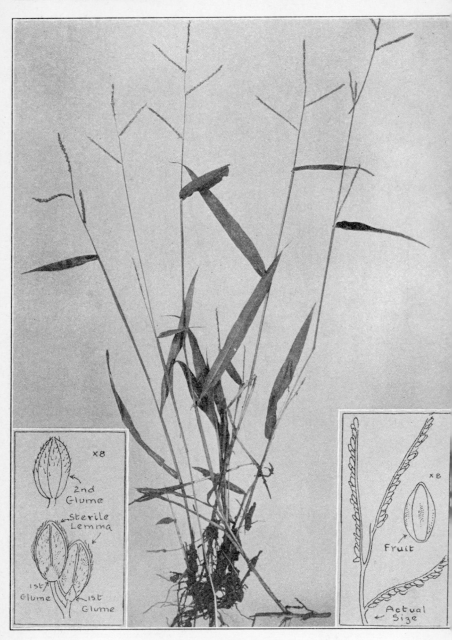

PASPALUM LANGEI

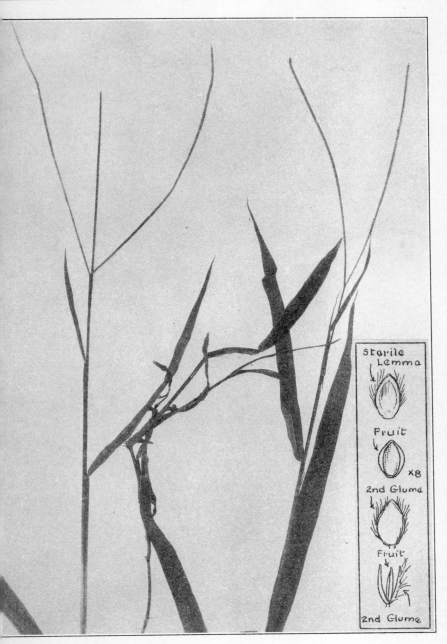

Sterile Lemma

Fruit ×8

2nd Glume

Fruit

2nd Glume

PASPALUM CONJUGATUM, Sour-grass

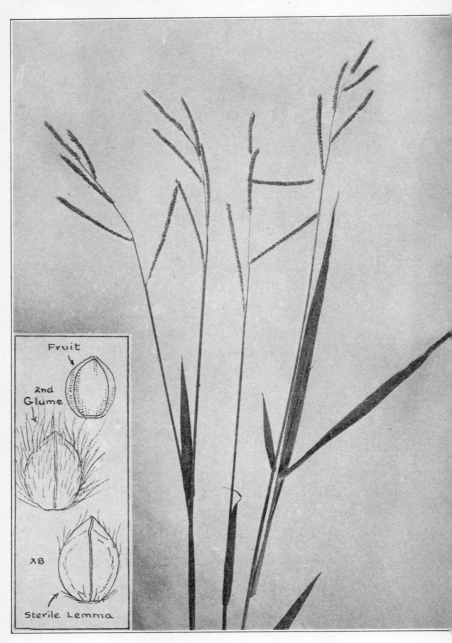

Fruit

2nd
Glume

x8

Sterile Lemma

PASPALUM DILATATUM, Dallis-grass

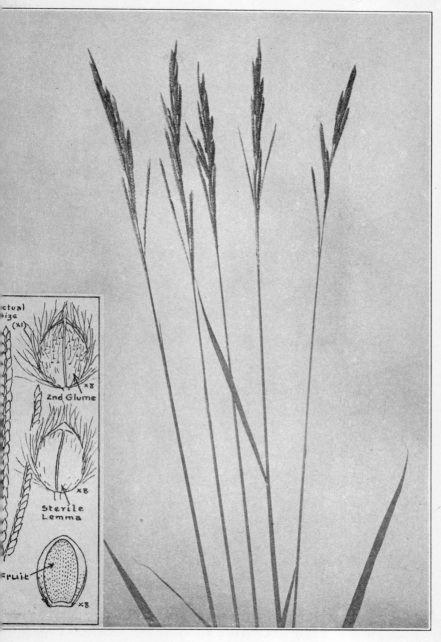

PASPALUM URVILLEI, Vasey-grass

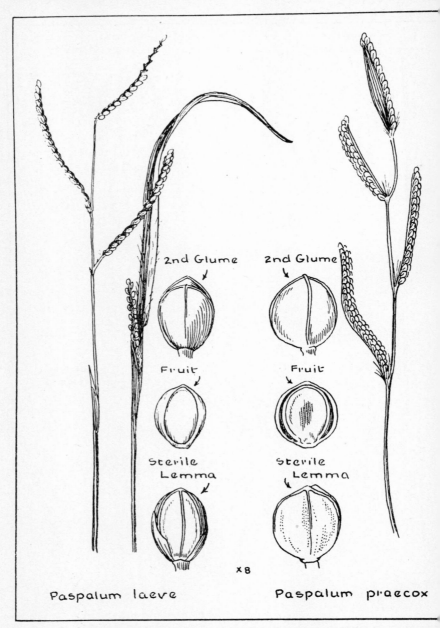

2nd Glume   2nd Glume

Fruit   Fruit

Sterile   Sterile
Lemma   Lemma

×8

Paspalum laeve   Paspalum praecox

PASPALUM LAEVE, PASPALUM PRAECOX

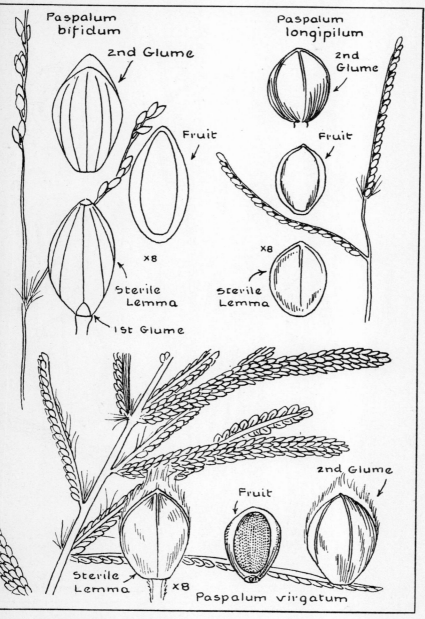

PASPALUM BIFIDUM, PASPALUM LONGIPILUM,
PASPALUM VIRGATUM

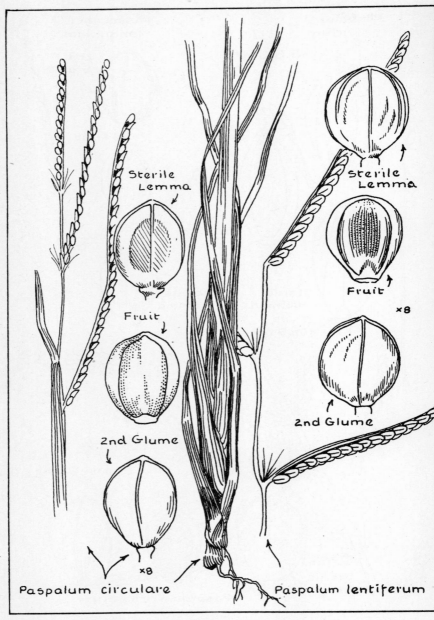

Sterile
Lemma

Fruit

2nd Glume

×8

Paspalum circulare

Sterile
Lemma

Fruit

×8

2nd Glume

Paspalum lentiferum

PASPALUM CIRCULARE, PASPALUM LENTIFERUM

2nd Glume
x8

Fruit

Sterile
Lemma

x8

P. floridanum
var. glabratum

PASPALUM FLORIDANUM, drawing of P. FLORIDANUM VAR.
GLABRATUM

PASPALUM PLICATULUM

88. PANICUM L. (păn'ĭ-kŭm)

Spikelets more or less compressed dorsiventrally, arranged in open or ompact panicles, rarely racemes; **Glumes** 2, herbaceous, nerved, usually ʾery unequal, the **First** often minute, the **Second** typically equaling the terile lemma, the latter of the same texture and simulating a third glume, ʾearing in its axil a membranaceous or hyaline palea and sometimes a taminate flower, the palea rarely wanting; **Fertile Lemma** chartaceous-ndurate, typically obtuse, the nerves obsolete, the margins inrolled over ᴀn inclosed palea of the same texture, a lunate line of thinner texture ᴀt the back just above the base, the rootlet protruding through this at ᵹermination.

Annual or *perennial* grasses of various habit confined mostly to the ᵥarmer regions; about 150 species in the United States, 85 in Texas.

A number of species here included in the genus *Panicum* depart in a measure from the generic characters: the subgenus *Paurochaetium* approaches *Setaria* in that the uppermost spikelet of each branchlet is sub- tended by a bristle-like prolongation of the axis; *P. geminatum* and *P. paludivagum* have a racemose inflorescence as in *Brachiaria,* but the spikelets are placed with the back of the fruit turned toward the rachis as in True *Panicum,* not in the reverse position as in *Brachiaria.*

In the genera *Axonopus, Eriochloa* and *Brachiaria,* the back of the lemma or fruit is turned from the rachis, while in *Digitaria, Paspalum* and *Panicum* the back of the fruit is turned toward the rachis. In all except *Panicum* (rarely in *Panicum*) the subsessile spikelets are borne on one side of a spikelike raceme. In *Axonopus* the first glume is suppressed, in *Eriochloa* it is reduced to a minute sheath or ring, in *Digitaria* it is some- times wanting, in *Paspalum* it is typically wanting, and in *Panicum* always present. The first glume in *Panicum* is typically not more than half the length of the spikelet, and is commonly much shorter than this, but in a few species, especially those included under "Miscellaneous Species" at the end of True *Panicum,* the first glume is nearly as long as the second.

Under "Miscellaneous Species" we have four in Texas: *P. obtusum* and *P. gymnocarpon,* with the first glume nearly as long as the spikelet, the last with the fruit about one-third as long as the spikelet; *P. hemitomon,* differing from the typical *Panicums* in that the fruit is less rigid and the tip of the palea is not entirely inclosed by the fertile lemma; and *P. hians* with the sterile palea enlarged at maturity.

Three subdivisions of this genus are recognized in the United States: subgenus *Paurochaetium,* with only a few species in the United States, three in Texas; *Panicum* proper, or True *Panicum,* sometimes known as the sub- genus *Eupanicum;* and the subgenus *Dichanthelium.* All the species of *Paurochaetium, Dichanthelium,* and *Miscellaneous Species* are perennials, while those of True *Panicum* include both *perennials and annuals.*

The group True *Panicum* and the subgenus *Dichanthelium* are sus- ceptible of further divisions into minor groups, the names of which are the plurals of the characteristic species of the group. These names are not intended to be formal and should have no nomenclatorial standing. The term *Angustifolia* is used as if we were to say *P. angustifolium* and its allies. The groups of these two main divisions are arranged to represent their relationship so far as this can be done in a linear sequence. In True *Panicum* the first group, the *Geminata,* is furthest removed from the typical species, the inflorescence resembling that of *Paspalum.*

The *Capillaria, Diffusa* and *Virgata,* typical groups, are near the cente of the series. In the same way the *Depauperata* are an outlying group o *Dichanthelium,* the typical groups being the *Dichotoma* and *Lanuginoso* The species of each group are also arranged to represent their affinities but it is impossible to indicate the difference in the degree of relationship Some of the groups are manifestly more homogeneous than others. Th group *Geminata,* for example, includes two closely allied species, *P. gemina tum* and *P. paludivagum,* and one, *P. purpurascens,* in which the affinity i less evident. The latter species is placed in the same group as the other tw partly as a matter of convenience.

In the preparation of the portion of this book relating to the genu *Panicum,* the writer is very much indebted to *The North American Specie of Panicum,* by A. S. Hitchcock and Agnes Chase. As far as applicable th groupings and keys, as well as explanations of same, have been copied fron this work. As *Panicum* is quite a large genus, with numerous species in Texas, it would be very difficult to collect a specimen of each species. Whei unable to collect a suitable specimen for photographing, the author, fo description and drawing, has rearranged the description of the species a described in that work, and had the artist copy the illustrations.

The photographs and drawings of each subgenus are placed im mediately following the description of the last species, *Miscellaneous Specie* being placed between True *Panicum* and *Dichanthelium.*

In a few cases the photographs show both forms, the vernal an autumnal. A drawing of a spikelet of each species is also shown.

KEY TO SUBDIVISIONS

AXIS OF BRANCHLETS EXTENDING beyond the base of the uppermost spike let as a point or bristle 1-6 mm. long.
See subgenus *Paurochaetium,* Pages 554-558.
AXIS OF BRANCHLETS NOT EXTENDING into a bristle.
Basal leaves usually distinctly different from those of the culm, forming winter rosette.
See subgenus *Dichanthelium,* Pages 609-655.
Basal leaves not forming a winter rosette.
See True *Panicum* (including Miscellaneous Species), Pages 559-608.

Subgenus PAUROCHAETIUM Hitchc. & Chase (pô-rō-kē′tĭ-ŭm).

Perennials; Culms tufted, erect; **Blades** not over 7 mm. wide **Inflorescence** narrow, more or less interrupted, the branches short an appressed, the ultimate branchlets bearing one-to-several spikelets, pro duced beyond the uppermost spikelet as a bristle 1-6 mm. long; **Spikelet** 1.5-3.5 mm. long, much swollen on the face, glabrous; **Fruit** transversel rugose, apiculate. This group approaches *Setaria* in having branchlet produced into bristles, and in the shape of the spikelets and rugose fruits

BRISTLES USUALLY SHORTER THAN THE SPIKELET. Spikelets about 2. mm. long; blades of the midculm usually more than 4′ long.
1. P. ramisetur
BRISTLES USUALLY LONGER THAN THE SPIKELET.
Spikelets 3.5 mm. long; blades usually more than 6′ long, narrowed towar the base. 2. P. reverchor
Spikelets about 3-3.2 mm. long; blades of the midculm usually less than 4′ long abruptly acute; second glume obscurely reticulate. 3. P. firmulur

1. P. RAMISETUM Scribn. (răm-ĭ-sē′tŭm) ; *P. subspicatum* Vasey.

Culms 1-3 feet tall, tufted, from short horizontal rootstocks, branch ing at the base and lower nodes, erect or ascending, sometimes decumben at the base, somewhat flattened, scabrous below the nodes, the node labrous to appressed-pubescent, more or less hirsute around the base; Blades mostly 3-7' long, 3-6 mm. wide, the lower shorter, flat or soon involute, not narrowed at the base, often sparsely-ciliate, more or less papillose-pilose on the upper surface, sometimes on the lower surface, the papillae sometimes without hairs; **Sheaths** longer or shorter than the internodes, not compressed, sparingly papillose-pilose, especially along the margins and at the summit; **Ligule** a dense ring of hairs 1.5-2 mm. long; **Panicle** finally exserted, 3-8' long, slender, 5-8 mm. thick, sometimes interrupted below, the appressed branches usually less than 10 mm. long, mostly crowded, with 1-3 spikelets on each branchlet, the branchlet extending into a short bristle usually not exceeding the short-pediceled pikelet (some plants have the bristles longer than the spikelet); **Spikelets** .4-2.6 mm. rarely 3 mm. long, 1.2-1.5 mm. wide, ovate-lanceolate, acute, turgid, plano-convex; **Glumes,** the first clasping, about half the length of the spikelet, subacute, 3-5-nerved, the second slightly shorter than the **Sterile Lemma,** acute, strongly 5-9-nerved; **Fruit** 1.9-2.2 mm. long, 1.2-.4 mm. wide, abruptly pointed, transversely rugose. (This species differs rom *P. reverchoni* in the smaller spikelets, having more spikelets to a branchlet and therefore a less number of bristles.) (Illustrated on photograph of *P. reverchoni*.)

Sandy plains and prairies, southern Texas to northern Mexico.

2. P. REVERCHONI Vasey (rĕv-ĕr-shō'nī).

Culms 12-27' tall, in large tufts, from short rootstocks, erect, simple or with one or two sterile branches toward the base, the slender nodes and lower internodes pubescent with appressed hairs, the numerous culms giving the plant a leafy aspect; **Blades** stiffly erect, 3-8' long, 2-5 mm. wide, flat, or involute at apex, narrowed toward the base, leaves of sterile shoots involute-setaceous, scabrous especially above, somewhat scabrous below, parsely papillose-ciliate on margins; **Sheaths** mostly longer than the internodes, ciliate on margins near the summit, villous at throat at each end of ligule; **Ligule** very short-ciliate, hairs 1 mm. long or less; **Panicles** somewhat included or long-exserted, very slender, 2-7' long, interrupted, branches short, appressed, branchlets bearing 1-2 short-pediceled or subsessile spikelets, the branchlets usually terminated by awn-like bristle 3-8 mm. long; **Spikelets** about 3.5 mm. long, about 2 mm. wide, turgid, elliptic, pointed; **Glumes,** the first about half as long as the spikelet, acute, 3-7-nerved, the second and **Sterile Lemma** slightly shorter than the fruit, strongly 5-7-nerved, often with a few short nerves between the prominent nerves; **Fruit** 3-3.3 mm. long, 1.8-1.9 mm. wide, elliptic, minutely pointed, and minutely transversely rugose.

Rocky or sandy prairies and limestone hills. Spring to fall.

3. P. FIRMULUM Hitchc. & Chase (fĭr'mū-lŭm).

Culms 10-30' tall, rather loosely tufted, ascending or decumbent at he base, simple or with a few appressed branches, glabrous or the nodes appressed-pubescent, from creeping knotted rootstocks; **Blades** 1-3' (1.5-4') long, 4-7 mm. wide, flat, stiffly ascending or spreading, the lower shorter and more spreading, abruptly acute, rounded at the base, wider than the sheath, smooth or slightly rough on the upper surface, sparsely papillose-ciliate, at least toward the base; **Sheaths** overlapping, striate, papillose or papillose-pubescent or nearly glabrous, often with a tuft of stiff hairs on both sides at the summit; **Ligule** a dense ring of hairs 1.5-2 mm. long, often of different lengths; **Panicles** finally exserted, mostly

3-5′ long, slender, interrupted, the short branches erect and appressed, th branchlets bearing 1-3 short-pediceled spikelets, the setiform prolongatio of the axis usually slightly longer or sometimes twice as long as the spike let; **Spikelets** 3-3.2 mm. long, about 1.8 mm. wide, obovate, subacute turgid, strongly nerved; **Glumes,** the first clasping, about half as long a the spikelet, pointed, 5-7-nerved, the second and **Sterile Lemma** subequal scarcely covering the fruit, 5-7-nerved, the glume reticulated toward th summit, sometimes obscurely so, subacute, slightly exceeded by the steril lemma; **Fruit** about 2.7 mm. long, 1.6-1.8 mm. wide, obovate-elliptic abruptly acute, very turgid, minutely scabrous at the apex.

This species resembles *P. ramisetum,* from which it differs in th larger spikelets, usually longer setae, broader, more or less ciliate blades and markedly knotty rootstocks.

Sandy prairies, southern Texas.   (Near Encino and Sarita.)   Spring

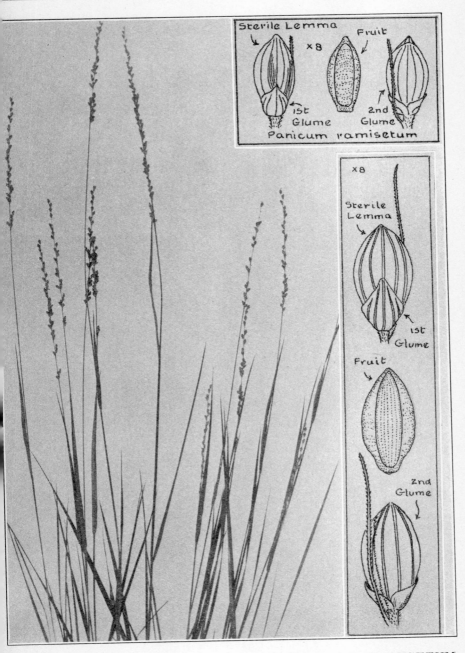

PANICUM REVERCHONI; drawings of Spikelet of P. RAMISETUM

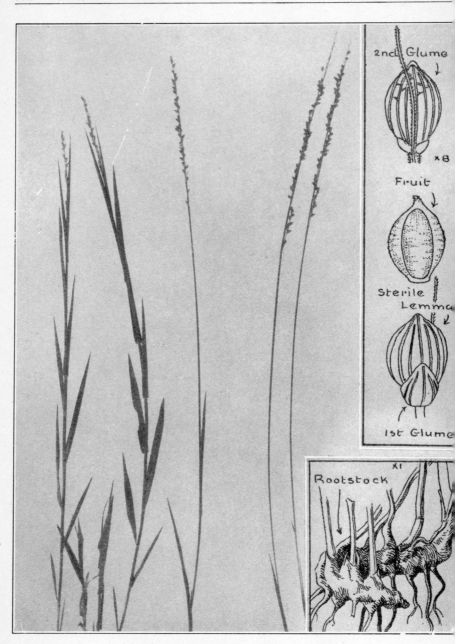

PANICUM FIRMULUM

TRUE PANICUM AND MISCELLANEOUS SPECIES
(Synopsis of groups—Key to miscellaneous species)

INFLORESCENCE CONSISTING OF SEVERAL MORE OR LESS SECUND spikelike racemes, the spikelets short-pediceled.
FRUITS TRANVERSELY rugose.
Racemes appressed; perennials. Geminata (p. 559)
Racemes ascending or spreading; annuals. Fasciculata (p. 561)
FRUITS NOT transversely rugose, spikelets glabrous; perennials. (Miscellaneous Species.)
FIRST glume nearly equaling the sterile lemma.
Racemes spreading; fruit not over one-third the length of the spikelet.
38. P. gymnocarpon
Racemes appressed; spikelets 3-3.8 mm. long, obtuse. 39. P. obtusum
FIRST glume about half the length of the sterile lemma.
Panicle very narrow; spikelets 2.4-2.7 mm. long; fruit not rigid.
40. P. hemitomon
Panicle open, but usually contracted; spikelet- or branchlet-bearing along the upper half or towards the ends only; sterile palea enlarged at maturity. 41. P. hians
INFLORESCENCE AN OPEN OR CONTRACTED PANICLE, OR IF WITH racemose branches fruit not transversely rugose.
PLANTS ANNUAL; panicles open, usually diffuse.
SPIKELETS glabrous, not warty nor rugulose; fruit polished.
First glume less than one-fourth the length of the spikelet, obtuse or truncate; sheaths glabrous. Dichotomiflora (p. 564)
First glume nearly half the length of the spikelet or more, acute or acuminate, sheaths hispid. Capillaria (p. 565)
SPIKELETS warty, rugulose or hispid; fruit not polished, margins of lemma not inrolled; spikelets 2 mm. or more long. Verrucosa (p. 578)
PLANTS PERENNIAL.
FRUIT transversely rugose (very faintly so in *P. plenum*); spikelets ellipsoid, glabrous; plants robust. Maxima (p. 570)
FRUIT not transversely rugose; spikelets not silky-villous.
Panicles more or less diffuse; spikelets long pediceled; spikelets pointed, glabrous; culms terete.
Rootstocks wanting; sheaths usually hirsute. Diffusa (p. 567)
Rootstocks present; sheaths glabrous. Virgata (p. 572)
Panicles more or less contracted, or the spikelets short-pediceled along the main branches; first glume usually more than one-third the length of the acute spikelets; culms erect, wiry, not geniculate.
Panicles few-flowered; contracted. Tenera (p. 574)
Panicles many-flowered; open or contracted; the short-pediceled pointed spikelets often secund. Agrostoidia (p. 575)

GEMINATA (jĕm-ĭ-nā′tá):—**Perennials; Culms** tall, spreading or creeping; **Inflorescence** consisting of several erect, or spreading in *. purpurascens*, spikelike racemes, distributed along an elongated axis; **pikelets** secund, glabrous; **Fruit** more or less transversely rugose or oughened. *Growing in water or wet places.*

P. *geminatum* and *P. paludivagum* are similar in aspect, but the latter iffers from the former by its succulent lower culms, the lower part submerged, branching and rooting at the lower nodes, the elongated aerial lades, and almost bladeless lower portion, the longer and less turgid spikets, and nearly smooth fruit.

Para grass has widely creeping stolons, sometimes as much as 10-15 eet long, the flower culms erect from a decumbent or prostrate base, comonly 3-6 feet tall, the nodes bearded. The panicles consist of several pikelike racemes, usually ascending or spreading. It is found growing long irrigation ditches, especially in the water and along the banks, often tangle of prostrate or decumbent culms and stolons. It is said to flower nfrequently.

NODES GLABROUS; panicle branches appressed.
  Spikelets not over 2.4 mm. long; glumes and sterile lemma not papery.
                                                                4. P. geminatu
  Spikelets 3 mm. long; glumes and sterile lemma papery.   5. P. paludivagu
NODES BEARDED; panicle branches ascending or spreading.   6. P. purpurasce

4. P. GEMINATUM Forsk. (jĕm-ĭ-nā'tŭm).

Culms commonly 2-3 feet tall, tufted, usually numerous, erect o
ascending from a more or less decumbent base or with stolons rooting ε
the nodes, scarcely succulent, sparingly branched; **Blades** 4-8' long, 3-
mm. wide, flat, or involute toward the apex, somewhat rough on uppe
surface; **Sheaths** overlapping, close; **Ligule** ciliate, about 1 mm. long
Panicle short-exserted or included at the base, 5-15' long, narrow, the axi
angled, hollowed out next to the racemes, scabrous toward the apex, tb
racemes commonly 12-18, appressed, erect or narrowly ascending, tb
lower distant, the upper gradually shorter and approximate, the lowe
25-35 mm. long, the rachis usually ending in a pointed prolongation, th
spikelets in two rows, single, on one side of a triangular winged rachis
Spikelets subsessile, about 2.3 mm. long, 1.4 mm. wide, turgid, abruptl
and minutely pointed; **Glumes,** the first about one-third the length of th
spikelet, obtuse or truncate, usually 3-nerved, the second nearly as long a
the fruit, exceeded only by the point of the fruit, 5-nerved; **Sterile Lemm**
5-nerved, abruptly pointed, equaling the fruit, and like the second glum
faintly reticulate toward the apex, inclosing a hyaline palea and usuall
an abortive staminate flower; **Fruit** about 2.2 mm. long, 1.2 mm. wide
elliptic, abruptly pointed, strongly transversally rugose.

Moist ground or shallow water, mostly near the coast, Texas an
southwest Florida. (Mitchell Lake, Bexar county.) Spring to fall.

5. P. PALUDIVAGUM Hitchc. & Chase (păl-ōō-dĭv'a-gŭm); WATER-GRASS

Culms erect or ascending, from a long creeping base, the uppe
portion out of the water 1-3 feet, the submerged portion often 3-4 fee
long, the upper internodes somewhat flattened, the lower more or les
swollen, soft and succulent, taking root at the dark constricted nodes
the lower portion sometimes branching; **Blades** 6-13' long, 3-7 mm
wide, conduplicate at the base, laxly ascending, the upper surfac
scabrous, those of the submerged portion often reduced or rudi
mentary, soon deciduous; **Sheaths** longer than the internodes, the uppe
flattened, loose at the summit, papery, smooth, mostly deciduous from th
submerged portion; **Ligule** ciliate, about 1 mm. long; **Panicle** exserted o
included at the base, blades often equaling or exceeding the panicle
narrow, 8-12' long, axis angled, the edges scabrous toward the summit
furrowed out next to each raceme, the racemes about 12-15, erect o
appressed, commonly 15-35 mm. long, the lower distant, the uppe
gradually shorter and approximate, the axis ending in a rudimentary
spikelet or slender pointed prolongation; the spikelets appressed, in twe
rows on one side of a triangular winged rachis, those on one side over
lapping about half way those of the other side, single, subsessile; **Spike**
lets 2.8-3 mm. long, about 1.4-1.6 mm. wide, narrowly ovate, subacute, no
turgid; **Glumes** papery, the first about one-fifth the length of the spike
let, nerveless, erose-truncate; the second half to two-thirds the length o
the spikelet, faintly 3-5-nerved; **Sterile Lemma** papery, as long as th
fruit, 5-nerved, enclosing a palea of about equal length and a staminat
flower; **Fruit** about 2.8-3 mm. long, 1.2-1.3 mm. wide, narrowly ovate
acute, very obscurely rugose, the margins scarcely inrolled.

More or less submerged in fresh water, rivers and lakes of the interior and along the coast. Texas, Florida and Mexico. (Sabinal River near Sabinal.) Spring to fall.

. P. PURPURASCENS Raddi (pûr-pū-răs′ĕns) ; *P. barbinode* Trin.; (has been wrongly referred to as *P. molle* Sw.) ; PARA GRASS.

Culms commonly 3-6 feet tall, erect or ascending from stout creeping stolons or a decumbent base, taking root at the lower nodes, robust, simple or producing leafy shoots, the swollen nodes densely-villous; **Blades** 4-12′ long, 10-15 mm. wide, flat, rounded at the base, lanceolate, ascending or spreading, margins scabrous; **Sheaths** mostly about equal to the internodes, from glabrous, especially toward the summit, to softly villous or merely papillose, but densely-pubescent at the collar and at the base close to the nodes; **Ligule** membranaceous, including the ciliate hairs slightly over 1 mm. long; **Panicle** finally exserted, oblong-pyramidal, 4-8′ long, one-third to one-half as wide, purplish or lead color, the axis 4-6′ long, scabrous on the edges, racemes commonly 10-18, the lower 4′ long or less, the upper shorter, densely-pubescent in the axils, ascending or spreading, rather distant, subracemose, densely-flowered, the spikelets mostly on short branchlets with a few to a dozen or more spikelets to a branchlet, alternate on one side of a flattened rachis, a few stiff hairs on the short pedicels; **Spikelets** 3-3.2 mm. long, 1.4 mm. wide, elliptic; **Glumes** membranaceous, the first about 1 mm. long, 1-nerved, acute; the second and **Sterile Lemma** about equal, both slightly exceeded by the sterile palea which is as long as the spikelet, 5-nerved, obtuse; the **Palea** often subtending a staminate flower; **Fruit** 2.3-2.5 mm. long, 1.1 mm. wide, obtuse, minutely transversely rugose or roughened.

Cultivated and waste ground escaped from cultivation; Texas to Florida. (Mercedes.) Summer and fall.

FASCICULATA (fă-sĭk-ū-lā′tà) :—**Annuals;** usually rather wide flat blades; **Ligule** ciliate or membranaceous-ciliate, not over 1 mm. long; **Inflorescence** of several narrow or spikelike racemes along a main axis; **Second Glume** and **Sterile Lemma** usually more or less reticulate-veined, at least toward the apex, the **Lemma** inclosing a palea of nearly equal length and often a staminate flower; **Fruit** transversely rugose.

SPIKELETS STRONGLY RETICULATE-VEINED, bronze to mahogany-colored, glabrous.
Spikelets 2.1-2.5 mm. long; blades 6-20 mm. wide, pubescent or glabrous.
8. P. fasciculatum

Spikelets 2.6-3.2 mm. long, blades narrow, 6-10 mm. wide, pubescent.
8a. P. fasciculatum var. reticulatum

SPIKELETS SCARCELY RETICULATE-VEINED, or only near the apex.
Spikelets 2 mm. long, glabrous; plants usually prostrate.   7. P. reptans
Spikelets 3.5-3.8 mm. long, pubescent, rachis sparsely hispid; sheaths papillose.
9. P. arizonicum

Spikelets 5-6 mm. long, sparsely pilose.   10. P. texanum

. P. REPTANS L. (rĕp′tăns).

Culms ascending, 4-12′ tall, above the decumbent or creeping base, usually prostrate, rooting at the nodes, freely branching, slender, nodes puberulent; **Blades** lanceolate or ovate-lanceolate, about 1.5-2.5′ long, 7-12 mm. wide, cordate, glabrous or puberulent on both surfaces, the undulate margins scabrous, papillose-ciliate with stiff hairs at base; **Sheaths** shorter than the internodes, loose, densely ciliate; **Ligule** a dense ring of hairs less than 1 mm. long; **Panicle** about 1-2.5′ long, finally long-exserted, consisting of about 5-13 spikelike racemes, ascending or spreading, solitary or somewhat fascicled, the lower 20-30 mm. long, upper shorter; rachises and pedicels scabrous, often sparsely pilose with rather long hairs, spikelet-bearing on one side of the rachis, rather densely clustered, branches very short, pedicels about 1 mm. long or less, with short rather stiff hairs **Spikelets** about 2 mm. long, about 1 mm. wide, acute; **Glumes**, the first about one-fifth the length of the spikelet, rounded or truncate, the second and **Sterile Lemma** slightly exceeding the fruit, strongly 5-7-nerved; **Fruit** slightly shorter and narrower than the spikelet, elliptic, apiculate.

Moist open ground and frequent weed in waste places and cultivated soil; Texas to Florida; Mexico. Spring and summer.

8. P. **FASCICULATUM** Swartz (fă-sĭk-ū-lā'tŭm); *P. fuscum* Swartz *P. fuscum* var. *fasciculatum* Griseb.

Plants erect or spreading from a decumbent base, the more robust becoming much branched from the lower nodes; **Culms** 12-40' tall, sometimes taller, glabrous or scabrous, or sometimes pubescent below the panicle or hispid below the appressed-pubescent nodes; **Blades** 1.5-12 long, 6-20 mm. wide, flat, glabrous, usually scabrous above, sometimes sparsely hispid on one or both surfaces, the nerves in the larger blades conspicuous, sometimes appearing somewhat plicate; **Sheaths** glabrous to papillose-hispid; **Ligule** a dense ring of hairs about 1 mm. long; **Panicle** 2-6' long, short-exserted or included at the base until maturity, consisting of a series of spikelike racemes arranged along a scabrous sometimes pilose main axis, the racemes 2-4' long, solitary or fascicled, narrowly ascending to spreading, spikelet-bearing from the base, or naked below, the short-pediceled spikelets approximate or somewhat crowded, borne singly or 2-3 together on short branchlets, along the under side of the rachis **Spikelets** bronze to mahogany colored, 2.1-2.5 mm. long, in occasional specimens as much as 3 mm. long, obovate, turgid, abruptly short-pointed glabrous; **Glumes,** the first clasping, about one-third the length of the spikelet, subacute, 5-7-nerved, the second glume and **Sterile Lemma** slightly exceeding the fruit, 9-nerved, faintly to strongly transversely wrinkled between the nerves; **Fruit** 1.9-2.3 mm. long, obovate, obscurely apiculate.

This species is variable in the amount of pubescence and in the size of the spikelets. The greater number of specimens from Mexico and the United States have spikelets 2.5-2.8 mm. long. There are many specimens intermediate between the species and subspecies. (Illustrated on photograph of *P. fasciculatum* var. *reticulatum*.)

Moist open ground, often a weed in fields and along roadsides, southern Florida and southern Texas, southward through Mexico. (Robstown.)

8a. P. **FASCICULATUM** var. **RETICULATUM** (Torr.) Beal (rē-tĭk-ū lā'tŭm).

Culms 6-30' tall, tufted, decumbent at the base, branching from lower nodes, spreading or erect, pubescent at and below the nodes, axis his pidulous just below panicles; **Blades** 2-6.5' long, 6-10 mm. sometimes 1 mm. wide, flat, flaccid, rough, especially above, ciliate on the margins usually harshly pubescent on both surfaces; **Sheaths** shorter than th internodes, upper inflated, densely ciliate, more or less hispid or papillose hispid; **Ligule** membranaceous-ciliate about 1 mm. long; **Panicle** exserted or included at base until maturity, 3-6' long, consisting of about 10 spike like racemes along a scabrous sometimes pilose axis, pubescent in the axils he racemes commonly less than 2′ rarely 4′ long, ascending or spreading, usually solitary and distant about one-half their length, spikelet-bearing nearly or to the base, the short-pediceled spikelets approximate or crowded, single or two or three together, on short branchlets, along the under side of the axis of the raceme, apex of pedicels often pilose; **Spikelets** 2.6-3.2 mm. long, about 1.7-1.9 mm. wide, obovate; **Glumes,** the first ovate, about one-third as long as the spikelet, 3-5-nerved; the second and **Sterile Lemma** about 7-nerved (7-9-nerved) as long as the spikelet and slightly exceeding the fruit, bronze to mahogany colored, strongly transversely wrinkled between the nerves; the **Lemma** enclosing a palea of nearly equal length; **Fruit** 2.3 mm. long and about 1.3 mm. wide, slightly obovate, obscurely apiculate, transversely rugose.

Prairies, fields and waste ground; Texas and Arizona to Mexico. (Common near San Antonio.) Spring and summer.

9. P. ARIZONICUM Scribn. & Merr. (ăr-ĭ-zŏn′ĭ-kŭm).

Culms 8-24′ tall, tufted, erect or ascending from a decumbent base, often rooting at the lower nodes, branching, bristly-hispid below the panicle and sometimes sparsely pubescent at the nodes; **Blades** 2-6′ long, 5-12 mm. wide, ascending or spreading, flat, rounded at the base, glabrous on both surfaces, or scabrous to papillose-hispid beneath, the scabrous, thin cartilaginous margin usually papillose-ciliate at the base; **Sheaths** shorter than the internodes, or the upper overlapping, rather loose, glabrous to strongly papillose-hispid; **Ligule** a ring of hairs about 1 mm. long; **Panicles** 3-8′ long, finally exserted, open, the solitary looselyflowered slender branches ascending, 2′ long or less, the spikelets borne on very short appressed branchlets, the pedicels, main axis and branches scabrous and more or less papillose-hirsute or hispid; **Spikelets** 3.5-3.9 mm. long, about 1.8 mm. wide (drawing was made from immature spikelets; they are plumper when more mature), obovate-elliptic, abruptly pointed, attenuate at the base, densely pubescent to glabrous, the hairs rather stiff, bronze or dirty-yellow; **Glumes,** the first about half the length of the spikelet, clasping, acute, 5-nerved, the second and **Sterile Lemma** pointed beyond the fruit, the glume 5-7-nerved, the lemma 5-nerved, the nerves often reticulate; **Fruit** 2.9-3 mm. long, 1.5-1.6 mm. wide, obovateelliptic, apiculate.

This species varies much as to size and amount of pubescence. Open sandy or rocky ground, western Texas to southern California and northern Mexico; introduced into North Carolina, South Carolina, Florida and Mississippi. (Rocky ground about 10 miles west of Van Horn, banks of foothills.) Fall.

10. P. TEXANUM Buckl. (tĕks-ā′nŭm); Colorado Grass, Congho Grass, Texas Millet.

Culms 1-5 commonly 2-3 feet rarely as much as 10 feet tall, tufted, erect or ascending, often decumbent and rooting at the lower nodes, branching from the middle and lower nodes, leafy, softly pubescent, at least below the nodes and beneath the panicles; **Blades** ascending or spreading, 3-8′ long, 7-16 mm. wide, flat, rounded at the base, softly pubescent on both surfaces, often finely papillose; **Sheaths,** the lower shorter than the internodes, the upper usually overlapping, densely ciliate, softly pubescent; **Ligule** about 1 mm. long, ciliate; **Panicles** finally exserted, 3-10′ long, 10-30 mm. thick, the main axis much exceeding the erect branches, the axis densely clothed with short pubescence having

long stiff hairs intermixed, the short-pediceled spikelets somewha
crowded on several narrow spikelike racemes, 1.5-4′ long, commonly 6-12
Spikelets 5-6 mm. long, about 2 mm. wide, fusiform, pointed, short
attenuate at the base, pilose; **Glumes,** the first more than half the lengtl
of the spikelet, 3-5-nerved (3-7), acute, the second and **Sterile Lemm:**
exceeding the fruit, often obscurely reticulate, 5-7-nerved; **Fruit** 3.7-3.:
mm. long, about 2 mm. wide, elliptic, apiculate, transversely rugose
(Illustrated on photograph of *P. reptans.*)

Prairies and open ground, often a weed in waste ground and culti
vated fields, especially in corn fields in late summer and fall. Texas anc
northern Mexico; introduced into North Carolina, Oklahoma, Florid:
and Oregon. Summer and fall.

DICHOTOMIFLORA (dī-kŏt-ō-mǐ-flō′rà):— **Annual** plants witl
mostly large, spreading panicles, the branchlets short and appressed alon:
the ascending or rarely spreading main branches; **Ligule** membranaceou:
below, densely ciliate above, 1-3 mm. long; **Spikelets** glabrous, narrow
acute or acuminate, the first glume one-fifth to one-fourth as long, truncat•
or with a broadly triangular tip; **Fruit** smooth and shining.

Our one species of this group, *P. dichotomiflorum,* is common alon:
irrigation canals and ditches, and low bottoms in the rice fields in south
east Texas.

This species as it occurs in the United States is usually glabrou
throughout but varies much in size of the blades and spikelets, the latte
varying from 2-3.2 mm. in length. Specimens are often found with th•
blades sparsely or even densely pilose. These variations cannot be in an;
way correlated, and each is connected by intergrading specimens with th•
typical form.

11. P. DICHOTOMIFLORUM Michx. (dī-kŏt-ō-mǐ-flō′rŭm); SPREADIN•
WITCH-GRASS.

Culms 1.5-3.5 feet sometimes over 6 feet long, usually freely branch
ing, at first erect, finally ascending, or spreading from a geniculate o
prostrate base, usually smooth throughout (in tropical forms more or les
pubescent), somewhat flattened, often thick and succulent, drying fur
rowed, the nodes swollen, at least the lower; **Blades** 3-20′ long, 3-20 mm
wide, flat, or sometimes folded, the white midnerve usually prominent
rough on the margins and surface except below near the base, or some
times sparsely pilose above; **Sheaths** usually longer than the internodes
somewhat flattened, loose, ciliate on the margins toward the summit
Ligule membranaceous, ciliate, 1-2 mm. long; **Panicles** terminal an•
axillary, included at the base or tardily exserted, 4-15′ long, the mai•
branches ascending or finally spreading or even reflexed, 3-6′ long
usually single or in twos, naked at the base, the main axis and branche
scabrous toward the summits, the short branchlets appressed, bearin:
short-pediceled, often rather crowded spikelets; **Spikelets** 2-3.2 mm
usually 2.5 mm. long, about 0.9 mm. wide, narrowly oblong, acute, ofte•
greenish-purple; **Glumes,** the first usually less than one-fourth the lengtl
of the spikelet, truncate or broadly triangular, 1-3-nerved, the second an•
Sterile Lemma about equal, somewhat pointed beyond the fruit, rathe
faintly 7-nerved, the palea of the sterile lemma nearly equal to the frui
or wanting; **Fruit** about 2 mm. long, 0.8 mm. wide, elliptic.

Moist ground, along streams, and a weed in waste places and culti
vated soil, Texas to Florida, north to Maine and Nebraska. (Common i•
the rice fields of southeast Texas.) Summer and fall.

CAPILLARIA (kăp-ĭ-lăr′ĭ-à) :—**Annuals;** papillose-hispid at least on e sheaths, or rarely glabrous; **Ligule** membranaceous, ciliate, 1-3 mm. ıg; **Panicles** many-flowered, more or less diffuse, often breaking away maturity and rolling before the wind; **Spikelets** pointed, glabrous, the ˑst **Glume** large and clasping, the **Fruit** often falling from the spikelet fore the disarticulation of the latter, smooth and shining, usually olive- own at maturity, the nerves showing as faint pale lines.

P. miliaceum, known as hog-millet, commonly 2-3 feet tall, with large ades and large heavy drooping panicles, is often cultivated for forage and dder, frequently escaping from cultivation. It is cultivated at many aces in Texas.

P. capillare, known as old-witch grass, has a large purplish panicle, at aturity often as broad as long, the numerous long-pediceled spikelets at ˌe ends of the many branches. At maturity the panicle breaks away and ˌlls before the wind as a tumble-weed. The plants, especially the larger ˌes, are conspicuous for their purplish panicles.

P. flexile, with a long but narrow panicle, and *P. capillare* var. *occi-ˌntale,* with a long broad panicle, have spikelets much larger than those of ˌ *capillare. P. philadelphicum* differs from *P. capillare* in the few- owered slender panicle and more divergent branches. *P. hirticaule,* ǃually with reddish-brown spikelets, has the first glume half to two-thirds ˌe length of the spikelet.

ANICLES MORE OR LESS DROOPING. Spikelets 4.5-5 mm. long; in culti-
vation; introduced.   **16. P. miliaceum**
ANICLES ERECT, USUALLY LONG.
PANICLES MORE than half the length of the entire plant; first glume one-
third to half as long as the spikelet.
  PANICLES narrow, usually less than half as broad as long; spikelets 3.1-3.5
  mm. long.   **12. P. flexile**
  PANICLES diffuse, as broad as long.
    Spikelets 2-2.2 mm. rarely 2.5 mm. long; blades not crowded toward the
    base.   **14. P. capillare**
    Spikelets 3-3.3 rarely 2.5 mm. long; blades usually crowded toward the
    base.   **14a. P. capillare var. occidentale**
PANICLES NOT more than one-third the entire length of the plant; first glume
two-fifths to two-thirds as long as the spikelet.
  Spikelets 1.7-2 mm. long, not turgid, acute but not long-acuminate; panicle
  diffuse; plants slender, with blades not over 6 mm. wide.
    13. P. philadelphicum
  Spikelets 2.7-3.3 mm. long; panicle branches narrowly ascending; blades
  4-13 mm. wide.   **15. P. hirticaule**

2. **P. FLEXILE** (Gattinger) Scribn. (flĕks′ĭl) ; WIRY WITCH-GRASS.

Culms 8-28′ tall, erect, slender, freely branching from the base, ˌlabrous or somewhat hispid below, the nodes pubescent; **Blades** as much ˌs 12′ long, 2-6 mm. wide, rarely narrower, erect but not stiff, glabrous or ˌparsely hispid; **Sheaths** papillose-hispid, the hairs shorter than in ˌˑ. *capillare;* **Panicles** 4-8′ rarely 12′ long, oblong, about one-third as wide, he branches at first narrowly ascending, somewhat spreading at maturity, he peduncles of the panicle not brittle and readily breaking as in ˌˑ. *capillare;* **Spikelets** long-pediceled, 3.1-3.5 mm. long, 0.9-1 mm. wide, anceolate, acuminate; **Glumes,** the first about one-third the length of the ǃpikelet, the second slightly longer than the **Sterile Lemma,** both 7-9- ˌnerved, much exceeding the fruit, the palea of the sterile floret wanting; **Fruit** 2 mm. long, 0.9 mm. wide, elliptic.

This species is distinguished from *P. capillare* by the more slender culms, less dense pubescence, narrower blades, less diffuse panicles and the

longer acuminate spikelets; and from *P. philadelphicum* by the narro
panicle and larger, acuminate and longer-pediceled spikelets. (See drawing

Sandy, mostly damp soil, meadows and open woods, east Texas
Florida, north to South Dakota and Ontario; introduced in Utah. Summe
fall.

13. P. PHILADELPHICUM Bernh. (fĭl-à-dĕl'fĭ-kŭm) ; Wood Witci GRASS.

Plants light-yellowish-green, in small tufts, freely branching, 8-2
tall, erect, or rarely decumbent at the base, depauperate, norther
specimens sometimes forming small mats; **Culms** slender, the lower inte
nodes much shortened, more or less zigzag at the base, papillose-hispid 1
nearly glabrous; **Blades** 1.5-6′ long, 2-6 mm. wide, erect or ascendin;
sparsely hirsute, rarely nearly glabrous; **Sheaths** mostly longer than th
internodes, papillose-hispid; **Panicles** exserted, diffuse, ovoid, 4-8′ lon;
forming one-third the entire length of the plant or more, few-flowere
the capillary scabrous branchlets solitary, bearing rather short-pedicele
spikelets, usually in twos at the ends; **Spikelets** 1.7-2 mm. long, 0.7 mn
wide, elliptic; **Glumes,** the first about two-fifths the length of the spikele
5-nerved, acute, the second and **Sterile Lemma** equal, only slightly excee
ing the fruit, the palea of the sterile lemma wanting; **Fruit** 1.5 mm. lon;
0.6 mm. wide, elliptic.

This species differs from *P. capillare* in its narrow, erect blades, mo
slender culms, and smaller, few-flowered panicles, with more divergen
branches, and spikelets mostly in twos. The spikelets are usually slightl
smaller, but the spikelets of the type of *P. philadelphicum* and of severa
other specimens are 2 mm. long. (See drawings of *P. flexile.*)

Dry open or sandy ground, Texas to Mississippi, Georgia, north t
Maine, Oklahoma and Wisconsin. (Dallas county.) Summer-fall.

14. P. CAPILLARE L. (kăp-ĭ-lăr'ē) ; Old-witch-grass.

Culms 9-34′ tall, tufted, erect, or ascending from a decumbent o
geniculate base, simple or sparingly branched especially at the base
papillose-hispid to nearly glabrous, densely hispid or pubescent at th
nodes; **Blades** 4-10′ long, 5-20 mm. wide, larger blades slightly narrowe
and rounded at the base, midrib prominent, papillose-hispid on th
margins, hispid on both surfaces or nearly glabrous above; **Sheath**
usually longer than the internodes, densely papillose-hispid; **Ligule** ver
short, ciliate; **Panicle** included at the base until maturity, 3-15′ long
often more than half as long as the plant, nearly as broad, erect, ovate o
pyramidal, diffuse, the scabrous and sparsely pilose branches in ones t
threes, 1-8′ long, ascending or at maturity divaricately spreading, the
main axis sparsely pilose, scabrous toward the apex, the numerou
capillary scabrous branchlets bearing toward their ends long-pedicele
spikelets, the whole panicle breaking away and rolling before the wind;
Spikelets 2-2.5 mm. long, about 0.9 mm. wide, elliptic; **Glumes,** the first
about half the length of the spikelet, acute, 5-7-nerved, the second and
Sterile Lemma equal or subequal, the glume often slightly longer, more
or less acuminate beyond the fruit; **Palea** of the sterile floret wanting;
Fruit about 1.5 mm. long, about 0.8 mm. wide, elliptic, shiny, brownish,
strongly nerved with several pale nerves.

Open ground, fields and waste places. Texas to Florida, north to
Maine, the Dakotas and Colorado. Spring and summer.

a. P. CAPILLARE var. OCCIDENTALE Rydb. (ŏk-sĭ-dĕn-tăl'ē) ;
P. barbipulvinatum Nash ; BARBED WITCH-GRASS.

Differs from the species chiefly in being on the average lower ;
ades shorter, crowded toward the base, less pubescent ; **Panicles** more
serted, the branches early divaricate ; **Spikelets** usually about 3 mm.
.5-3.3) long, acuminate. (See drawings of *P. flexile*.)

Open ground and waste places, Texas to California and north to
nada. (Abilene.)

P. HIRTICAULE Presl (hĭr-tĭ-kô'lē).

Culms 6-28' tall, erect, simple or nearly so, or sometimes branching
d decumbent at the base, papillose-hispid to glabrous, nodes hispid, the
irs spreading ; **Blades** 2-6' long, 4-13 mm. wide, often cordate at the
se, sparsely hispid or nearly glabrous, ciliate toward the base ; **Sheaths**
pillose-hispid, but sometimes sparsely so ; **Panicle** exserted, 2-6' long,
rcely one-third the entire length of the plant, rather many-flowered,
 branches ascending, the lower usually narrowly so, scabrous but not
ose, bearing rather short and appressed-pediceled spikelets along half
two-thirds their length, the glabrous pulvini inconspicuous ; **Spikelets**
'-3.3 mm. long, 1-1.1 mm. wide (smaller in occasional specimens)
iceolate-fusiform, acuminate, typically reddish-brown ; **Glumes,** the first
lf to three-fourths the length of the spikelet, acuminate, the midnerve
ibrous toward the apex, the second slightly longer than the **Sterile**
mma, both much exceeding the fruit, strongly many-nerved, the mid-
rves scabrous toward the summit, the palea of the sterile floret small,
rveless ; **Fruit** 2 mm. long, 1 mm. wide, elliptic, a scar sometimes showing
either side at the base.

This species is variable ; the Mexican specimens are mostly fairly
pical, but the more northern are often rather freely branching, or the
nicles are less strict, or the spikelets not reddish. (See drawings of
flexile.)

Rocky or sandy soil, western Texas to southern California, and south
rough Mexico. (El Paso.)

. P. MILIACEUM L. (mĭl-ĭ-ā'sē-ŭm) ; BROOMCORN MILLET.

Culms 8-36' tall, stout, erect, or decumbent at the base, usually
anching from the basal nodes, hispid below the pubescent nodes or
ibrous ; **Blades** as long as 12', as wide as 25 mm., rounded at the base,
adually narrowed to the apex, more or less pilose on both surfaces,
irgins scabrous, sometimes almost glabrous ; **Sheaths** usually shorter
an the internodes, papillose-hispid ; **Ligule** a ring of hairs about 1 mm.
ig ; **Panicle** 4-12' long, usually more or less included at the base, com-
inly nodding, rather compact, the numerous very scabrous branches
rrowly ascending, several inches long, spikelet-bearing toward the sum-
t ; **Spikelets** 4.5-5 mm. long, ovate, acuminate, strongly many-nerved ;
umes exceeding the fruit, the first about half the length of the spikelet
even longer, acuminate, the second and **Sterile Lemma** subequal, the
rile lemma subtending a small palea ; **Fruit** about 3 mm. long, 2 mm.
de, elliptic, stramineous to reddish-brown.

Waste places or in cultivation. Abundant in the northeastern states,
re and there over most of the United States. Spring and summer.

DIFFUSA (dĭf-ū'zà) :—**Perennials** ; **Culms** stiff, somewhat tufted,
eaths mostly hirsute ; **Blades** long and narrow ; **Ligule** membranaceous,

ciliate, 1-3 mm. long; **Spikelets** mostly narrowly ovate, acuminat
glabrous; first glume clasping, the equal second glume and **Sterile Lemn**
exceeding the fruit and pointed beyond it, the **Palea** and sterile flor
about half as long as its lemma; **Fruit** smooth and shining. The speci
of this group often resembles those of *Capillaria*, especially in their spik
lets, but the latter are all annuals.

   P. hirsutum, a stout plant 3-5 feet tall, with blades 20 mm. wide mo
or less, is found in the United States only in the Rio Grande Valley fro
Mercedes to Brownsville; *P. capillarioides*, with the fruit about one-thi
as long as the second glume and sterile lemma, is confined to southern Tex
and northern Mexico; *P. hallii*, with spikelets 3-3.2 mm. long and *P. filip*
with spikelets 2.2-2.6 mm. long, both 1-2 feet tall, have blades glaucous
the upper surface and less than 8 mm. wide, the uppermost blades
P. filipes usually equaling or exceeding the panicle.

SECOND GLUME AND STERILE LEMMA ELONGATED, at least three tin
   as long as the fruit; spikelets 5-6 mm. long.   17. P. capillarioic
SECOND GLUME AND STERILE LEMMA NOT ELONGATED; panic
   usually more or less diffuse.
   BLADES 20 mm. WIDE more or less; plants stout, 3-5 feet tall, ascending
       spreading; spikelets 2-2.2 mm. long.   20. P. hirsutu
   BLADES LESS than 8 mm. wide, usually glabrous on both surfaces, glauco
       above; plants erect, usually 1-2 feet tall.
       Panicles much exceeding the blades; spikelets 3-3.5 mm. long.   19. P. ha
       Panicles usually equaled or exceeded by the uppermost blades; spikelets 2-
           mm. long.   18. P. filip

17. P. CAPILLARIOIDES Vasey (kăp-ĭ-lăr-ĭ-oi'dēz).

   Culms 10-30' tall, in small or large spreading tufts, sparing
branched, erect or ascending, flattened, almost glabrous to appresse
pubescent, the nodes densely-pubescent; **Blades** 4-12' long, 4-9 mm. wic
slightly rounded at the narrowed base, flat, stiffly ascending, margi
papillose-ciliate, papillose-pubescent on both surfaces, slightly so belov
Sheaths about equal to the internodes, harshly papillose-pubescent; **Ligu**
loose, hairs about 1.5-2 mm. long; **Panicle** commonly short-exserted, 4-1
long, often as wide as long, diffuse, few-flowered, branches stiffly sprea
ing, as much as 8' long, mostly single and alternate, scabrous, naked
base, axils pubescent, bearing short-pediceled spikelets near the en
Spikelets 5-6 mm. long, about 1.2 mm. wide, lanceolate, acuminate; **Glum**
the first about 2.5 mm. long, acute, 5-7-nerved; the second and **Steri**
Lemma about equal, acuminate, many-nerved and about three times
long as the fruit; **Fruit** about 1.8 mm. long and nearly 1 mm. wide, obtus
elliptic, pale, shining.
   Prairies, southern Texas and northern Mexico. Spring and fall.

18. P. FILIPES Scribn. (fĭl'ĭ-pēz).

   Culms 1-2.5 feet tall, in small to rather large dense tufts, erect
spreading, stiff, simple or sparingly branched, glabrous except t
sparsely-appressed pubescent nodes, the panicles readily disarticulati
at the first node below the panicle; **Blades** 4-12' long, 3-7 mm. wide, t
uppermost blades often equaling or exceeding the panicles, thin, ascen
ing or laxly spreading, flat, or those of the sterile shoots narrow and i
volute, the upper surface and margins usually rough, glabrous or sparse
pubescent on the upper surface toward the base, or sparsely papillo
hirsute on the midrib on the under surface toward the base; **Sheat**
shorter or sometimes longer than the internodes, villous at the throa
otherwise glabrous or sparsely papillose-hispidulous; **Ligule** me

anaceous, ciliate, 1-3 mm. long; **Panicle** purple, usually erect, finally
serted, 3-10' long, about three-fourths as wide, the slender axis and
anches rather rigid and rough, the axils especially the lower often more
less pilose, the branches ascending or spreading, in ones to fours, the
wer usually 4-7' long, naked at the base, some specimens branchlet- and
ikelet-bearing only at the extremities and others on the upper three-
urths, the comparatively few spikelets on scabrous pedicels 1-3 times the
ngth of the spikelet; **Spikelets** green to purple, 2.2-2.6 rarely 2.8 mm.
ng, about 1 mm. wide, pointed; **Glumes,** the first half to two-thirds as
ng as the spikelet, 3-5-nerved, acute or acuminate, the second and **Sterile**
emma about equal, 5-7-nerved or the glume 9-nerved, the **Sterile Palea**
bout as long as the fruit; **Fruit** 1.5-1.8 mm. long, about 0.9 mm. wide,
liptic, shining and smooth, dimly nerved.

(Specimens collected near Hempstead had a few spikelets at the ex-
emities of the branches, while those collected at San Antonio were spike-
t-bearing on the upper two-thirds.)

Low open ground, often in sandy land; Texas, Louisiana and Mexico.
pring.

9. P. HALLII Vasey (häl′ĭ-ī).

Plants glaucous, green, especially on the upper surface of blades;
ulms 1-2 feet tall, usually in small tufts, erect, simple, or sparingly
ranched from the lower nodes, the nodes appressed-pubescent; **Blades**
.5-8' long, 2-5 mm. wide, flat, not equal to or exceeding the panicle, but
rowded at the base, commonly sparsely papillose-ciliate toward the base,
therwise glabrous, or with a few long delicate hairs on the upper surface,
r sparingly papillose-hispid beneath toward the base, often with a
arrow, scabrous, white cartilaginous margin; **Sheaths,** the lower overlapping, the upper about as long as the internodes, glabrous to sparsely
papillose-hispid; **Ligule** about 1.5 mm. long, a short membrane, ciliate
with hairs about 1 mm. long; **Panicle** commonly long-exserted, exceeding
the leaves, 1.5-8' long, the few branches stiffly ascending, mostly single, or
whorled at one or sometimes two nodes, naked at the base, the longest
mostly less than 3' long, bearing short-appressed branchlets usually less
than 1' long, the approximate appressed spikelets on pedicels commonly
less than the length of the spikelet; **Spikelets** 3-3.2 mm. (3-3.7) long, 1.2
mm. (1.1-1.5) wide, turgid, green or purplish; **Glumes,** the first half to
two-thirds the length of the spikelet, 3-5-nerved, acute, the second and
Sterile Lemma prominently 5-7-nerved, often with 1 or 2 additional
obscure nerves; **Fruit** 1.7-2 mm. long, 1-1.3 mm. wide, oval, obtuse, dark
olive-brown at maturity.

Dry prairies, rocky and gravelly hills, canyons and in bottom lands,
Texas to Arizona, and south into Mexico.

20. P. HIRSUTUM Swartz (hĕr-sū′tŭm).

Culms 3-5 feet tall, tufted, erect, stout, the culms as much as 10 mm.
thick, from short rootstocks, glabrous or with a few scattered stiff hairs,
the nodes appressed-pubescent; **Blades** 6-28' long, 12-20 mm. sometimes
35 mm. wide, slightly narrowed toward the base, flat, ascending or spreading, sometimes reflexed, margins and surface smooth or rough, glabrous
or sparsely pubescent, especially toward the base on the upper surface;
Sheaths grayish-hairy, mostly longer than the internodes, the lower
crowded and overlapping, often hirsute at the collar, commonly densely
papillose-hispid, the prominent papillae between the strong nerves with or

without hairs, the rather long hairs appressed, ascending or erect, har and sometimes irritating to the skin; **Ligule** membranaceous, about (mm. long or reduced to a mere line on the upper leaves, often with a den row of stiff hairs 3-5 mm. long back of the ligule; **Panicles** final exserted, erect, 6-15′ long, somewhat fan-shaped, axis scabrous, t branches single or in half whorls, ascending or slightly spreading, t lower often distant and as much as 10′ long, with branchlets as much 4′ long, naked at the base; **Spikelets** 2-2.3 mm. long, about 0.8 mm. wid lanceolate, acute, glabrous; **Glumes,** the first about two-fifths as long the spikelet, 3-5-nerved, acute, the second and **Sterile Lemma** exceedin the fruit, the lemma slightly longer than the glume, 7-9-nerved, the glum 7-nerved; **Sterile Palea** about as long as the fruit; **Fruit** 1.4-1.6 mm. lon about 0.7 mm. wide, elliptic, smooth and shining, the nerves evident.

In dry or moist places, banks of ditches or rivers, often among shrub Southern Texas and Mexico. (Rio Rico, near Mercedes.)

MAXIMA (măks′ĭ-mȧ) :—**Perennials; Culms** mostly robust and mor than 3 feet high, simple or branching at the base only, or with smal sterile shoots from the lower nodes; **Blades** linear, flat; **Ligule** men branaceous, ciliate; **Panicles** large, many-flowered; **Spikelets** ellipsoid glabrous, mostly faintly nerved, the sterile lemma with a well-developec palea, and in *P. maximum* a staminate flower; **Fruit** strongly to ver obscurely rugose, puberulent at the apex.

CULMS WITH A CORM-LIKE BASE.
Blades mostly over 5 mm. wide; culms more than 3.5 feet tall.   23. P. bulbosun
Blades less than 5 mm. wide; culms rarely as much as 3.5 feet tall.
                                                   23a. P. bulbosum var. minus
CULMS FROM A CREEPING ROOTSTOCK, NOT CORM-LIKE BASE.
Nodes hirsute; ligules 4-6 mm. long; fruit strongly rugose.   21. P. maximum
Nodes glabrous; ligules 3 mm. long; fruit very obscurely rugose.
                                                   22. P. plenum

21. **P. MAXIMUM** Jacq. (măks′ĭ-mŭm) ; GUINEA GRASS.

Culms 3-8 feet tall, even taller in cultivation, robust, in small or large tufts, from creeping rootstocks, erect or sometimes geniculate and rooting at the lower nodes, the nodes commonly densely hirsute; **Blades** 7-30′ long, 8-35 mm. wide, flat, erect or ascending, very scabrous on the margins, often hirsute on the upper surface near the base; **Sheaths** shorter than the internodes, ciliate, pubescent at collar, otherwise papillose-hirsute to glabrous; **Ligule** membranaceous at base, stiffly and densely ciliate with rather long hairs; **Panicle** long-exserted, 8-20′ long, usually about one-third as wide, stiffly erect, branches single or in whorls, ascending, naked at the base, axils pilose, the branchlets short, appressed, bearing more or less clustered short-pediceled spikelets; **Spikelets** about 2.8-3.3 mm. long, 1-1.2 mm. wide, oblong-ellipsoid, faintly nerved; **Glumes,** the first about one-third the length of the spikelet, obtuse, the second and **Sterile Lemma** about equal, slightly exceeding the fruit, usually purple, thin, the lemma inclosing a staminate flower; **Fruit** about 2.4 mm. long, 1 mm. wide, elliptic, strongly transversely rugose, minutely puberulent at the apex, acute.

Guinea grass has been cultivated for forage in the Gulf states, especially in Florida and southwest Texas. (Riviera and Padre Island causeway.) Spring and fall.

P. PLENUM Hitchc. & Chase (plē′nŭm).

Culms 1-6 feet tall, growing in rather large clumps from stout root-
ocks, robust, flattened, glabrous to minutely pubescent, often glaucous,
anching at the lower nodes; **Blades** 8-15′ long, 7-15 mm. wide, erect or
cending, flat, revolute on drying, margins and toward the apex scabrous,
metimes sparsely hairy on both surfaces near the base; **Sheaths** over-
pping on the lower short internodes (shorter than the upper), glabrous
the lower sometimes pubescent toward the summit, flattened; **Ligule**
nsely ciliate, about 1.5 mm. long; **Panicle** 8-24′ long, the lower branches
long or less, slender, 1-5 at a node, somewhat spreading, naked at the
se, with numerous slender branchlets; **Spikelets** 2.5-3.4 mm. (3-3.4) long,
2 mm. wide, oblong-elliptic, strongly nerved; **Glumes,** the first 3-nerved,
1.5 mm. long, scarcely half the length of the spikelet, subacute, slightly
abrous on the midnerve toward the apex, the second and **Sterile Lemma**
early equal, scarcely exceeding the fruit; the **Palea** of the sterile floret
bout as long as its lemma; **Fruit** about 3 mm. long, 1 mm. wide, elliptic,
cute, very obscurely rugose, minutely pubescent at the apex.

Moist places in canyons and on rocky hillsides. Texas to Arizona
nd Mexico. (San Antonio and Natalia.) Summer and fall.

3. P. BULBOSUM H. B. K. (bŭl-bō′sŭm) ; Bulbous Panic-grass.

Culms 3-7 feet tall, in tufts of few-to-several culms, robust, erect,
lattened, the lowest internode thickened into a hard corm-like base 8-20
m. thick, sometimes with one or more of the corms of the previous year
ttached, simple, the roots strong, scaly; **Blades** 8-16′ long, 3-12 mm.
vide, flat, erect or ascending, margins and upper surface scabrous, more
r less papillose-pilose, especially near the base; **Sheaths** shorter than
he internodes, glabrous to appressed-pubescent toward the base, some-
imes villous at throat, often papillose; **Ligule** membranaceous, truncate,
bout 1 mm. long, fimbriate; **Panicle** exserted, open, usually 8-13′ some-
imes as much as 25′ long, usually about half as wide, the slender flexuous
branches ascending or spreading, commonly in ones, twos or threes, often
ne long and other or others shorter, the lower sometimes as much as 17′
long, with branchlets as much as 7′ long, naked at the base, the ultimate
branchlets bearing rather short-pediceled spikelets; the axis and pedicels
scabrous; **Spikelets** 3-3.5 mm. (3.5-4.2) long, about 1.2 mm. wide, subacute,
glabrous, usually purplish; **Glumes,** the first about half as long as spikelet,
usually 3-nerved, the second at maturity shorter than the **Sterile Lemma**
and fruit, the sterile lemma rarely inclosing a staminate flower, both
usually 5-nerved; **Fruit** about as long as the spikelet, narrowly ovate,
transversely rugose, the subacute apex minutely puberulent.

Moist places in valleys and canyons; west Texas to Arizona and
Mexico. (Alpine.) Summer.

23a. P. BULBOSUM var. MINUS Vasey (mī′nŭs) ; *P. bulbosum sciaphilum*
(Rupr.) Hitchc. & Chase.

Plants less than 3.5 feet sometimes only 12-16′ tall; **Culms** slender,
few-to-several in loose clusters, the corms smaller, not over 8 mm. in
diameter, commonly many together attached at the base to a rootstock;
Blades 4-16′ usually less than 10′ long, 2-4 mm. wide; **Spikelets** 2.8-3.2 mm.
long. As limited here, this subspecies includes only those specimens having
both the smaller spikelets and narrower blades. Many intergrading forms
are included in the species. (No illustration, as spikelets similar but

smaller.) This grass has been collected in New Mexico and near Ft. Dav Texas.

Gravelly river banks, ravines, mesas and similar situations in t mountains from Texas to New Mexico and Arizona and central Mexic

VIRGATA (vẽr-gā′tȧ):—**Perennials** from stout rootstocks; most maritime species, with stout simple culms and firm foliage; **Ligule** me branaceous, ciliate; **Panicles** open or contracted; **Spikelets** glabrou mostly large, terete or thicker than wide, usually gaping owing to t well-developed staminate floret and its palea in addition to the perfe one, the **Glumes** and **Sterile Lemma** firm in texture, the **Fruit** relativel rather small, smooth and shining, in some species the margins of th lemma scarcely inrolled.

All of our species of this group are usually large robust plants, ofte glaucous, and with large spikelets.

P. amarum, first collected in Texas by the writer, and *P. amarulum,* taller plant, both with narrow elongated panicle, are stout woody plants o the seacoast.

P. havardii, with spikelets 6-8 mm. long, confined to extreme wester Texas, New Mexico and northern Mexico, and *P. virgatum,* with a wid range, have diffuse open panicles.

P. virgatum is very variable as to aspect, size of plants and spikelets and thrives under a diversity of soil and climate. The plants are sometime robust and rigid, attaining a height of 7 feet. Frequently these plants hav abortive spikelets, the writer having found this form at many places in eas Texas, at San Antonio and Ft. Worth, and often on higher and drier soi nearby were plants with fully developed spikelets. It is claimed that thes plants are affected by a smut, this sometimes resulting in abnormal forms This form should be further investigated.

SPIKELETS NOT OVER 2.5 mm. LONG. FIRST GLUME LESS THAN HALF
 as long as the spikelet. Panicle loosely-flowered, first glume truncate
 about one-fifth the length of the spikelet. 24. P. repens
SPIKELETS 3-7 mm. LONG; FIRST GLUME MORE THAN HALF THE
 length of the spikelet.
PANICLES ELONGATED, contracted; seacoast plants.
 Culms rarely 3.5 feet tall, solitary, from the nodes of horizontal rootstocks.

 Culms 3-7 feet tall, in dense tufts. 27. P. amarum
PANICLES DIFFUSE, or only slightly contracted; plants from creeping root- 28. P. amarulum
 stocks, sometimes of salt marshes but not littoral.
 Spikelets 6-8 mm. long; culms solitary with a creeping base. 26. P. havardii
 Spikelets 3.5-5 mm. long, long-beaked; culms erect. 25. P. virgatum

24. P. REPENS L. (rē′pĕns).

Culms 1-2.5 feet tall, rigid, erect or ascending from the nodes of strong horizontal often extensively creeping rootstocks, simple, clothed at the base with bladeless overlapping sheaths; **Blades** 1.5-6′ long, 2-5 mm. wide, flat or folded, or those of the sterile shoots sometimes longer and wider, firm, long-pilose at the base on the upper surface, otherwise sparsely pilose to glabrous on both surfaces; **Sheaths** usually overlapping, rather loose, more or less pilose, especially along the margins, or some- times glabrous; **Ligule** about 1 mm. long; **Panicles** stramineous, rather short-exserted, 2.5-5′ long, one-third to two-thirds as wide, the somewhat distant branches stiffly ascending, rarely spreading, usually naked at the base, bearing short-appressed branchlets with short-pediceled spikelets toward the ends; **Spikelets** 2.2-2.5 mm. long, 1-1.1 mm. wide, ovate, sharply

ointed; **Glumes,** the first about one-fifth as long as the spikelet, broad,
ose and truncate, obscurely nerved, the second and **Sterile Lemma** equal,
7-nerved; **Fruit** 1.8-1.9 mm. long, about 1 mm. wide, obovate-elliptic.
See photograph of *P. virgatum* for drawings.)

Seabeaches, extensively creeping and acting as a sandbinder, along
ie coast, Texas to Alabama.

5. P. VIRGATUM L. (vĕr-gā′tŭm) ; Switch-grass.

Culms commonly 3-5 feet tall, rarely taller, solitary or in small or
irge clumps, simple, robust, with numerous scaly creeping rootstocks,
iostly glabrous throughout, often glaucous or purple-tinged; **Blades**
-24′ long, 3-15 mm. wide, flat, long, attenuate, margins scabrous, some-
mes pilose or sparsely pubescent on the upper surface near the base,
irely extending to the apex; **Sheaths** shorter than the internodes, or
inger below, often ciliate, sometimes villous at the throat; **Ligule** a dense
ing of hairs 3-4 mm. long; **Panicles** long-exserted, 5-20′ long, ovate to
yramidal, mostly one-third to half as wide as long, sometimes contracted,
sually many-flowered, the slender, scabrous, single or fascicled branches
aked at the base, ascending or spreading, with many branchlets along the
pper half or two-thirds; **Spikelets** prominently nerved, rather short-
ediceled, commonly 3.5-5 mm. long (ranging from 3-6 mm.), 1.2-1.5 mm.
ride, elliptic-ovate, acuminate; **Glumes,** the first clasping, about two-
iirds the length of the spikelet, rarely equaling the sterile lemma,
cuminate to cuspidate, 5-nerved, the second longer than the **Sterile**
emma, both much exceeding the fruit, 5-7-nerved; **Fruit** about three-
ourths as long as the spikelet, narrowly ovate, the margins of the lemma
irolled only at the base.

Prairies, moist open ground, open woods and salt marshes, over most
f the United States, except the Pacific coast. Spring to fall.

6. P. HAVARDII Vasey (hā-vär′dĭ-ī) ; *P. virgatum macranthum* Vasey.

Plants 3 feet tall or more, pale-green, glaucous, glabrous throughout;
'ulms robust, solitary, erect from creeping rootstocks, simple; **Blades**
rect or ascending, 10-16′ long, 5-10 mm. wide, broadest at the base,
ipering into a long involute-setaceous tip, sometimes pilose on the upper
urface at the base; **Sheaths** longer than the internodes; **Ligule** about
mm. long, dense; **Panicle** short-exserted, as much as 16′ long, half to
hree-fourths as wide, loosely-flowered, the mostly verticillate branches
scending or finally spreading; **Spikelets** 6-8 mm. long, about 2 mm. wide,
vate-acuminate, strongly nerved; **Glumes,** the first clasping, half to two-
iirds the length of the spikelet, the second slightly shorter than the
terile Lemma, both exceeding the fruit, 7-9-nerved; **Fruit** 4.5-5 mm. long,
bout 1.8 mm. wide, narrowly ovate, the margin of the lemma inrolled
nly at the base.

This apparently rare species resembles *P. virgatum* from which it
iffers in the decumbent base of the solitary culms and in the larger spike-
its. (No illustration, as spikelets similar to *P. virgatum* except larger.)

Arroyos and sandhills, western Texas to New Mexico and northern
Iexico. (Guadalupe Mountains.)

7. P. AMARUM Ell. (ăm′ȧ-rŭm).

Plants glaucous and glabrous throughout; **Culms** commonly 2-3
arely 4.5 feet tall, solitary, in small or large colonies, sparingly branched
t the base, erect or ascending, from extensively creeping horizontal root-

stocks, the culms and rootstocks thick, woody and rigid, the large roo
stocks making the plant a good sand-binder; **Blades** ascending or sprea
ing, 6-16′ long, 6-16 mm. wide, flat, soon becoming involute toward th
tip, broadest at the base, thick, leathery; **Sheaths** mostly longer than th
internodes, the collar often purplish; **Ligule** membranaceous, short, th
ciliate hairs about 2-3 mm. long; **Panicles** short-exserted, or included a
the base, contracted, commonly 6-12′ long, 20-30 mm. wide, one-fourth t
one-third the length of the plant, rather densely-flowered, the leaves ofte
exceeding the panicles, the appressed or slightly ascending branches di
tant, usually several to a node, commonly 2-4′ long, bearing scattere
short-appressed branchlets, the pedicels short; **Spikelets** 4.5-5.5 mn
(5-6.5) long, 1.8-2 mm. wide, as much as 3 mm. thick, narrowly ovat
acuminate, prominently nerved; **Glumes,** the first clasping, usually abou
two-thirds as long as the spikelets, acuminate, 5-7-nerved (7-9), the mi
nerve usually scabrous toward the apex, the second usually slightly longe
than the **Sterile Lemma,** both much exceeding the fruit, 7-9-nerved, th
midnerve scabrous toward the apex; **Fruit** about three-fifths as long a
the spikelet, 1.5 mm. wide, narrowly ovate.

(Specimens collected at Galveston and Corpus Christi have panicle
shorter, more densely-flowered, and spikelets smaller than usual for th
species.)

Sandy seashores and coast dunes, Texas to Mississippi, Georgia t
Connecticut.   Fall.

28. P. AMARULUM Hitchc. & Chase (à-mâr′ū-lŭm).

Plants less glaucous than *P. amarum*, glabrous throughout, tufted, i
small or large bunches, sometimes 3-7 feet across, the rootstocks vertica
or ascending; **Culms** 3-6 feet tall, simple above the base, stout, sometime
10 mm. thick; **Blades** 5-20′ long, 5-12 mm. wide, erect or ascending, broad
est at the base, more or less involute, sometimes pilose on the upper sur
face near the base; **Sheaths** mostly shorter than the internodes (or over
lapping); **Ligule** a densely ciliate membrane, 2-3 mm. long; **Panicl**
finally exserted, 10-18′ long, 1-4′ wide, often one-third the length of th
plant, slightly nodding, the branches longer, and not so densely-flowere
or compact as in *P. amarum*, the branches erect or narrowly spreading a
their tip, often 4-6′ long, fascicled, mostly spikelet-bearing to the base
Spikelets short-pediceled, 4.3-5.5 mm. long, about 1.8 mm. wide, narrowl
ovate, acuminate, strongly nerved; **Glumes,** the first half to two-third
as long as the spikelet, acuminate, 5-7-nerved, scabrous on the midnerv
toward the apex, the second slightly longer than the **Sterile Lemma,** bot
7-9-nerved, pointed beyond the fruit; **Fruit** 3-3.5 mm. long, 1.2-1.5 mm
wide, narrowly ovate, bluntly pointed. (No illustration, as spikelet
similar to those of *P. amarum* except usually smaller.)

Sandy seashores and coast dunes, Texas to Louisiana, Florida t
Virginia.   (Sand dunes south of Corpus Christi.)   Fall.

TENERA (tĕn′ẽr-à):—**Perennials;** **Culms** slightly compressed, wiry
the internodes much elongated; **Blades** linear, at the base narrower tha
their sheaths; **Ligule** membranaceous, about 0.5 mm. long; **Panicles** small
narrow, nearly simple; **Spikelets** short-pediceled, glabrous or nearly so
Palea of sterile floret a small nerveless scale; **Fruit** elliptic, smooth an
shining.

In our single species the panicle is 1-3′ long, the pointed spikelet
2.2-2.8 mm. long.

9. P. TENERUM Beyr. (tĕn'ēr-ŭm).

Plants in small tufts from a knotted crown, 1-3 feet high, olivaceous; Culms erect, stiff and wiry, producing small, solitary panicles from the upper nodes or remaining simple, glabrous; **Blades** 1-6' long, 2-4 mm. wide the uppermost much reduced), erect, firm, drying involute at least toward the summit, pilose on the upper surface toward the base, or the lower sometimes on both surfaces; **Sheaths** much shorter than the internodes, the upper glabrous, the lower sparsely to copiously papillose-pubescent toward the summit with soft spreading or reflexed hairs; **Panicles** rather short-exserted, 1-3' long, rarely over 5 mm. wide, the short-appressed subracemose branches bearing rather crowded spikelets throughout their length, the pedicels usually with a few long hairs at the summit; **Spikelets** 2.2-2.8 mm. long, 0.8-1 mm. wide, narrowly ovate, pointed; **Glumes,** the first clasping, half as long as the spikelet or more, 1-nerved, glabrous or obscurely strigose toward the summit, the second and **Sterile Lemma** equal, exceeding the fruit, 5-7-nerved, glabrous; **Fruit** 1.7-1.8 mm. long, about 0.8 mm. wide.

This species has been described under the name of *P. stenodes* (Griseb.) Nash. (See drawings of *P. flexile.*)

Margins of swamps and wet places in flatwoods and pine barrens near the coast, Texas to Florida and North Carolina. (Nona, Texas.) Spring and fall.

AGROSTOIDIA (ăg-rŏs-toi'dĭ-à):—Tufted **Perennials; Culms** erect, compressed, sheaths more or less keeled; **Ligule** membranaceous, short, sometimes ciliate; blades long and narrow; **Spikelets** lanceolate, glabrous; **First Glume** keeled, scabrous on the keel toward the apex, the **Second Glume** and **Sterile Lemma** pointed beyond the fruit, more or less keeled, the spikelet thus often appearing laterally compressed, the palea of the sterile floret about half as long as its lemma; **Fruit** elliptic, smooth and shining, a *minute tuft* of thickish hairs at the apex.

SPIKELETS SET OBLIQUELY ON THEIR APPRESSED PEDICELS. Culms but little compressed; rootstocks present.
  Panicles open; spikelet 3-3.8 mm. (usually 3.4-3.8) long.   34. P. anceps
  Panicles more or less contracted; spikelets not over 2.8 mm. long.
                                               35. P. rhizomatum
SPIKELETS NOT OBLIQUELY DISPOSED. Culms strongly compressed with keeled sheaths; rootstocks absent.
  LIGULES CILIATE, 2-3 mm. long; basal leaves half as long as the culm or more; panicle much exceeding the upper blades; spikelets not over 2.7 mm. usually 2.5 mm. long, the first glume less than half the length of the spikelet.   33. P. longifolium
  LIGULES EROSE or lacerate, not ciliate; basal blades in short tufts, the upper usually nearly equaling the terminal panicle.
  FRUIT stipitate; spikelets 2.5-2.8 mm. long, conspicuously secund.
                                               32. P. stipitatum
  FRUIT not stipitate; spikelets not conspicuously secund.
    Spikelets 1.8-2 mm. long, in occasional specimens 2.2 mm. long; panicle branches ascending or spreading.   30. P. agrostoides
    Spikelets about 2.5 mm. long; panicle branches erect or nearly so.
                                               31. P. condensum

30. P. AGROSTOIDES Spreng. (ăg-rŏs-toi'dēz); Red-top Panic-grass, Munro-grass.

Culms 1.5-3 feet tall, commonly in dense clumps, from a short caudex, erect, glabrous throughout except as noted, rather stout, flattened, with numerous shoots of short leaves at the base, much shorter than those of

the culm; **Blades** 7-24′ long, the upper shorter, 5-12 mm. wide, erect, coi
duplicate, or revolute at the base on drying, flat above, narrowed som<
what toward the base, rough on the margins and midnerve underneath
Sheaths longer than the internodes, keeled, often pilose on the sides at th
union with the blade; **Ligule** membranaceous, erose, less than 1 mm. long
Panicles terminal and axillary, finally long-exserted, at first purplisl
finally pale, 4-10′ long, rarely longer, usually half to two-thirds as wid<
the stiff branches as long as 7′, ascending or sometimes spreading a
maturity, with more or less divergent densely-flowered branchlets, con
monly from the lower side, the ultimate branchlets and short pedice]
appressed, scabrous, the pedicels usually bearing at their summit one-t<
several delicate white hairs; **Spikelets** 1.6-2 mm. rarely 2.2 mm. long
0.7-0.8 mm. wide, at first purple, finally pale; **Glumes,** the first about hal
the length of the spikelet, 3-5-nerved, scabrous on the midnerve towar<
the apex, the second and **Sterile Lemma** subequal, 5-nerved, the midnerv
scabrous at the summit, the sterile palea nearly equal to the fruit; **Frui**
1.2-1.3 mm. long, about 0.6 mm. wide, a minute tuft of thickish hairs at th
apex.   The panicles much resemble those of red-top, *Agrostis alba* L.

Low places and wet meadows, eastern Texas to Florida, north t
Maine and Kansas.   (Orange.)   Summer and fall.

31. P. CONDENSUM Nash (kŏn-dĕn′sŭm).

Culms 3-6 feet tall, erect, sometimes geniculate at the base, rathe
stout, flattened, branched above; **Blades** 5-25′ long, 7-12 mm. wide, fla
and thin above, conduplicate with a very large midrib toward the base
smooth or margins and upper surface rough; **Sheaths** shorter than th
internodes, flattened, appressed-pubescent toward the summit; **Ligul**
membranaceous, less than 1 mm. long, erose; **Panicles** terminal and axillary
4-10′ long, narrowly oblong, commonly less than 2′ wide, slightly nodding
greenish-purple, the axillary smaller and more slender, the branche
mostly 1-6′ long, the lower naked at the base, distant, solitary or severa
to a node, appressed, erect or narrowly ascending, the short-appresse<
branchlets crowded with spikelets on short scabrous pedicels; **Spikelet**
about 2.2 mm. long, about 0.8 mm. wide, lanceolate, green to purplish
Glumes, the first half to slightly more than half as long as the spikelet
keeled, acuminate, very scabrous on midnerve toward the apex, the secon<
slightly longer than the **Sterile Lemma,** both acuminate, the tips slightl
spreading, scabrous on the midnerve toward the apex; **Palea** about half a
long as its lemma; **Fruit** about 1.3 mm. long (1.4-1.5), about 0.7 mm. wide
elliptic, shining, smooth, with a minute tuft of hairs at the apex.

In wet places along borders of streams and ponds; Texas to Florid<
and north to Pennsylvania.

32. P. STIPITATUM Nash (stĭp-ĭ-tā′tŭm) ; TALL FLAT PANIC-GRASS.

Plants like *P. agrostoides* in habit, often purple-tinged throughout
Culms on the average stouter, strongly compressed; **Blades** usually equal
ing or exceeding the terminal panicles, often scabrous on the lower sur
face; **Sheaths** much overlapping; **Panicles** usually several to a culm, some
times as many as five axillary panicles, commonly dark-purple, short
exserted, 4-8′ long, one-third to half as wide, densely-flowered, th<
numerous stiff branches ascending, with numerous divaricate branchlets
mostly from the lower side and beginning at the base, bearing crowde<
subsecund spikelets, the short scabrous pedicels only rarely with one o}
two erect hairs; **Spikelets** 2.5-2.8 mm. long, about 0.7 mm. wide, ofter

rved at the point; **Glumes,** the first about half the length of the spikelet,
e second and **Sterile Lemma** subequal, scabrous on the midnerve at the
uminate apex; **Fruit** about 1.5 mm. long, about 0.6 mm. wide, short-
pitate. (See drawings of *P. flexile.*)

Typical specimens of this species are characteristic and readily dis-
guished from *P. agrostoides,* but less densely-panicled forms, with smaller
kelets, approach that species.

Moist soil, east Texas to Missouri, Kentucky, South Carolina and north
Connecticut. Summer.

P. LONGIFOLIUM Torr. (lŏn-jĭ-fō′lĭ-ŭm) ; LONG-LEAVED PANIC-GRASS.

Culms in dense tufts, 14-32′ tall, usually surrounded by basal leaves
arly half as long as the culm, slender, stiff, much compressed; **Blades**
6′ long, 2-5 mm. wide, conduplicate at the base, flat above or somewhat
rolute, erect or sometimes recurved or tortuous, pilose on the upper
rface near the base, sometimes also on the lower surface; **Sheaths**
stly shorter than the internodes or longer at the base, keeled, usually
iry on the sides at the junction with the blades, otherwise glabrous or
lous toward the summit, sometimes densely so; **Ligule** fimbriate-ciliate,
mm. long, the ciliae usually at the sides only, not meeting at the back;
nicles finally long-exserted, much exceeding the leaves, the lateral
nicles few or none, 4-10′ long, usually half to two-thirds as wide, but
netimes rather contracted, the distant slender branches solitary or
scicled, ascending, usually naked at the base, bearing short-appressed
her closely-flowered branchlets, these and the pedicels scabrous, the
ter sometimes with a few hairs at the summit; **Spikelets** 2.4-2.7 mm.
ng, about 0.7 mm. wide; **Glumes,** the first two-fifths to scarcely half the
gth of the spikelet, acute, the second slightly longer than the **Sterile**
mma, both keeled, usually spreading at the tip, scabrous on the mid-
rve at the apex; **Fruit** 1.6 mm. long, 0.6 mm. wide. (See drawings of
flexile.)

Moist sandy land, mostly along the coast, central Texas to Florida,
rth to Connecticut and Rhode Island. (Jefferson.) Summer.

P. ANCEPS Michx. (ăn′sĕps) ; *P. rostratum* Muhl.; BEAKED OR FLAT-
STEMMED PANIC-GRASS.

Culms commonly 1.5-3 feet tall, sometimes taller, in small or large
ts, rather stout, from stout scaly branching rootstocks, somewhat
ttened, one side channeled, glabrous to sparsely pubescent; **Blades** 4-22′
g, 6-13 mm. wide, flat or slightly conduplicate at the base, erect, the
per surface slightly roughened, sometimes papillose, commonly ciliate
l densely pubescent on the upper surface toward the base, otherwise
brous to sparsely pubescent; **Sheaths** mostly longer than the internodes
id to be usually shorter), somewhat flattened, glabrous to densely
oillose-pilose, especially at the summit; **Ligule** membranaceous, very
rt; **Panicles** terminal only, or narrow panicles produced from the upper
aths, partly included, or sometimes long-peduncled, the terminal finally
g-exserted, open, 4-12′ long, often equaled or exceeded by the long
des, the rather long slender remote branches single, branching near
base and often appearing verticillate, ascending or spreading, bearing
rt mostly-appressed branchlets, the distant or approximate branchlets
h rather crowded spikelets, somewhat secund, the spikelets *set obliquely* on
ir short appressed scabrous pedicels, usually shorter than the spikelets,
first glume toward the axis, the axis and branches scabrous; **Spikelets**

3-3.2 mm. (3-3.8) long, 1-1.2 mm. wide, lanceolate, glabrous; **Glumes,**
first keeled, one-third to one-half as long as the spikelet, 3-5-nerv
scabrous on the keel toward the apex, acute; the second and **Sterile Lem**
subequal, the glume often slightly longer, forming a beak beyond
fruit, the tips open and often curved at maturity, the glume 5-7-nerv
midnerve often scabrous toward the apex, the lemma 5-nerved, with pa
about half as long; **Fruit** 2-2.2 mm. long, about 1 mm. wide, ellip
smooth and shining, a minute tuft of thickish hairs at the apex.

Moist sandy land, New Jersey to Florida and west to Kansas and Tex
Summer-fall.

35. P. RHIZOMATUM Hitchc. & Chase (rī-zō-mā′tŭm).

Plants like *P. anceps* in habit; **Culms** less robust, the scaly rhizor
slender and more numerous, the leaves more or less clustered at the ba
Blades 4-16′ commonly less than 12′ long, 5-10 mm. wide, pubescent
both surfaces or sometimes glabrous except on the upper surface near
base; **Sheaths** shorter than the internodes; or the lower overlappi
densely to sparsely villous along the margins and toward the summit
dense ring of pubescence at the junction of the blade; **Ligule** nearly obsol
Panicles, the terminal long-exserted, the usually numerous smaller axill
ones short-peduncled or partially included, 4-10′ long, usually less tl
one-third as wide, more or less contracted and densely-flowered, rat
more compound than in *P. anceps*, the distant primary branches asce
ing, bearing numerous branchlets 10-30 mm. long, these with appress
short, approximate branchlets, with crowded spikelets *set obliquely*
their short appressed pedicels as in *P. anceps,* but hardly at all secur
Spikelets 2.4-2.8 mm. long, about 1 mm. wide; **Glumes,** the first one-th
to scarcely half as long as the spikelet, acute, the second and **Ste**
Lemma subequal, beaked as in *P. anceps* but less strongly so, but li
exceeding the fruit; **Fruit** 1.9 mm. long, 0.9 mm. wide.

It is distinguished from *P. anceps* by the somewhat contracted, m
densely-flowered panicles of smaller spikelets, and by the short leaves m
or less crowded at the base. Usually the panicle is less open than
P. anceps. (See drawings of *P. flexile.*)

Moist sandy woods, Texas to Florida and north to Maryland. (Piel
Texas.) Summer.

VERRUCOSA (vĕr-ōō-kō′sà) :—Glabrous **Annuals** with weak, div
cately branching culms, decumbent at base and usually provided w
aerial braceroots at the lower nodes, the lower internodes much shor
than the middle and upper; **Ligule** ciliate, not over 0.5 mm. long; **Pani**
with divaricate capillary branches, spikelet-bearing toward the en
Spikelets tuberculate; **Fruit** minutely papillose, the margins of the lem
flat, inrolled only at base.

SPIKELETS about 2 mm. long, glabrous.	36. P. verrucos
SPIKELETS over 3 mm. long, hispid.	37. P. brachyantl

36. P. VERRUCOSUM Muhl. (vĕr-ōō-kō′sŭm).

Culms 0.6-5 feet tall, slender (plants light-green), solitary or few
gether, lax, at first erect but soon decumbent at base, and ascending
widely spreading; **Blades** 2-8′ long, 4-10 mm. wide, flat, thin, lax, sor
what narrowed toward the base, gradually narrowed to the acuminate t
Sheaths shorter than the internodes, ciliate; **Ligule** ciliate, not over
mm. long; **Panicles** finally exserted, diffuse, 2-12′ long, about as wi

all panicles often produced at the lower nodes, at least the ultimate anchlets scabrous, the branches mostly solitary, the branchlets bearing a w short-pediceled spikelets mostly in twos toward the ends; **Spikelets** 3-2.1 mm. long, about 1 mm. wide, elliptic-obovate, subacute; **Glumes,** e first one-fourth the length of the spikelet or less, the second and **erile Lemma** warty, glabrous, the glume shorter than the fruit at turity; **Fruit** 1.8-2 mm. long, 1 mm. wide, elliptic, acute. (See drawings *P. flexile.*)

Wet, mostly shady soil, Atlantic Coastal Plain, southeast Texas to orida and north to Massachusetts. Also Indiana and Tennessee. efferson.) Spring-fall.

. P. BRACHYANTHUM Steud. (brăk-ĭ-ăn'thŭm); *P. sparsiflorum* Vasey.

Culms 1-3.5 feet tall, slender, freely branching from the lower nodes, e plants weakly ascending or spreading from a decumbent base; **Blades** 6' long, 2-3 mm. wide, narrowed toward the base, often involute and abrous toward the tip, the uppermost usually reduced; **Sheaths** shorter an the internodes, minutely ciliate; **Ligule** ciliate, not over 0.5 mm. long; anicles finally exserted, 2-6' long, about as wide, the branches few, abrous, the lower sometimes as much as 4' long, bearing a few short-ediceled spikelets, mostly in twos, toward the ends; **Spikelets** 3.2-3.6 mm. ng, 1.5 mm. wide, elliptic-obovate, abruptly pointed; **Glumes,** the first inute, the second and **Sterile Lemma** subequal, the tubercles bearing iff spreading hairs; **Fruit** 2.9-3 mm. long, 1.4 mm. wide, obovate-elliptic, bacute. (See drawings of *P. flexile.*)

Sandy soil, Texas, Louisiana and Oklahoma. (Jacksonville, College tation, Galveston.)

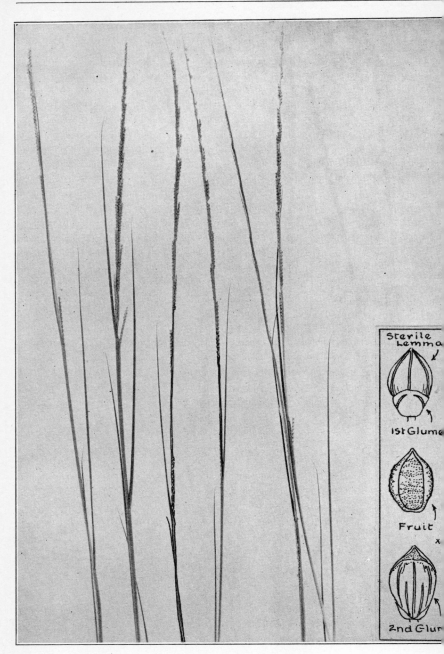

PANICUM GEMINATUM

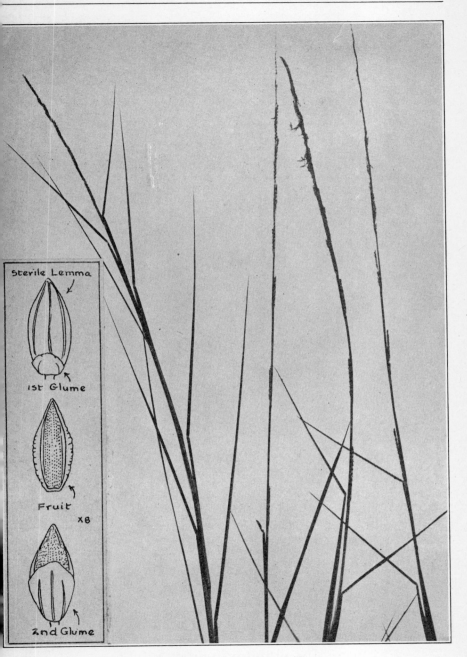

PANICUM PALUDIVAGUM

PANICUM PURPURASCENS; Para Grass

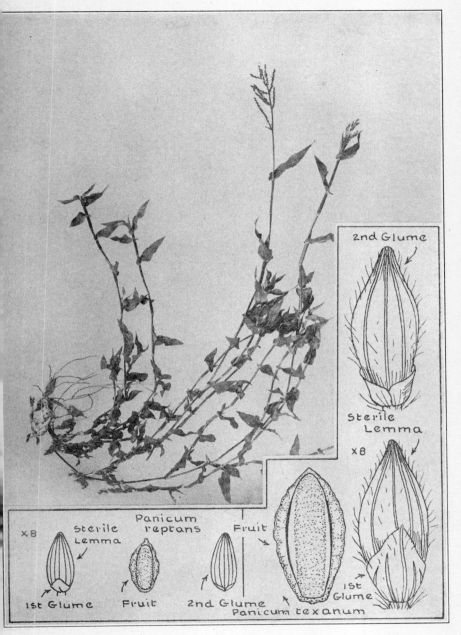

PANICUM REPTANS; drawings of PANICUM TEXANUM

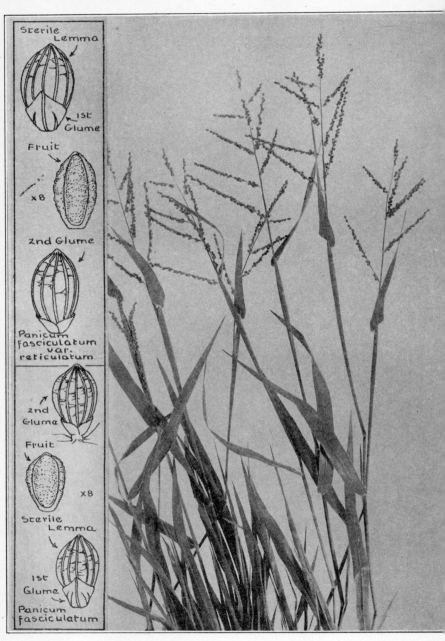

PANICUM FASCICULATUM var. RETICULATUM; drawing of
PANICUM FASCICULATUM

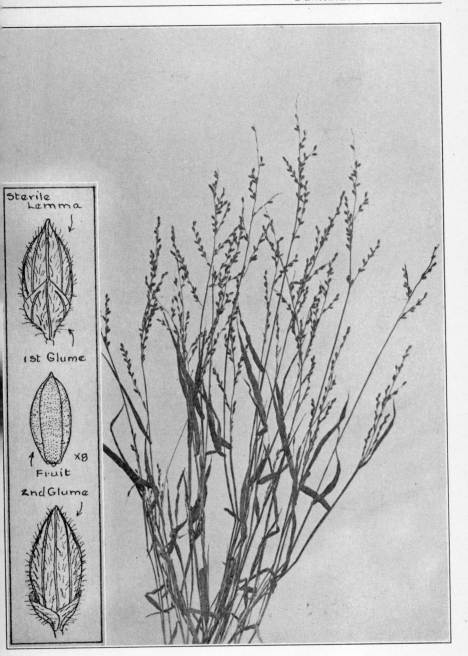

Sterile Lemma

1st Glume

Fruit ×8

2nd Glume

PANICUM ARIZONICUM

PANICUM TEXANUM; Colorado Grass, Congho Grass, Texas Mille
(See *P. reptans* for drawing of spikelet)

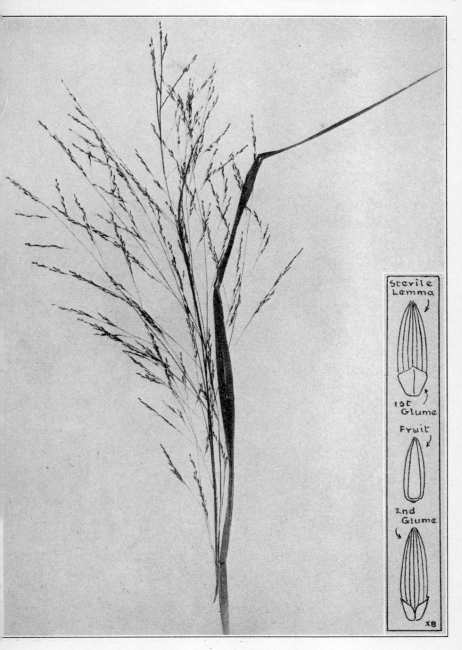

Sterile
Lemma

1st
Glume

Fruit

2nd
Glume

x8

PANICUM DICHOTOMIFLORUM

PANICUM CAPILLARE; Old-witch-grass

PANICUM MILIACEUM; Proso Millet

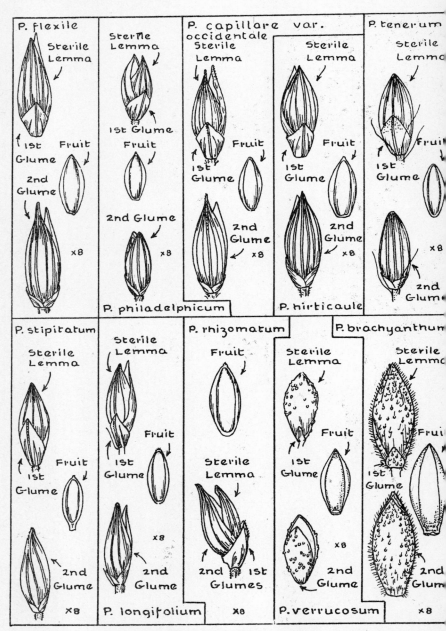

PANICUM FLEXILE; P. PHILADELPHICUM; P. CAPILLARE va
OCCIDENTALE; P. HIRTICAULE; P. TENERUM; P. STIPITATUM
P. LONGIFOLIUM; P. RHIZOMATUM; P. VERRUCOSUM;
P. BRACHYANTHUM

PANICUM CAPILLARIOIDES

PANICUM HIRSUTUM

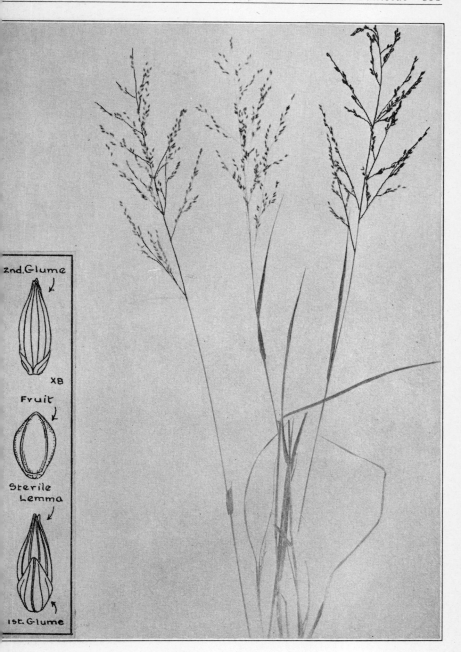

PANICUM HALLII

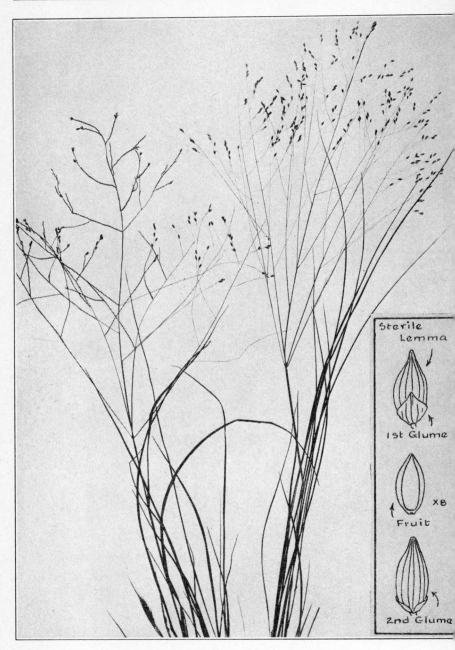

PANICUM FILIPES

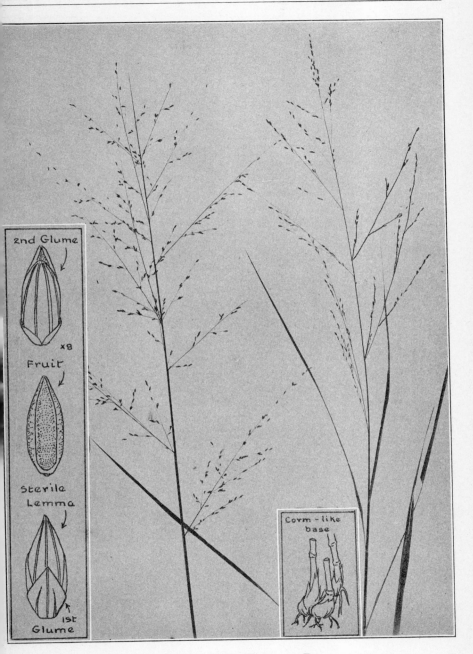

PANICUM BULBOSUM; Bulbous Panic-grass

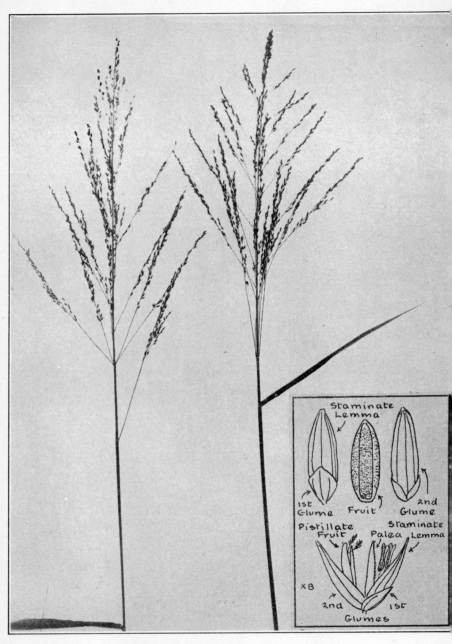

PANICUM MAXIMUM; Guinea-grass

Sterile
Lemma

1st Glume

Fruit
×8

2nd Glume

PANICUM PLENUM

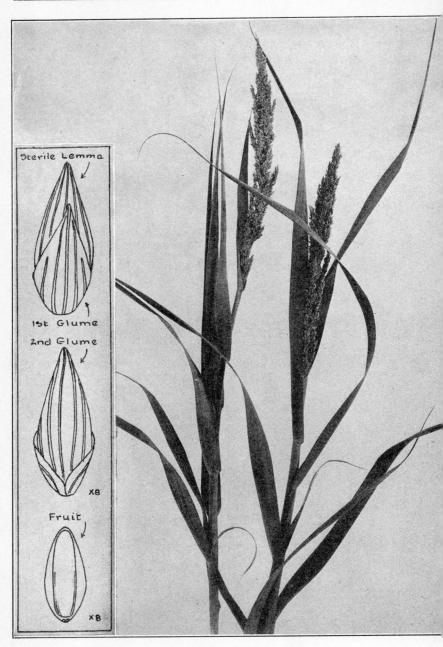

PANICUM AMARUM

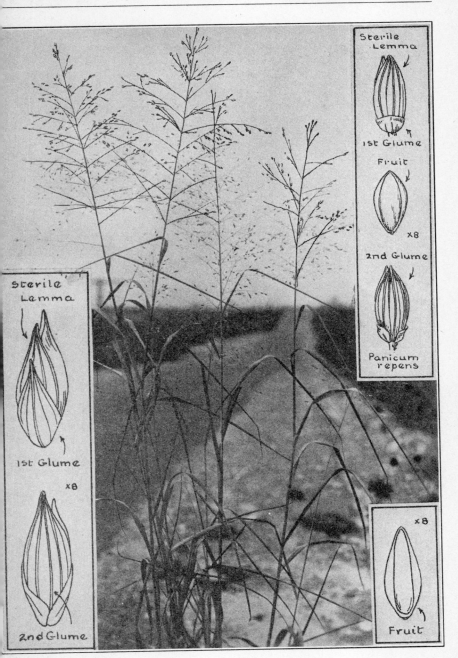

PANICUM VIRGATUM; Switch-grass, and drawing of PANICUM
REPENS

PANICUM ANCEPS

PANICUM AGROSTOIDES

PANICUM CONDENSUM

MISCELLANEOUS SPECIES

P. GYMNOCARPON Ell. (jĭm-nō-kär′pŏn) ; *Phanopyrum gymnocarpon* Nash.

Culms 2-6 feet tall, erect or ascending from a decumbent or prostrate e, branching and rooting at the usually dark lower nodes, succulent, tened, the erect or ascending portion usually 2-3 feet tall, often grow- in a tangled mass of culms, glabrous or nearly so throughout; **Blades** ′ long, the upper and lower shorter, 15-30 mm. wide, flat, slightly rowed at the cordate-clasping base, lanceolate, margins scabrous, some- es sparingly ciliate toward the base; **Sheaths** shorter than the inter- es, sometimes margins ciliate toward the summit, flattened, usually loose; **Ligule** membranaceous, about 1 mm. long, somewhat decurrent vn the margins of the sheath; **Panicles** finally exserted, ovate to amidal, 6-15′ long, consisting of several-to-many rather rigid spikelike emes, solitary or fascicled along the rigid and angular main axis, fly ascending or spreading, mostly less than 7′ long, except the lower kelet-bearing to the base, the spikelets short-pediceled on one side of rt appressed branchlets, thus appearing in somewhat scattered sters; **Spikelets** about 6 mm. long, about 1.2 mm. wide when closed, ongly nerved; **Glumes** and **Sterile Lemma** acuminate-pointed, the first rly as long as the sterile lemma, 3-nerved, the second exceeding the rile lemma, both much exceeding the fruit and at maturity spreading l exposing it, 5-nerved, the summit of the lemma arcuate, the sterile ea about 2.5 mm. long or obsolete, hyaline; **Fruit** 1.7-2 mm. long, out 1 mm. wide, obovate, stipitate, smooth and shining.

Marshes, ditches and muddy banks of streams and lakes, Texas to rida. (Along the Sabine River at Orange.) Fall.

P. OBTUSUM H. B. K. (ŏb-tū′sŭm) ; GRAPEVINE MESQUITE.

Grapevine mesquite is a perennial forage grass of the southwest, with f, erect culms, 1-2 feet high, often with stolons several feet long, and is uspicuous for the *swollen woolly nodes on the stolons.*

Culms 8-30′ tall, erect, rather rigid, simple, flattened, glabrous, l *nodes glabrous*, decumbent at base, with knotted rootstocks, stolons en several feet long, with swollen bearded or *woolly nodes;* **Blades** ′ commonly 4-7′ long, 2-6 mm. wide, and of the stolons 1.5-3′ long, 2-4 . wide, margins scabrous, surface smooth to rough, firm, erect, long crow-pointed, sparsely hairy on upper surface near the base; **Sheaths** rter than the internodes, the very lowest pubescent or villous; **Ligule** mbranaceous and about 1 mm. long; **Panicle** included or short-exserted, .5′ long, narrow, with a few appressed raceme-like branches, densely- wered, usually 0.6-1.5′ long; **Spikelets** about 3.2-3.8 mm. long, commonly -1.8 mm. wide and about 2 mm. thick, obovate, blunt, green at first, er turning brownish, often in pairs along one side of rachis, short- diceled; **Glumes**, the first about one-fourth shorter than the spikelet, erved, sometimes 5-nerved, the second glume and sterile lemma about ual, the second glume 5-7-nerved, sometimes 9-nerved; **Sterile Lemma** ′-nerved, subtending a palea and staminate flower; **Fruit** about 3-3.5 . long, 1.5-1.7 mm. wide, subacute, smooth and shining, slightly nutely pubescent near the apex.

Sandy or gravelly soil, mostly along the banks of streams and ditches, xas, south to Mexico and west to Arizona, north to Colorado and ssouri. Spring to fall.

40. P. HEMITOMON Schultz (hē-mĭt′ō-mŏn); Maiden Cane or Simpso Grass.

Plants aquatic or semi-aquatic, pale-green, leafy, with extensiv creeping rootstocks, often producing numerous sterile shoots with ov lapping, sometimes densely hirsute, sheaths; **Culms** (fertile) 1.5-4 f tall, erect, stout; **Blades** 4-10′ long, 7-12 mm. (7-15) wide, ascending spreading, flat, acuminate, rounded at the base, rough on the marg and sometimes on the upper surface; **Sheaths** (aerial) shorter than internodes, glabrous or ciliate on the margins, rarely hirsute toward summit like those of the sterile shoots, or the lower hirsute throughou **Ligule** lacerate-ciliate, about 1 to 1.5 mm. long; **Panicles** usually sho exserted, 6-10′ long, very narrow, the branches erect or ascendi solitary or 2 or 3 in a fascicle, the lower distant, mostly 1-2.5′ long sometimes longer, bearing short appressed branchlets or subsessile spi lets along the triquetrous scabrous rachis; **Spikelets** about 2.5 mm. lo about 0.9 mm. wide, or when spreading open about 1.2 mm. wide, lanc late, acute, often somewhat laterally compressed (i. e. the glume so kee that the spikelet lies on its side); **Glumes,** the first clasping, about h the length of the spikelet, acute, 3-nerved, midnerve scabrous toward t apex, the second strongly keeled, somewhat boat-shaped, acute, 3-5-nerve slightly shorter than the 5-nerved **Sterile Lemma,** the latter inclosing membranaceous scabrous-nerved palea of nearly equal length, often su tending a staminate flower; **Fruit** about 2.2 mm. long, 0.7 mm. wic slightly boat-shaped, elliptic, acute, smooth and shining, not rigid, t margins of the lemma inrolled toward the base only, the apex of the lemn scarcely inclosed. In this species the spikelets rarely perfect their grain It departs somewhat from the typical species of *Panicum* in that the fru is less rigid and the tip of the palea is not entirely inclosed by the ferti lemma. The fruit is not rugose as in the closely related subdivisio *Geminata*.

In moist soil, along river banks and ditches, borders of lakes and pond often in water, Texas to Florida and north to Delaware. (Bellville.)

41. P. HIANS Ell. (hī′ăns); *Steinchisma hians* (Ell.) Nash.

Culms 10-25′ tall, tufted, simple or sparingly branched, erect or oute culms sometimes geniculate, taking root at the lower nodes; **Blades** 2-(long, 2-6 mm. wide, flat, erect or ascending, sparingly pilose on the uppe surface near the base; **Sheaths** shorter than the internodes, keeled; **Ligul** membranaceous, less than 1 mm. long; **Panicle** commonly 3-5′ sometime 8′ long, at first included at the base, finally exserted, mostly open, erec or nodding, the primary branches usually few, 5-10, distant, slender appressed or spreading, naked below, the spikelets more or less secund crowded in continuous or interrupted clusters; **Spikelets** on short pedicels 2.2-2.4 mm. long, before maturity lanceolate-terete, nearly 1 mm. wide finally on opening becoming much broader, strongly nerved; **Glumes,** the first half to two-thirds as long as the spikelet, 1-1.5 mm. long, 3-nerved acute; the second and **Sterile Lemma** subequal, 3-7-nerved, at maturity slightly exceeded by the *enlarged indurated sterile palea;* **Fruit** 1.8-1.9 mm. long, 0.7 mm. wide, the margins of the lemma scarcely inrolled. It is only at maturity that the sterile palea becomes noticeably enlarged and in durated.

In damp soil, along ditches and streams, in most or all of the southern states and extending into New Mexico. Spring to fall.

PANICUM OBTUSUM; GRAPEVINE MESQUITE

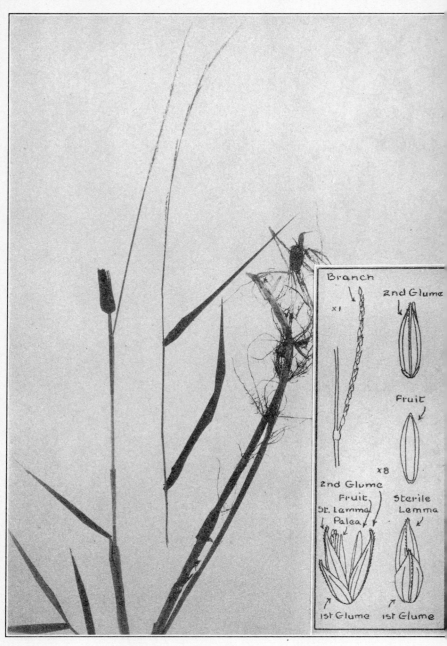

PANICUM HEMITOMON; Maiden Cane

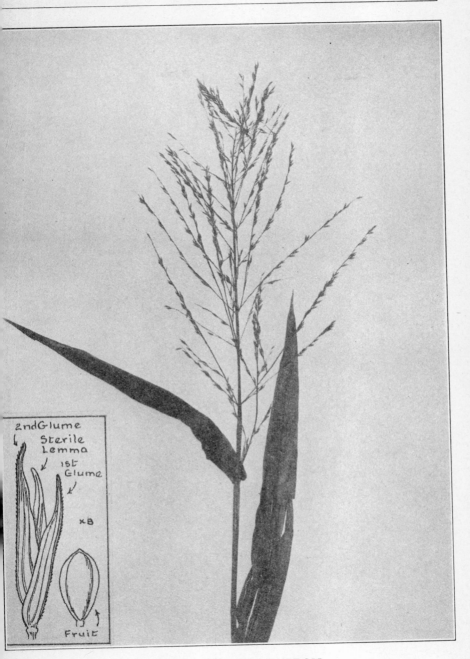

2ndGlume
Sterile
Lemma
1st
Glume

×8

Fruit

PANICUM GYMNOCARPON

PANICUM HIANS

bgenus DICHANTHELIUM Hitchc. & Chase (dī-kăn-thē'lĭ-ŭm).

Perennial, from a crown, rarely from short, matted rootstocks, sur-
ınded by a more or less *well-marked rosette of usually short winter leaves,*
spring producing *simple culms with mostly narrowly-lanceolate blades
d terminal panicles with numerous spikelets, these rarely perfecting seed;*
ə early culms branching at some or all of the nodes (in a few species
ɔm the base only) after the maturity of the primary panicles or some-
ıes before; the branches often repeatedly branching, the short branchlets
ɔre or less fascicled and bearing usually much reduced leaves; the terminal
ɐ or two joints of the primary culms often finally falling, the whole pro-
.cing an *autumnal form usually strikingly different from the vernal
·m;* the secondary panicles reduced, the latest more or less included in
ə sheaths, *cleistogamous* and *perfecting their grains.*

In this group there is an intermediate stage of branching, in which the
ɐnts do not show the characteristic vernal or autumnal habit. Vernal
lms are sometimes produced on plants during the branched condition be-
use of renewal of activity due to increased moisture, excess of nutriment,
jury, or other causes.

SYNOPSIS OF GROUPS

.ADES ELONGATED, NOT OVER 5 mm. WIDE, MOSTLY 20 TIMES OR
  more as long as wide; autumnal form branching from the base only (from
  the lower nodes in *P. werneri*).   Depauperata (p. 613)
.ADES NOT ELONGATED (OR IF SO MORE THAN 5 mm. WIDE AND
  autumnal form not branching from base).
PLANTS BRANCHING from the base, finally forming rosettes or cushions,
  foliage soft and lax; blades prominently ciliate.   Laxiflora (p. 615)
PLANTS BRANCHING from the culm nodes or rarely remaining simple.
  BLADES long, stiff, autumnal form bushy-branched above. Spikelets turgid,
    attenuate at base, mostly pustulose-pubescent; blades conspicuously
    striate, tapering from base to apex.   Angustifolia (p. 615)
  BLADES not long and stiff (somewhat so in *P. oligosanthes*).
    Plants not forming a distinct winter rosette; spikelets attenuate at base,
      papillose; blades narrow.   Pedicellata (p. 633)
    Plants forming a distinct winter rosette; spikelets not attenuate at base.
      Spikelets turgid, blunt, strongly nerved (not strongly turgid in
        P. oligosanthes); blades rarely as much as 15 mm. wide (sometimes
        20 mm. in *P. ravenelii*).
        Sheaths, or some of them, papillose-hispid (sometimes all glabrous in
          P. helleri); spikelets 3-4 mm. long.   Oligosanthia (p. 630)
        Sheaths glabrous or minutely puberulent; spikelets 1.5-2.5 mm. long,
          unsymmetrically pyriform; culms wiry.   Lancearia (p. 629)
      Spikelets not turgid, blunt, not strongly nerved (see *P. roanokense*).
        Ligule of conspicuous hairs, usually 3-5 mm. long.
          Sheaths glabrous or only the lowermost somewhat pubescent.
                                                            Spreta (p. 622)
          Sheaths strongly pubescent.   Lanuginosa (p. 623)
        Ligule obsolete or nearly so.
          SPIKELETS SPHERICAL AT MATURITY; blades glabrous, firm,
            cordate; plants sparingly branching.   Sphaerocarpa (p. 627)
          SPIKELETS USUALLY OBOVATE OR ELLIPTIC.
            BLADES OF THE midculm elongated, less than 15 mm. wide; culms
              usually tall; spikelets pointed, abruptly so in the velvety
              P. scoparium.   Scoparia (p. 634)
            BLADES OF THE midculm not elongated.
              BLADES cordate, 10-30 mm. long, wide; spikelets pubescent.
                Spikelets 2.5-3 mm. long; sheaths glabrous or minutely puberu-
                  lent.   Commutata (p. 636)
                Spikelets 3-5 mm. long (sometimes only 2.7 mm. long in the
                  hispid-sheathed *P. clandestinum*).   Latifolia (p. 637)

BLADES not cordate, less than 10 mm. wide. Sheaths glabrou
vernal culms slender but not delicate, rarely less than 16' ta
lower internodes not shortened; vernal culms about ever
leafy throughout, spikelets elliptic or obovate, not over 2.5 m
long.   Dichotoma (p. 61

KEY TO SPECIES

SPIKELETS GLABROUS, RARELY SPARSELY PUBESCENT.
SPIKELETS 3 mm. LONG or more, strongly nerved.
Spikelets pointed or beaked 3.5 mm. long; blades elongated.
                                                  42. P. depauperatu
Spikelets blunt, blades not elongated.
Spikelets 3.2-3.3 mm. long; blades firm; sheaths or some of them hispi
                                                  74. P. scribnerianu
Spikelets not over 3 mm. long; blades rather thin; sheaths glabrous
sparsely hispid.   73. P. helle
SPIKELETS LESS than 3 mm. long.
SECOND glume and sterile lemma exceeding the fruit and pointed beyond i
spikelet 2.3-2.6 mm. long; blades not clustered toward the base.
Sheaths, at least the secondary, hispid.   80. P. scabriusculu
Sheaths glabrous; blades firm; fruit, 1.5 mm. long.   81. P. cryptanthu
SECOND glume and sterile lemma not pointed beyond the fruit.
Ligule manifest, 1-3 mm. long. Culms rather stout; sheaths glabrous.
                                                  59. P. spretu
Ligule obsolete; spikelets 1.5-2.4 mm. long.
Spikelets 1.5 mm. long or less; nodes bearded.   53. P. microcarp
Spikelets 2 mm. long or more.
Blades elongated, some of them 20 times as long as wide; spikele
2.1-2.4 mm. long; blades erect; branches, when present, from t
lower nodes only.   45. P. werne
Blades not elongated, about 10 times as long as wide.
CULMS SOON PROSTRATE, VINE-LIKE; BRANCHES DIVAR
CATE; plants bright-green; spikelets not over 2.1 mm. long.
                                                  58. P. lucidu
CULMS NOT VINE-LIKE; BRANCHES NOT DIVARICATE; spik
lets 2 mm. long (1.5-1.6 mm. long in P. portoricense).
CULMS CRISP-puberulent, wiry, blades ciliate at the base.
Spikelets 2.1 mm. long; blades firm, glabrous above.
                                                  71. P. lanceariu
Spikelets 1.5-1.6 mm. long.   70. P. portoricens
CULMS GLABROUS; blades not ciliate.
BLADES erect, firm; spikelets turgid; strongly nerved; plant
grayish-olive.   57. P. roanokens
BLADES spreading; spikelets not turgid.
Nodes glabrous; autumnal form erect, branched like a tree.
                                                  55. P. dichotomu
Nodes, at least the lowest, usually bearded; autumnal form top
heavy-reclining.   56. P. barbulatu
SPIKELETS PUBESCENT, RARELY GLABROUS.
SPIKELETS 3 mm. LONG, or more.
BLADES elongated, those of the midculm at least 15 times as long a
wide; secondary panicles from the basal sheaths only.
Spikelets pointed, about 3.5 mm. long.   42. P. depauperatu
Spikelets 2.7-3.2 mm. long.   43. P. perlongu
BLADES not elongated, usually less than 10 times as long as wide.
Blades velvety pubescent beneath.
Spikelets 3 mm. long; plants very villous throughout.
                                                  72. P. malacophyllu
Spikelets 4 mm. long or more; ligule 3-4 mm. long. 76. P. raveneli
Blades not velvety-pubescent beneath.
Sheaths glabrous or minutely puberulent only.
Nodes bearded; spikelets 4 mm. long, or more.   85. P. bosci
Nodes not bearded; spikelets scarcely more than 3 mm. long.
Spikelets turgid, blunt; blades mostly less than 10 mm. wide.
                                                  73. P. helleri

Spikelets not turgid; blades more than 10 mm. wide; panicles as broad as long; branches spreading.
Culms erect or autumnal form leaning; blades symmetrical, broadly cordate.   82. P. commutatum
Culms decumbent; blades usually unsymmetrical and falcate, narrowed to the scarcely cordate base.   83. P. joorii
Sheaths pubescent, the hairs spreading to appressed.
Pubescence ascending or appressed; spikelets 3.5-4 mm. long; first glume not remote.   75. P. oligosanthes
Pubescence spreading; sometimes sparse.
PLANTS ROBUST, OVER 3.5 FEET TALL; blades usually 20 mm. wide or more.   84. P. clandestinum
PLANTS RARELY MORE THAN 20' TALL; blades rarely over 15 mm. wide; panicles about as wide as long; blades ascending or spreading.
SPIKELETS ATTENUATE at base, 3.5-4 mm. long (no distinct winter rosette).
CULMS erect or leaning; blades thin, 2-4' long, narrowed toward the base.   77. P. pedicellatum
CULMS decumbent; blades thick, not over 2' long, not narrowed toward base.   78. P. nodatum
SPIKELETS NOT attenuate at the base, not over 3.3 mm. long.
SPIKELETS 3.2-3.3 mm. long; blades firm; sheaths, some of them more or less hispid.   74. P. scribnerianum
SPIKELETS not over 3 mm. long; blades thin, sheaths, or some of them, glabrous, or sparsely hispid.   73. P. helleri
SPIKELETS LESS than 3 mm. long.
BLADES elongated, not over 5 mm. wide; secondary panicles at the base only or wanting.
Culms single or a few in a tuft; spikelets turgid, 2.7-3 mm. long.   43. P. perlongum
Culms in large tufts; spikelets not turgid, not over 2.7 mm. long.
Sheaths pilose.   44. P. linearifolium
Sheaths glabrous.   45. P. werneri
BLADES usually not elongated; secondary panicles not at the base.
Spikelets attenuate at the base, mostly prominently pustulose; blades narrow, stiff, strongly nerved, tapering from base to apex.
Nodes bearded; plants grayish-villous; autumnal blades flat.
Spikelets 2 mm. long.   48. P. chrysopsidifolium
Spikelets 2.5-2.8 mm. long.   49. P. consanguineum
Nodes not bearded; plants villous only at the base, or nearly glabrous.
Autumnal blades flat; lower panicle branches spreading or deflexed.   50. P. angustifolium
Autumnal blades involute; lower panicle branches more or less ascending.
PLANTS GLABROUS OR NEARLY SO; autumnal culms erect; spikelets not subsecund; panicle loose and open.   52. P. ovinum
PLANTS PUBESCENT, AT LEAST ON THE LOWER HALF.
SPIKELETS ABOUT 2.4 mm. long; vernal blades 3-5' long, autumnal blades not falcate.   51. P. arenicoloides
SPIKELETS NOT over 2 mm. long; vernal blades 1.5-2.5' long, autumnal blades falcate.   47. P. aciculare
Spikelets not attenuate at the base.
Sheaths retrorsely pilose; blades soft and lax. Panicle branches loosely spreading; blades ciliate and more or less pilose on the surface; spikelets 2 mm. long.   46. P. xalapense
Sheaths not retrorsely pilose.
Ligule manifest, mostly 2-5 mm. long.
SHEATHS, OR ALL BUT THE LOWEST, GLABROUS; spikelets not over 1.6 mm. long.
Panicles narrow, one-fourth to one-third as wide as long.   59. P. spretum
Panicle open, nearly as wide as long; spikelets 1.5 mm. long.   60. P. lindheimeri
SHEATHS PUBESCENT, SPIKELETS NOT POINTED AT MATURITY; blades not cordate; ligule 2-5 mm. long.

SPIKELETS NOT over 1 mm. long.   61. P. wrightianu

SPIKELETS MOSTLY more than 1.5 mm. long, if less, pubescen
spreading.

PLANTS grayish, velvety-pubescent.

Plants dark or olive-green when dry; sparingly branching fr
middle nodes, erect; vernal blades sparingly pilose
upper surface.   64. P. thurov

Plants light- or yellow-green when dry; autumnal form a
cending or spreading, branching from the middle a
upper nodes; the reduced fascicled blades strongly cilial
culms 16-28' tall, autumnal culms usually 8-20' tall.
63. P. lanuginosu

PLANTS pubescent, often villous, but not velvety.

Culms conspicuously pilose with long, horizontally spreadi
hairs; branching before the expansion of primary panic
65. P. praecoc

Culms variously pubescent, if pilose the hairs not long a
horizontally spreading; vernal blades pubescent on
upper surface, sometimes pilose near base and marg
only.

Spikelets 1.6-1.8 mm. long; vernal blades pilose
pubescent; upper surface of blades appressed-pubesce
or pilose toward the base only; autumnal form
decumbent-spreading.

Blades stiffly erect.   62. P. huachu

Blades lax, spreading.
62a. P. huachucae var. fasciculat

Spikelets 2.2 mm. long or more; pubescence on culms h
zontally spreading; autumnal form freely branching.
66. P. villosissim

Spikelets 2.7-2.9 mm. long; culms stiff; blades conspicuou
ciliate.   67. P. ov

Ligule obsolete or less than 1 mm. long.

NODES BEARDED (*P. SCOPARIUM MAY APPEAR TO*
bearded).

SPIKELETS NEARLY 3 mm. long; plants velvety-villous throu
out.   72. P. malacophyll

SPIKELETS RARELY as much as 2.5 mm. long; plants
pubescent throughout.

Spikelets 1.5-1.6 mm. long.   53. P. microcar

Spikelets 2 mm. long; blades glabrous or only the lo
pubescent or velvety; autumnal form profusely branchi
fruits slightly exposed at maturity; upper sheaths vis
spotted.   54. P. nitid

NODES NOT BEARDED.

PLANTS DENSELY gray-velvety throughout, a viscid glabr
ring below the nodes.   79. P. scopari

PLANTS NOT gray-velvety.

SHEATHS or some of them pilose or hispid; pubesce
papillose-hispid.

Spikelets ovate, pointed, 2.3-2.6 mm. long.
80. P. scabriuscu

Spikelets obovate obtuse, nearly 3 mm. long; blades ab
20 mm. wide.   84. P. clandestin

SHEATHS glabrous or puberulent only.

Spikelets spherical, not over 1.8 mm. long; blades cord
ciliate at the base.

Culms spreading; panicle nearly as broad as long.

Blades lanceolate.   68. P. sphaerocar

Blades with the margins parallel two-thirds of th
length.   68a. P. sphaerocarpon var. inflat

Culms erect or ascending; panicle never more than t
thirds as broad as long; spikelets 1.5 mm. long; bla
lanceolate, the upper not reduced.   69. P. polyant

Spikelets not spherical.
  Culms soon prostrate, vine-like; branches divaricate; plants
    bright-green; spikelets not over 2.1 mm. long.
                                              58. P. lucidum
  Culms not vine-like; branches not divaricate; spikelets un-
    symmetrically pyriform; strongly nerved; culms wiry.
    Spikelets 1.5-1.6 mm. long.   70. P. portoricense
    Spikelets 2.1 mm. long; blades firm, glabrous above.
                                              71. P. lancearium

DEPAUPERATA (dē-pô-pĕr-ā′tà) :—**Culms** simple, mostly 4-16′ tall;
lades much elongated, 2-14′ long, 2-5 mm. wide, narrowed at the base,
ng-acuminate at apex, basal blades shorter, but not forming a distinct
sette in the autumn; **Ligule** less than 1 mm. long; **Spikelets** 2.2-3.8
m. long, strongly 7-9-nerved; **Autumnal Form** bearing simple branches
om the basal or lower nodes, the reduced panicles more or less concealed
the foliage at the base of the plants.

PIKELETS ABOUT 3.5 mm. LONG, BEAKED.   42. P. depauperatum
PIKELETS 3 mm. LONG OR LESS (sometimes 3.2 mm. long in P. *perlongum*),
    not beaked.
  CULMS SINGLE or few in a tuft; spikelets turgid, blunt, 2.7-3.2 mm. long;
    prairie plants.   43. P. perlongum
  CULMS IN large tufts; spikelets not turgid, 2.2-2.7 mm. long; plants of dry
    woods.
  Sheaths pilose; spikelets 2.2-2.7 mm. long, pilose.   44. P. linearifolium
  Sheaths glabrous; spikelets 2.2-2.3 mm. long; glabrous to sparingly pilose.
                                              45. P. werneri

2. P. DEPAUPERATUM Muhl. (dē-pô-pĕr-ā′tŭm) ; STARVED PANIC-GRASS.

Vernal Form with the culms several-to-many in a tuft; **Culms** 8-16′
ll, slender, but rather stiff, erect or spreading at the summit, glabrous,
uberulent or sometimes pilose, nodes ascending pubescent; **Blades** linear,
.5-6′ long, 2-5 mm. wide, the lower shorter, often involute in drying,
zabrous on both surfaces, sometimes pubescent beneath; **Sheaths**, except
he lowest, shorter than the internodes, glabrous to papillose-pilose;
anicles exserted, usually not much exceeding the leaves, 1.5-3′ long,
arely longer, few-flowered, the rather strict remote branches narrowly
scending at maturity; **Spikelets** 3.2-3.8 mm. rarely only 3 mm. or as much
s 4 mm. long, 1.5-1.7 mm. wide, elliptical, pointed, glabrous or sparsely
ubescent; **Glumes**, the first one-third to half the length of the spikelet,
ubacute, the second and **Sterile Lemma** equal, extending beyond the fruit
orming a beak, strongly 7-9-nerved; **Fruit** 2.1-2.3 mm. long, 1.4-1.5 mm.
vide, oval, minutely umbonate at the apex. **Autumnal Form** similar to the
ernal, the reduced secondary panicles produced on branches from the
asal or lower nodes, more or less concealed in the tuft of basal leaves.

This species is variable as to pubescence and size of spikelets. (See
rawings on photograph of P. *xalapense*.)

Open sterile woods, Texas to Georgia, north to Maine and Minnesota.
Denison.) Summer and fall.

3. P. PERLONGUM Nash (pĕr-lŏn′gŭm) ; LONG-STALKED PANIC-GRASS.

Vernal Form similar to that of P. *depauperatum*, more strict in habit
nd in smaller tufts, more constantly pilose and usually papillose, the
lades on the average longer and narrower, sometimes 10′ long, pubescent
n the lower surface; **Panicles** smaller and narrower, the branches erect,
ence appearing more densely flowered; **Spikelets** 2.7-3.2 mm. long, 1.6-
.7 mm. wide, oval, blunt, sparingly pilose; **Glumes**, the first one-fourth
r one-third the length of the spikelet, acute or obtuse, the second and

Sterile Lemma equal, obtuse, not extended beyond the fruit, strong 7-9-nerved; **Fruit** 2.4 mm. long, 1.5-1.6 mm. wide, obovate-oval, round and minutely unbonate at the summit. **Autumnal Form** with seconda panicles usually more numerous than in *P. depauperatum* and sometim produced from the second node. (See drawings on photograph *P. xalapense*.)

Prairies and dry soil, Texas to Michigan and Manitoba. (Lla county.) Spring-summer.

44. P. LINEARIFOLIUM Scribn. (lĭn-ē-ăr-ĭ-fō′lĭ-ŭm) ; Low WHITE-HAIR PANIC-GRASS.

Vernal Form light-green, in dense tufts, often accompanied by t more or less curved withered leaves of the previous year; **Culms** 8-18′ ta very slender, erect or spreading, often somewhat drooping, glabrous minutely puberulent, rarely pilose, the nodes often pubescent to pilos all the nodes being at or near the base; **Blades** 4-12′ long, 2-5 mm. wi (the lower shorter), erect, usually overtopping the panicle before maturit usually scabrous on both surfaces, or sometimes smooth below, glabrou or often pubescent on the lower and sometimes on the upper surfac usually papillose-ciliate near the base, the hairs rather long and stif **Sheaths** usually exceeding the internodes, sparsely to densely pilose, mo or less papillose, the papillae often obscure; **Ligule** a ring of hairs le than 1 mm. long; **Panicles** finally exserted on very slender peduncle 2-4′ long, half to two-thirds as wide, few-flowered, the flexuous branch remote and ascending; **Spikelets** 2-2.7 mm. (2.2-2.7) long, about 1.3 mm wide, oblong-elliptic, obtuse or subacute, sparsely pilose with weak sprea ing hairs; **Glumes,** the first one-third to one-fourth as long as the spik let, obtuse or pointed by the inrolling of the margins, ovate, 1-nerved, th second and **Sterile Lemma** subequal, about equal to the fruit, sometimes th second glume seems to be shorter at maturity, 7-9-nerved; **Sterile Pale** about one-third as long as its lemma, thin, pale; **Fruit** about 2 mm. lon about 1.2 mm. wide, oval, obscurely umbonate at the summit. **Autumn Form** similar, the reduced secondary panicles produced on the short bas branches mostly concealed in the tuft of basal leaves.

Dry woods, rocky or sandy soil, Texas to Georgia, north to Main and Kansas. (Oak wood, Bastrop; also Palestine and Jacksonville.) Sprin

45. P. WERNERI Scribn. (wẽr′nẽr-ī) ; WERNER'S PANIC-GRASS.

Vernal Form similar to *P. linearifolium*, typical specimens differin as follows: **Culms** stiffer, nodes usually sparingly pilose; **Blades** firme shorter and wider, 6′ long or less, the lower culm blades 1.5-2′ long, 3- mm. wide, a few long hairs at the rounded base, scabrous on both surface not pubescent; **Sheaths** often shorter than the internodes, glabrous **Spikelets** 2.1-2.4 mm. long, 1.2-1.3 mm. wide, nearly or quite glabrou **Autumnal Form** similar to the vernal, remaining simple or late in th season bearing simple branches from the lower, rarely from the basa nodes.

This species intergrades with *P. linearifolium*, but is distiguished by combination of stiffer habit, glabrous sheaths, shorter, broader and firme blades, and less pubescent spikelets. In habit, especially as seen in the field *P. werneri* often suggests *P. depauperatum*. (See drawing on photograp of *P. xalapense*.)

Sterile woods and knolls, Texas and Virginia to Ohio, Maine and Minne sota. (Dallas.) Spring-summer.

LAXIFLORA (lăk'sĭ-flō-rà) :—**Plants** light-green, vernal culms 4-16′ gh, numerous in tufts; **Blades** flat, soft, mostly ciliate, basal blades orter, but not forming true rosettes in the autumn; **Ligule** nearly solete; primary **Panicles** long-exserted; **Spikelets** 1.3-2.3 mm. long, ovate, obtuse, turgid, 5-7-nerved; **Autumnal Form** freely branch-g near the base, forming close, flat, soft tufts, the reduced panicles often ceeded by the leaves.

Our only species has the sheaths retrorsely pilose, blades ciliate, and e spikelets 1.9-2 mm. long, papillose-pilose.

P. XALAPENSE H. B. K. (zăl-à-pĕn'sē).

Vernal Form; Culms in dense, soft light-green tufts, 4-20′ tall, often niculate at the base, the nodes densely villous with reflexed hairs, the sal leaves numerous, slender, erect or ascending; **Blades** 2-6.5′ long, orter at the base, 4-8 mm. wide, flat, acuminate, narrowed toward the se, the upper blade somewhat convolute at the base around the culm, nally papillose-ciliate, pilose on one or both surfaces, especially on the ver blades, or glabrous; **Sheaths** shorter than the internodes, or the ver longer, conspicuously retrorsely pilose, sometimes papillose, collar bescent; **Ligule** almost obsolete; **Panicles** long-exserted, the peduncle nder and weak, 3.5-4′ long, about two-thirds as wide, comparatively v-flowered, lax, the branches flexuous, spreading or ascending, or the ver sometimes reflexed, the main axis and capillary branches more or s pilose; **Spikelets** 1.9-2 mm. long, 1.1 mm. wide, oblong-obovate, obtuse; imes, the first about one-third to one-fourth as long as the spikelet, the ond and **Sterile Lemma** short-pilose, minutely papillose, the glume 7-·ved, shorter than the 5-7-nerved sterile lemma, exposing the fruit at turity; **Fruit** 1.5-1.6 mm. long, about 1 mm. wide, oval, minutely bonate. **Autumnal Form** branching at the base, forming soft, spreading ts, the sheaths overlapping and blades reduced, exceeding the ondary panicles.

Woods, Texas to Florida, Maryland, Illinois and Missouri; also xico. (Alvin.) Spring.

ANGUSTIFOLIA (ăn-gŭs-tĭ-fō'lĭ-à) :—**Plants** mostly dull grayish-en, cespitose; **Vernal Culms** erect or ascending from a spreading base, stly 12-16′ rarely as much as 40′ high, appressed-villous at base or some-es above, or rarely smooth even at base; **Blades** narrow, ascending, nally firm and rigid, more or less striate with prominent nerves, and netimes longitudinally wrinkled besides, often ciliate at the base; ·ule ciliate, less than 1 mm. long; **Spikelets** attenuate at base, rather ongly 7-nerved, usually pubescent, the hairs arising from bullate billae; **First Glume** narrow and sheathing at base. **Autumnal Culms** eatedly forming bushy crowns, these remaining erect or becoming umbent or widely spreading; **Blades** much reduced, often involute; a inct rosette of basal leaves formed in the fall. Species of the Atlantic in and Gulf states.

DES BEARDED; PLANTS GRAYISH-VILLOUS; autumnal blades flat.
bikelets 2 mm. long.
bikelets 2.5-2.8 mm. long.
              48. P. chrysopsidifolium
              49. P. consanguineum
DES NOT BEARDED; PLANTS VILLOUS ONLY AT BASE, or nearly glabrous; autumnal blades involute or flat.
UTUMNAL BLADES flat; lower panicle branches spreading or deflexed.
              50. P. angustifolium

AUTUMNAL BLADES involute; lower branches more or less ascending
  spikelets less than 3 mm. long, not pointed, or obscurely so.
PLANTS glabrous or nearly so; autumnal culms erect; spikelets not su
  secund; panicle loose and open.   52. P. ovinu
PLANTS pubescent, at least on the lower half.
  Spikelets about 2.4 mm. rarely only 2.1 mm. long; vernal blades 3-5′ lon
    autumnal blades not falcate.   51. P. arenicoloid
  Spikelets not over 2 mm. long; vernal blades 40-60 mm. long, autumn
    blades much crowded, falcate.   47. P. acicula

47. P. ACICULARE Desv. (ă-sĭk-ū-lā′rē) ; this species has been confuse
with *P. neuranthum* Griseb.

Vernal Culms 8-20′ or taller, in shaded situations, numerous in a tu
ascending from a decumbent base, the nodes more or less pubescent b
not bearded; **Blades,** those at the middle of the culm 1.5-2.5′ long, rare
longer, 2-5 mm. wide, the uppermost shorter, usually 10-20 mm. lon
1-2 mm. wide, stiff, spreading or ascending, narrowed to an involute poi
glabrous or the lower sparsely pilose, somewhat papillose-hispid on t
margins at the base; **Sheaths,** the lower villous, the upper ciliate, othe
wise glabrous; **Panicles** open, 1.5-2.5′ long, the flexuous branches sprea
ing at maturity; **Spikelets** 1.9-2 mm. long, 1.1 mm. wide, obovate, blu
basal attenuation short; **Glumes,** the first about one-fourth the length
the spikelet, obtuse or pointed, the second and **Sterile Lemma** equ
papillose-pubescent; **Fruit** 1.6 mm. long, 1 mm. wide, oval-ellipt
glabrous at the apex. **Autumnal Form** consisting of numerous bush
branched culms 4-12′ long, spreading and forming dense cushions, t
short blades involute, sharp-pointed and usually arcuate, mostly 10-
mm. long; spikelets more turgid than in the vernal form.

This species is abundant in the coast region and can be distinguish
from all the other species of this group within its range by the sm
spikelets and the awl-like blades of the autumnal state. (See drawings
P. consanguineum.)

Sandy pine woods of the coastal plains from eastern Texas to Flori
and north to New Jersey. (Waller county.)

48. P. CHRYSOPSIDIFOLIUM Nash (krī-sŏp-sĭd-ĭ-fō′lĭ-ŭm).

Vernal Form 12-18′ tall, ascending or spreading; **Culms** rath
slender, purplish, grayish-villous, especially below, the nodes bearde
Blades 2-4′ long, 3-5 mm. wide, tapering from base to apex, villous
both surfaces; **Sheaths** much shorter than the internodes, villous like
culm, densely so at the summit; **Panicles** finally long-exserted, 1.5-2
long, about three-fourths as wide, the flexuous branches ascending
spreading; **Spikelets** 2 mm. long, 1.2-1.3 mm. wide, obovate, blunt a
turgid; **Glumes,** the first one-third the length of the spikelet, subacute
obtuse, the second and **Sterile Lemma** subequal, scarcely covering
fruit at maturity, villous, the bullate papillae prominent; **Fruit** 1.7 m
long, 1.2 mm. wide, broadly elliptic, minutely puberulent at the ap
Autumnal Form spreading and forming mats, the **culms** slender, of
zigzag toward the tip; **Blades** numerous, flat, becoming papery with a
mostly 10-30 mm. long, 1.5 mm. wide; **Spikelets** more turgid than us
in the primary panicle. This species can be distinguished fr
P. consanguineum by the smaller spikelets, and from *P. aciculare* by
bearded nodes, the lax culms and flat blades of the autumnal form.

Sandy pine woods of the coastal plain, Texas to Florida. (Har
county.)

9. P. CONSANGUINEUM Kunth (kŏn-săn-gwĭn'ē-ŭm).

Vernal Form with culms ascending or spreading, often geniculate at the base, 8-22' tall, rather stout, densely felty-villous below, less so above, nodes bearded; **Blades** erect or ascending, 2.5-5' long, 5-8 mm. wide (the lowermost shorter and broader), tapering slightly toward the base, more or less involute-pointed, villous on both surfaces, or nearly glabrous above, the longitudinal wrinkling conspicuous in the lower blades; **Sheaths** villous, the upper often sparsely so; **Panicles** 1.5-3' long, one-half to two-thirds as wide, the lower branches usually narrowly ascending; **Spikelets** 2.6-2.8 mm. long, 1.6-1.8 mm. wide, obovate, blunt, turgid; **Glumes**, the first one-third the length of the spikelet or less, the second and **Sterile Lemma** equal, scarcely covering the fruit at maturity, densely papillose-villous, the bullate papillae prominent; **Fruit** 2 mm. long, 1.5-1.7 mm. wide, minutely puberulent at the apex. **Autumnal Form** spreading or decumbent, the numerous branches somewhat flabellately fascicled, the blades mostly 1-1.5' long, 2-3 mm. wide, flat, thin and papery.

The *vernal form* of this species may be distinguished from *P. angustifolium* by the greater amount of pubescence, the bearded nodes and the ascending panicle branches, and the *autumnal form* by the widely spreading habit of shorter blades. (See drawings.)

Sandy pine woods of the coastal plain from Virginia to northern Florida and west to Arkansas and eastern Texas. (Beaumont.) Spring and summer.

50. P. ANGUSTIFOLIUM Ell. (ăn-gŭs-tĭ-fō'lĭ-ŭm); NARROW-LEAVED PANIC-GRASS.

Vernal Form with erect or nearly erect **Culms** 12-22' tall, the lowermost internodes gray-crisp-villous, the middle and upper glabrous, nodes glabrous or the lower villous, not bearded; **Blades** 3-5' rarely 6' long, 4-8 mm. wide, lowermost blades shorter and broader and longitudinally wrinkled, stiffly ascending, the upper more appressed, long-acuminate, scarcely narrowed at the base; **Sheaths**, the upper ciliate, the lower more or less appressed-villous; **Panicles** long-exserted, 1.5-4' long, nearly as wide, loosely flowered, the branches at anthesis widely spreading, the lower 30-40 mm. long, often reflexed; **Spikelets** 2.5-2.8 mm. long, 1.4-1.6 mm. wide, elliptic-obovate, turgid; **Glumes**, the first about one-third the length of the spikelet, pointed or obtuse, the second and **Sterile Lemma** equal, covering the fruit at maturity, not beaked beyond it, papillose-villous; **Fruit** 2 mm. long, 1.3-1.5 mm. wide, broadly elliptic, minutely puberulent at the obscurely umbonate apex. **Autumnal culms** stiffly ascending or somewhat top-heavy, reclining, not spreading or mat-like; blades very numerous, flat, appressed, rather thin and papery, panicles reduced (the later ones often to two or three spikelets), overtopped by the leaves; spikelets commonly more turgid and blunt than those of the primary panicles.

The flat papery blades of the autumnal form as seen in the spring still attached to the plants bearing the vernal culm are characteristic of this species and of one other of this group with flat autumnal blades, *P. consanguineum.* (See drawings of *P. consanguineum.*)

Sandy pine woods along the coastal plain from eastern Texas to Florida and north to Pennsylvania. (Beaumont and Houston.) Spring-fall.

51. P. ARENICOLOIDES Ashe (ăr-ĕn-ĭ-kō-loi′dēz).

Vernal Form intermediate in appearance between that of *P. angust* *folium* and *P. aciculare*, grayish-green, slender, the **Culms** mostly 12-2(tall; **Blades** 2.5-5′ long, the lower shorter, 3-4 rarely 5 mm. wide, taperin from the base to a more or less involute tip, softly villous; **Sheaths** softl villous; **Panicles** 40-60 mm. long, two-thirds to three-fourths as wide, th lower branches ascending; **Spikelets** 2.1-2.5 mm. long, 1.2-1.3 mm. wid obovate, obtuse; **Glumes**, the first one-third the length of the spikele truncate or pointed, the second and **Sterile Lemma** scarcely covering th fruit at maturity, papillose-pubescent; **Fruit** 1.8-1.9 mm. long, 1.1-1.2 mn wide, obscurely puberulent at the apex. **Autumnal Form** bushy-brancl ing, erect or top-heavy, the blades involute; spikelets more turgid, th attenuate base in exceptional specimens elongated, lengthening the spik(let to as much as 2.8 mm. long.

The vernal form of this species can be distinguished from *P. aciculaı* by the larger spikelets and longer blades, and from *P. angustifolium* b the smaller spikelets and the ascending branches of the panicle; th autumnal form is distinguished by the involute blades, longer than those (*P. aciculare*. (See drawings of *P. consanguineum*.)

Sandy pine woods, mostly near the coast, Texas to Florida, Nort Carolina and Arkansas. (Houston.)

52. P. OVINUM Scribn. & Smith (ō-vī′nŭm).

Vernal Form with culms usually few in a cluster, erect or nearly s(glabrous, 12-20′ tall; **Blades** erect or ascending, stiff, glabrous, the low(somewhat ciliate at the base, the lowermost ovate or lanceolate, as muc as 10 mm. wide, those of the midculm 4-6′ long, 3-6 mm. wide, the upper most shorter and narrower; **Sheaths** glabrous or the lowermost appressec pubescent; **Panicles** usually short-exserted, 2-4′ long, three-fourths a wide or less, loosely flowered, the lower branches ascending; **Spikelet** 2.1-2.2 mm. long, 1.2-1.3 mm. wide, obovate-elliptic, obtuse, basal attenua tion short; **Glumes**, the first about one-fourth the length of the spikele usually truncate, the second and **Sterile Lemma** scarcely equaling th fruit at maturity, papillose-pubescent, sometimes minutely so; **Fruit** 1. mm. long, 1.1 mm. wide, oval, puberulent at the apex. **Autumnal For** erect or nearly so, the blades becoming loosely involute, not much shorte than the vernal blades, spikelets more turgid, sometimes slightly shorte than those of the primary panicle.

P. ovinum in its vernal form differs from *P. aciculare* in being nearl glabrous and having broader spikelets and larger less exserted panicle: the uppermost blades being proportionately longer. (See drawings o *P. consanguineum*.)

Dry or moist open ground, eastern Texas to Mississippi and Arkansa: In Texas this species occurs on open prairies, on dry ground, and also i swales. (Dallas and Hempstead.)

DICHOTOMA (dī-kŏt′ō-mà):—**Culms** few-to-many in a tuft, glabrou or the nodes only pubescent; **Blades** lanceolate, rarely as much as 10 mn wide, mostly glabrous; **Sheaths** glabrous, or the lower sometime pubescent, never conspicuously hirsute; **Ligule** ciliate, 0.7 mm. long o less; **Panicle** usually open; **Spikelets** elliptical, not turgid (except i *P. roanokense*), 1.5-2.5 mm. long; second **Glume** and **Sterile Lemma** 5-7 nerved. **Autumnal Form** usually branching, erect, reclining or prostrate secondary leaves and panicle much reduced.

ODES, AT LEAST THE LOWER, BEARDED.
  SPIKELETS 1.5-1.6 mm. LONG, glabrous (occasional individuals with
    pubescent spikelets).   53. P. microcarpon
  SPIKELETS 2 mm. OR more long.
    Spikelets glabrous, 2 mm. long; autumnal form top-heavy-reclining.
                                                            56. P. barbulatum
    Spikelets pubescent. Upper sheaths viscid-spotted; blades glabrous, or only
      the lower pubescent or velvety, autumnal form erect or reclining, pro-
      fusely branching; spikelets 2 mm. long; fruit slightly exposed at maturity.
                                                            54. P. nitidum
ODES NOT BEARDED; SPIKELETS GLABROUS or sometimes pubescent in
    P. lucidum.
  CULMS LAX, soon prostrate or vine-like; plants bright-green; spikelets not
    over 2.1 mm. long.   58. P. lucidum
  CULMS ERECT, or the autumnal top-heavy, never prostrate.
    SPIKELETS 2 mm. long or more; panicles open; blades erect, firm; spikelets
      turgid, strongly nerved; plants grayish olive-green. 57. P. roanokense
    SPIKELETS not over 2 mm. long, not pointed.
      Autumnal form erect, branched like a little tree; primary blades rarely over
        5 mm. wide; second glume shorter than the fruit and sterile lemma.
                                                            55. P. dichotomum
      Autumnal form top-heavy-reclining; primary blades 6-10 mm. wide; second
        glume equaling fruit and sterile lemma.   56. P. barbulatum

3. P. MICROCARPON Muhl. (mī-krō-kär′pŏn) ; BARBED PANIC-GRASS.

Vernal Form tufted; Culms commonly 1-2 sometimes 3 feet tall, erect, or sometimes geniculate at the base, the nodes densely bearded with reflexed hairs; Blades 4-5′ long, 8-15 mm. wide, narrowed toward the base, thin, spreading, the upper often reflexed, glabrous, more or less papillose-ciliate at the base, or the whole blade (in a rare form) papillose-pubescent; Sheaths glabrous or pubescent, or just the lower pubescent, ciliate on the margins, often somewhat papillose; Ligule ciliate, the hairs short; Panicles 3-5′ long, finally long-exserted, ovate in outline, many-flowered, the branches ascending; Spikelets about 1.6 mm. long, about 0.8 mm. wide, elliptic, glabrous, rarely minutely pubescent; Glumes, the first about one-fourth the length of the spikelet, acute, the second shorter than the Sterile Lemma (which is about equal to the fruit), and exposing the fruit at maturity, obtuse, prominently 5-7-nerved; Fruit 1.4 mm. long, 0.7 mm. wide, elliptic, narrowly obtuse. Autumnal Form much branched from all the nodes, reclining from the weight of the dense mass of branches; Blades much reduced, flat, mostly 20-40 mm. long, the ciliate hairs at the base of the blades and margins of sheaths more conspicuous; Panicles much reduced and loosely flowered; the tufted basal blades often large, sometimes as much as 3′ long and 15 mm. wide. The author collected his specimen in a sphagnum bog near Otine, Texas, same being pubescent throughout; this is a rare form. (See drawings of *P. consanguineum.*)

Wet woods and swampy places, marshes, east Texas to Florida, north to Illinois and Massachusetts. Fall.

54. P. NITIDUM Lam. (nĭt′ĭ-dŭm).

Vernal Form tufted; Culms erect or somewhat spreading, 12-24′ sometimes 36′ tall, the nodes bearded with reflexed hairs; Blades 1.5-4′ (2-5′) long, 4-10 mm. wide, flat, ascending or finally reflexed, sometimes sparsely papillose-ciliate toward the narrowed base; Sheaths longer or shorter than the internodes, ciliate on the margins, otherwise glabrous or the lower papillose or papillose-pubescent, more or less glandular or mottled, especially the upper; Ligule ciliate, the hairs less than 1 mm.

long; **Panicles** long-exserted, purplish, 2-4.5′ long, the spikelets on pedice.
1-4 times as long as the spikelets; **Spikelets** purplish, about 2 mm. lon
and about 1.1 mm. wide, oval or elliptic, sparsely short-pubescent; **Glume**
the first one-third to one-fourth the length of the spikelet, broadly acut
the second and **Sterile Lemma** about equal, the slightly shorter glum
scarcely covering the fruit at maturity, both 7-nerved; **Fruit** elliptic, 1.!
1.7 mm. long, about 1 mm. wide, subobtuse. **Autumnal Form** erect o
more or less reclining from the weight of the foliage, the branchlets an
foliage forming large clusters from the nodes of the vernal culm; reduce
Blades numerous, 10-30 mm. long, 1-3 mm. wide, flat or soon becomin
involute; **Panicles** mostly reduced to a few long-pediceled spikelets.

This species is distinguished from *P. microcarpon* by its pubescer
spikelets 2 mm. long, and by the erect autumnal form with involute blade
The viscid spots on the sheaths are often conspicuous.

Low moist or marshy ground, Texas to Florida and Virgini
(Houston.)   Spring.

55. P. DICHOTOMUM L. (dī-kŏt′ō-mŭm); FORKED PANIC-GRASS.

Vernal Form often purplish; **Culms** 12-20′ tall, erect, from a knotte
crown, the nodes naked or the lower with a few spreading hairs; **Blade**
2-4.5′ long, 4-8 mm. wide, slightly narrowed toward the base, acuminat
spreading, glabrous on both surfaces, sometimes with a few long hairs o
the margins at the base, the basal blades lanceolate-ovate, long-ciliate nea
the base; **Sheaths** less than half the length of the internodes, sometime
ciliate, otherwise glabrous, or the lowermost rarely sparingly pubescent
Panicles long-exserted, 1.5-4′ long, the axis and spreading branche
flexuous, spikelet-bearing toward the ends; **Spikelets** 2 mm. long, 0.9 mn
wide, elliptic, glabrous or rarely pubescent; **Glumes,** the first one-thir
the length of the spikelet, subacute, the second and **Sterile Lemma** rathe
faintly nerved, the glume shorter than the fruit at maturity; **Fruit** 1.
mm. long, 0.9 mm. wide, elliptic. **Autumnal Culms** much branched at th
middle nodes, the lower portion usually erect and devoid of blades, thu
giving the plants the appearance of diminutive trees as described b
Gronovius and Linnaeus; **Blades** much reduced and very numerous, ofte
involute.

This common and widely distributed species can be distinguished by it
lack of pubescence, its smooth spikelets, 2 mm. long, and its erect autumna
form. (See drawings of *P. consanguineum.*)

Dry or sterile woods, eastern Texas to Florida and north to Michiga
and New Brunswick. (Beaumont.)   Summer.

56. P. BARBULATUM Michx. (bär-bū-lā′tŭm).

Vernal Form in large tufts; **Culms** slender, 20-32′ tall, erect o
spreading at the summit, the lower nodes usually bearded; **Blades** spreac
ing, 2.5-4′ long, 6-10 mm. wide, the lower shorter, acuminate, rounded a
the base, glabrous, the lower rarely puberulent; **Sheaths** with a puberulen
ring at the summit, otherwise glabrous, or the lower usually softl
pubescent; **Panicles** long-exserted, 2.5-4.5′ long, as wide or wider, th
slender flexuous branches fascicled, the lower spreading or drooping a
maturity, spikelet-bearing at the ends; **Spikelets** 2 mm. long, 1 mm. wid
oval, glabrous; **Glumes,** the first one-fourth to one-third as long as th
spikelet, acute, the second and **Sterile Lemma** equal, covering the fruit a
maturity; **Fruit** elliptic, 1.8 mm. long, 1 mm. wide, obscurely apiculat
Autumnal Form diffusely branched, forming very large, top-heavy reclir

ıg bunches, the slender branchlets recurved, the numerous flat blades
orizontally spreading.

Closely allied to *P. dichotomum* from which it differs in the vernal
ɔrm in having usually wider blades, bearded lower nodes and fruit covered
y the equal second glume and sterile lemma; the autumnal form is dis-
inguished by the large top-heavy reclining tufts. (See drawings of *P. con-
anguineum*.)

Sterile or rocky woods, eastern Texas to Georgia, north to Michigan and
lassachusetts. (Houston and Mineola.) Summer.

7. P. ROANOKENSE Ashe (rō-à-nōk-ĕn'sē); *P. curtivaginum* Ashe.

Vernal Form tufted, somewhat glaucous olive-green; **Culms** 20-40′
all, erect or ascending; **Blades** 2.4-3.6′ long, 3-8 mm. wide, at first stiffly
ɛrect, later ascending or spreading, tapering to both ends, glabrous or
vith a few hairs around the base; **Sheaths** half as long as the internodes
ɔr less, glabrous or the lowermost sometimes sparsely pubescent; **Panicles**
l.6-3.2′ long, scarcely as wide, the branches spreading; **Spikelets** 2 mm.
ong, 1 mm. wide, ellipsoid-obovoid, very turgid, glabrous; **Glumes**, the
first about one-third the length of the spikelet, the second and **Sterile
Lemma** strongly nerved, subequal, the glume rather conspicuously purple-
tinged at the base, scarcely covering the fruit at maturity; **Fruit** 1.6 mm.
ong, 0.9 mm. wide, ellipsoid. **Autumnal Form** erect or decumbent,
branching at the middle or upper nodes, the branches numerous but not
ɩn tufts, the primary internodes elongating and becoming arched about the
time the branches appear; the reduced blades more or less involute, not
exceeding the 0.6-1.6′ long panicles, basal blades firm, erect, often as
much as 2-2.4′ long.

The plant is glabrous throughout with the exceptions mentioned; the
glaucous olive-green color and very turgid spikelets, purple stained at the
base, are characteristic. (See drawings of *P. consanguineum*.)

Open swampy woods or wet peaty meadows, eastern Texas to Florida,
north to Virginia. (Waller county.)

58. P. LUCIDUM Ashe (lū'sĭ-dŭm); Bog Panic-grass.

Vernal Form at first erect and resembling that of *P. dichotomum*,
but the weak culms soon becoming decumbent, sometimes rooting at the
lower nodes; **Blades** 1.5-3′ long, 4-6 mm. wide, at first erect but soon
widely spreading, thin, bright-green, shining, glabrous; **Sheaths** usually
ciliate on the margins; **Panicles** resembling those of *P. dichotomum* but
fewer-flowered; **Spikelets** 2-2.1 mm. long, 1 mm. wide, elliptic, glabrous
(rarely obscurely pubescent); **Glumes**, the first about two-fifths the
length of the spikelet, pointed, the second and **Sterile Lemma** more
strongly nerved than in *P. dichotomum*, both shorter than the fruit at
maturity; **Fruit** 1.7 mm. long, 0.9 mm. wide, slightly pointed. **Autumnal
Form** repeatedly branched, forming large clumps or mats of slender, weak,
vine-like culms, the branches elongated and diverging at a wide angle, not
fascicled, the blades 20-40 mm. long, waxy, flat and spreading; panicles
much reduced.

Under a lens the oblong epidermal cells are visible between the
nerves in the blades, especially on the lower surface, giving a minutely
bullate surface characteristic of this species and of no other in this
group. (See drawings of *P. consanguineum*.)

Wet woods and sphagnum swamps, along the coastal plain from eastern Texas to Florida and north to New York. (Colmesneil.) Summer fall.

SPRETA (sprē'tà) :—**Culms** tufted, rather stiff, mostly glabrous o nearly so; **Blades** not over 8 mm. wide; **Ligule** densely hairy, 3-5 mm long; **Spikelets** 1-1.6 mm. long, pubescent or rarely glabrous; **Secon Glume** and **Sterile Lemma** 5-7-nerved.

Autumnal Forms with more or less tufted branchlets and much re duced leaves and panicles.

PANICLE NARROW, ONE-FOURTH TO ONE-THIRD AS WIDE AS LONG
59. P. spretun
PANICLE OPEN, TWO-THIRDS AS WIDE AS LONG or more.
Spikelets 1.5 mm. long. 60. P. lindheimer
Spikelets 0.95-1 mm. long, 0.5 mm. wide; culms and sheaths appressed
pubescent. 61. P. wrightianu

59. P. SPRETUM Schult. (sprē'tŭm) ; *P. eatoni* Nash; includes *P. paucipi lum* Nash; EATON'S PANIC-GRASS.

Vernal Culms tufted, 12-36' tall, erect or slightly decumbent at th base, sometimes sending out rootlets from the lower nodes, the nodes swollen **Blades** 2.8-4' long, 4-8 mm. wide, firm, ascending or often reflexed sparingly long-ciliate at the rounded base, otherwise glabrous; **Sheath** shorter than the internodes, loose, usually ciliate toward the summit, o the lower slightly pubescent; **Panicles** 3.2-4.8' long, one-fourth to one-thir as wide, rather densely flowered, the branches ascending or appressed short spikelet-bearing branchlets in the axils; **Spikelets** 1.4-1.6 mm usually 1.5 mm. long, 0.7-0.9 mm. wide, elliptic, obscurely pointed; **Glumes** the first one-fourth to one-third the length of the spikelet, obtuse or sub acute, the second and **Sterile Lemma** equaling the fruit at maturity pubescent or rarely glabrous; **Fruit** 1.3 mm. long, 0.7 mm. wide, elliptic slightly pointed. **Autumnal Form** more or less reclining, branching afte maturity of the primary panicle, the earlier branches elongated, ascending but not appressed, bearing exserted panicles, the subsequent branchlet in short fascicles, the blades much reduced, sometimes minutely pubescent overtopping the small ultimate panicles; winter rosette appearing rathe early, the blades glabrous or nearly so. (For drawing see photograph o vernal form of *P. lindheimeri*.)

Wet and usually sandy soil, mostly near the coast, Texas to Maine also in northern Indiana. (Waller county.) Spring-summer.

60. P. LINDHEIMERI Nash (lĭnd-hī'mēr-ī) ; LINDHEIMER'S PANIC-GRASS

Vernal Culms 8-40' tall, tufted, stiffly ascending or spreading, node swollen, glabrous, or the lower internodes pubescent, the sheath node pubescent, the lower often villous; **Blades** lanceolate, 1-4' long, the uppe short, 6-10 mm. wide, flat, at first ascending, finally spreading, papillose ciliate at the rounded base, glabrous on both surfaces, or minutely puberu lent beneath, sometimes a few scattered hairs on the upper surface nea the base; **Sheaths** less than half as long as the elongated internodes, long ciliate on the margins, otherwise glabrous, or the lower ascending pubescent; **Ligule,** densely hispid hairs 3-5 mm. long; **Panicle** 1.5-3' long nearly as wide, ovate, branches ascending or spreading, 30 mm. long o less, naked at the base, loosely flowered; **Spikelets** about 1.5 mm. long about 0.9 mm. wide, obovate, turgid, obtuse, pubescent, the pedicels about the length of the spikelet, the terminal ones longer; **Glumes,** the first bout one-fourth as long as the spikelet, obtuse, the second and **Sterile emma** scarcely equaling the fruit at maturity, about 7-nerved; **Fruit** 3-1.4 mm. long, 0.8 mm. wide, elliptic, obtuse. **Autumnal Form** usually ,iffly spreading or radiate-prostrate, internodes elongated, with tufts of 1ort, appressed branches at the nodes; blades reduced, involute-pointed 1d often conspicuously ciliate at the base.

(See photographs of each form.)

Dry sandy or sterile woods or open ground, Texas to Florida and [aine, also west to California. Spring-summer.

l. P. WRIGHTIANUM Scribn. (rīt-ĭ-ā'nŭm).

Vernal Culms 6-16' rarely 24' tall, weak and slender, ascending from decumbent base, or rarely at first erect, minutely puberulent; **Blades**)-40 mm. long, 3-5 rarely 6 mm. wide, spreading, glabrous or puberulent ∍neath and minutely pilose above; **Sheaths** shorter than the internodes, riate, summit and margin ciliate, otherwise glabrous or puberulent; igule 2-3 mm. long; **Panicles** 30-60 mm. long, oblong-ovate, one-third to alf as wide, the branches ascending, the minute spikelets long-pediceled; **pikelets** 0.95-1 mm. long, 0.5 mm. wide, ellipsoid, turgid, subacute, 1bescent; **Glumes**, the first about one-fourth the length of the spikelet, 1e second shorter than the fruit and **Sterile Lemma; Fruit** 0.8 mm. long, 5 mm. wide, subacute. **Autumnal Form** decumbent spreading, the culms)reading out from the lower and middle nodes, the numerous ascending ranches becoming somewhat bushy-branched, the flat or subinvolute [ades and secondary panicles not much reduced. (For drawing see hotograph of vernal form of *P. lindheimeri.*)

Along the margins of streams and ponds in sandy or mucky soil,)utheastern Texas to Florida and north to New Jersey. Summer and Ll.

LANUGINOSA (lȧ-nū-jĭ-nō'sȧ):— **Plants** more or less pubescent 1roughout, usually conspicuously so; **Blades** not over 10 mm. wide, sually narrower; **Ligule** densely hairy, 2-5 mm. long; **Spikelets** 1.3-3 mm. ■ng, pubescent, the **Second Glume** and **Sterile Lemma** 5-7- or in the larger)ikelets 7-9-nerved. **Autumnal Form** usually freely branching, secondary ■aves and panicles much reduced.

These species were usually referred by the earlier American authors to *. pubescens* Lam. or Michx.

PIKELETS NOT OVER 2 mm. LONG.
  PLANTS GRAYISH, velvety-pubescent; spikelets 1.8-2 mm. long; autumnal blades flat.
    PLANTS dark or olive-green when dry, sparingly branching from middle nodes, erect; vernal blades sparingly pilose on upper surface.
64. P. thurowii
    PLANTS light or yellow green when dry. Autumnal form ascending or spreading, branching from middle and upper nodes, the reduced, fascicled blades strongly ciliate; culms 16-28' high, autumnal culms usually 16-20' long. 63. P. lanuginosum
  PLANTS PUBESCENT, often villous, but not velvety.
    CULMS conspicuously pilose with long, horizontally spreading hairs; branching before expansion of primary panicles. 65. P. praecocius
    CULMS variously pubescent; if pilose the hairs not long and spreading; upper surface of blades appressed-pubescent or pilose toward the base only.
    Blades stiff, erect. 62. P. huachucae
    Blades lax, spreading. 62a. P. huachucae var. fasciculatum

SPIKELETS 2.2 mm. LONG OR MORE.
  Spikelets 2.2-2.3 mm. long; pubescence on culms horizontally spreading
    autumnal form freely branching.   66. P. villosissimu
  Spikelets 2.7-2.9 mm. long; culm stiff; blades conspicuously ciliate.
                                                      67. P. ova

62. P. HUACHUCAE Ashe (wä-chū'sē); (Some American authors hav referred to this species as *P. unciphyllum* Trin.) ; HAIRY PANIC-GRAS

  Vernal Forms tufted, 8-24′ tall, usually stiffly upright, ligl olivaceous, often purplish, harsh to the touch from the copious spreadin papillose-pubescence of culms and blades, the nodes bearded with sprea ing hairs; **Blades** 1.4-3.2′ long, 6-8 mm. wide, stiffly erect or ascendin firm, the veins inconspicuous, the upper surface copiously short-pilos especially toward the base, the lower surfaces densely pubescent; **Sheatl** shorter than the internodes; **Ligule** 3-4 mm. long; **Panicles** rather shor exserted until maturity, 40-60 mm. long, nearly as wide, rather densel flowered, the axis and often the branches pilose, flexuous, fascicle branches ascending or spreading, short spikelet-bearing branchlets at ba of the fascicles; **Spikelets** 1.6-1.8 mm. long, 1 mm. wide, obovate, obtus turgid, papillose-pubescent; **Glumes,** the first about one-third the lengt of the spikelet, the second and **Sterile Lemma** subequal, scarcely coverin the fruit at maturity; **Fruit** 1.5-1.6 mm. long, 1 mm. wide, ellipti obscurely apiculate. **Autumnal Form** stiffly erect or ascending, the culn and sheaths sometimes papillose only, the branches fascicled, the reduce crowded leaves ascending, the blades 20-30 mm. long, much exceeding th reduced panicles.

  This species is variable as to the amount of pubescence and stiffness leaves, and intergrades with the subspecies *P. huachucae* var. *fasciculatu* (Torr.) Hubb. (See drawings of *P. lanuginosum.*)

  Prairies and open ground, Texas to California and north to Sout Dakota; also Mexico. (El Paso.)

62a. P. HUACHUCAE var. FASCICULATUM (Torr.) Hubb. (fă-sĭk-ĭ lā'tŭm; *P. huachucae silvicola* Hitchc. & Chase.

  Vernal Form taller and more slender, brighter green and less densel pubescent than *P. huachucae.* **Culms** 12-30′ tall, suberect or ascendin papillose-pilose with spreading hairs, the nodes bearded with reflex hair usually a glabrous ring below; **Blades** 2-4′ long, 6-12 mm. wide, thin, la and spreading, the veins inconspicuous, the upper surface sparsely shor pilose, or with copious long hairs at the base, the lower surface pubescen and with a satiny lustre; **Sheaths** papillose-pilose; **Panicles** exserted, 2- rarely 4′ long, nearly as wide, rather densely flowered, the axis pilose, th flexuous fascicled branches spreading, with short spikelet-bearing brancl lets at the base of the fascicles; **Spikelets** 1.6-1.8 mm. long, 0.8-1 mm. wid elliptic-obovate, at maturity subobtuse, pubescent with spreading hairs **Glumes,** the first one-fourth to one-third as long as the spikelet, obtuse o subacute, the second and **Sterile Lemma** subequal, slightly shorter tha the fruit at maturity; **Fruit** 1.5 mm. long, 0.8-0.9 mm. wide, elliptic, sul acute. **Autumnal Form** more or less decumbent, the numerous fascicle branches shorter than the primary internodes, at least late in the seasor the reduced spreading leaves sometimes nearly glabrous above excep for a few hairs near the base. Some specimens represent an extreme forr with the upper surface of the blades nearly or quite glabrous, thu *approaching P. tennesseense.* (See drawings of *P. lanuginosum.*)

Open woods and clearings, east Texas to Florida, north to Maine and
est to Michigan; also Nebraska and Arizona. (Gillespie and Waller
ounties.)

3. P. LANUGINOSUM Ell. (lå-nū-jǐ-nō'sŭm) ; WOOLLY PANIC-GRASS.

Vernal Form grayish olive-green, velvety to the touch; Culms 16-28′
ll, usually in large clumps, slender, lax, spreading, densely villous with
ne soft hairs arising from small papillae, nodes villous, often a glabrous
ng below; Blades 2-4′ long, 5-10 mm. wide, the uppermost much smaller,
ickish but not stiff, ascending or spreading, somewhat incurved or
oon-shaped, acuminate, narrowed toward the rounded base, the margins
metimes papillose-ciliate, the upper surface clothed with short soft hairs
termixed with long soft hairs, especially toward the margins and base,
e lower surface densely velvety-pubescent; Sheaths shorter than the
ternodes, soft-villous like the culm, or the upper puberulent only,
liate; Ligule 3-4 mm. long; Panicles exserted, 2.4-4.8′ long, about as
ide, loosely flowered, the axis pubescent, the slender flexuous branches
reading or ascending, the lower often drooping; Spikelets 1.8-1.9 mm.
ng, 1 mm. wide, obovate-elliptic, subobtuse, pubescent; Glumes, the first
e-third the length of the spikelet, obtuse or obscurely pointed, the
cond and Sterile Lemma equal, slightly shorter than the fruit at
aturity; Fruit 1.6 mm. long, 0.9 mm. wide, elliptic, subacute. Autumnal
orm widely spreading or decumbent, freely branching from the middle
odes, the branches repeatedly branching and much exceeding the inter-
odes, the ultimate branchlet forming flabellate fascicles; leaves and
anicles much reduced, the flat blades almost always ciliate and exceed-
g the panicles; winter rosette not appearing until late, the blades
)-50 mm. long, usually ciliate, otherwise minutely velvety or nearly
labrous.

The plant bears some resemblance in color and pubescence to
. *scoparium*, but is smaller and much more slender. The vernal form also
sembles *P. huachucae* var. *fasciculatum*, but is larger and more velvety,
nd is gray-green in color rather than bright-green. (See drawings of
. *lanuginosum*.)

Moist sandy woods, mostly near the coast, eastern Texas to Florida and
orth to New Jersey. (Silver Lake.) Summer.

4. P. THUROWII Scribn. & Smith (thŭr-ō'ĭ-ī).

This is a grayish densely villous plant, usually in small tufts, mostly
rowing in open woods. The photograph shows both vernal and autumnal
orms, the autumnal form with three short crowded branches to the left.
he densely villous culms usually have a glabrous ring just below the
earded nodes.

Vernal Form bluish-green; Culms 12-28′ tall, mostly in small tufts,
ect or ascending, at first simple, finally branching, villous, usually a
labrous or almost glabrous ring below the bearded nodes; Blades 2-5.5′
ng, 6-10 mm. wide, the upper and lowermost shorter than the middle
es, flat, acuminate, somewhat involute toward the tip, narrowed toward
e rounded base, ascending or spreading, both upper surface and margins
ward the base sparsely hairy with rather long stiff hairs, the lower
irface densely villous, rather velvety; Sheaths long, the upper shorter
an the internodes, the lower overlapping and densely papillose-hirsute,
e upper rather densely villous, sometimes sparsely so; Ligule about 4
m. long; Panicle finally exserted, 3-4′ long, nearly as wide, greenish to

purplish, rather densely flowered, the axis sparingly villous, especiall
below, the branches ascending or spreading, usually the longest less tha
2.5′ long; **Spikelets** about 2 mm. long, 1 mm. wide, elliptic, somewha
obovate at maturity, obtuse, pubescent with soft spreading hairs; **Glume**
the first slightly distant below, about one-fifth the length of the spikele
obtuse, or slightly pointed, the second and **Sterile Lemma** equal, scarcel
equaling the fruit at maturity, obtuse or slightly pointed; **Sterile Pale**
about half as long as its lemma; **Fruit** about 1.6 mm. long, 0.9 mm. wid
elliptic, subacute, smooth, striate, pale. **Autumnal Form** erect, after th
maturity of the primary panicle bearing at the distant nodes a few
appressed or ascending fascicled branches scarcely longer than th
primary internodes, the reduced blades flat or somewhat involute at th
tips, ciliate.

Prairies and dry open woods, Texas to Alabama. (Houston an
Beaumont.) Spring.

65. P. PRAECOCIUS Hitchc. & Chase (prē-kō′shŭs); EARLY-BRANCHIN PANIC-GRASS.

Vernal Culms tufted, 6-10′ tall, early branching and elongating, some
times to 12-18′, at first erect, soon becoming geniculate and spreading, ver
wiry, slender, abundantly papillose-pilose, with weak spreading hairs 2-
mm. long; **Blades** 2-4′ long, 4-6 mm. wide, rather firm, erect or ascending
the margins parallel about two-thirds their length, acuminate, long-pilos
on both surfaces, the hairs of the upper surface 4-5 mm. long, erect from
the plane of blade, the under surface prominently papillose; **Sheaths,** even
the lowest much shorter than the very long internodes, those of th
branches usually only 10-20 mm. long, pilose like the culms but mor
prominently papillose; **Ligule** 3-4 mm. long; **Panicles** at first usually over
topped by the upper leaf, but at or past maturity exserted, 40-60 mm
long, about as wide, loosely flowered, the axis pilose, the branche
flexuous, spreading or ascending; **Spikelets** 1.8-1.9 mm. long, 1 mm. wid
obovate, turgid, obtuse, pilose; **Glumes,** the first one-third to half th
length of the spikelet, triangular, the second and **Sterile Lemma** subequa
the glume slightly shorter than the fruit at maturity; **Fruit** 1.6 mm. long
1 mm. wide, broad-elliptic. **Autumnal Form** ascending from a geniculat
base, or in prairie sod, erect, forming close bunches 4-8′ tall, the uppe
portion of the primary culms early deciduous, the branches appresse
the scarcely reduced blades erect or narrowly ascending, much exceedin
the reduced panicles; winter rosette appearing late, the blades 20-30 mm
long, long-pilose.

This species scarcely has a simple state, the branches appearing ofte
before the first panicle is expanded. (See drawings of *P. lanuginosum.*

Dry prairies and clearings, Texas to Minnesota, Michigan and Indiana
(Waller county.) Spring-summer.

66. P. VILLOSISSIMUM Nash (vĭl-ō-sĭs′ĭ-mŭm); WHITE-HAIRED PANIC GRASS.

Vernal Plants light olive-green; **Culms** densely tufted, 10-18′ tal
slender, erect or ascending, papillose-pilose, the spreading hairs 3 mm
long; **Blades** 2-4′ long, 5-10 mm. wide, often subinvolute toward the acum
nate apex, little narrowed toward the base, rather firm, ascending o
sometimes spreading, pilose on both surfaces, the hairs of the upper sur
face appressed, longer and less copious; **Sheaths** shorter than the inter
nodes, pilose like the culm; **Ligule** 4-5 mm. long; **Panicles** short-exserte

5-3′ long, usually as wide, loosely flowered, the spikelets long-pediceled,
e axis sparsely pilose, the branches rather stiffly ascending or spreading;
ikelets 2.2-2.3 mm. long, 1.1 mm. wide, oblong-elliptic, obtuse or
scurely pointed, papillose-pubescent with spreading hairs; **Glumes,** the
:st one-third to nearly half the length of the spikelets, acute, sometimes
abrous, the second and **Sterile Lemma** subequal, the glume slightly
orter than the fruit at maturity; **Fruit** 1.9 mm. long, 1. mm. wide,
liptic, subacute. **Autumnal Form** at first decumbent, often with geni-
late nodes and arched internodes, the first branches appearing at about
e maturity of the primary panicle, late in the season prostrate, the leaves
the fascicled branchlets appressed, giving a combed-out appearance, a
aracter conspicuous in the field but less so in the herbarium; blades not
:eatly reduced, often with only a few hairs on the upper surface, over-
pping the much reduced panicles; winter rosette appearing rather early,
ades long, bluish-green, densely pilose. (See drawings of *P. lanuginosum.*)
    Dry sandy or sterile soil, open woods and hillsides, eastern Texas to
lorida, north to Massachusetts and Minnesota. (Denison and Weather-
rd.) Spring-summer.

7. P. OVALE Ell. (ō′văl-ē).
    Vernal Plants light olive-green; **Culms** 8-20′ tall, tufted, erect or
scending, rather stout, long-pilose below with spreading or appressed
airs, often nearly glabrous above, usually leafy at the base, the nodes
ensely bearded with short spreading hairs; **Blades** 2-4′ long, 5-10 mm.
ide, the uppermost much smaller, sharply acuminate, rounded at the base,
rm, ascending, the upper surface usually nearly glabrous except for long
airs on or near the margin and base thus giving the blades the appearance
f being strongly ciliate, these hairs occasionally wanting except at the base,
he lower surface appressed-pubescent; **Sheaths** shorter than the inter-
odes or the lower overlapping, ascending pilose, the upper less densely
o, rarely nearly glabrous; **Ligule** composed of a ring of hairs about 1 mm.
ng with a second sparse ring 2-3 mm. long above it; **Panicles** usually
hort-exserted, 2-4′ long, about as wide when fully expanded, the lower
ranches finally spreading, rarely drooping; **Spikelets** 2.7-2.9 mm. long,
.3 mm. wide, oblong-elliptic, obtuse, pilose, sometimes rather sparsely so;
Glumes, the first one-third to nearly half as long as the spikelet, usually
ointed, the second slightly shorter than the fruit and sterile lemma at
aaturity; **Fruit** 2.2 mm. long, 1.2 mm. wide, elliptic, obtuse. **Autumnal
Form** spreading-decumbent, the stiff culms rather loosely branching from
he middle and upper nodes, the ultimate branchlets crowded at the ends
f the primary branches, the reduced blades erect; winter leaves very firm,
onspicuously ciliate; short culms with tufted branches sometimes formed
luring the winter, the green bushy crown persistent at the base of the tall
vernal culms. (See drawings of *P. lanuginosum.*)
    Dry sandy woods, eastern Texas to Florida; North Carolina and Kansas.
(Waller county.) Spring-summer.

    SPHAEROCARPA (sfē-rō-kär′på):—**Culms** usually few in a tuft,
ather stout, glabrous; **Blades** mostly thick and firm, cordate and ciliate
at base, margins strongly cartilaginous; **Ligule** obsolete or nearly so;
Spikelets obovoid-spherical at maturity, oval when young, 1-1.8 mm. long,
puberulent; **Second Glume** and **Sterile Lemma** 5-7-nerved; **Panicle**
branches mostly viscid. **Autumnal Form** remaining simple or but sparingly
branching, the thick, white-margined blades of the winter rosette conspicuous.

CULMS SPREADING; BLADES OBSCURELY NERVED; panicle nearly
broad as long.
Ligules obsolete or wanting; blades lanceolate.   68. P. sphaerocarp
Ligules evident, 0.3-1 mm. long; margins of blades parallel for at least tw
thirds their length.   68a. P. sphaerocarpon var. inflatu
CULMS ERECT OR ASCENDING; BLADES RATHER STRONGLY NERVE]
panicle never more than two-thirds as broad as long, usually less; spikele
1.5-1.6 mm. long; blades lanceolate, the upper not reduced.   69. P. polyanth

68. P. SPHAEROCARPON Ell. (sfē-rō-kär'pŏn) ; ROUND-FRUITED PANI
GRASS.

Vernal Form, plants light-green; Culms 10-22′ tall, tufted, radiat
spreading or ascending, leafy toward the base, the nodes glabrous (
appressed puberulent (appressed pubescent) ; Blades 2.5-5′ long, 7-12 mm
wide, flat, the upper and lower shorter, ascending, thick and firm, acum
nate, slightly narrowed to the subcordate base, rough on the margins an
upper surface, the cartilaginous margins stiffly ciliate and sometim
serrulate toward the base, often papillose; Sheaths, the upper short
and the lower longer than the internodes, loose toward the summit, cilia
on the margin, sometimes with viscid tubercles between the nerves; Ligu
obsolete or nearly so; Panicles long-exserted, 2-5′ long, nearly as wid
green to dark-purple, the axis and the ascending branches with visc:
spots; Spikelets about 1.6 mm. (1.5-1.8) long, about 1.2 mm. (1-1.3) wid
oval to obovoid-spherical, dark-purple, puberulent; Glumes, the fir
about one-fourth the length of the spikelet, obtuse; the second and Steri
Lemma equaling the fruit at maturity, 5-7-nerved; Fruit 1.4 mm. (1.4-1.!
long, 1.1 mm. (1-1.2) wide, obovoid-spherical, china-white.   Autumn.
Form prostrate-spreading, sparingly branching late in the season fro
the base or lower and middle nodes, the branches short, mostly simple, tl
blades and panicles not greatly reduced; winter rosette of many thic
ovate or ovate-lanceolate, white-margined leaves, appearing early.
Sandy soil, Texas south through Mexico, east to Florida and north
Vermont, Illinois and Kansas. (Houston.) Spring and summer.

68a. P. SPHAEROCARPON var. INFLATUM (Scribn. & Smith) Hitch
(ĭn-flā'tŭm).

Vernal Form similar to that of the species, more ascending, n
radiate-spreading; Culms on the average taller, more slender; Blades 5-1
mm. wide, narrower, the margins nearly parallel for two-thirds the
length, with fewer ciliae at the base; Sheaths rather loose, more common
and prominently viscid-tuberculate; Ligule 0.3-1 mm. long; Panicles mo
closely flowered; Spikelets slightly smaller, 1.4-1.5 mm. long, 1 mm. wid
Autumnal Form decumbent, rather freely branching from the midd
nodes before the maturity of the primary panicles, these early branch
long and again branching more freely than in the species, the ultima
blades and panicles not greatly reduced.   This subspecies is distinguishe
by the ligules, slightly smaller spikelets, and narrower parallel-margine
blades, taken in combination, and in autumnal specimens by the mo
freely branching habit.
(See photograph of *P. sphaerocarpon* for drawing of spikelet.)
Moist sandy ground, eastern Texas to Florida and north to Marylan
also north to Missouri.

69. P. POLYANTHES Schult. (pŏl-ĭ-ăn'thēz).

Vernal Plants light-green, in tufts of few to several culms; Culm
12-36′ tall, stout, erect, the nodes glabrous or nearly so; Blades 5-9′ lon

25 mm. wide, the upper seldom reduced, rather thin, prominently
·ved, long-acuminate, scarcely narrowed toward the cordate base, rough
smooth on the upper surface, smooth below, the cartilaginous scabrous
.rgins ciliate toward the base; **Sheaths** long, usually overlapping, finely
iate on the margins, otherwise glabrous; **Ligule** obsolete or wanting;
nicles exserted, 3-10′ long, one-fourth to half as wide, densely flowered,
₃ lower branches narrowly ascending, often distant, the upper fascicled,
ikelet-bearing to the base; **Spikelets** 1.5-1.6 mm. long, 1-1.1 mm. wide,
ovoid-spherical at maturity, minutely puberulent; **Glumes,** the first one-
ird to two-fifths the length of the spikelet, obtuse or obscurely pointed,
e second and **Sterile Lemma** equaling the fruit at maturity; **Fruit**
ovoid-spherical. **Autumnal Form** remaining erect and simple or pro-
.cing from the lower or middle nodes simple branches with smaller
ides and panicles; winter rosette like those of *P. sphaerocarpon,* but the
ives larger.

This species is distinguished from *P. sphaerocarpon* by its erect habit,
ller and more leafy culms, wider blades and narrow panicles. (See photo-
aph of *P. sphaerocarpon* for drawings of spikelet.)

Damp grounds, woods and openings, Texas to Georgia and north to
ilahoma and New Jersey. (Palestine and Burnet.) Summer-fall.

LANCEARIA (lăn-sē-ā′rĭ-à):—**Plants** olive-green, often purplish;
ernal Culms wiry, minutely crisp-puberulent or glabrous; **Blades**
.abrous or puberulent, usually strongly ciliate, at least near the base;
heaths glabrous or puberulent, at least at the summit; **Ligule** nearly
»solete; **Spikelets** unsymmetrically pyriform, that is, more swollen on the
ice than on the back; **First Glume** thin and shining, broad at the summit,
otuse or truncate; **Second Glume** and **Sterile Lemma** strongly 7-9-nerved,
uberulent or glabrous. Species of the Atlantic coastal plain, two in
exas.

PIKELETS 1.5-1.6 mm. long.   70. P. portoricense
PIKELETS 2-2.1 mm. long; culms stiffly ascending; blades firm, glabrous
   above.   71. P. lancearium

). P. PORTORICENSE Desv. (pōr-tō-rĭ-sĕn′sē); *P. pauciciliatum* Ashe.

Vernal Culms 6-12′ tall, tufted, erect or geniculate at the base,
lender, stiff and wiry, the internodes commonly reddish-purple, crisp-
uberulent to nearly glabrous; **Blades** 20-50 mm. long, 3-6 mm. wide, firm,
scending or spreading; glabrous to puberulent, ciliate near the base;
heaths much shorter than the internodes, striate, glabrous or crisp-
uberulent; **Panicles** 20-40 mm. rarely 60-70 mm. long; two-thirds as wide,
he flexuous branches spreading, or the lower reflexed, the pedicels and the
ltimate branchlets often directed toward the under side; **Spikelets** 1.5-1.6
ım. long, 1 mm. wide; **Glumes,** the first one-third to half as long as the
pikelet, obtuse or truncate, the second and **Sterile Lemma** puberulent, the
;lume shorter than the fruit and sterile lemma; **Fruit** 1.4 mm. long, 1 mm.
vide, elliptic-obovoid, obscurely pointed. **Autumnal Culms** ascending
rom a decumbent base, branching from all but the uppermost node before
he maturity of the primary panicles, the primary internodes often
elongated, the terminal joint with its panicle together with the internode
below it often falling early, thus giving the appearance of short culms
oranching at all the nodes, characteristic of this species; early branches
about equaling these shortened primary culms, repeatedly branching, the
ultimate branchlets in fascicles toward the ends, the reduced blades spread-

ing, involute-pointed; winter rosette appearing late, not conspicuous. (S drawings of *P. lanuginosum.*)

Sandy woods of the coastal plain, mostly in moist places southeast Tex and along the Gulf to Florida, north to North Carolina. (Narcoosse Texas.)

71. P. LANCEARIUM Trin. (lăn-sē-ā′rĭ-ŭm).

Vernal Culms tufted, usually purplish, 8-20′ tall, wiry, stiffly ascend ing, from a more or less geniculate base, minutely grayish crisp-puber lent; **Blades** 20-60 mm. long, 3-7 mm. wide, firm, ascending or spreadin usually glabrous on the upper surface, strongly ciliate toward the base, c sometimes nearly to the apex; **Sheaths** much shorter than the internode puberulent at least near the margins; **Panicles** 30-60 mm. long, two-third as wide, rather few-flowered, the flexuous branches spreading or the lowe reflexed; **Spikelets** 2-2.1 mm. long, 1-1.2 mm. wide; **Glumes**, the first on third to half as long as the spikelet, obtuse or truncate, the second an **Sterile Lemma** puberulent or sometimes glabrous, the glume slightl shorter than the fruit and sterile lemma; **Fruit** 1.6-1.7 mm. long, 1 mm wide, obovate-elliptic, minutely puberulent at the apex. **Autumnal Culm** geniculate-spreading, ascending at the ends, the stiff internodes occasionall elongated, branching from the middle nodes, the branches much longer tha the internodes, late in the season bearing fascicles of short branchlets tc ward the summit, the reduced flat or involute-pointed blades spreading, th ultimate panicles reduced to a few spikelets, partly inclosed in the sheaths (See photograph of *P. helleri.*)

Low sandy woods of the coastal plain, Texas to Florida and Virginia

OLIGOSANTHIA (ŏl-ĭ-gō-săn′thĭ-à):—**Culms** rather stout, usuall erect; **Blades** firm, not over 20 mm. wide, usually narrower; **Sheaths** mor or less hirsute, villous, or sometimes glabrous; **Ligule** inconspicuous ex cept in *P. ravenelii;* **Spikelets** about 3-4 mm. long, obovate, turgid usually papillose-hirsute, strongly 7-9-nerved. **Autumnal Form** with branches more or less crowded toward the summit.

NODES BEARDED; BLADES VELVETY-PUBESCENT BENEATH.
Plants lax, soft-velvety throughout; spikelets not over 3 mm. long.
72. P. malacophyllun
Plants stiff, pubescence harsh; spikelets about 4 mm. long. 76. P. raveneli
NODES NOT BEARDED; BLADES NOT VELVETY; panicle about as wide a long.
Spikelets narrowly obovate, subacute; plants olivaceous, appressed-pubescent
75. P. oligosanthes
Spikelets 3.2-3.3 mm. long; blades firm; sheaths or some of them more or less hispid. 74. P. scribnerianum
Spikelets not over 3 mm. long; blades rather thin; sheaths or some of them glabrous or sparsely hispid. 73. P. helleri

72. P. MALACOPHYLLUM Nash (măl-à-kō-fĭl′ŭm); SOFT-LEAVED PANIC- GRASS.

Vernal Form velvety or velvety pilose throughout; **Culms** few-to- several in tufts, 10-28′ tall, slender, more or less geniculate at the base with arched internodes, ascending or spreading, papillose-pilose with soft reflexed hairs, the nodes retrorsely bearded; **Blades** 3-4′ long, 6-12 mm. wide, tapering to the rounded base, acuminate, rather thin, velvety on both surfaces, ciliate at least toward the base, spreading or ascending; **Sheaths** shorter than the internodes, usually less copiously pilose than the culm, loose; **Ligule** 1-1.5 mm. long; **Panicles** usually short-exserted, 30-70 mm. long, at first narrow, the lower branches finally spreading, with

ort-spikelet-bearing branchlets in the axils; **Spikelets** 2.9-3 mm. long,
-1.7 mm. wide, elliptic-obovate, obscurely pointed, turgid at maturity,
pillose-pilose; **Glumes,** the first about one-third as long as the spikelet,
second and the **Sterile Lemma** equaling the fruit at maturity; **Fruit**
mm. long, 1.5 mm. wide, elliptic. **Autumnal Form** spreading, freely
anching from the middle and upper nodes before the maturity of the
mary panicle, at length forming bushy, topheavy clumps with reduced
des and numerous secondary panicles.

(For drawings see photograph of *P. oligosanthes.*)

Sandy woods, eastern Texas to Missouri, Kansas and Tennessee. (Dallas
d Denison.) Spring-summer.

P. HELLERI Nash (hĕl′ĕr-ī).

Vernal Form in clumps of few-to-several culms, usually somewhat
ish light-green, 8-20′ tall, slender, ascending or spreading, often from
hort decumbent base, the internodes glabrous, or the lower appressed-
bescent; **Blades** 1.5-4.5′ long, the upper short, 6-12 mm. wide, tapering
ward both ends, thin, ascending or spreading, papillose-ciliate toward
base, otherwise glabrous or pubescent beneath; **Sheaths** mostly longer
n the internodes, ciliate on the margins, sparsely papillose-hispid to
brous, the papillae often without hairs as in *P. scribnerianum;* **Ligule**
iliate ring about 1 mm. long; **Panicle** 2-5′ long, about three-fourths
wide, finally long-exserted, the branches mostly single, usually with several
rt branchlets, more open and loosely flowered than in *P. scribnerianum;*
ikelets about 3 mm. long, 1.5-1.7 mm. wide, on short pedicels, longer or
orter than the spikelets, obovate, turgid, blunt, glabrous, or with a few
ttered hairs; **Glumes,** the first about one-third the length of the spike-
, acute, the second and **Sterile Lemma** subequal, slightly exposing the
it at maturity, strongly nerved, usually 7-9-nerved; **Fruit** 2.4-2.5 mm.
g, 1.5-1.6 mm. wide, oval, obscurely apiculate. **Autumnal Form** branch-
at all but the lowest nodes, forming loose sprawling tufts, the branches
newhat divaricate, with sheaths more commonly pubescent than those
the primary culm, the blades widely spreading, not much reduced, the
g-pedicled spikelets rather conspicuous among the foliage.

The smaller spikelets, thinner blades tapering to both ends, and the
habit, taken in combination, distinguish this species from *P. scribneri-
um,* a closely related species. In both of these plants little weight can be
en to pubescence or lack of it.

Open woods and prairies, New Mexico, Texas, Louisiana, north to
lahoma and Missouri. Spring.

P. SCRIBNERIANUM Nash (skrĭb-nĕr-ĭ-ā′nŭm).

Vernal Form in clumps of few-to-many culms; **Culms** 8-20′ tall, erect
ascending, often geniculate at the base, sometimes widely spreading,
brous to harshly puberulent, or sometimes ascending-pilose, or the
ver internodes sometimes densely pubescent; **Blades** 2-4′ rarely 6′ long,
2 mm. wide, rounded and ciliate at the base, wide at the base, rarely
rrowed toward the base as in *P. helleri,* acuminate, firm, ascending or
ct, glabrous on the upper surface, sometimes sparsely pubescent on the
der surface; **Sheaths** longer than the internodes, loose, the nerves
ominent, villous at the throat, ciliate, papillose-hispid or papillose only
ween the nerves, the lower often densely short-pubescent or glabrous;
gule about 1 mm. long; **Panicles** included at the base or finally short-
serted, mostly 2-3′ long rarely longer, two-thirds to three-fourths as wide,

the branches ascending or finally spreading; **Spikelets** 3.2-3.3 mm. lo
1.9-2 mm. wide, obovate, turgid, strongly nerved, blunt, sparsely pubesc«
to glabrous; **Glumes,** the first about one-third the length of the spike
acute, the second and **Sterile Lemma** subequal, broad, about 9-nerved, 1
glume slightly shorter than the nearly equal sterile lemma and fru
Fruit 2.8-2.9 mm. sometimes only 2.5 mm. long, 1.8-1.9 mm. sometimes o1
1.6 mm. wide, broadly elliptic, minutely apiculate. **Autumnal Fo**
branching from the middle and upper nodes (rarely from the low«
at about the maturity of the primary panicles; the branches longer th
the internodes, and late in the season producing crowded branchlets w
ascending, not greatly reduced, blades and small partially inclu0
panicles from their upper nodes. This species is very variable in 1
matter of pubescence. Glabrous and hispid sheaths are commonly fou
on the same specimen in this species. (The photograph shows both 1
vernal and autumnal forms.)

Sandy soil or dry prairies, south Texas to Maryland, to Mai
Ontario, and westward to the Pacific coast. (Sandy land below Cor]
Christi.) Spring-summer.

75. P. OLIGOSANTHES Schult. (ŏl-ĭ-gō-săn′thēz).

Vernal Form 14-40′ tall, olivaceous, in loose tufts of few-to-seve
culms, erect, often purplish, appressed-pubescent, especially below; **Bla«**
1.5-5.5′ long, 4-8 mm. rarely 10 mm. wide, stiffly spreading or ascendi
sharply acuminate, narrowed toward the base, upper surface with a f
long hairs or glabrous, harshly puberulent beneath, stiffly ciliate (papillo:
near the base; **Sheaths** shorter than the internodes, or the lower long
glabrous to papillose-pubescent, the hairs ascending, or papillose-his]
between the strong nerves; **Ligule,** hairs 1-2 mm. long with longer o»
intermixed; **Panicles** long-exserted, 2.5-5′ long, about as wide, ovate
ovate-pyramidal, loosely flowered, the branches stiffly spreading
ascending, the spikelets usually on long pedicels; **Spikelets** 3.5-4 mm. lo»
about 1.8 mm. wide (smaller in exceptional specimens), oblong-ovate, s«
acute, sparsely pubescent, sometimes papillose; **Glumes,** the first less th
half the length of the spikelet, acute, the second slightly shorter than 1
fruit and **Sterile Lemma,** 7-9-nerved; **Fruit** 2.8-3 mm. long, 1.5-1.7 m
wide, elliptic. **Autumnal Form** erect or spreading, sometimes top-hea`
prostrate, branching sparingly from the lower and freely from the up]
nodes, late in the season the short branchlets aggregate at the summit
the branches, the crowded blades ascending or widely spreading, 1
panicles more or less included and reduced to a few spikelets, these co
monly more turgid and blunt than of the primary panicle.

Very sandy land, usually moist or dry open woods, Texas to Flori«
north to New Jersey and Illinois. (Natalia, in very sandy wood
Summer and fall.

76. P. RAVENELII Scribn. & Merr. (răv-ĕn-ĕl′ĭ-ī).

Vernal Form in loose tufts, grayish olive-green; **Culms** 12-28′ t;
erect or ascending, densely papillose-hirsute with ascending hairs, 1
nodes short-bearded; **Blades** 3-6′ long, 10-20 mm. wide, sharply acumina
rounded at the base, thick, ascending or spreading, glabrous on the up]
surface, densely velvety-hirsute beneath, usually short-ciliate nearly to t
apex; **Sheaths** shorter than the lower internodes, about equaling the sh«
upper ones or overlapping, papillose-hirsute like the culm; **Ligule** 3-4 m
long; **Panicles** short-exserted, or included at the base, 2.5-5′ long, as wi

wider, loosely flowered, the branches finally spreading; **Spikelets** 4-4.3
1. long, 2-2.2 mm. wide, obovate, turgid and blunt, sparsely papillose-
bescent; **Glumes,** the first one-third to two-fifths the length of the
kelet, the second and **Sterile Lemma** subequal, scarcely equaling the
1it at maturity, strongly nerved; **Fruit** 3.2 mm. long, 2 mm. wide,
iptic, minutely apiculate. **Autumnal Form** more or less spreading,
inching from the middle and upper nodes, the short branchlets crowded
the summit late in the season, overtopping the small panicles. (See
awings of *P. lanuginosum.*)

Sandy or gravelly woods or open ground, Texas to Florida, north
Maryland and Missouri. (Waller county.) Summer-fall.

PEDICELLATA (pĕd-ĭ-sĕl-ā′tȧ) : — **Culms** slender, more or less
·sute; **Blades** not over 6 mm. wide, ciliate; **Ligule** of short hairs; **Spike-
**s 3.5-4 mm. long, attenuate at base, papillose, 7-9-nerved; **Autumnal
·rm** freely branching, the branches appearing before the maturity of
ɔ primary panicle; no distinct winter rosette formed.

This group of two species appears to be intermediate between the sub-
ɪus *Dichanthelium* and True *Panicum.* The plants bear a general re-
ɪblance to *Oligosanthia* but in the absence of a winter rosette and in the
anching habit, especially of *P. nodatum,* they show a departure from
chanthelium.

JLMS erect or leaning; blades thin, 2-4′ long, narrowed toward the base.
77. P. pedicellatum
JLMS decumbent; blades thick, not over 2′ long, not narrowed toward the base.
78. P. nodatum

. P. **PEDICELLATUM** Vasey (pĕd-ĭ-sĕl-ā′tŭm).

Vernal Form in tufts of few-to-several erect or ascending culms from
short knotted rootstock; **Culms** 8-20′ tall, slender, usually ascending-
rsute, at least below, a few spreading hairs on the nodes; **Blades** 2-3.6′
ng, 3-6 mm. wide, ascending or spreading, the margins toward the
rrowed base sparsely ciliate with long hairs, both surfaces glabrous or
metimes minutely hispid; **Sheaths** ciliate on the margin, papillose,
aringly hirsute; **Ligule** dense, about 1 mm. long; **Panicles** 30-60 mm.
ng, about three-fourths as wide, the branches few, spreading or ascend-
g; **Spikelets** 3.5-3.7 mm. long, 1.4 mm. wide, elliptic, prominently
ipillose-hispid; **Glumes,** the first nearly or quite half the length of the
·ikelets, narrow, acute, the second shorter than the fruit and **Sterile
ɔmma** at maturity; **Fruit** 3 mm. long, 1.3 mm. wide, elliptic, subacute.
utumnal Form erect or leaning, branching from all but the uppermost
ɔdes before the maturity of the primary panicle, the branches slightly
varicate, the blades and panicles not greatly reduced.

(See photograph of *P. nodatum* for drawings of spikelet.)

Dry woods and prairies, Texas. (Kerrville and Austin.) Spring-
ɪmmer.

3. P. **NODATUM** Hitchc. & Chase (nō-dā′tŭm).

Vernal Form in tufts from a knotted crown; **Culms** 10-24′ tall, as-
ɪnding or spreading, slender, hard and wiry, harshly puberulent and
nely papillose, growing in tufts from a knotted crown; **Blades** 1-2′ long,
6 mm. wide, or the lowermost sometimes as much as 3′ long and 8 mm.
ide, ascending, rather firm, broadest just above the slightly narrowed
ɪd rounded base, abruptly acute, puberulent on both surfaces, papillose-

ciliate with stiff hairs 2-3 mm long; **Sheaths** shorter than the internode papillose-hispid between the strong nerves; **Ligule** dense, 1-2 mm. long less; **Panicles** 40-70 mm. long, half to nearly as wide, few-flowered, t few branches mostly 1-1.5′ long, usually single, sometimes in twos, ascen ing or spreading, puberulent, the more or less appressed spikelets puberulent pedicels one to two times as long as the spikelets, 1-6 to branch; **Spikelets** about 4 mm. long, 1.5-1.7 mm. wide, pyriform, papillos pubescent; **Glumes,** the first about one-third the length of the spikel acuminate, 1-nerved; the second and **Sterile Lemma** 7-9-nerved, the glun slightly exceeded by the sterile lemma and fruit, obtuse; **Sterile Pal** about one-third the length of the sterile lemma, thin; **Fruit** about 3 m long, 1.3-1.5 mm. wide, obovate-elliptic, minutely white-puberulent at t subacute apex. **Autumnal Form** widely-geniculate-decumbent, ear branching from all but the uppermost node, the branches somewh divaricate, equaling or exceeding the main culm, with numerous swoll nodes, the internodes 20-30 mm. long, the whole forming a loose tuft, t blades and panicles not reduced.

This species differs from *P. pedicellatum* in its stiffer, short-joint culms, shorter, puberulent, prominently ciliate blades, and pyriform spik lets with a shorter first glume.

Oak woods, sandy ground, southern Texas to northern Mexico. (Nea Encino, Falfurrias-Edinburg Road, and Sarita.) Spring.

Scoparia (skō-păr′ĭ-à):—**Vernal Culms** tall; **Blades** flat, elongate not over 15 mm. wide; **Ligule** short; **Spikelets** pointed, 7-9-nerved.

PUBESCENCE SOFT-VILLOUS OR VELVETY. Vernal culms erect or ascen
   ing; plants velvety throughout, a viscid ring below the villous nodes; spik
   lets about 2.5 mm. long, abruptly pointed.   79. P. scopariu
PUBESCENCE WHEN PRESENT NOT VELVETY. Spikelets ovate, i.e., broade
   below the middle; fruit 2 mm. long or less.
   Sheaths or some of them hispid, rarely glabrous; autumnal form with crowd
      branchlets.   80. P. scabriusculu
   Sheaths glabrous; autumnal form sparingly branching.
                                                            81. P. cryptanthu

79. P. SCOPARIUM Lam. (skō-păr′ĭ-ŭm) ; VELVETY PANIC-GRASS.

Vernal Form grayish olive-green, velvety-pubescent throughout e cept where noted; **Culms** 2-4 feet tall, rather stout, erect or ascendin usually geniculate at the base, the nodes villous with reflexed hairs, *glabrous viscid ring* below; **Blades** 3-7′ long, 10-17 mm. wide, flat, ascenc ing or spreading, often reflexed late in the season, rather thick, long acuminate, slightly narrowed to the rounded base, the uppermost blade often much reduced, the pubescence short; **Sheaths** about half as long a the long internodes, the velvety pubescence wanting on the back towar the summit, the surface here viscid when fresh; **Ligule** a ring of soft hair about 1-1.5 mm. long; **Panicles** finally long-exserted, 3-6′ long, nearly a wide, many-flowered, the axis, branches and pedicels with viscid blotche the branches ascending or spreading, spikelet-bearing to the base; **Spike lets** 2-2.6 mm. long, about 1.4-1.5 mm. wide, obovate, turgid at maturit abruptly pointed, papillose-pubescent with spreading hairs; **Glumes,** th first about one-fourth the length of the spikelet, mostly acute or truncate the second and **Sterile Lemma** strongly 7-9-nerved, the glume obtuse shorter than the fruit at maturity, the lemma abruptly pointed anc equaling it; **Fruit** 1.8-2 mm. long, about 1.4 mm. wide, obovate-elliptic apiculate. **Autumnal Form** (often forming very large billowy cushions ning or spreading, branching from the middle nodes after the maturity the primary panicle, the branches usually longer than the primary ternodes, repeatedly branching, often more or less scorpioid, the ulti- ate branchlets in fan-like fascicles, the sheaths often swollen toward the mmit, contracted at the throat, the blades much reduced, overtopping e small, partially included panicles.

A well-marked and constant species, easily recognized by its velvety bescence, the glabrous, viscid ring below the nodes, and the viscid pper portion of the sheath. The viscidity disappears in drying, but the andular surface is evident.

Wet or damp soil, east Texas to Florida, north to Massachusetts, west rough Kentucky and Missouri to Oklahoma. (Beaumont.) Spring and ll.

0. **P. SCABRIUSCULUM** Ell. (skăb-rĭ-ŭs′kū-lŭm) ; TALL SWAMP PANIC-GRASS.

Vernal Form grayish olive-green ; **Culms** 3-5 feet tall, erect, scabrous t least below the nodes, sometimes puberulent, the nodes glabrous or uberulent ; **Blades** 6-10′ long, 9-12 mm. rarely 15 mm. wide, stiffly ascend- ng or spreading, often reflexed, gradually tapering to an involute point, lightly narrowed toward the base, scabrous or smooth, glabrous but often nore or less pubescent beneath ; **Sheaths** shorter than the internodes, glabrous to more or less hispid at least toward the summit, often mottled r white-spotted, commonly swollen at the base and contracted toward he summit ; **Ligule** short-membranaceous, usually with a ring of hairs bove ; **Panicles** finally exserted, 4-8′ long, half to two-thirds as wide, nany-flowered, the axis glabrous or pubescent, often viscid, the flexuous ranches ascending, spikelet-bearing from near the base ; **Spikelets** 2.3-2.6 nm. long, 1.1-1.3 mm. wide, ovate, pointed, glabrous or obscurely puberu- lent ; **Glumes**, the first less than one-sixth as long as the spikelet, the second and **Sterile Lemma** strongly nerved, exceeding the fruit and form- ing an abrupt point beyond it ; **Fruit** 1.8 mm. long, 1 mm. wide, elliptic. **Autumnal Form** erect, branching from the middle and upper nodes, the branches appressed, somewhat longer than the internodes, finally bearing fascicled branchlets and forming dense oblong masses along the upper part of the primary culm, the sheaths, especially the later ones, densely papillose-hirsute, the flat reduced blades ovate-lanceolate, reduced in length much more than in width, the panicles partly or entirely inclosed in the sheaths.

This species is very variable in the amount of pubescence ; even on the same plant are often found glabrous and hispid sheaths or glabrous and pubescent blades. Otherwise it is an unusually uniform species.

(See photograph of autumnal form of *P. scoparium* for drawings of spikelet.)

Moist ground, especially along ditches, streams and swamps, near the coast, eastern Texas to Florida and north to New Jersey. (Nona.) Spring-summer.

81. **P. CRYPTANTHUM** Ashe (krĭp-tăn′thŭm).

Vernal Form tufted ; **Culms** 32-40′ tall, erect, glabrous except the usually bearded nodes ; **Blades** 4-6′ long, 7-9 mm. wide, stiffly ascending or spreading, acuminate, involute-pointed, glabrous, sparingly ciliate at the base ; **Sheaths** glabrous, or the lowermost sparsely hirsute, the upper somewhat inflated, all more or less ciliate on the margins and pilose at the summit; **Ligule** membranaceous, erose, scarcely 0.5 mm. long; **Panic** short-exserted, 2.5-4′ long, nearly as wide, the axis and ascending branc viscid-spotted; **Spikelets** 2.2-2.4 mm. long, 1 mm. wide, lanceolate-ellipt pointed; **Glumes,** the first one-fourth to one-third as long as the spike the second and **Sterile Lemma** equal, longer than the fruit, and point beyond it, glabrous or sparsely pilose; **Fruit** 1.5 mm. long, 0.9 mm. wi elliptic. **Autumnal Form** erect, glabrate on the nodes, sparingly bran ing from the middle and upper nodes, the branches stiffly ascending at angle of 30-45 degrees; blades flat, stiffly ascending, 20-50 mm. long, ξ mm. wide, involute-pointed; panicles reduced to a narrow cluster partia hidden in the sheaths. The habit of this species suggests a small *P. scabri culum.* (See photograph of autumnal form of *P. scoparium* for drawings spikelet.)

Low swampy land, southeast Texas to northern Florida, north to Nor Carolina. Rare. (Kountze.)

COMMUTATA (kŏm-ū-tā′tà) : — **Culms** rather stout, glabrous puberulent; **Blades** usually 10 mm. or more wide, cordate and more less ciliate at base; **Ligule** obsolete or nearly so; **Spikelets** 2.4-3.2 m long, **elliptic,** not very turgid, pubescent, 7-9-nerved. **Autumnal For** usually not very freely branching.

CULMS ERECT, or autumnal form leaning; blades symmetrical, broadly corda
82. P. commutati
CULMS DECUMBENT; blades usually unsymmetrical and falcate, narrowed
the scarcely cordate base.   83. P. joo

82. P. COMMUTATUM Schult. (kŏm-ū-tā′tŭm) ; Variable Panic-gras

Vernal Form usually purple-tinged; **Culms** 15-27′ tall, in clumps few-to-many, erect, sometimes softly puberulent, nodes puberulent, final sparingly branching; **Blades** 3-4.5′ long, 11-17 mm. (12-25) wide, flat, t lower and upper smaller than those of the midculm, rather abrupt tapering to an acuminate apex and narrowed to the cordate-clasping bas margin scabrous and ciliate, or papillose-ciliate toward the base, glabrou or sometimes puberulent, especially the under surface; **Sheaths** short than the internodes, close, ciliate on the margin, a densely puberule ring at the summit, otherwise glabrous or puberulent between the nerve **Ligule** obsolete or a very short truncate membrane; **Panicles** green, final exserted, 3-4.5′ long, as wide or wider, loosely flowered, the axis glabrou its branches ascending or spreading; **Spikelets** 2.5-3 mm. long, 1.1-1.3 m wide, oblong-elliptic, obtuse, softly pubescent; **Glumes,** the first about on fourth the length of the spikelet, usually acute, the second and **Steri Lemma** barely covering the fruit at maturity, 7-nerved; **Fruit** 2.2-2.5 mr long, 1-1.2 mm. wide, elliptic, umbonate. **Autumnal Form** erect or lea ing, branching from the middle nodes, the portion of the primary cul above the uppermost branch commonly falling away leaving the branc with its shortened internodes, crowded rather loose sheaths, scarcely ϵ not at all reduced blades, and hardly exserted panicles, as the appare termination of the primary culm; secondary branchlets crowded towar the summit, the reduced blades exceeding the partly included much r duced panicles; winter rosette appearing rather early, the blades firn ovate. This species is typically almost glabrous, with stiff culms an firm blades, but often puberulent.

Woods, Texas to Florida, north to Illinois, Missouri, Michigan an Massachusetts. (Sandy land in woods, Houston.)

P. JOORII Vasey (jōōr'ĭ-ī).

Vernal Form rather pale grayish-green; **Culms** in clumps of few-many, 8-22′ tall, slender, spreading or ascending from a decumbent base, ιbrous or rarely pubescent, at least the lower internodes purplish-red; **ades** 2.4-6′ rarely 7′ long, 7-18 mm. wide, ascending or spreading, thin t firm, often subfalcate, acuminate, narrowed toward the rounded base, ually ciliate at the base, otherwise glabrous; **Sheaths** shorter than the :ernodes, ciliate, otherwise glabrous or rarely puberulent between the rves; **Ligule** nearly obsolete; **Panicles** short-exserted, 2-4′ long, about o-thirds as wide, loosely flowered, the branches ascending or spreading; •ikelets 3-3.1 mm. long, 1.2-1.3 mm. wide, elliptic, abruptly short-pointed, bescent; **Glumes,** the first one-third to two-fifths as long as the spike-·, acute, the second and **Sterile Lemma** more or less pustulate-papillose tween the nerves, the glume slightly shorter than the usually involute-inted sterile lemma; **Fruit** 2.4 mm. long, 1.2 mm. wide, elliptic, minutely ιbonate. **Autumnal Form** widely spreading, bearing more or less varicate branches from all the nodes, these primary branches longer an the internodes and branching from all or from their upper nodes, the timate branchlets in short, dense fascicles, the reduced blades ascending, ·ceeding the numerous, small, partly included panicles; winter rosette a own of a few short leafy basal shoots with evident internodes.

The type specimen of *P. joorii* is exceptional, having unusually large ιdes. As a whole this species has glabrous culms, sheaths and blades, but casional specimens more or less puberulent are found. (See photograph *P. commutatum* for drawings of spikelets.)

Low or swampy woods, southeast Texas to Florida, north to Arkansas d Virginia. (Waller county.) Spring-fall.

LATIFOLIA (lăt-ĭ-fō′lĭ-à):—**Culms** rather stout, usually more than ′ high; **Blades** ample, usually more than 15 mm. wide, cordate; **Ligule** •t over 1 mm. long; **Spikelets** 2.7-4.5 mm. long, rather turgid, pubescent, 9-nerved. **Autumnal Form** not very freely branching.

¶EATHS STRONGLY papillose-hispid, at least the lower and those of the branches; spikelets 2.7-3 mm. long. 84. P. clandestinum
¶EATHS GLABROUS or softly villous; blades glabrous or nearly so on both surfaces; nodes bearded; spikelets 4-4.5 mm. long. 85. P. boscii

. P. CLANDESTINUM L. (klăn-dĕs-tī′nŭm); DEER-TONGUE GRASS.

Vernal Form in large dense clumps, sometimes with strong root-ocks, 2-4′ long; **Culms** 28-58′ tall, erect, scabrous to papillose-hispid, at ast below the nodes; **Blades** 4-8′ long, 12-30 mm. wide, spreading or ially reflexed, slightly tapering to the cordate-clasping base, acuminate, abrous on both surfaces, at least toward the end, usually ciliate at the ιse; **Sheaths** as long as the internodes, or overlapping until after the ·anches appear, loose, strongly papillose-hispid to nearly glabrous, a ιberulent ring at the summit; **Ligule** 0.5 mm. long; **Panicles** finally ither long-exserted, 3-6′ long, about three-fourths as wide, many-owered, the flexuous branches in distant fascicles, short spikelet-bearing ·anchlets in the axils; **Spikelets** 2.7-3 mm. long, 1.4-1.5 mm. wide, •ovate-oblong, sparsely pubescent; **Glumes,** the first one-third the length : the spikelet, subacute or obtuse, the second slightly shorter than the uit and **Sterile Lemma**; **Fruit** elliptic 2.1-2.3 mm. long, 1.2-1.3 mm. wide. utumnal Form erect or leaning, sparingly branching, often before matur-y of the primary panicles, from the middle and upper nodes, the branches

leafy, the swollen bristly sheaths overlapping on the shortened internoc
and inclosing wholly or partially the secondary panicles; spikelets me
turgid than those of the primary panicles.   (See drawings of *P. lanu
nosum.*)

Moist, mostly sandy ground, Texas to Florida, north to Maine a
Kansas.   (Dallas.)   Spring-summer.

85. P. BOSCII Poir. (bŏs′kĭ-ī).

Vernal Form in large clumps; **Culms** purplish, 12-26′ tall, erect
ascending, nodes bearded with reflexed hairs, otherwise glabrous
minutely puberulent, rarely somewhat papillose; **Blades** spreading, 2.5
long, 12-25 mm. (15-30) wide, flat, acuminate, tapering very much towa
the sparsely short-ciliate cordate base, glabrous, or puberulent on t
under surface and sparsely pubescent on the upper surface; **Sheat**
shorter than the internodes, ciliate, collar pubescent, otherwise glabro
or sparsely to densely downy-pilose, especially the lower, sometimes t
lower papillose; **Ligule** a ring of hairs about 1 mm. long; **Panicles** gree
2.5-5′ long, as wide or wider, the main axis and the flexuous spreading
ascending branches puberulent; **Spikelets** 3.8-4.5 mm. long, 1.5-1.7 m
(2-2.2) wide, oblong-obovate, papillose-pubescent, green; **Glumes,** the fir
one-third to two-fifths the length of the spikelet, pointed, the seco
slightly shorter than the fruit and **Sterile Lemma** at maturity, both
nerved, obtuse; **Fruit** 3.2-3.5 mm. long, 1.5-1.6 mm. wide, elliptic, minute
pubescent and usually black at the tip.   **Autumnal Form** more or le
spreading, freely branching from the middle nodes, sometimes top-heav
reclining, not much reduced, the small panicles partly included, the upp
leaves of the branches crowded and spreading.

Woods, Texas to Florida, north to Massachusetts, Wisconsin and Okl
homa.   (Palacios River near Bay City.)   Spring.

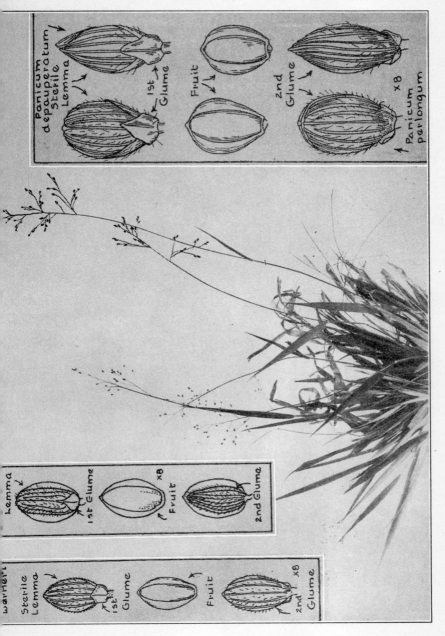

ANICUM XALAPENSE; drawings of P. WERNERI, P. DEPAUPER-
ATUM, P. PERLONGUM

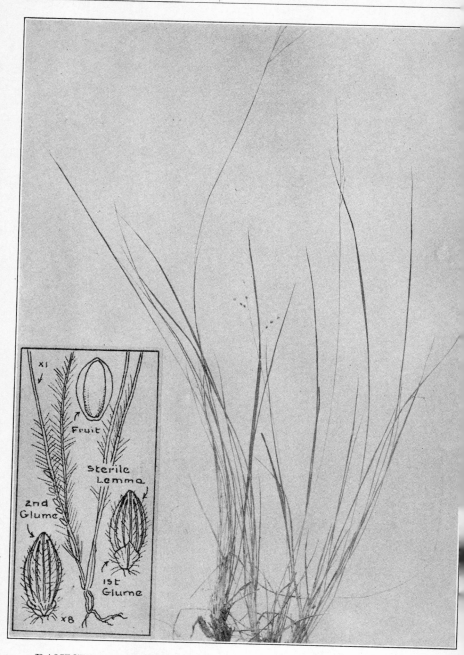

PANICUM LINEARIFOLIUM; Low White-haired Panic-grass

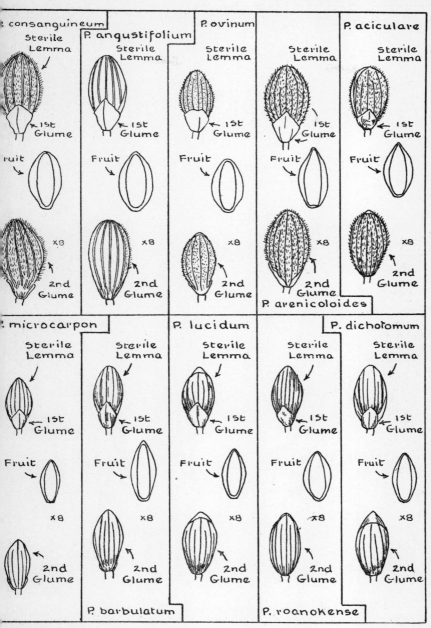

NICUM CONSANGUINEUM; P. ANGUSTIFOLIUM; P. OVINUM; ARENICOLOIDES; P. ACICULARE; P. MICROCARPON; P. BAR-LATUM; P. LUCIDUM; P. ROANOKENSE; P. DICHOTOMUM

PANICUM NITIDUM

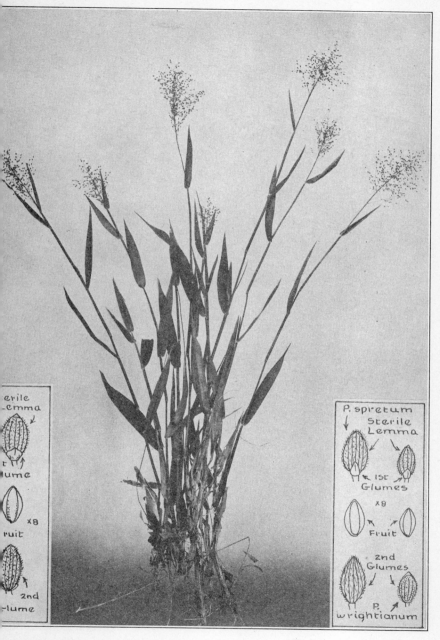

PANICUM LINDHEIMERI, Vernal Form; also drawing of
P. SPRETUM and P. WRIGHTIANUM

PANICUM LINDHEIMERI, Autumnal Form

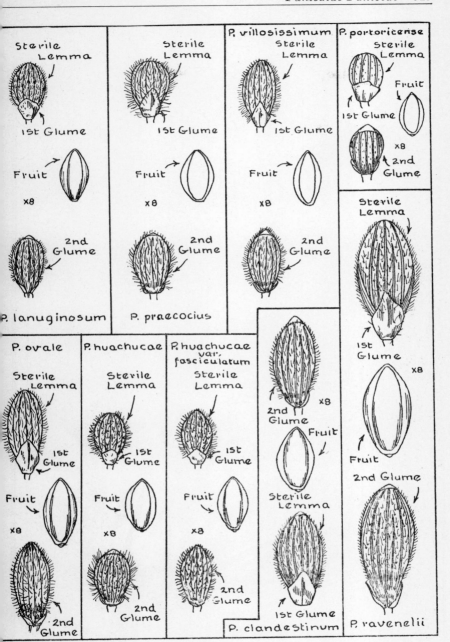

ANICUM LANUGINOSUM; P. PRAECOCIUS; P. VILLOSISSIMUM;
. PORTORICENSE; P. OVALE; P. HUACHUCAE; P. HUACHUCAE
VAR. FASCICULATUM; P. CLANDESTINUM; P. RAVENELII

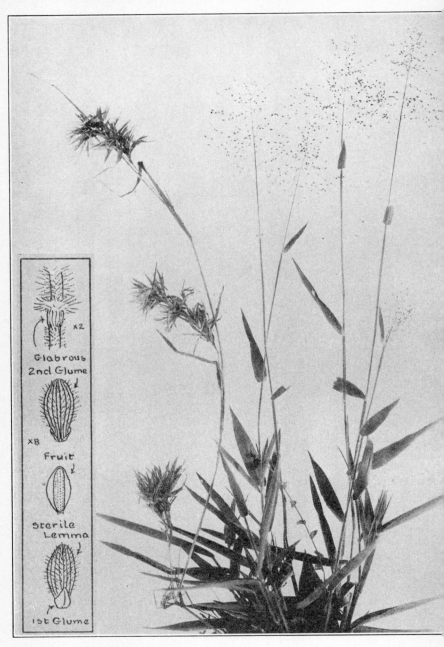

PANICUM THUROWII; Vernal and Autumnal Forms

NICUM SPHAEROCARPON; drawings of P. POLYANTHES AND
P. SPHAEROCARPON VAR. INFLATUM

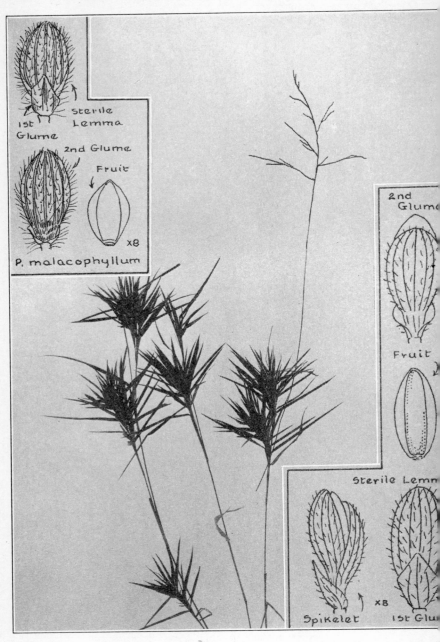

PANICUM OLIGOSANTHES, Vernal and Autumnal Forms; drawi
of P. MALACOPHYLLUM

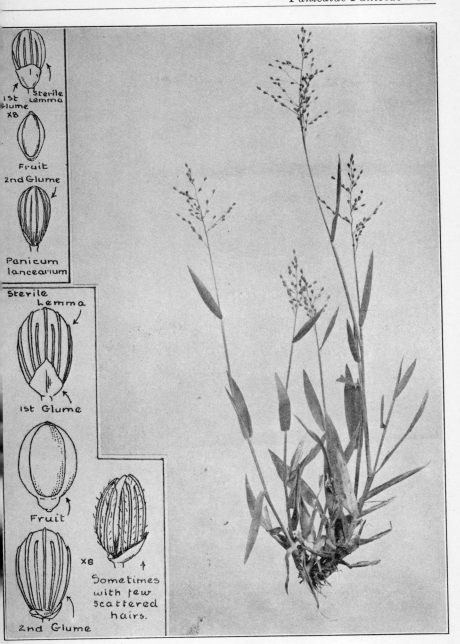

Sterile
Lemma

1st
Glume
X8

Fruit
2nd Glume

Panicum
lancearium

Sterile
Lemma

1st Glume

Fruit

2nd Glume

X8

Sometimes
with few
scattered
hairs.

PANICUM HELLERI

PANICUM SCRIBNERIANUM; Vernal and Autumnal Forms

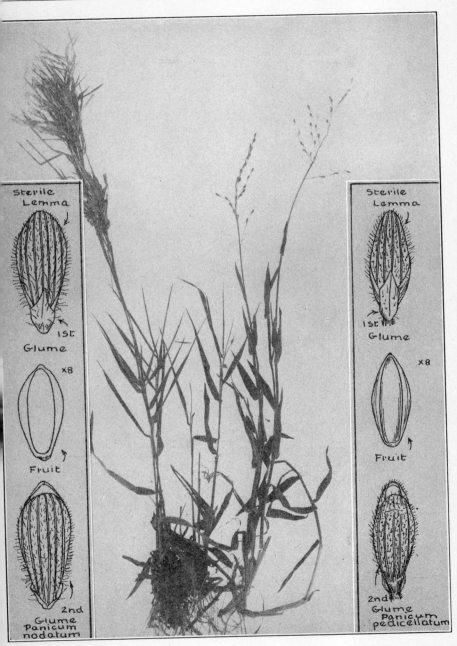

PANICUM NODATUM, Vernal and Autumnal Forms; also drawings of spikelet of P. PEDICELLATUM

PANICUM SCOPARIUM, Vernal Form.   (See photograph of autumn
form for drawings.)

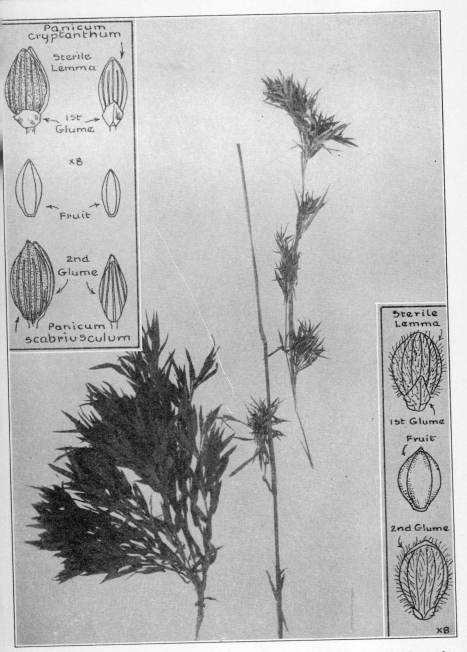

PANICUM SCOPARIUM, Autumnal Form; drawings of spikelets of
P. CRYPTANTHUM and P. SCABRIUSCULUM

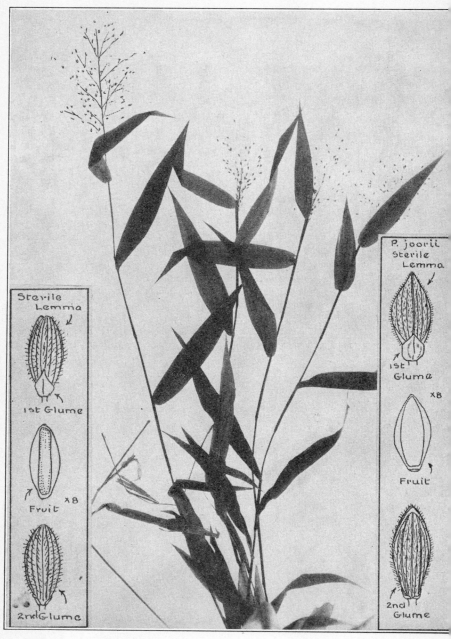

PANICUM COMMUTATUM; also drawings of spikelet of **P. JOORII**

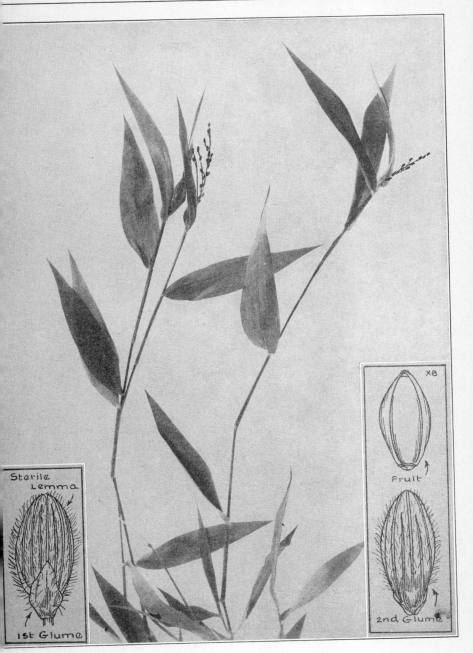

Sterile
Lemma

1st Glume

×8

Fruit

2nd Glume

PANICUM BOSCII

89. SACCIOLEPIS Nash (săk-ĭ-ŏl'ē-pĭs)

Spikelets oblong-conic; **First Glume** small, much shorter than tl spikelet; **Second Glume** broad, inflated-saccate, strongly many-nervec **Sterile Lemma** narrower, flat, fewer-nerved, its palea nearly as lon often subtending a staminate flower; **Fertile Lemma** stipitate, ellipti chartaceous-indurate, the margins inrolled, the palea not inclosed at tl summit.

Annuals or *perennials,* of wet soil, usually branching, the inflorescen a dense, usually elongate, spikelike panicle. Species about 12, in the Tropi of both hemispheres, one extending into the southern United States.

Our species is a *stoloniferous perennial,* 2-6 feet tall, often rather wea and tangled with other vegetation.

S. STRIATA (L.) Nash (strī-ā'tà); *S. gibba* (Ell.) Nash; *Panicu gibbum* Ell.; GIBBOUS PANIC-GRASS.

Culms 2-3 sometimes 6 feet tall, rather slender, erect or ascendir from a decumbent base, taking root at the lower nodes, stoloniferou nodes with a few hairs or glabrous, sparingly branched; **Blades** 2.5-7' lon 5-9 mm. (4-20) wide, flat, margins rough, sometimes sparsely-ciliate ɛ the base; **Sheaths** longer or shorter than the internodes, the lower som times rough, one margin toward the summit densely-ciliate, the upp often glabrous, the lower densely papillose-hirsute or hispid; **Ligule** very short membrane less than 0.5 mm. long; **Panicle** exserted, 2- (2.5-12') long, 8-15 mm. thick, spikelike, the erect or slightly ascendir branches short, usually less than 15 mm. long, pale-green, the spikelets c smooth and glabrous pedicels 2-4 mm. long; **Spikelets** 3.5-4 mm. lon 1.5 mm. wide, ovate-lanceolate; **Glumes,** the first usually less than 1 mɪ long, triangular, subacute, 3-nerved, the second slightly shorter than tl **Sterile Lemma,** both obtuse, purplish tipped, the glume 11-nerved, gibboɪ at the base, the sterile lemma 3-5-nerved, its palea about as long, acut often with a notch or two about 1 mm. below the apex; **Fruit** 1.6-1.8 mɪ long, 0.6-0.7 mm. wide, slightly stipitate, elliptic, obtuse, shining, smoot (See photograph of Natal grass for illustration.)

In very wet marshes, New Jersey to Oklahoma and south to Florid and Texas. (Marsh near Gonzales, Texas.) Summer-fall.

90. OPLISMENUS Beauv. (ŏp-lĭs'mĕn-ŭs)

Spikelets terete or somewhat laterally compressed, subsessile, solitary r in pairs, in two rows crowded or approximate on one side of a narrow cabrous or hairy rachis; **Glumes** about equal, emarginate or 2-lobed, wned from between the lobes; **Sterile Lemma** exceeding the glumes and ruit, notched or entire, mucronate or short-awned, inclosing a hyaline alea; **Fertile Lemma** elliptic, acute, convex or boat-shaped, the firm margins clasping the palea, not inrolled.

Freely branching, creeping, shade-loving *annuals* or *perennials,* with rect flowering shoots, flat, thin, lanceolate or ovate blades, and several one-ided, thickish, short spikes rather distant on a main axis. Species about 10, n the Tropics of both hemispheres, 1 extending into the southern states.

Our only species is a low annual, freely branching, creeping, with erect flowering culms, the flat lanceolate or ovate blades rounded or abruptly narrowed at the base, and the several short rather distant spikes arranged along the main axis. The short-pediceled spikelets solitary or in pairs. The author usually found this grass growing along with *Muhlenbergia schreberi* in the open shade of rather large trees.

O. SETARIUS (Lam.) Roem. & Schult. (sē-tā'rĭ-ŭs).

Culms 6-12' tall, sparingly branched, erect or ascending from a de-cumbent or creeping base, rooting at the nodes, weak, flattened, nodes pubescent, otherwise glabrous to pubescent; **Blades** 20-40 mm. long, 5-9 mm. wide, abruptly narrowed at the base, acute, thin, rough, sparsely-pilose on both surfaces or glabrate; **Sheaths** about as long as the inter-nodes, villous along the margins, pubescent at or near the collar; **Ligule** a very short ciliate membrane; **Panicle** long-exserted, racemose, the main axis 1-3 inches long, scabrous or puberulent, the spikes usually 3-5 some-times as many as 8, the rachis short, 2-5 mm. long, pubescent or villous at the base, the spikelets solitary or in pairs, usually 3-9 to a spike, the pedicels short, the lower spikelet often abortive; **Spikelets** exclusive of the awns 2.5-3 mm. long, pubescent at the base; **Glumes** about equal, about two-thirds the length of the spikelet, the second only slightly longer, pubescent to almost glabrous, scabrous on the midnerve, each bearing a stout blunt almost smooth straight awn, the awn sometimes viscid, the first 1-3-nerved, lanceolate, the awn 5-9 mm. long, the second ovate, 5-nerved, the awn usually slightly shorter than the glume; **Sterile Lemma** and fruit about equal, 2-2.5 mm. long, the sterile lemma broadly-oval, pubescent, the awn similar to those of glumes but less than 1 mm. long, and usually ascending; **Fruit** lance-ovate, about 2-2.5 mm. long, 0.8 mm. wide, shining.

In low lands and swamps, usually in open woods, a tropical plant, Texas to Florida, North Carolina and Arkansas. (Woods, Mission Burial Park, San Antonio, Texas.) Summer-fall.

OPLISMENUS SETARIUS

91. ECHINOCHLOA Beauv. (ĕk-ĭ-nŏk′lō-à)

Spikelets plano-convex, often stiffly hispid, subsessile, solitary or in regular clusters on one side of the panicle branches; **First Glume** about half the length of the spikelet, pointed; **Second Glume** and sterile lemma equal, pointed, mucronate, or the glume short-awned and the lemma long-awned, sometimes conspicuously so, inclosing a membranaceous palea and sometimes a staminate flower; **Fertile Lemma** plano-convex, smooth and shining, acuminate-pointed, the margins inrolled below, flat above, the apex of the palea not inclosed.

Coarse, often succulent, *annual* or *sometimes perennial*, grasses, with compressed sheaths, linear flat blades, and rather compact panicles composed of short, densely-flowered racemes along a main axis. Species about 30, in the warm and temperate regions of both hemispheres; 4 annuals in the United States, all in Texas.

This genus differs from *Panicum* in the awned glumes (the first awnless in some species), sterile lemma and pointed fertile lemma. The species intergrade and overlap a great deal.

In all the species in the United States the *ligule* is absent, and all have distinctly awn-pointed or awned second glume and sterile lemma except *E. colonum*. In *E. colonum* the spikelets are merely apiculate or mucronate, and the racemes are simple and rather distant.

E. crusgalli, known as barnyard grass, erect and stout in water and wet places, and spreading in fields and waste places, is rather common over most of the United States. The panicles vary much as to size, color (green to purple), and length of awns.

E. walteri, usually taller and stouter, more robust than *E. crusgalli*, with at least the lower sheaths papillose-hirsute or hispid, has long-awned spikelets. It is mostly confined to the coastal plains and adjacent to the Great Lakes.

The author has not only obtained much information, but has copied many paragraphs from Contributions from U. S. National Herbarium, Vol. 22, Part 3, by A. S. Hitchcock.

RACEMES SIMPLE, RATHER DISTANT, 10-20 mm. LONG. Spikelets crowded in about 4 rows, the awn of the sterile lemma reduced to a short point; blades usually less than 5 mm. wide.   1. E. colonum

RACEMES USUALLY MORE OR LESS BRANCHED, more than 20 mm. long. Spikelets usually irregularly crowded or fascicled, not arranged in rows; awns variable; fruit 2.5-3 mm. long, blades commonly more than 5 mm. wide.

  SHEATHS SMOOTH; awns variable, but the panicle not a dense mass of long-awned spikelets.

    PANICLE erect or usually nodding, the branches often spreading.

      Spikelets awned.

        Awn of the sterile lemma usually not over 10 mm. long; spikelets rather small, not strongly hispid; panicle soft.   2. E. crus-pavonis

        Awn of the sterile lemma usually 5-10 mm. long.   3. E. crusgalli

      Spikelets awnless, or the awn of the sterile lemma less than 3 mm. long.   3a. E. crusgalli var. mitis

    PANICLE usually erect, dense, the racemes appressed.

      Racemes thick, incurved; spikelets awnless, mostly purple.   3b. E. crusgalli var. edulis

      Racemes mostly single; spikelets awnless or nearly so, not strongly hispid, not papillose, usually green.   3c. E. crusgalli var. zelayensis

  SHEATHS, AT LEAST the lower, papillose-hispid or hirsute; panicle dense, the spikelets long-awned.   4. E. walteri

1. E. COLONUM (L.) Link (kō-lō′nŭm) ; JUNGLE RICE.

Culms 10-28′ tall, tufted, the larger plants freely branching towa
the base, prostrate-spreading, ascending or erect, flattened, nod
glabrous or puberulent, often rooting at the lower node; **Blades** 2-7′ lon
3-6 mm. wide, rarely 10 mm. wide, flat, sometimes scabrous on the margi
(occasionally bearing transverse purple bands, "zonate"); **Sheat**
shorter than the internodes, flattened, glabrous or the lower sometim
sparsely pubescent near the base; **Ligule** wanting, sometimes a few hai
at the junction of blade and sheath; **Panicles** finally exserted, 2-6′ lon
racemes several, usually 6-12, mostly 10-20 mm. sometimes 30 mm. lon
appressed or ascending, commonly single, occasionally two approxima
the lower distant about 10 mm. sometimes even 20 mm., racemose
arranged along a smooth or slightly scabrous axis, the spikelets crowde
in pairs in two rows appearing in four rows, the rachis triangular-fl
tened, scabrous; **Spikelets** 2.2-3 mm. long, about 1.5 mm. wide, more
less hispidulous; **Glumes**, the first about half the length of the spikel
3-nerved, broad, pointed, the second and **Sterile Lemma** about equ
short-pointed but not awned, 5-nerved; **Sterile Palea** nearly as long as
lemma, obtuse, thin; **Fruit** 2-2.5 mm. long, about 1.4 mm. wide, the sho
point minutely scabrous. The specimens collected seem to have spikel
from 2-3 mm. long, but perhaps some were immature.

Ditches and moist places, southern United States, extending in
Mexico, north to Kansas and here and there over most of the Unit
States. Spring and summer.

2. E. CRUS-PAVONIS (H. B. K.) Schult. (krŭs-på-vō′nĭs) ; *E. crusga*
var. *crus-pavonis* (H. B. K.) Hitchc.

Culms erect or sometimes decumbent at the base, as much as 40′ ta
Blades 5-15 mm. wide; **Panicles** 4-8′ long, nodding, rather soft, purp
pale or pinkish; **Racemes** mostly ascending or appressed, the lower son
what distant; **Spikelets** about 3 mm. long, hispid on the nerves, hispid
lous on the internerves, the awn usually about 10 mm. long.

Marshes and wet places, often in water, southern Texas and throug
out tropical America at low altitudes.

3. E. CRUSGALLI (L.) Beauv. (krŭs-găl′ī).

Culms commonly 2-3 feet rarely 5 feet tall, erect or sometimes
cumbent at the base, branching at the base; **Blades** 6-24′ long more or le
6-30 mm. wide more or less, scabrous on the margins and sometimes on t
upper surface; **Sheaths** glabrous and smooth; **Ligule** wanting, the ligul
area sometimes pubescent; **Panicle** 4-8′ long, erect or nodding, purplish
green, the axis scabrous; **Racemes** spreading, ascending or appressed, t
lower somewhat distant, as much as 4′ long, sometimes branching, t
upper approximate and shorter, the rachis scabrous or hispid, especial
on the base, the spikelets crowded on the branches; **Spikelets** excludi
the awns about 3 mm. long, strongly hispid or papillose-hispid on t
nerves, hispidulous on the internerves; **Sterile Lemma** with a well-c
veloped palea, neuter, the awn variable in length, mostly 5-10 mm. lor
on at least a part of the spikelets sometimes as much as 30 mm. lon
Fruit whitish or brownish, 2.5-3 mm. long, elliptic, turgid, narrowed in
a cusp or point.

Moist open ground, ditches, waste places and cultivated fiel
throughout most of the United States. Summer-fall.

. E. CRUSGALLI var. MITIS (Pursh) Peterm. (mī'tĭs).

Differs from the typical form in having the **Spikelets** awnless or nearly , the awns being less than 3 mm. long. In the southwest this form passes to *E. crusgalli* var. *zelayensis*. A specimen from San Antonio, Texas, . ιs scabrous sheaths. This specimen, collected by the author at San ιntonio, has **Spikelets** exclusive of the short awn 3-3.5 mm. long. The ιnicle is usually more open than shown in the photograph.

Moist places, Texas to Florida, north to Massachusetts and British ɔlumbia, Oklahoma to Oregon and northern Mexico to California. Summer- ll.

. E. CRUSGALLI var. EDULIS Hitchc. (ē-dū'lĭs) ; *E. crusgalli frumen- tacea* W. F. Wight; *E. frumentacea* Link; Japanese Barnyard Millet.

Differs from the typical form in having dense panicles, the **Racemes** ick, appressed, incurved; **Spikelets** awnless, mostly purple; **Fruits** pale, ually exposed before maturity, contrasting with the purple glumes. In e United States this is sometimes cultivated as a forage grass under the ιme of Japanese barnyard millet. For a time it was exploited under e name of billion-dollar grass. In India the seed is used as human food. Escaped from cultivation, eastern Texas, Alabama, North Carolina to e New England states and the central states. Summer.

. E. CRUSGALLI var. ZELAYENSIS (H. B. K.) Hitchc. (zē-lā-ĕn'sĭs).

Differs from E. crusgalli var. mitis in having less succulent culms, ɔstly simple more or less appressed racemes, the spikelets less strongly spid, but papillose, usually green.

Moist, often alkaline places, Texas south through Mexico to Argentina, d north to Oklahoma, Oregon and California. (El Paso, Big Spring, ɔuston, Eagle Pass.)

E. WALTERI (Pursh) Heller (wăl'tēr-ī) ; *E. longearistata* Nash; Salt Marsh Cockspur-grass.

Culms 3-6 rarely 10 feet tall, as much as 1′ thick at the base, erect decumbent at the base, sometimes rooting at the lower nodes, freely anching when growing in water or mud; **Blades** commonly 5-15′ long, -18 mm. wide, in the larger plants 36′ long and 30 mm. wide, flat, the ιrgins and both surfaces toward the tip scabrous; **Sheaths** at least the wer papillose-hispid or papillose only or merely hispid-ciliate or just abrous, the collar sometimes pubescent; **Ligule** wanting, the ligular area ten pubescent; **Panicle** finally exserted, 8-12′ long, the axillary panicles ually smaller (one large plant had eight branches, each with a panicle), een to purplish, erect or nodding, loose, the axis scabrous, more or less pillose-hispid on the angles, the racemes densely-flowered, appressed ascending, sometimes spreading, single or in the larger plants fascicled, proximate, or the lower somewhat distant, sometimes branching, 0.5-5′ ng, the rachis hispidulous on the angles, also more or less papillose- spid, the spikelets on the many racemes or the short branches; **Spikelets** clusive of the awns 3-3.5 mm. long, brownish-purple or green, ovate- nceolate, the glumes and sterile lemma hispid or papillose-hispid on the rves, hispidulous on the internerves; **Glumes**, the first about half as ng as the sterile lemma, ovate, awn-pointed, the second and **Sterile mma** about equal, the second glume short-awned, and sterile lemma com- ɔnly long-awned, the awn 4-30 mm. long, rarely much longer, all on the

same panicle; **Palea** of sterile floret neuter; **Fruit** about 3 mm. lon
about 1 mm. wide, ovate-lanceolate, pointed, shining, narrower and mo
fusiform than in *E. crusgalli*.

Along streams and ditches, in marshes, often in water, along t
coast.   Coastal plain, Texas to Florida, north to Massachusetts, New Yo
to Wisconsin, Iowa and Kentucky.   (Brackenridge Park, San Anton
Texas.)   Summer-fall.

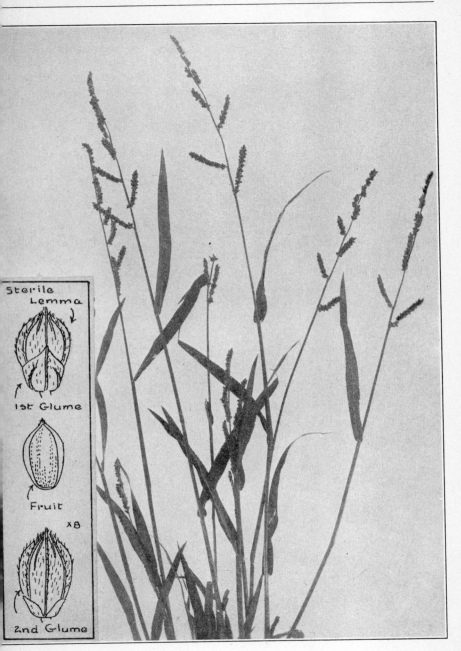

ECHINOCHLOA COLONUM

Four Echinochloa

E. crusgalli var. zelayensis   E. crusgalli var. edulis

E. crus-pavonis   E. crusgalli var. mitis

ECHINOCHLOA CRUSGALLI var. ZELAYENSIS, ECHINOCHLO
var. EDULIS, ECHINOCHLOA CRUS-PAVONIS and ECHINOCHLO
CRUSGALLI var. MITIS

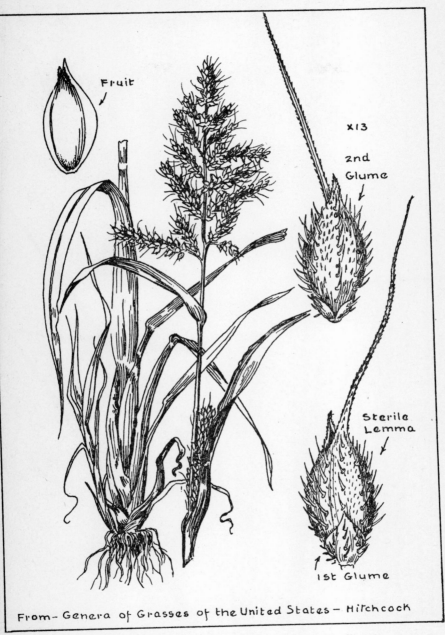

Fruit

×13

2nd Glume

Sterile Lemma

1st Glume

From— Genera of Grasses of the United States — Hitchcock

ECHINOCHLOA CRUSGALLI; Barnyard Grass

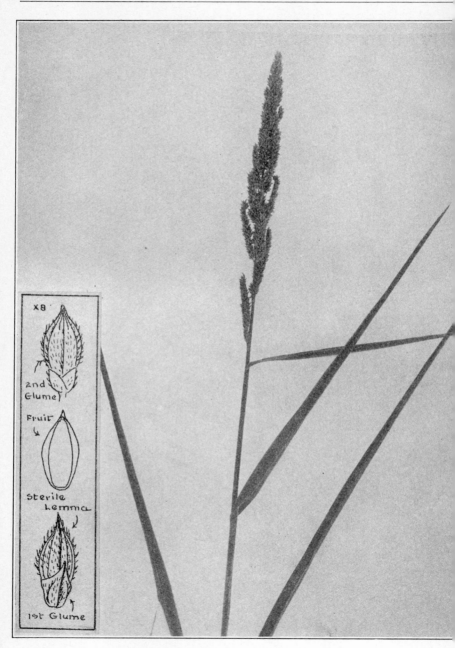

ECHINOCHLOA CRUSGALLI VAR. MITIS

ECHINOCHLOA WALTERI; Salt Marsh Cockspur-grass

92.   TRICHOLAENA Schrad. (trī-kō-lē'nà)

Spikelets on short capillary pedicels; **First Glume** small, much short
than the spikelet, villous; **Second Glume** and **Sterile Lemma** equal, rais
on a stipe above the first glume, emarginate or slightly lobed, short-awne
covered except toward the apex with long silky hairs, the palea of th
sterile lemma well developed; **Fertile Lemma** shorter than the spikele
cartilaginous, smooth, boat-shaped, obtuse, the margins thin, not inrolle
inclosing the margins of the palea.

Natal grass, our single species, is an upright, rather slender perennia
about 3 feet tall, with beautiful nodding purple to pink panicles, about
long. It is an important forage grass in Florida, and is found growing i
sandy land at Donna, Texas, and several other places in the Rio Gran
Valley.

T. ROSEA Nees (rōz'ē-à); NATAL GRASS.

Culms 2-4 feet tall, tufted, rather slender, branching, especially ne
the base, smooth or rough and papillose-pilose below, nodes mostl
pubescent; **Blades** 2-8' long, 3-6 mm. wide, acuminate, thin, sometim
papillose-pilose near the base; **Sheaths** mostly shorter than the inte
nodes, smooth or the lower rough, papillose-pilose, and finely pubescen
Ligule a ring of rather stiff hairs; **Panicle** pinkish to rose, usually 4-
long, nodding, ovate to pyramidal, the branches commonly 2.5' long or les
single or in whorls, capillary, the axis flexuous; **Spikelets** purple to pin
including the hairs 6-8 mm. long, excluding the hairs about 3.5 mm. lon
on pedicels 1-3 mm. long; **Glumes,** the first minute, villous, the secon
and sterile lemma about 3.5 mm. long, short-awned, long-villous; th
Palea of the sterile lemma about 2.5 mm. long, inclosing three stamen
Fruit about 2 mm. long, with **Palea** about the same length.

In sandy loam, near the coast, Texas to Florida. (Donna, Texas.
Spring-fall.

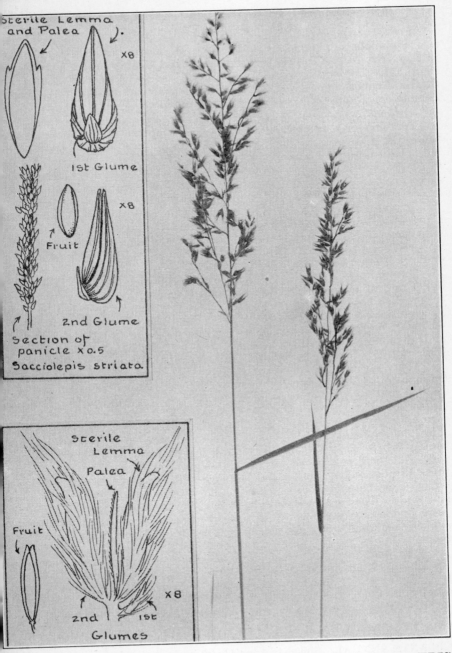

Sterile Lemma and Palea
×8
1st Glume
Fruit
×8
2nd Glume
Section of panicle ×0.5
Sacciolepis striata

Sterile Lemma
Palea
Fruit
2nd
1st
×8
Glumes

TRICHOLAENA ROSEA, NATAL GRASS; also drawings of SACCIOLEPIS STRIATA

93. SETARIA Beauv. (sē-tā'rĭ-à)
(Chaetochloa Scribn.)

Spikelets subtended by one-to-several bristles (sterile branchlets falling free from the bristles, awnless; **First Glume** broad, usually le than half the length of the spikelet, 3-5-nerved; **Second Glume** an **Sterile Lemma** equal, or the former shorter, several-nerved; **Fertil Lemma** coriaceous-indurate, smooth or rugose.

Annual or *perennial* grasses, with narrow terminal panicles, these dens and spikelike or somewhat loose and open. Eighteen species in the Unite States, 10 in Texas.

The genus *Setaria* is closely allied to *Panicum* from which it is dis tinguished by the presence of one or more bristle-like sterile branches belov each spikelet. In a small group of species of *Panicum* the ultimate branch lets are produced beyond the few to several spikelets as short bristles.

Two species with five or more bristles below each spikelet, *S. geniculata* a perennial with short rootstocks, and yellow foxtail, an annual, have th same general appearance except the latter has the blades twisted so that th upper surface is beneath. All our other species have one or sometimes tw or three bristles below each spikelet.

Two annuals, green foxtail, with a somewhat pointed head, and foxtai millet or Italian millet (*S. italica*), with larger and denser bristly yellow or purplish heads, are closely related, the latter being considered by many as a cultivated form of green foxtail. Small heads of Italian millet re semble green foxtail, but can be distinguished by the fact that a ripe head of Italian millet rubbed between the palms of the hands yields free seed while in green foxtail the spikelets fall as a whole from the pedicels.

There are many varieties of Italian millet, such as Hungarian millet, German millet and Golden Wonder. To these the general term millet is applied and should not be confused with the common millet, *Panicum miliaceum*, often cultivated in the United States under the name of broom-corn millet, proso millet and hog millet.

S. macrostachya and *S. scheelei*, perennials, are closely related, the first having two forms in Texas, the narrow-leaved form with blades 3-5 mm. wide, and the broad-leaved form with blades as much as 10 mm. and some times 15 mm. wide. The second has larger, looser panicles with the lower branches of the panicle as much as 35 mm. long and blades as much as 20 mm. wide. The former is found in open dry ground and woods, and the latter in open rocky woods. *S. grisebachii*, an annual, usually with a purple panicle, somewhat resembles the last species, but is found in open ground or fields.

S. magna, an annual, the tallest of our species, sometimes growing to a height of 12 feet or more, has very large, dense, almost cylindric panicles. It is found along streams and ditches. *S. verticillata*, another annual, usually less than three feet tall, is easily distinguished by its backwardly barbed bristles causing the panicles to cling to everything they touch.

BRISTLES BELOW EACH SPIKELET NUMEROUS, AT LEAST MORE THAN five; panicles dense, cylindric, spikelike.
  PLANTS ANNUAL. Spikelets 3 mm. long; blades twisted.   1. S. lutescens
  PLANTS PERENNIAL. Spikelets mostly 2-2.5 mm. long; plant with short rootstocks.   2. S. geniculata
BRISTLES BELOW EACH SPIKELET ONE, OR BY ABORTION OF THE spikelet two or three.
  BRISTLES DOWNWARDLY barbed. Spikelets about 2 mm. long, not globose; plants annual.   3. S. verticillata

BRISTLES UPWARDLY barbed.
  PLANTS annual. Fruit at maturity finely cross-lined or nearly smooth.
    Panicle loosely flowered, tapering above (usually purplish).
                                                    4. S. grisebachii
    Panicle compactly flowered, sometimes interrupted at the base.
      Plants as much as 12 feet tall, bristles 10-20 mm. long; fruit smooth or
        nearly so.   5. S. magna
      Plants mostly less than 3 feet tall; axis of the panicle villous.
        Panicle cylindric, tapering above, green; spikelets falling entire.
                                                    6. S. viridis
        Panicle lobed or interrupted, often large and heavy, purple or yellow;
          fruit deciduous from glumes and sterile lemma.   7. S. italica
  PLANTS perennial.
    Spikelets 2-2.5 mm. long. Panicle pale or greenish, often narrowed to-
      ward the summit but not attenuate; branches of the panicle short or
      only the lower as much as 20-30 mm. long; the bristles irregular in
      length, the longer sometimes 10-15 mm. long.
      Blades mostly less than 10 mm. wide, often folded; panicle usually loosely
        or interruptedly spikelike, the branches usually not over 10 mm.
        long.   8. S. macrostachya
      Blades flat, as much as 20 mm. wide; panicle tapering from near the
        base, the lower branches as much as 35 mm. long.   9. S. scheelei
    Spikelets 3 mm. long. Bristles 15-25 mm. long; blades villous.
                                                    10. S. villosissima

. S. LUTESCENS (Weigel) Hubbard (lū-tĕs'ĕns); *Chaetochloa lutescens*
(Weigel) Stuntz; *C. glauca* of authors; YELLOW FOXTAIL OR PIGEON-
GRASS.

 Culms 1-3.5 feet tall, tufted, erect or spreading, branching mostly toward the base, flattened, succulent at the base, the culms and leaves often
with a purplish tinge; **Blades** 4-11′ long, 7-11 mm. wide, flat, some of the
blades twisted, rough above, often pilose or papillose-pilose above toward
the base; **Sheaths** shorter than the internodes, flattened-keeled; **Ligule**
membranaceous, ciliate, about 1 mm. long; **Panicle** tawny-yellowish at
maturity, exserted, 1.5-3′ long, spikelike, erect, about 10 mm. thick, dense,
cylindric, sometimes slightly interrupted at the base, axis densely
pubescent, branches very short, usually less than 1 mm. long, densely
pubescent, each branch bearing one developed spikelet and below this a
cluster of short branchlets ending in bristles, sometimes a second small
and undeveloped spikelet borne in one of these secondary clusters, branchlets various in length, usually about 1 mm. long, bearing one to several
bristles, the whole cluster on each branch having more than 5 and sometimes as many as 20, bristles tawny to yellow, upwardly barbed, various
in length, usually 2-3 times as long as the spikelets; **Spikelets** about 3 mm.
long, flat on one side and strongly convex on the other, oval in outline but
slightly narrowed toward the apex; **Glumes,** the first ovate, about half as
long as the spikelet, 3-5-nerved, the second about two-thirds as long as the
spikelet, 5-9-nerved; **Sterile Lemma** about as long as the fruit, 5-nerved,
the lower edges folded around the fruit, with well developed palea but
no stamens; **Fruit** strongly marked with numerous transverse ridges.

 Common weed in cultivated soil and waste places in the eastern and
southern states, extending into Texas; also New Mexico and California.
(San Antonio, Texas.) Summer-fall.

2. S. GENICULATA (Lam.) Beauv. (jē-nĭk-ū-lā'tà); *Chaetochloa geniculata* (Lam.) Millsp. & Chase.

 Culms 2-3 feet tall, erect or spreading, often from a geniculate base,
often tufted, from short rootstocks, smooth except below the panicle,
resembling *S. lutescens* but perennial; **Blades** 2-9′ long, 1-4 mm. (1-8) wide,

numerous at the base, flat, long acuminate, usually narrow, not twiste
glabrous except sometimes villous at the base, more or less rough; **Sheat**
shorter than the internodes, or the lower longer, flattened, smooth
sometimes rough towards the summit; **Ligule** membranaceous, sho:
ciliate; **Panicle** long-exserted, 1-3′ long, erect, cylindric, densely-flowere
truncate or rounded at the top, green, yellowish or purple, includii
bristles about 10 mm. wide, the axis densely pubescent, with about
bristles below each spikelet, sometimes many more, as long as to sever
times the length of spikelet, usually 2-3 times as long, upwardly barbe
Spikelets about 2-2.5 mm. long, plano-convex, ovoid; **Glumes,** the fii
about one-third as long as the spikelet, 3-nerved, the second about tw
thirds as long as the spikelet, 5-nerved; **Sterile Lemma** 5-7-nerved, stai
inate or neuter with a well-developed palea; **Fruit** subacute, about equ
to the sterile lemma, finely transversely-undulate-rugose.

Open ground, cultivated soil, along ditches; Texas to Florida, nor
to Illinois, Kansas and New England; also California. Spring to fall.

3. S. VERTICILLATA (L.) Beauv. (vĕr-tĭs-ĭ-lā′tà) ; *Chaetochloa vҽ
ticillata (L.) Scribn.; Foxtail-grass.

Culms 1-3 feet usually 1-2 feet rarely 3.5 feet talĺ, erect or geniculai
spreading, freely branching, scabrous below the panicles; **Blades** 3-
long, 5-12 mm. wide, narrowed toward both ends, flat, thin, mostly roug
especially toward the tip, glabrous to sparsely pubescent with short hair
Sheaths shorter than the internodes, keeled, glabrous or sometimes cilia
rarely rough toward the summit; **Ligule** membranaceous-ciliate, includii
the hairs about 1.5 mm. long; **Panicles** exserted, or those of the branch
sometimes included at the base, erect, interrupted below, somewhat tape
ing above, cylindric, 2-5′ long, mostly about 10-12 mm. thick, green, tl
bristles turning pale, the axis scabrous, the angles retrorsely hispi
scabrous, the short branches many-flowered, scabrous-hispid on the angl
like the axis, the branchlets very short, bearing 1-4 spikelets, a brist
below each spikelet, sometimes by abortion of spikelets 2-4, 1-3 times
long as the spikelets, *downwardly barbed* to the flattened base; **Spikele**
about 2 mm. long, about 1 mm. wide, oblong-elliptic; **Glumes,** the fii
about one-third as long as the spikelet, 3-nerved, obtuse, the second ai
Sterile Lemma equal, about equal to the elliptic fruit, 5-7-nerved, tl
Sterile Palea small; **Fruit** about 1.8 mm. long, 0.9 mm. wide, ellipti
minutely transverse-rugose.

Waste or cultivated land, here and there throughout the Unii
States. (Corn-field near Brownsville, Texas.) Spring to fall.

4. S. GRISEBACHII Fourn. (grī-sē-băk′ĭ-ī) ; *Chaetochloa grisebach
(Fourn.) Scribn.

Culms 1-4.5 mostly about 3 feet tall, tufted, erect or spreadii
branching below, smooth or scaberulous below the pubescent nodes, tl
hairs usually appressed, and below the panicle; **Blades** erect or ascendin
3-12′ usually 4-7′ long, 10 mm. sometimes 14 mm. wide, flat, narrowed
the rounded base, scabrous, puberulent; **Sheaths** mostly shorter than tl
internodes, strongly-nerved, smooth or sometimes slightly rough, sparing
puberulent or hispidulous, densely-ciliate, often papillose, pubescent
hirsute on the collar; **Ligule** a short membrane about 0.5 mm. lon
densely ciliate, the hairs about 1 mm. long; **Panicles** purplish, the termin
exserted, those of the branches shorter and often included at the bas
3-7′ long, loosely-flowered, tapering toward the apex, the axis scabrou

re or less villous except toward the base, the branches rather densely-
wered, sometimes as much as 20-25 mm. usually 5-10 mm. long, approxi-
te or the lower somewhat distant (a few branches at the base often
rter than those just above), the ultimate branchlets (some might call
m pedicels) about 0.5 mm. long, bearing a single bristle below the spike-
s, sometimes rudimentary, thus bringing the bristles in pairs; **Bristles**
5 mm. long, sometimes shorter and sometimes longer, upwardly barbed,
xuous, purplish or green; **Spikelets** purple to green, about 2 mm. long;
mes, the first about one-third the length of the spikelet, acute, 3-
ved, the second a little shorter than the spikelet, finally exposing the
it, obtuse, 3-5-nerved; **Sterile Lemma** about equal to the fruit, 5-nerved,
te; **Sterile Palea** about half the length, narrow; **Fruit** about 1.9 mm.
g, acute, pointed, finely cross-wrinkled.

Open ground, often stony soil, weed in fields, Texas to Arizona,
xico. (Tippit Ranch 15 miles north of Alpine, 15 miles west of Junction,
rrville, Austin, New Braunfels.) Fall.

S. MAGNA Griseb. (măg′nà); *Chaetochloa magna* (Griseb.) Scribn.;
GIANT FOXTAIL-GRASS.

Culms commonly 4-10 feet rarely 13 feet tall, erect, robust, as much
20 mm. thick at the base, sparingly branched above, rarely, at the base,
branches erect, aerial roots about 1-3 joints above the usual roots
ilar to those of corn, scabrous below the panicle, otherwise smooth;
des 18′ long more or less, 20-35 mm. wide more or less, flat, usually
gh on both surfaces; **Sheaths** longer or shorter than the internodes,
se, scabrous at the summit, especially on the keel, hispid-ciliate on the
rgins; **Ligule** v-shaped, the short membrane densely and stiffly hispid,
mm. long; **Panicles** green, finally tawny with age, densely-flowered,
4′ long, commonly 20-40 mm. thick, those of the branches small, nod-
g, often interrupted below, tapering at each end, the axis rough, densely
bescent and villous with ascending hairs 1-2 mm. long, the branches
ct or ascending, as much as 50 mm. long, commonly about 15-20 mm.
g; **Bristles** somewhat flexuous, 1 or 2 (usually 1) below each spikelet,
0 mm. long; **Spikelets** 2 mm. long, 1.1 mm. wide; **Glumes,** the first
ut one-third as long as the spikelet, 3-nerved, broadly acute, the second
ghtly shorter than the fruit, 5-7-nerved, obtuse; **Sterile Lemma** exceed-
· the fruit, 7-nerved, acute, the sterile palea about as long as the fruit;
uit about 1.6 mm. long, about 1 mm. wide, elliptic, smooth, shiny, his-
lulous at the acute tip.

Marshes and wet places along the coast, Texas to Florida and Dela-
re. (Between Port Arthur and Ferry on the Orange road.) July-
gust.

S. VIRIDIS (L.) Beauv. (vĭr′ĭ-dĭs); *Chaetochloa viridis* (L.) Scribn.;
GREEN FOXTAIL-GRASS.

Culms 8-36′ tall, tufted, erect or geniculate-spreading, simple or
nched at the base, scabrous below the panicle, otherwise smooth and
brous; **Blades** 3-6′ long, 5-10 mm. sometimes 15 mm. wide, flat, linear-
ceolate, not twisted, scabrous especially on the upper surface; **Sheaths**
rter than the internodes, flattened, smooth except sometimes scabrous
vard the summit, ciliate on the margins; **Ligule** very short, densely
ate; **Panicle** green or purple, erect or somewhat nodding, usually about
.5′ (1.5-5′) long, densely-flowered, excluding the bristles about 8 mm.
ck, cylindric, tapering at the apex, the axis densely villous with hairs

about 1 mm. long, the branches very short, bearing mostly 5-6 spikel
1-3 bristles usually 2-3, mostly 3-4 times the length of the spikel
rachis pubescent; **Spikelets** 2-2.5 mm. long, elliptic, spikelets fall
entire; **Glumes,** the first about one-third to one-fourth the length of
spikelet, acute, 3-nerved, the second and **Sterile Lemma** about as long
the fruit, or the glume a little shorter, 5-nerved, the sterile palea
fully developed; **Fruit** finely transversely wrinkled or ridged.

Cultivated soil or waste ground, common throughout cooler parts
the United States extending into the southern states, rarely into Mexi
Summer and fall.

7. S. ITALICA (L.) Beauv. (ĭ-tăl'ĭ-kȧ); *Chaetochloa italica* (L.) Scrib
Italian Millet.

Culms usually about 3 feet tall, robust, erect, simple or branching
the base, scabrous below the panicle; **Blades** 6-16' long, 6-25 mm. wi
flat, rough on both surfaces and margins, narrowed at both ends; **Shea**
overlapping, ciliate on the margins, pubescent at the collar; **Ligule** a ri
of stiff hairs 1-2 mm. long; **Panicle** yellow, green or purple, 1-9' lo
even longer, one-half to an inch thick or even thicker, dense, cylind
erect or nodding, often much lobed, the rachis densely villous; **Brist**
1 or sometimes 2 or 3 to each spikelet, upwardly barbed, 1-3 times as lo
as the spikelet; **Spikelet** about 3 mm. long; **Glumes,** the first ovate,
nerved, about one-third as long as the spikelet, the second and **Ster**
Lemma 5-7-nerved, the glume about three-fourths as long as the spike
the sterile lemma longer than the fruit; **Fruit** deciduous from the glun
and sterile lemma, plano-convex, finely transversely wrinkled or ridg

Cultivated and in waste places in United States, especially fr
Texas to Nebraska and Kansas. (Boerne, Texas.) Spring-summer.

8. S. MACROSTACHYA H. B. K. (măk-rō-stăk'ĭ-ȧ); *Chaetochloa mac*
stachya (H. B. K.) Scribn. & Merr.; It has also been referred
C. composita (H. B. K.) Scribn.

Culms commonly 1-3 feet tall, pale-green, tufted, flattened, erect
spreading, often from a geniculate base, branching at the base and low
nodes, scabrous below the panicle and usually below the glabrous, h
pidulous or appressed-pubescent nodes, often sparsely hirsute around t
base, not so robust as *S. scheelei;* **Blades** 3-16' long, the narrow-leav
form with blades 3-5 mm. wide, flat or folded, narrowed toward ba
scabrous on the upper surface, usually smooth beneath, sometimes pil
at the base on the upper surface, rarely pubescent on both surfac
Sheaths in the larger plants shorter than the internodes, flattened, cili
on the margin, glabrous, pubescent or hirsute at the collar, or sometim
pubescent over entire surface; **Ligule** densely ciliate-villous, 1-3 m
long; **Panicles** mostly spikelike, the terminal exserted mostly 3-10' lo
those of the branches shorter, narrow, rather densely-flowered, t
branches usually short, the lower longest, sometimes as much as 20 m
long, somewhat tapering above but not attenuate, more or less interrupt
or lobed, sometimes rather open below, the main axis pubescent and al
sparsely villous, bristles mostly single below each spikelet, 10-15 mm. lo
with shorter ones intermixed; **Spikelet** 2.5 mm. long, 1.5 mm. wide, pa
green; **Glumes,** the first about two-fifths as long as the spikelet, broac
acute, 3-nerved, the second about three-fourths as long as the spikelet,
nerved (5-7), obtuse; **Sterile Lemma** equal to the fruit, 5-nerved, acu
its palea about three-fourths as long as the fruit; **Fruit** 2 mm. long, 1

5 mm. wide, elliptic, incurved at the apiculate apex, finely transversely
rinkled.

Open dry ground and dry woods, southwestern United States, Colo-
do and Mexico. (San Antonio, Texas.) Spring to fall.

S. SCHEELEI (Steud.) Hitchc. (shē′lē-ī); *Chaetochloa scheelei*
(Steud.) Hitchc; *C. polystachya* Scribn. & Merr.; *S. polystachya*
Scheele.

Culms commonly 2-4 feet tall, usually more robust than *S. macrostachya,*
ect or spreading, geniculate at the base, tufted, branching at or near the
ase, flattened, especially the lower internodes puberulent or appressed-
ilose or sparsely hirsute, the hairs mostly appressed; **Blades** commonly
-10′ sometimes 15′ long, 5-15 mm. rarely 20 mm. wide, flat, narrowed
ward the base, scabrous except sometimes smooth beneath toward the
ase, glabrous or sparsely hirsute on the upper surface at the base, some-
mes pubescent on both surfaces; **Sheaths** shorter than the internodes
bove, or the lower longer, scabrous toward the summit or on the keel,
he collar from sparsely to densely hirsute, or the upper sometimes
labrous, sometimes papillose, margins ciliate; **Ligule** a ring of rather
tiff hairs 1-2 mm. long; **Panicle** rather loose, erect or slightly nodding,
ommonly 6-8′ sometimes 13′ long, those of the branches shorter, tapering
rom the base to the apex, the axis scabrous-pubescent or sparsely villous,
he branches ascending, as long as 35 mm. at the base, not so densely
lowered as *S. macrostachya,* bristles usually 10-15 mm. long, mostly one
elow each spikelet, or 2-3 by reason of abortive spikelets; **Spikelets** pale,
cute, at maturity about 2.4 mm. long, 1.2 mm. wide; **Glumes,** the first
bout two-fifths as long as the spikelet, 3-nerved, broadly acute, the
econd about two-thirds as long as the spikelet, obtuse, 5-nerved; **Sterile
emma** about equal to the fruit, 5-nerved, acute, its palea about half as
ong as its lemma, narrow; **Fruit** about 2.2 mm. long, elliptic, incurved
t apiculate apex, finely transversely wrinkled.

Open or rocky woods, southern and western Texas and Arizona. (San
Antonio, Kerrville, Austin, Brownsville, Kingsville, Abilene.) Spring to
all.

0. S. VILLOSISSIMA (Scribn. & Merr.) Schum. (vĭl-ō-sĭs′ĭ-mà); *Chaetochloa villosissima* Scribn. & Merr.

Culms as much as 39′ tall, erect or decumbent at the base, glabrous or
the nodes more or less pubescent; **Blades** 6-12′ long, 5-8 mm. wide,
scabrous and villous or scabrous only; **Sheaths** flattened-keeled, especially
the lower, glabrous or somewhat hispidulous, often scabrous toward the
summit, hispid on the collar, especially the lower, villous on the margin;
Ligule densely pilose, 2-3 mm. long; **Panicles** rather loose, more or less
interrupted, tapering at the summit, as much as 9′ long, the branches
ascending, the lower as much as 20 mm. long, the axis angled, scabrous,
villous; **Bristles** single below each spikelet, flexuous, 15-25 mm. long;
Spikelets about 3 mm. long, lanceolate-ovate, acutish, not strongly turgid
on the convex side, pale or greenish; **Glumes,** the first one-third as long as
the spikelet, 3-nerved, the second nearly as long as the fruit, 5-nerved
(rarely 7-nerved); **Sterile Lemma** as long as the fruit, 5-nerved, convex
or sulcate, the palea narrow, less than 1 mm. long; **Fruit** lanceolate, the
tip rather pointed, incurved, the surface finely but sharply cross-wrinkled.

Open woods along streams, Texas; a rare species. (San Diego,
Limpia Canyon, Texas.) Spring.

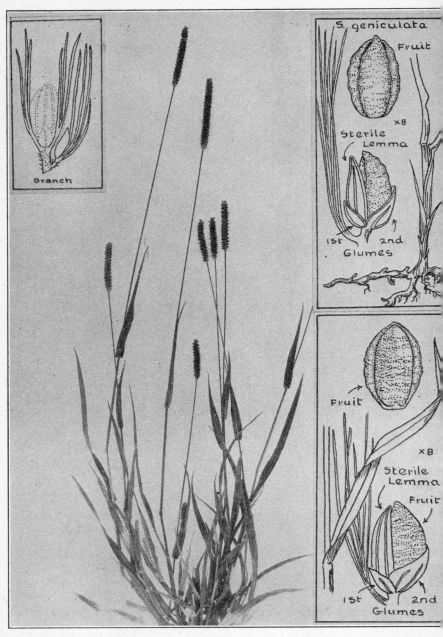

SETARIA LUTESCENS, Yellow Foxtail; also drawings of SETARI
GENICULATA

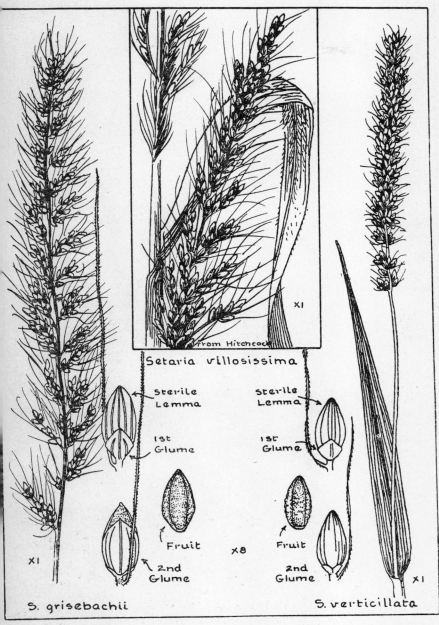

Setaria villosissima

sterile
Lemma

1st
Glume

Fruit

2nd
Glume

from Hitchcock

×1

sterile
Lemma

1st
Glume

Fruit

2nd
Glume

×8

×1

S. grisebachii

S. verticillata

×1

SETARIA GRISEBACHII, S. VERTICILLATA AND S. VILLOSISSIMA

SETARIA MAGNA, Giant Foxtail-grass

SETARIA VIRIDIS, Green Foxtail

SETARIA ITALICA, Italian Millet

Sterile
Lemma

1st Glume
Fruit

Sterile
Palea

x8

2nd Glume

ETARIA MACROSTACHYA to the left; SETARIA SCHEELEI to the
right

94. PENNISETUM Rich. (pĕn-ĭ-sē'tŭm)

Spikelets solitary or in groups of two or three, surrounded by a involucre of bristles, these not united except at the very base, ofte plumose, falling attached to the spikelets; **First Glume** shorter than th spikelet, sometimes minute or wanting; **Second Glume** shorter than o equaling the sterile lemma; **Fertile Lemma** chartaceous, smooth, th margin thin, inclosing the palea.

Annual or *perennial*, often branched grasses, with usually flat blad and dense spikelike panicles. Plants of tropical or subtropical climates, in Texas.

The spikelets are solitary or in groups, surrounded by distin apparently whorled bristles called an involucre. These bristles are suppose to be sterile branchlets.

In *Setaria* and *Cenchrus* the spikelets are also subtended by bristle but in *Cenchrus* the bristles are united at the base.

All of our species are *perennials* except *P. glaucum*, an annua *P. glaucum*, the most important grass of this genus, and *P. purpureum*, well known African species called elephant grass, are very tall, stout grasse and at a distance much resemble corn. Both are cultivated in the souther states as forage plants. *P. glaucum*, known as pearl millet, differs fro the other *Paniceae* in having an enlarged deciduous caryopsis burstin through its lemma and palea, leaving the bristles and floral bracts on th panicle. *P. ruppelii*, known as fountain grass, with pinkish-purple feather panicle, and *P. villosum*, with a white feathery panicle, are cultivated fo ornament, as borders in parks and lawns, sometimes escaping from cult vation. *P. nervosum*, a South American species, has been introduced a Brownsville, Texas, and is also used to some extent for ornamental purpose

PANICLE FEATHERY, ABOUT 1' THICK. Plants perennial, 1-3.5 feet ta
   erect or spreading, blades 3-5 mm. wide; involucral bristles 10-35 mm. lon
   PANICLE WHITE or pale, 2-4.5' long.   1. P. villosu
   PANICLE PURPLE or pink, 4-12' long.   2. P. ruppel
PANICLE NOT FEATHERY, PINKISH-PURPLE OR FINALLY TAWN
   Plants robust, 3-12 feet tall, blades long and about an inch wide.(*P. nervosu*
   3-6 feet tall, blades 4-10 mm. wide.)
   PLANTS ANNUAL. Panicle about an inch thick, 6-12' long; involucr
      bristles about as long as the spikelet, usually two spikelets to a cluste
                                  3. P. glaucu
   PLANTS PERENNIAL. Panicles about 0.5' thick.
     INVOLUCRAL bristles unequal, 4-12 mm. long, 1 or 2 villous at the bas
      spikelets 2-5 to a cluster.   4. P. purpureu
     INVOLUCRAL bristles unequal, 3-8 mm. long; spikelets 1, or sometimes
      to a cluster.   5. P. nervosu

1. P. VILLOSUM R. Br. (vĭl-ō'sŭm); *P. longistylum* of florists, n Hochst.

Culms 1-3 feet tall, usually in rather large tufts, erect or decumber at the base, branched below, arising from numerous branching rootstock somewhat flattened, glabrous to villous; **Blades** 6-25' long, 3-5 mm. wid flat or slightly conduplicate, long acuminate, rough on the margins an toward the apex, sometimes sparsely pubescent at the base and papillos ciliate on the margins near the base; **Sheaths**, the lower crowded an overlapping, the upper shorter than the internodes, loose, ciliate towar the summit and villous at the throat, otherwise glabrous to sparsel pubescent; **Ligule** a ring of hairs about 1 mm. long; **Panicle** pale or whit 2-4.5' long, finally exserted, ovate to oblong, dense, the axis triangula

uberulent, more or less pilose on the margins, the spikelets solitary or
-3 in a cluster, in the involucre bristles, the bristles plumose below and
ommonly 1-1.5′ long; **Spikelets** 8-10 mm. long; **Glumes,** the first minute
r about 1 mm. long, triangular or truncate, the second usually 3-4 mm.
ong, lanceolate, acute; the **Sterile** and **Fertile Lemmas** lanceolate,
.cuminate, 7-9-nerved, minutely scabrous toward the apex, the sterile
.emma shorter; **Palea** of fertile lemma nearly as long as its lemma; **Style**
;-12 mm. long.

Cultivated for ornament, escaped from cultivation, Texas and other
.outhern states; also Michigan and California. Summer-fall.

2. P. RUPPELII Steud. (rŭp-ĕl′ĭ-ī); Fountain Grass.

Culms mostly 2-3.5 feet tall, usually in large dense tufts, erect,
;ranching, especially toward the base; **Blades** 10-25′ long more or less,
;-4 mm. wide when spread open, semi-conduplicate, long-attenuate, rough
;n the margins, often sparsely papillose-ciliate on the margins, the hairs
rather long and weak; **Sheaths** commonly longer than the internodes,
villous at the throat, ciliate toward the summit; **Ligule** a ring of hairs
about 0.5 mm. long; **Panicles** pink or purple, exserted, erect or finally
nodding, 4-12′ long, cylindric, about an inch thick, the culm pubescent
below the panicle, the rather stout axis scabrous and more or less
pubescent, the short branches ascending or finally spreading, usually
solitary, the villous peduncle 2-3 mm. long, often with one or two in-
volucres of bristles below without spikelet, commonly with 3-4 subsessile
or short-pediceled spikelets above, each spikelet with an involucre of
bristles, or sometimes apparently two spikelets to an involucre, the upper
two spikelets perfect, usually with stigmas about the length of the spikelet exposed, and lower apparently staminate; **Bristles** numerous, unequal
in length, 10-20 mm. long, the rachis or branch often produced into a
bristle sometimes 30 mm. long, scabrous or scabrous and feathery below;
Spikelets 6-7 mm. long, lanceolate, purplish; **Glumes,** the first wanting,
the second 2-2.5 mm. long, 1-nerved, acuminate; **Sterile Lemma** 4.5-5 mm.
long, 3-nerved, acuminate; **Lemma** about 6-7 mm. long, acuminate,
pointed, 5-nerved, scabrous on the back; **Palea** about 6 mm. long, acuminate, pointed.

Cultivated in nurseries for ornamental purposes, chiefly for lawns.
(San Juan, Texas.) Thrives well in Rio Grande Valley, and if permitted
to escape cultivation it might become a troublesome weed. Summer-fall.

3. P. GLAUCUM (L.) R. Br. (glô′kŭm); *P. typhoideum* Rich.; *Penicillaria
spicata* (L.) Willd.; Pearl Millet.

Culms 4-8 feet tall, erect, stout, commonly 10-20 mm. thick, branching
at or near the base, woolly below the spikelike panicle; **Blades** 10-35′
long more or less, 20-30 mm. wide more or less, flat, scabrous on the
margins, sparsely hairy on the upper surface and margins near the base,
sometimes papillose; **Sheaths** mostly about as long as the internodes,
margins toward the summit often ciliate, the dark collar sometimes
pubescent; **Ligule** membranaceous, about 1 mm. long, ciliate with dense
stiff hairs 2-3 mm. long; **Panicle** spikelike, cylindric, exserted or included
at the base, 6-12′ long, 1′ thick or less, the axillary narrower and

shorter, solitary, erect, densely-flowered, the spikelets single or in pairs,
a cluster, the cluster with villous peduncles 4-5 mm. long, plumose bristl
(branchlets) at first purple, finally yellowish, surrounding and about a
long as the spikelets; **Spikelets** 4-5 mm. long, lanceolate when young, a
maturity obovate, the large oval seed bursting through the fertile lemm
and palea and dropping to the ground leaving the remainder of the spik
let and involucre of bristles attached to the spike; **Glumes** short, rath
broad, truncate, ciliate, sparsely pubescent, the first about 1 mm. long o
less, the second broader, about 1.5 mm. long; **Sterile Lemma** and i
Palea about equal, subtending a staminate flower, oblong, the steri
lemma 5-7-nerved, hairy at the apex and upper margins, the **Palea** moi
or less pubescent; **Lemma** 3-3.5 mm. long, broad, 5-7-nerved, scabrous t
ward the apex, rather long-hairy near and along the margins; **Pale**
similarly shaped and ciliate along the margins; **Grain** obovate, about
mm. long, about 2.3 mm. wide, pearl-gray.

Cultivated in Texas and other southern states. (Experimental farr
Angleton, Texas.)   Fall.

4. **P. PURPUREUM** Schum. (pûr-pū'rē-ŭm); ELEPHANT GRASS. (
smaller form is called Napier grass.)

Culms 6-12 feet tall more or less, robust in large tufts, erect, often
thick, branched, often more or less glaucous; **Blades** 2-3 feet long more o
less, about 1′ wide, flat, the surface rough to smooth, margins rougl
Sheaths commonly longer than the internodes; **Ligule** a ring of rath
stiff hairs about 4 mm. long; **Panicle** tawny, finally exserted, spikelik
commonly 6-9′ long, about 10-12 mm. thick, cylindric, erect, the axis rigi
rough, densely pubescent, densely-flowered, the spikelets 1-5 commonl
2-3 in a cluster, the cluster with a hairy callus at the base, including tl
bristles mostly 10-12 mm. long, the involucre of tawny scabrous bristl
as many as 50, often with one or two villous at the base and much stoute
and longer, sometimes 10-15 mm. long, the shorter ones mostly 4-8 mn
long; **Spikelets** 4-6 mm. long, when more than one to a cluster one sul
sessile and the others with pedicels about 1.5 mm. long, the middle spikel
usually larger and longer, lanceolate, straw-colored; **Glumes** lanceolat
pale, the first 1-3 mm. long, 1-nerved, thin, scabrous on the margins an
keel, the second about half as long as the spikelet, acuminate, awn-pointe
or short-awned, 3-nerved, sometimes ciliate on one margin; **Sterile Lemm**
about 4 mm. long, 5-nerved, acuminate, awn-pointed, puberulent, slightl
ciliate on the margins; **Lemma** slightly shorter than the sterile lemm
3-nerved; **Stigmas** long, plumose; **Stamens** 3.

Introduced from Africa, grown for forage in southern Texas an
southern Florida. (Cuero, Texas.)   Fall.

5. **P. NERVOSUM** (Nees) Trin. (nĕr-vō'sŭm).

Culms 3-6 feet tall, tufted or solitary, erect or ascending from
decumbent or prostrate base, sometimes taking root at the swollen lowe
nodes, strongly flattened, branching; **Blades** 4-15′ long, 4-10 mm. wid
flat, narrowed, and soon folded toward the base on drying, upper surfac
and margins rough; **Sheaths** shorter than the internodes, flattened, loose
sometimes ciliate on the margins; **Ligule** membranaceous, ciliate, abou

mm. long; **Panicle** spikelike, exserted or included at the base, 4-6′ long,
ylindric, about 12 mm. thick, at first pinkish or purplish, finally tawny,
lense, nodding, the spikelets solitary or sometimes 2 inclosed in an in-
olucre of approximately 20-30 bristles of unequal length, 3-8 mm. long,
cabrous; **Spikelets** 5-6 mm. long, lanceolate, pale; **Glumes,** the first about
-2.5 mm. long, lanceolate, 1-nerved, acute or awn-pointed, the second and
terile Lemma subequal, about 5 mm. long, lanceolate, acuminate,
ften awn-pointed, strongly about 9-nerved; **Lemma** as long as the spike-
et, acuminate, 5-nerved, minutely papillose; **Palea** nearly as long as its
emma and similar except 2-nerved.

South American species, introduced along Rio Grande, southern
'exas. (Brownsville, Texas.) Fall.

PENNISETUM VILLOSUM

PENNISETUM RUPPELII, Fountain Grass

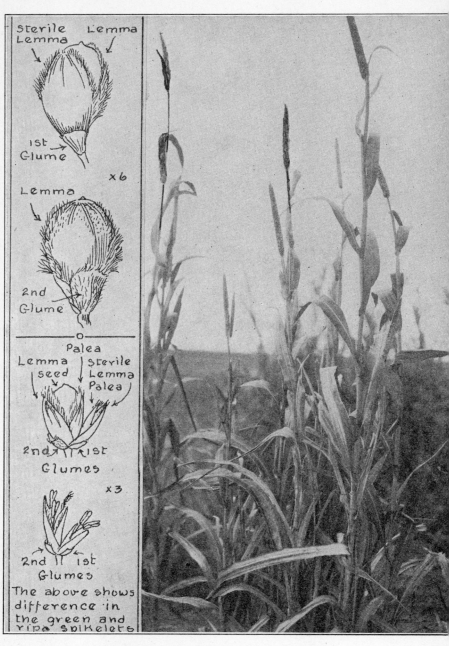

PENNISETUM GLAUCUM, Pearl Millet

PENNISETUM PURPUREUM

PENNISETUM NERVOSUM

95. CENCHRUS L. (sĕn′krŭs)
(Sand-bur)

Spikelets solitary or few together, surrounded and inclosed by a ▪iny **bur** composed of numerous coalescing bristles (sterile branchlets), .e bur globular, the peduncle short and thick, articulate at base, falling ith the spikelets and permanently inclosing them, the seed germinating ithin the old involucre, the spines usually retrorsely barbed.

Annual or sometimes *perennial*, commonly low branching grasses, with at blades and racemes of burs, the burs readily deciduous. Seven species in e United States, chiefly in the southern portion.

C. myosuroides, a robust erect perennial 3-6 feet tall, differs from the her species of this genus in the longer, more densely-flowered, spikelike ,cemes and the bristles of the bur or involucre being united only at the .se.

C. echinatus, known as hedge-hog grass, is an annual with a rather .ick purplish raceme 1.5-4′ long, the bur having at the base a ring of ort slender bristles.

C. pauciflorus, known as sand-bur, usually densely tufted, often forms rge mats, the globose burs with many sharp spreading spines rendering it pernicious weed.

C. incertus differs from *C. pauciflorus* by its perennial base, its taller alms, erect or spreading habit, and the ovate bur usually with a long abrous base. The bur varies much as to the number of spines, commonly .e or two spines on the outer face besides a ridge or one or two knots at e base of the body. It is sometimes as spiny as some burs of *C. pauciflorus.*

One of the spikelets in the bur is usually better developed; the illustra-ns are of the better developed spikelets.

\VOLUCRAL LOBES UNITED AT THE BASE ONLY; RACEMES DENSE.
  Involucral lobes terete, scabrous; plants perennial.   1. C. myosuroides
\VOLUCRAL LOBES UNITED ABOVE THE BASE; RACEMES USUALLY NOT DENSE.
  INVOLUCRE WITH a ring of slender bristles at base. Bristles retrorsely barbed, not much exceeding the involucral lobes; lobes villous at base within, erect or nearly so, or rarely 1 or 2 lobes loosely interlocking, the tips spinelike; burs excluding the bristles 5-7 mm. wide; plants annual.
                                                            2. C. echinatus
  INVOLUCRE with flattened spreading spines, no ring of slender bristles at base.
    BODY of the bur pubescent, ovate, 3-3.5 mm. wide, tapering at base; spines 3-4 mm. long; plants perennial.   3. C. incertus
    BODY of the bur finely pubescent, globose, not tapering at base, including the spines 7-8 mm. wide; plants annual.   4. C. pauciflorus

C. MYOSUROIDES H. B. K. (mī-ō-sū-roi′dēz); *Cenchropsis myosu-roides* (H. B. K.) Nash.

Culms commonly 3-6 feet tall, solitary or tufted, often in clumps, ect or ascending from a geniculate base, often branching from the lower ›des, some of the branches flowering, the rather woody robust culms ›rete, glabrous and often glaucous, from stout rootstocks; **Blades** as-nding or spreading 6-16′ long, 5-12 mm. wide, tapering from a round at base to an attenuate often involute tip, rough on the upper surface; .eaths shorter than the internodes, loose, firm, strongly nerved; **Ligule** embranaceous, about 1 mm. long, densely ciliate, the hairs about 2 mm. ng; **Raceme** spikelike, commonly long-exserted, 4-8′ long, about 6-10 m. thick, cylindric, dense, the common axis slender, angled, puberulent,

with numerous burs at first appressed, spreading in age, 5-7 mm. lon
the bristles retrorsely scabrous, united at the base only, the lowest rc
shorter, slender and spreading, the inner bristles slender, not flattened
nerved, about equaling the spikelet, erect or nearly so; **Spikelets** usual
one to a bur, 4.5-5 mm. long, 1.5-1.8 mm. wide, acuminate; **Glumes,** t
first about 1.5 mm. long, one-third the length of the spikelet, 1 or
nerved, acute, the second 3-7-nerved, wide at the base, about 4 mm. lon
sometimes mucronate; the **Sterile Lemma** slightly longer than the secoi
glume, 3-5-nerved; **Fruit** about equal to the sterile lemma.

In sandy open ground, often near the coast, Texas to Floriê
(Asherton, Mercedes, Texas.) Spring-fall.

2. C. ECHINATUS L. (ĕk-ĭ-nā'tŭs) ; Hedge-hog Grass.

Culms commonly 1-2 sometimes 3 feet long, ascending from a decui
bent or geniculate base, often rooting at the lower nodes, branching frc
the base and lower nodes, flattened, scabrous below the spike; **Blad**
3-8' long, 3-12 mm. wide, flat or somewhat folded, especially toward t
apex, rough except on under surface near the base, sometimes sparse
pilose on upper surface near the base especially on the younger plant
Sheaths on the larger plants shorter than the internodes, loose, flattene
glabrous or pubescent on the margins at the summit, rarely sparse
pilose; **Ligule** ciliate, hairs about 1-1.5 mm. long; **Racemes** spikelik
1.5-4' long, terete, commonly 12-15 mm. thick, at first included, lat
exserted, green to purplish, axis flexuous, often interrupted below; **Bu**
commonly numerous, truncate at the base, the body 4-7 mm. high, as broa
or broader, pubescent, tawny, the outer slender bristles scabrous, 1-3 m;
long, the inner stout, broadened at the base, the longest of them usual
about equaling the lobes of the body but sometimes longer or much r
duced, ascending or spreading, the lobes of the body commonly ten, ere
or bent inward, or sometimes one or two lobes inflexed, often with l
green lines or nerves down the back, the tips hard and spinelike, retrorse
barbed, villous within; **Spikelets** 3-6 to a bur, commonly 4 mm. long, abo
equaling the lobes or shorter, 4-5.5 mm. long; **Glumes,** the first 1-nerve
narrow, about one-third to one-half as long as the spikelet, the secoi
broad, 5-nerved and about three-fourths as long as the spikelet; **Ster**
Lemma and **Fruit** subequal, the sterile lemma with palea about as lon
often subtending a staminate flower.

In sandy open ground or waste places, Texas to Florida and Sou
Carolina, west to New Mexico and south to Mexico. Spring-fall.

3. C. INCERTUS M. A. Curtis (ĭn-sĕr'tŭs).

Culms 1-4 feet tall, sometimes taller, often in dense clumps, erect
ascending, from a decumbent base, sometimes prostrate, freely branchir
flattened, scabrous below the raceme, mostly glabrous; **Blades** folded
sometimes flat, 2.5-15' long, 2-5 mm. wide, rough on the upper surfae
pilose or sparsely pilose at or near the base; **Sheaths,** upper shorter th
the internodes, the lower overlapping, loose and open, sometimes pilc
near the summit; **Ligule** ciliate with fine hairs about 0.5 mm. lon
Racemes spikelike, 1.5-4' long, long-exserted, or those of the branches i
cluded at the base or short-exserted, the burs not crowded, the slend
axis flexuous, scabrous, sometimes pilose; **Burs** 3-5 mm. wide, excludi
the spines, the body finely and densely pubescent, the base glabrous
sparsely pubescent; **Spines** spreading, flat, broadened at the base, t
lower often obsolete on the outer face of the bur and represented by l

lobs or ridges, the upper few, rarely more than 5 mm. long; *body of the
ur* usually not deeply cleft on the outer face, the lobes commonly 5-7, erect
: spreading, 4-6 mm. long, rigid, spinelike, long-ciliate at the base;
pikelets 1-3 to a bur, 5-6 mm. long, about 2 mm. wide; **Glumes** the first
arrow, pointed, usually present; the second about three-fourths the
ngth of the subequal **Sterile Lemma** and **Fruit; Fruit** attenuate, the
alea minutely puberulent toward the summit. (Drawings on photograph
f *C. pauciflorus.*)

In open sandy soil, North Carolina to Florida and west to Texas.
pring-fall.

. C. PAUCIFLORUS Benth. (pô-sĭ-flō'rŭs); *C. tribuloides* and *C. carolinianus* of authors.) Sand-bur.

Culms 6-24' (8-36') tall, tufted, sometimes forming large mats, freely
ranching, spreading, ascending or suberect from a decumbent base,
lattened, scabrous or rarely pubescent below the racemes; **Blades** 1-6'
ong, 2-7 mm. wide, flat, sometimes folded, spreading, tapering from the
ase to the apex, scabrous on the margins and upper surface, and some-
imes below, often pilose above near the base; **Sheaths** mostly shorter
han the internodes, pubescent along the margins, rarely throughout,
ometimes with a tuft of hairs at the summit, those below the raceme
ometimes inflated, loose; **Ligule** ciliate, about 1 mm. long; **Racemes**
pikelike, solitary on main axis and many branches, partly included or
hort-exserted, 1-4' commonly 1.5-3' long, the burs rather crowded, the
lender axis flexuous, scabrous, sometimes pilose; **Burs** exclusive of
pines 3-7 mm. wide, pubescent, rarely nearly glabrous; **Spines** numerous,
preading or reflexed, flat, broadened at the base, the lowermost shorter
ind more slender, some of the upper ones 4-5 mm. long, usually villous at
he base, the bur with a deep cleft exposing the spikelets; **Spikelets** commonly two to a bur, 5-7 mm. long, about 2 mm. wide; **Glumes**, the first
isually not over one-third the length of the spikelet, the second glume and
sterile lemma subequal, or the lemma nearly as long as the turgid acuminate-pointed fruit.

In sandy open ground, Massachusetts to Florida, west through
Texas to California, south throughout Mexico. Spring to fall.

CENCHRUS MYOSUROIDES

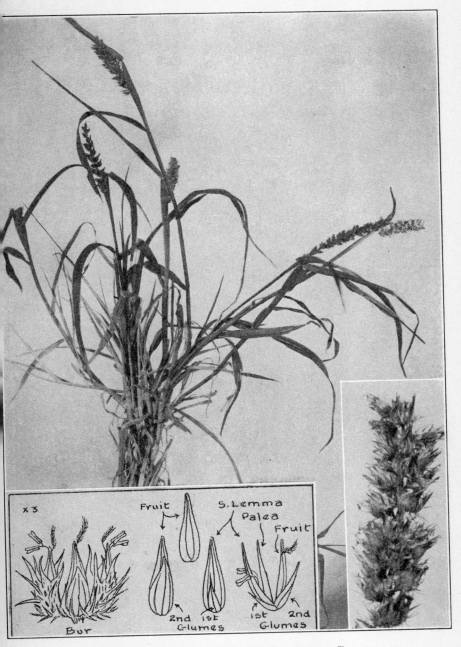

CENCHRUS ECHINATUS, Hedge-hog Grass

CENCHRUS PAUCIFLORUS, SAND-BUR, AND CENCHRUS INCERTU

XII. ANDROPOGONEAE, THE SORGHUM TRIBE

96. IMPERATA Cyrillo (ĭm-pē-rā'tȧ)

Spikelets all alike, awnless, in pairs, unequally pedicellate on a lender continuous rachis, surrounded by long silky hairs; **Glumes** about qual, membranaceous; **Sterile Lemma, Fertile Lemma,** and **Palea** thin nd hyaline.

Perennial, slender, erect grasses, with terminal narrow woolly panicles. *wo species in the United States, one in Texas.

They are not found in sufficient abundance to be of agricultural value.

The illustrations and descriptions are taken from U. S. Dept. Agr. Div. 3ot. Bull. No. 13, *Grasses of the Pacific Slope,* by Dr. Geo. Vasey.

l. I. HOOKERI Rupr. (hŏŏk'ĕr-ī).

Culms 2-3 feet tall, a few to a tuft, from short-jointed rootstocks, ather coarse, erect, simple; **Blades** 3-18' long, the upper short and ippressed, the lower or basal numerous and long, narrowed toward the ɔase, flat, margins and lower surface slightly rough, villous on the upper ;urface toward base; **Sheaths** longer than the internodes, more or less villous at the throat; **Ligule** membranaceous, truncate, 2 mm. long; **Panicle** exserted, white-hairy, 6-16' long, narrow, about 1' in diameter; branches mostly in threes and fours, ascending or appressed, densely-flowered, the hairs giving the panicle a feathery appearance flecked with yellow or brown anthers and stigmas; **Spikelets** nearly sessile, 3 mm. long, narrowly lanceolate; **Glumes** indistinctly 5-7-nerved, lance-ovate, obtuse, the first about 3 mm. long, the second about 2.5 mm. long, both glumes covered with white hairs 8-12 mm. long; **Lemma** about 2.5 mm. long, 1-nerved, ovate, acute, membranaceous; **Palea** about 1.5 mm. long, irregularly dentate; **Grain** about 0.7 mm. long, obovate, amber-colored, falling with the spikelet entire.

Along watercourses; west Texas to southern California. Fall.

IMPERATA HOOKERI

97. MISCANTHUS Anderss. (mĭs-kăn'thŭs)

Spikelets all alike, in pairs, unequally pedicellate along a slender ntinuous rachis; **Glumes** equal, membranaceous or somewhat coriaceous; erile **Lemma** a little shorter than the glumes, hyaline; **Fertile Lemma** aline, smaller than the sterile lemma, extending into a delicate bent and xuous awn; **Palea** small and hyaline.

Robust *perennials*, with long flat blades and terminal panicles of aggre- te spreading slender racemes, our species with a tuft of silky hairs at the se of the spikelet, surrounding it and of about the same length as the imes, the palea of the short-pedicellate spikelet about one-fourth as long the lemma, the palea of the long-pedicellate spikelet obsolete. Species out eight, in southeastern Asia and South Africa; one cultivated in the iited States.

Our species, *M. sinensis,* has at least three varieties: *M. sinensis* var. *brinus,* with banded blades, which is illustrated by a photograph and fully scribed; *M. sinensis* var. *variegatus,* with striped blades; and *M. sinensis* r. *gracillimus,* with very narrow blades. The species and varieties are ten grown in Texas as ornaments in nurseries and on lawns.

.ADES not banded or striped.
Blades 8-16 mm. wide.   1. M. sinensis
Blades very narrow.   1b. M. sinensis var. gracillimus
.ADES banded or striped.
Blades banded.   1a. M. sinensis var. zebrinus
Blades striped.   1c. M. sinensis var. variegatus

M. SINENSIS Anderss. (sī-nĕn'sĭs) ; EULALIA.

Culms 4-10 feet tall, in large dense tufts, erect; **Blades** numerous, as uch as 3 feet long, usually 8-12 mm. wide, mostly basal, tapering to a ender point, the margins sharply serrate; **Sheaths** somewhat flattened, liate; **Ligule** 1-2 mm. long; **Panicles** 5-15′ long, somewhat fan-shaped, e numerous silky aggregate racemes erect or ascending; **Spikelets** about mm. long, with a tuft of silky hairs at base surrounding them, the hairs out as long as the glumes.

Cultivated as an ornament, occasionally growing wild; eastern and uthern states. (Rio Grande Valley.) Fall.

. M. SINENSIS var. ZEBRINUS Beal (zē-brī'nŭs).

Culms 3-6 feet tall, in rather large tufts, erect, nodes barbed; **Blades** 24′ long, the upper short, 3-10 mm. wide more or less, crowded at the ise, flat, soon becoming revolute on drying, margins very rough, more r less papillose toward the base, the upper surface and sometimes the wer hirsute at the base, the hairs usually appressed, the blades with a hite or pale midrib and transverse bands of cream or brown, often eckled with brown; **Sheaths** longer than the internodes, glabrous or arsely hirsute toward the summit; **Ligule** membranaceous, about 1.5 im. long, ciliate; **Panicle** tawny, commonly 10-15′ long, somewhat fan- aaped, the axis 4-6′ long, the numerous silky racemes 4-10′ long, com- ionly in whorls of 3-4, distant about 1′, sometimes branching, the ivergent spikelets alternate on the slender scabrous rachis, one pedicel f the pair about 1.5 mm. long and the other 4-5 mm. long; **Spikelets** 3.5-4 im. long, narrowly lanceolate, with silky hairs about as long as the spike- t at and surrounding its base; **Glumes** about equal, longer than the sterile emma, the first flattened, obtuse, slightly scabrous toward the apex, the econd keeled, acute, scabrous on the midnerve, ciliate on the margins;

Sterile Lemma slightly shorter than the glumes, hyaline, 2-toothed, ciliat **Lemma** about equal to the sterile lemma, ciliate, deeply bifid with twisted geniculate awn 6-7 mm. long from the sinus.

Cultivated as an ornamental here and there over the United State (San Antonio.) Fall.

1b. M. SINENSIS var. GRACILLIMUS Hitchc. (grăs-ĭl′ĭ-mŭs).
Similar to the species except **Blades** very narrow.

1c. M. SINENSIS var. VARIEGATUS Beal (vā-rĭ-ē-gā′tŭs).
Similar to the species except **Blades** striped.

Blades

Actual Size

Sterile Lemma

Lemma

x4

Palea

2nd 1st

Glumes

MISCANTHUS SINENSIS VAR. ZEBRINUS; also drawings of banded, striped and plain blades

98.   SACCHARUM L. (săk′á-rŭm)

Spikelets in pairs, one sessile, the other pedicellate, both perfec
awnless, arranged in panicled racemes, the axis disarticulating below th
spikelets; **Glumes** somewhat indurate; **Sterile Lemma** similar but hyaline
Fertile Lemma hyaline, sometimes wanting.   *Perennial* grasses of tropic:
regions; about 10 species, two in Texas.

S. officinarum, sugar cane, a tall stout grass often more than 12 fee
tall, has solid juicy culms, with broad flat blades and large plume-lik
panicles 1-2 feet long.   The glumes and delicate sterile lemma are about th
same length, the fertile lemma and palea being absent.   Sugar cane is
tropical plant; it is cultivated in the southern states chiefly for the pro
duction of sugar and molasses, and is also used for forage.   Although cult
vated several places in Texas, the author did not find any in bloom.   Rarel
blooms in the United States.

S. narenga, with nearly oblong purplish panicles, has been introduce
at Angleton by R. S. Stanfield, Superintendent of Substation No. 3, Texa
Agricultural and Mechanical College.

BASAL HAIRS 2-3 times as long the spikelet.	1. S. officinarun
BASAL HAIRS about as long as the spikelet.	2. S. narengi

1. S. OFFICINARUM L. (ŏf-ĭs-ĭ-nā′rŭm) ; Sugar Cane

Culms 10-16 feet tall, 10-30 mm. thick, solid, juicy, the lower inter
nodes short, swollen; **Blades** mostly elongated, mostly 40-60 mm. wide
with a very thick midrib; **Sheaths** overlapping, the lower usually falling
from the culm; **Panicle** plumelike, 8-24′ long, the slender racemes drooping; **Spikelets** 2.5-3 mm. long, obscured in a basal tuft of hairs 2-3 times
as long as the spikelet.

Cultivated in the southern states, especially in Louisiana for sugar
and molasses, and for forage; a tropical plant.   (Lytle, Texas.)

2. S. NARENGA Hamilt. (nā-rĕn′gá).

Culms 3-8 feet tall, erect, rather slender for their height, villous at
the base of the panicle; **Blades** 1-2 feet long, 3-14 mm. wide, flat above,
folded and narrowed below; margins and upper surface rough; **Sheaths**
longer than the internodes, smooth to rough, glabrous to woolly, the
lower very hirsute at the throat; **Ligule** membranaceous; **Panicle** exserted,
5-12′ long, oblong or nearly so, erect or slightly nodding, purple, the
numerous racemes ascending, finally spreading, mostly less than 2′ long,
the rachis-joint and pedicels slightly shorter than the spikelets, pilose;
Spikelets about 2.7 mm. long, oblong, brownish-purple, the hairs at the
base about as long as the spikelet; **Glumes** indurated, smooth on the back,
ciliate on margins; **Sterile Lemma** nearly equal to the glumes; **Palea** about
two-thirds as long as the glumes.

Introduced at Angleton.

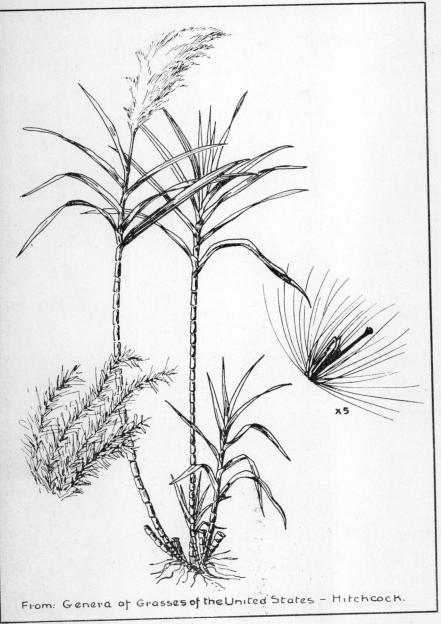

x5

From: Genera of Grasses of the United States - Hitchcock.

SACCHARUM OFFICINARUM; Sugar Cane, Ribbon Cane

SACCHARUM NARENGA

99. ERIANTHUS Michx. (ĕr-ĭ-ăn′thŭs)
(Plume-grass)

Spikelets all alike, in pairs along a slender axis, one sessile the other ᵉdicellate, the rachis disarticulating below the spikelets, the rachis-joint ʰd pedicel falling attached to the sessile spikelet; **Glumes** coriaceous, ꞯual, usually copiously clothed, at least at the base, with long silky ᵖreading hairs; **Sterile Lemma** thin and hyaline; **Fertile Lemma** hyaline, ᵗe midnerve extending into a slender awn; **Palea** small and hyaline.

Perennial reedlike grasses, with flat blades and terminal oblong, usually ᵊnse, silky panicles. Species about 20, in the warmer regions of both ᵊmispheres; about six in the United States, at least five in Texas.

All of our species are rather tall, robust perennials, usually growing in ᵊw moist soil, mostly in central and eastern Texas. All except one have ᵒng hairs at the base of the spikelet and woolly panicles. All except one ᵃve awns 10-20 mm. long.

E. saccharoides, our most common species, has straight awns and basal ᵃirs more than the length of the spikelet. *E. contortus* and *E. alope-* ᵘroides have flat twisted geniculate awns, the first with dark-brown ᵃnicles, the hairs not exceeding the spikelet, the second with pale panicles, ᵗe hairs exceeding the spikelet. *E. strictus,* a reddish-brown plant, has long narrow glabrous panicle, the hairs at the base of the panicle wanting.

E. ravennae, a native of the Mediterranean region, has hairs about as ᵒng as the spikelet and awns 3-5 mm. long or awnless. It is often cultivated ᵒr ornament because of the large silky panicles sometimes 2 feet long.

ᴀWN 3-5 mm. LONG, TERETE, STRAIGHT. Basal hairs about as long as the
   spikelet.   1. E. ravennae
ᴀWN 10-20 mm. LONG, TERETE OR FLAT.
  AWN FLAT, closely spiral at the base, geniculate; apex of the lemma deeply
    2-cleft; spikelets 5-7 mm. long.
    BASAL hairs twice or nearly twice as long as the yellowish spikelets which
      are nearly concealed in the copious hairs of the cream-colored or pale
      panicle.   2. E. alopecuroides
    BASAL hairs sometimes equaling but not exceeding the brown spikelets
      which are plainly visible through the brown panicle.   3. E. contortus
  AWN TERETE or flat only at the very base, not spiral at the base, straight;
    apex of the lemma entire or slightly 2-toothed.
    BASAL hairs exceeding the spikelets, sometimes twice as long; spikelets
      4-6 mm. long.   4. E. saccharoides
    BASAL hairs wanting; spikelets 8-11 mm. long; glumes strongly appressed
      hispid.   5. E. strictus

ⁱ. E. RAVENNAE (L.) Beauv. (rà-vĕn′ē); Raᴠᴇɴɴᴀ Grass, Hardy Pampas-grass, Woolly Beard.

Culms 6-13 feet tall, robust, as much as 15 mm. thick at the base, ᵉrect, growing in large clumps, glabrous or a few hairs at or near the nodes and the lower internodes; **Blades,** those of the culm 1-2.5 feet long, of the sterile shoots as much as 3.5 feet or even longer, 5-12 mm. wide, flat above the middle, narrowed, thick, folded or grooved toward the base, especially those of the sterile shoots, the upper often revolute toward the base, usually rough, sometimes very much so, densely long-villous at the base on both surfaces, or those of the sterile shoots densely villous on the upper surface the entire length of the narrowed portion, more or less papillose, especially toward the base; **Sheaths** longer than the internodes, usually rough, the upper glabrous or sparsely hairy, the lower and those of the sterile shoots densely appressed hirsute or hispid, all more or less papillose; **Ligule** about 1 mm. long, minutely ciliate; **Panicles** silky-brown,

purple or cream-silky, exserted, finally nodding, 1-2 feet long, 5-8' thic
densely flowered, the lower branches as much as 7' long, appressed, a
cending or spreading, the numerous branchlets 1-1.5' long, each wit
several short sessile racemes, the rachis-joints and pedicels villous an
about half as long as the spikelets; **Spikelets** 4.5-5 mm. long, densel
villous at the base, the hairs as long as or slightly longer than the spikele
Glumes about equal, both 3-nerved, lanceolate, awn-pointed, often ɔ
toothed, usually more or less pilose; **Sterile Lemma** about three-fourth
as long as the glumes, hyaline; **Lemma** about three-fifths as long as th
spikelet, hyaline, 3-nerved, with a straight terete awn 3-5 mm. long, o
awnless; **Palea** shorter than its lemma, 2-toothed, hyaline, ovate, acut

Native of Mediterranean region, occasionally cultivated in the Unite
States for ornament because of its silky plumes. (Arcadia Floral Com
pany, Ft. Worth Pike, Dallas.)   Summer-fall.

2. E. ALOPECUROIDES (L.) Ell. (ăl-ō-pē-kū-roi'dēz); *E. divaricatu*
(L.) Hitchc.; WOOLLY BEARD-GRASS.

Culms 5-10 feet tall, stout, erect, nodes naked or villous, axis o
panicle and the internodes below the panicle sparsely to densely long
villous, the hairs appressed; **Blades** 2-24' long or even longer, 5-15 mm
(5-25) wide, narrowed toward the base, often papillose-hirsute on th
upper surface near the base; **Sheaths** mostly shorter than the internodes
hirsute at the throat; **Ligule** a short-ciliate membrane scarcely 1 mm
long; **Panicle** finally exserted, pale silky, 6-12' long, 2-3' wide, oblong
rather densely-flowered; **Spikelets** 5-7 mm. long, yellowish, crowded, con
cealed by the hairy panicle; **Glumes** subequal, two-thirds as long as the
basal hairs, lanceolate, acuminate, long-pilose, scabrous towards the tip
the first 2-toothed, 5-6-nerved, the second acute, 3-nerved; **Sterile Lemma**
slightly shorter than the glumes, 3-nerved, thin, ciliate above on the
margins; **Lemma** about 3 mm. long, deeply 2-cleft at the apex, the teeth
about 2 mm. long, acuminate, the flat scabrous awns 12-18 mm. long,
closely spiral for about 6 mm. at the base, the remainder loosely spiral,
having usually 3-4 twists; **Palea** about 1 mm. long, thin, obtuse, long-
ciliate for about two-thirds of its length. (See photograph of *E. contortus*
for drawings.)

In damp soil, east Texas to Florida, north to New Jersey, thence to
Missouri and Oklahoma. (Texarkana.)   Fall.

3. E. CONTORTUS Baldwin (kŏn-tôr'tŭs); BEARD-GRASS.

Culms 3-9 feet tall, tufted, erect, stout, often 15 mm. in diameter,
glabrous, or sparsely pubescent below the panicle and at the nodes;
Blades 6-36' long, 5-24 mm. wide, flat or folded at the narrowed base,
smooth or rough, densely hirsute on the upper surface at the base near the
ligule, often more or less papillose on both surfaces; **Sheaths** mostly
longer than the internodes, smooth or rough, often sparsely hirsute at
the throat; **Ligule** 1-2 mm. long, firm, minutely ciliate; **Panicles** rather
dark-purplish-brown, exserted, erect, 5-17' long, 1.5-2' thick, densely
flowered, the main axis stout, rigid, somewhat 4-sided, more or less ciliate
on the edges, scabrous, the somewhat flattened zigzag branches as much
as 4' long, usually in ones or twos, distant about one inch, appressed or
slightly spreading, pubescent at the base, the branches with numerous
racemes 1-3' long; the rachis-joints and pedicels more or less ciliate, half
to two-thirds as long as the spikelets; **Spikelets** about 7 mm. long, equaling or exceeding the basal hairs; **Glumes**, the second often slightly longer,

oth more or less hirsute on the back and margins, especially the first,
he hairs often as long as the basal, scabrous toward the apex, the first
ften 2-toothed; **Sterile Lemma** shorter than the glumes, more or less
ubescent; **Lemma** about half as long as glumes, 2-toothed, hyaline, the
nidnerve extending into a scabrous awn 12-20 mm. long, flattened toward the base, loosely spiral above.

In moist soil, Texas to Florida, north to Maryland, Tennessee and
Oklahoma. (Near Tyler.) Summer-fall.

. E. SACCHAROIDES Michx. (săk-à-roi′dēz).

Culms 4-8 feet tall, tufted or solitary, erect, stout, rigid, densely
appressed-villous below the panicle and also the axis, the nodes bearded
with ascending or finally appressed hairs; **Blades** 2-30′ long, the upper
hort, the basal long, 4-15 mm. (4-25) wide, the long blades at the base
olded and narrowed for about half their length, flat above, rough,
glabrous, sparsely or densely hirsute, especially toward the base, some-
imes papillose near the base; **Sheaths** longer or the upper shorter than
he internodes, smooth or rough, glabrous or usually sparsely to densely
appressed hirsute, especially at the throat and collar; **Ligule** membranaceous, 4-5 mm. long; **Panicle** exserted, purple or brownish, 5-15′
ong, rarely longer, 2-5′ broad, broadly oblong, erect or slightly nodding,
he axis rather rigid, densely villous, the branches 3.5′ long or less, freely
branching, erect or ascending, crowded, spikelet-bearing to the base;
Rachis-joints and pedicels more than half as long as the spikelets, pilose,
the ring of hairs at the base of the spikelet from about as long to twice
as long as the spikelet; **Spikelets** exclusive of the awns 5-7 mm. long,
lanceolate; **Glumes,** the first slightly longer, scabrous toward the apex,
both naked or pilose above the base, the first 2-toothed, flattened or
slightly 2-keeled, the second keeled, acuminate, sometimes awn-pointed;
Sterile Lemma about three-fourths as long as the glumes; **Lemma** slightly
shorter than the sterile lemma, ovate, with a straight or nearly straight
awn 10-25 mm. long, terete, or flattened and slightly twisted near the
base, scabrous.

In moist sandy soil, Texas to Florida, north to New Jersey, Maryland and Kentucky. Summer and fall.

Note: A common form of this species with a small compact panicle has
been segregated as *E. compactus* Nash.

5. E. STRICTUS Baldw. (strĭk′tŭs).

Culms 4-7 feet tall, a few culms to a tuft, comparatively slender,
rigid, erect, terete, sparsely pubescent at the nodes, otherwise smooth and
glabrous, the whole plant, especially when old, more or less reddish-
brown; **Blades** 6-25′ long, 4-12 mm. wide, flat, narrowed toward the base,
on drying soon becoming conduplicate toward the base, attenuate into a
long slender point, sometimes short-pubescent or hirsute above near the
base, margins rough; **Sheaths** shorter than the internodes, glabrous;
Ligule membranaceous, truncate, about 1-2 mm. long, fringed; **Panicles**
reddish-brown, 8-16 rarely 28′ long, strict, 10-20 mm. wide, erect, exserted,
the branches mostly 2-4′ as much as 8′ long, appressed, the main axis
smooth and rigid; **Rachis-joints** usually about two-thirds as long as the

spikelets, the pedicels about half as long as the spikelets, angled an
slightly scabrous; **Spikelets** appressed to the rachis, linear-lanceolate, ex
clusive of awns 8-11 mm. long, the basal hairs wanting or sparse and ver
short; **Glumes** subequal, the second slightly longer, strongly appressed
hispid, the first 2-toothed, dorsally flattened or slightly 2-keeled, th
second keeled above; **Sterile Lemma** 6-7 mm. long, acute, dark-purple
Lemma 5-6 mm. long, 3-nerved, 2-toothed, with a scabrous straight o
almost straight awn 12-20 mm. long; **Palea** 1.5-2.5 mm. long.

In moist soil, east Texas to Florida, North Carolina, Tennessee an
Missouri.   (Orange, Beaumont.)   Fall.

ERIANTHUS RAVENNAE; Ravenna Grass, Hardy Pampas-grass

ERIANTHUS CONTORTUS; also drawing of spikelet of ERIANTHU
ALOPECUROIDES

ERIANTHUS STRICTUS, three culms to the left; ERIANTHUS
SACCHAROIDES to the right

100. ANDROPOGON L. (ăn-drō-pō′gŏn)

Spikelets in pairs at each node of an articulate rachis, one sessile and perfect, the other pedicellate and either staminate, neuter or reduced to the pedicel, the rachis and the pedicels of the sterile spikelets often villous, sometimes conspicuously so; **Glumes** of the fertile spikelet coriaceous, narrow, awnless, the first rounded, flat or concave on the back, several-nerved, the median nerve weak or wanting; **Sterile Lemma** shorter than the glumes, empty, hyaline; **Fertile Lemma** hyaline, narrow entire or bifid, usually bearing a bent and twisted awn from the apex or from between the lobes; **Palea** hyaline, small or wanting; **Pedicellate Spikelet** awnless, rarely short-awned, sometimes staminate and about as large as the sessile spikelet, sometimes consisting of one or more reduced glumes, sometimes wanting, only the pedicel present.

Rather coarse *perennials* (in the United States), with solid culms, the spikelets arranged in racemes, these numerous, aggregate on an exserted peduncle, or single, in pairs, or sometimes in threes or fours, the common peduncle usually inclosed by a spathe-like sheath, these sheaths often numerous, forming a compound inflorescence, usually narrow but sometimes in dense subcorymbose masses. Species about 150; about 30 species in the United States, 18 in Texas.

Our species are divided into three groups: the first (constituting the genus *Schizachyrium* of some authors) with the racemes solitary on each peduncle, the rachis-joints and pedicels with a cup-shaped appendage at the apex; the second (constituting the genus *Amphilophis* of some authors) with the racemes numerous and aggregate toward the naked summit of the culms and branches, the rachis-joints and pedicels sulcate (channeled), the median portion translucent and margins thickened; the third, with the racemes in pairs, sometimes as many as six, on each peduncle, the rachis joints and pedicels not cup-shaped at the apex or sulcate.

Of the first group we have five species in Texas, four with the racemes appressed, and one, *A. scoparius*, with the pedicellate spikelet spreading at maturity. *A. scoparius*, little bluestem, having a wide range, is the best known of this group; *A. hirtiflorus,* a west Texas plant, and *A. littoralis*, a coast plant, have hairy racemes; *A. tener* of east Texas, and *A. cirratus* of west Texas, have almost naked racemes; *A. exaristatus* has awnless spikelets.

Of the second group, we have four species: *A. perforatus*, with a pit like depression on the back of the first glume of the sessile spikelet, the culm nodes barbed; *A. barbinodis*, with a short fan-shaped panicle, the culm nodes barbed; and *A. saccharoides* with an elongated oblong panicle, the culm nodes usually naked. In the last three species the length of the panicle the axis and the spikelets vary much, some plants seemingly a mixture of two or more species.

Our other species belong to the third group. *A. furcatus*, big blue stem, and *A. hallii*, have much the same aspect, but in the latter the racemes are more hairy and the spikelets awnless or with an imperfect awn. The former is the best known of this group. Two of this group have been introduced.

PEDICELLATE SPIKELETS MUCH SMALLER THAN THE SESSILE, empty, one or two glumes or wanting.
  RACEMES SOLITARY; rachis-joints and pedicels with a cup-shaped appendage at the apex. (*Section Schizachyrium*)
    RACEMES hairy; rachis-joints and pedicels villous.
      Hairs at the apex of the rachis-joint 1-3 mm. long; spikelets 5-7 mm. long; first glume merely scabrous; plants green or purplish, rarely glaucous. Foliage not villous.
        Pedicels short-villous; rachis mostly zigzag.   1. A. scoparius
        Pedicels copiously villous; rachis mostly nearly straight.
          1a. A. scoparius var. neomexicanus
        Foliage villous; plants usually stout.
          1b. A. scoparius var. villosissimus
      Hairs at the apex of the rachis-joint 4-6 mm. long; spikelets 7 mm. long; first glume merely scabrous; plants glaucous; sheaths strongly compressed-keeled.   2. A. littoralis
      Hairs at the apex of the rachis-joint 2 mm. long; spikelets 8 mm. long, appressed.
        First glume densely villous.   3. A. hirtiflorus
        First glume minutely papillose, sparsely pubescent.
          3a. A. hirtiflorus var. feensis
    RACEMES naked or nearly so; rachis-joints and pedicels glabrous, or a few hairs at the apex of the pedicels and rachis-joints; spikelets appressed.
      Sessile spikelet 7-9 mm. long; blades 3-5 mm. wide.   4. A. cirratus
      Sessile spikelet 4-5 mm. long; blades 1-2 mm. wide.   5. A. tener
  RACEMES NUMEROUS, forming a dense, oblong to obovate, hairy panicle; rachis-joints and pedicels sulcate, the median portion translucent and margins thickened. (*Section Amphilophis.*)
    FIRST glume of the sessile spikelet with a deep pit-like depression on the back; culm nodes bearded.   6. A. perforatus
    FIRST glume of the sessile spikelet not pitted on the back.
      Axis of the panicle elongated; panicle linear-oblong, the branches scattered; culm nodes usually naked or nearly so.
        Spikelets awned.   7. A. saccharoides
        Spikelets awnless.   8. A. exaristatus
      Axis of the panicle short; panicle fan-shaped or obovate, the branches congested; culm nodes bearded.   9. A. barbinodis
  RACEMES MOSTLY in pairs, 2-6; rachis-joint and pedicels not clavate, sulcate nor the apex cup-shaped.
    RACEMES usually shorter than the spathe (upper sheath) which incloses the common peduncle.
      Inflorescence oblong, obovate or oval, many times divided, in dense corymbiform clusters.   10. A. glomeratus
      Inflorescence long, linear, the branches not much divided.   11. A. virginicus
    RACEMES, at least one of them on peduncles beyond the spathe.
      Upper sheaths inflated, overlapping; racemes flexuous, at least one exserted beyond the others.   12. A. elliottii
      Upper sheath not inflated; racemes stout, strict.   13. A. ternarius
PEDICELLATE SPIKELETS EQUALING OR EXCEEDING THE SESSILE spikelets, usually staminate. Rachis-joints and pedicels villous.
  PLANTS USUALLY 3-5 feet tall, stout; spikelets 7-10 mm. long; rachis-joints and pedicels clavate-thickened.
    AWN perfect with a well defined column.
      Sessile spikelet hispidulous; rachis-joint and pedicel hairs 2 mm. long or less, not conspicuously hairy.   14. A. furcatus
      Sessile spikelet minutely roughened; rachis-joint and pedicel long-ciliate on the upper half; first glume of the pediceled spikelet short-awned.
          16. A. divergens
    AWN imperfect, rarely spiral at the base or wanting; rootstocks horizontal, long.   15. A. hallii
  PLANTS USUALLY 1.5-2.5 feet tall, slender, weak. (Introduced at Experimental Station, Angleton.)
    Racemes slender, spikelets 3-4 mm. long, lanceolate; rachis-joint and pedicel about two-thirds as long as the sessile spikelet.   17. A. ischaemum
    Racemes stout; spikelets crowded; sessile spikelet 4-5 mm. long, broad, oblong-elliptic; pedicel and rachis-joint about one-third as long as the sessile spikelet.   18. A. annulatus

1.   A.   SCOPARIUS Michx.   (skō-pâr'ĭ-ŭs) ;   *Schizachyrium scoparium* (Michx.) Nash ; LITTLE BLUESTEM, BROOM-SEDGE.

Culms commonly 2-4 feet rarely 5 feet tall, branching above, usually tufted, slender, erect, green or purplish, rarely glaucous; **Blades** mostly 4-8' long, sometimes longer, 2-8 mm. wide, flat, usually rough, sparsely hirsute on the upper surface near the base (rarely conspicuously villous) **Sheaths** shorter than the internodes, flattened, rough, glabrous to sparsely hairy; **Ligule** membranaceous, truncate, about 1 mm. long; **Racemes** numerous, 1-2.5' long, mostly long-exserted, solitary on slender peduncles 1-4 from a single sheath, including those of the branches the whole inflorescence narrow and often 10-15' long, the rachis slender, flexuous, commonly with 4-8 joints, the rachis-joints and pedicels ciliate with hairs 1-3 mm. long; **Sessile Spikelets** 5-7 mm. long, somewhat longer than the pedicels and rachis-joints; **Glumes** nearly equal, acuminate, awn-pointed, the first flattened below, scabrous, obscurely nerved, the second thinner, keeled, scabrous on the keel, ciliate on the margins; **Sterile Lemma** nearly as long as the glumes, acuminate; **Lemma** shorter than the sterile lemma, with an awn 8-15 mm. long from the deeply bifid apex, the awn geniculate about 3 mm. from the base, twisted, scabrous; **Pedicellate Spikelet** finally divergent, usually 2-3 mm. long, reduced to a single glume.

In dry sandy soil, over most of the United States west of the Rocky Mountains.   Spring-fall.

1a.   A. SCOPARIUS var. NEOMEXICANUS (Nash) Hitchc. (nē-ō-mĕks-ĭ-kā'nŭs) ;   *Schizachyrium neomexicanum* Nash.

This form has pedicels copiously villous, the rachis mostly nearly straight.   In the southwest the species verges into this variety.

Sandy soil and rocky hills, Texas to Arizona.   (Refugio and Wheeler counties.)

1b.   A. SCOPARIUS var. VILLOSISSIMUS Kearney (vĭl-ō-sĭs'ĭ-mŭs) ; *Schizachyrium villosissimum* Nash.

A form with villous foliage has been segregated; the pediceled spikelet sometimes as long as the sessile, rarely staminate.

Eastern Texas.   (Lufkin.)

2.   A. LITTORALIS Nash (lĭt-ō-rǎl'ĭs) ;   *Schizachyrium littorale* (Nash) Bicknell ; SEACOAST BEARD-GRASS.

Culms 2.5-4 feet tall, tufted, erect, or decumbent at the base, from short rhizomes, flattened, freely branching above, the slender branches terminated with 1-3 solitary racemes on a slender common peduncle, resembling *A. scoparius,* but culms more compressed with broad keeled overlapping lower sheaths; **Blades** 2-18' long, the upper short, 2-5 mm. wide, usually rough except the under surface toward the base, sparsely hairy above, and sometimes densely so at the base; **Sheaths** longer than the internodes, strongly keeled, more or less scabrous on the keel; **Ligule** membranaceous, ciliate, 1-3 mm. long; **Racemes** solitary, 1-3 on each branch, about 30 mm. long, the slender peduncle (also the common peduncle) glabrous; the rachis-joints and pedicels about two-thirds as long as the sessile spikelet, ciliate-villous, the terminal hairs about 4-5 mm. long; **Sessile Spikelets** about 7 mm. long, narrow, with tufts of hairs at the base; **Glumes** subequal, first two-keeled, scabrous on the keels, about 7-nerved, acuminate, 2-toothed or awn-pointed; the second usually slightly shorter, awn-pointed, the midnerve prominent, keeled, ciliate on the

margins; **Sterile Lemma** about 5 mm. long, lanceolate, hyaline, ciliate on
the margins; **Lemma** shorter than the sterile lemma, 2-toothed, the slender
scabrous awn twisted at the base, slightly above, mostly 7-10 mm. long;
Pedicellate Spikelet including the pedicel about as long as the sessile one,
the 1 or 2 scales about 2-3 mm. long, with an awn 1-2 mm. long.

In sand along the coast; Texas, Virginia, north to New York.
Summer and fall.

3. A. HIRTIFLORUS (Nees) Kunth (hẽr-tĭ-flō'rŭs).

Culms mostly 2-3 feet tall, sometimes taller, densely tufted, erect,
reddish, slender, wiry, generally with two single branches from the upper
nodes, the lower internodes flattened, furrowed on one side, from a short
rootstock; **Blades** 1-8' long, 2-4 mm. wide, upper few and short, the lower
crowded and longer, flat, erect and rather firm, scabrous, sparsely ciliate
with long hairs toward the base; **Sheaths** mostly shorter than the internodes, lower flattened, with a few scattering hairs, or lower often hirsute,
especially at the throat; **Ligule** membranaceous, truncate, about 1.5 mm.
long; **Racemes** exserted, terminating the culm and branches, mostly 2
branches, one from each node, 2-3' long, 8-13 (10-20) joints, with appressed
spikelets, the rachis-joints and pedicels about equal, 6 mm. long, villous,
hairs 2 mm. long or less, cup-toothed and ciliate; **Sessile Spikelet** about 8
mm. long, acuminate; **Glumes,** the first green, several nerved, roughened
on the back, covered with long white hairs, the second thinner, slightly
shorter, minutely scabrous on the keel, slightly ciliate toward the apex;
Sterile Lemma hyaline, shorter than the glumes; **Lemma** hyaline, deeply
bifid, slightly ciliate, a twisted and bent awn 12-18 mm. long, from the
sinus; **Pedicellate Spikelet** about 4-5 mm. long, often with short awn,
flattened, lanceolate, green, hispid, the first glume inclosing a hyaline
second and shorter one.

West Texas to Arizona and Mexico. Summer-fall.

3a. A. HIRTIFLORUS var. FEENSIS (Fourn.) Hack. (fē-ĕn'sĭs).

Blades scabrous; **Sessile Spikelets** as much as 9 mm. long, the first
Glume minutely papillose, the pubescence less copious than in the species.
(See photograph of *A. hirtiflorus* for drawings.)

Canyons and rocky slopes; west Texas to Arizona and Mexico.

4. A. CIRRATUS Hack. (sĭr-ā'tŭs).

Culms 2-2.5 feet tall, slender, erect, branching below and above, the
branches arising singly; **Blades** 1-6' long, the upper short, 2-5 mm. wide,
flat, attenuate into a long slender sharp point, rigid, margins rough;
Sheaths shorter than the internodes, close, narrow; **Ligule** membranaceous,
2 mm. long, almost truncate; **Racemes** 3-5, 1.5-2.5' long, 1.5 mm. thick, of
about 10-15 joints, single, on long peduncles terminating the culm and
lateral branches, rachis-joint and pedicel about equal, 3-4 mm. long;
Rachis-Joint glabrous or the cup-like appendage sometimes ciliate with a
few hairs, and also a small tuft at the base of the joint; **Sessile Spikelet**
about 7 mm. long; **Glumes,** the first flattened, linear-lanceolate, thick, 2-
toothed at the apex, smooth except the scabrous margins and keels, 7-9-
nerved, the second slightly shorter, linear-oblong, obtuse, thin, acute,
smooth, 3-nerved; **Sterile Lemma** and **Fertile Lemma** about equal, both
shorter than the first glume, the sterile lemma obtuse, the fertile lemma
deeply bifid, the awn from the sinus, twisted at the base, straight or
usually geniculate, only slightly scabrous, about 10 mm. (10-16) long;

Pedicellate Spikelet slightly shorter than the sessile, sometimes reduced awnless, glabrous except a tuft of hairs near the apex, often 2-3 mm. long staminate or neuter.

Canyons and rocky slopes, western Texas to Arizona, southern California and Mexico. Summer-fall.

5. A. TENER (Nees) Kunth (tĕn'ĕr) ; *Schizachyrium tenerum* Nees.

Culms 1-3 feet tall, tufted, very slender, often weak, sparingly branching near the base ; **Blades** 0.5-7′ long, the uppermost very short and bristle-like, 0.5-2 mm. wide, soon involute, sometimes sparingly pilose above at the base ; **Sheaths** shorter than the internodes, sometimes keeled ; **Racemes** 3-8, solitary, usually on long peduncles, often nodding, of 10-15 joints, 1.5-2.5′ long, slender, appearing naked, the rachis-joints short-ciliate at the base and the rim of the cup, the pedicels with a few hairs near the apex or glabrous ; **Sessile Spikelets** 4-5 mm. long, appressed ; **Glumes** about equal, acute, the first somewhat rounded on the back, obscurely several-nerved, the second compressed-keeled, about 3-nerved ; **Sterile Lemma** about three-fourths as long as the glumes ; **Lemma** about 3 mm. long, awned from the sinus, the awn bent and twisted below, 6-12 mm. long ; **Palea** about two-thirds as long as its lemma ; **Pedicellate Spikelet** of a single scale about 4-5 mm. long, awnless or awn-pointed, the pedicel linear, narrow, sparingly pilose near the summit or glabrous.

In dry soil, east Texas to Florida, South Carolina. (Hardin county, on cut-over long-pine land.) Late summer and fall.

6. A. PERFORATUS (Trin.) Fourn. (pĕr-fō-rā'tŭs).

Culms 2-3.5 feet rarely 4.5 feet tall, often rather stout, tufted, erect, branching, bearded at the nodes ; **Blades** 3-15′ long, the upper short, 2-7 mm. wide, flat, smooth or rough, or the upper surface sparingly villous, especially toward the base ; **Sheaths** shorter than the internodes, villous at the throat ; **Ligule** membranaceous, truncate, ciliate, 2-4 mm. long ; **Panicle** exserted, or those of the branches included at the base, 2.5-6′ long, the axis 1-2′ shorter, the panicle narrow, finally the branches and racemes somewhat spreading, becoming narrowly obovate or fan-shaped and silvery-white, commonly with 5-8 branches, each branch often again sub-divided into 3-8 racemes 1-2′ long, the racemes at first appressed, the rachis-joints and pedicels villous, the hairs 3-7 mm. long ; **Sessile Spikelets** 4.5-5.5 mm. long, lanceolate, flattened, acute ; **Glumes,** the first with a pit-like depression on the back, more or less villous toward the base, the second glabrous or the inrolled margins ciliate ; **Sterile Lemma** about as long as the glumes ; **Lemma** shorter than the sterile lemma, tapering into a scabrous geniculate and twisted awn 15-20 mm. long ; **Pedicellate Spikelet** of a single awnless glume about 3-3.5 mm. long, with pedicel of about equal length.

Mesas, rocky hills and plains. Texas and Mexico. Summer to fall.

7. A. SACCHAROIDES Swartz (săk-à-roi'dēz) ; *A. torreyanus* Steud. ; SILVER BEARD-GRASS.

Culms 1.5-3.5 feet tall, tufted, slender, simple or freely branching, erect, or ascending from a decumbent base, the nodes from glabrous to appressed hispid ; **Blades** 2-6′ long or sometimes longer, 2-7 mm. wide, upper surface and margins somewhat rough ; **Sheaths** shorter than the internodes ; **Ligule** membranaceous, 1-2 mm. long ; **Panicle** long-exserted, or those of the branches short-exserted, 2-6′ commonly 2-4′ long, the panicle at first narrow and green, finally somewhat spreading, becoming narrowly oblong, silvery-white, the axis 1-5' commonly 2-3' long, with 5-10 branches as much as 2' long, usually again divided into 2-6 racemes 10-40 mm. long, rachis-joints about 2 mm. long, with terminal hairs 4-6 mm. long; **Sessile Spikelets** 3-4 mm. long, lanceolate, somewhat flattened; **Glumes,** the first several nerved, 2-toothed, villous on the lower half and at the base, ciliate on the margins at and near the apex, scabrous toward the apex, the second 3-nerved, ciliate at or near the apex; **Sterile Lemmas** and **Lemma** about equal, the latter with a twisted awn 8-15 mm. long; **Pedicellate Spikelet** consisting of a single scale or glume 2-3 mm. long on a villous pedicel about 2 mm. long, the hairs 4-6 mm. long.

In dry soil, prairies and rocky slopes, Texas to Kansas, Arizona, Mexico, Missouri, Colorado and Alabama. Summer.

8. **A. EXARISTATUS** (Nash) Hitchc. (ĕks-âr-ĭs-tā'tŭs).

Resembling A. saccharoides; **Panicle** slender; **Spikelets** slightly smaller, awnless or nearly so, rare. (Drawings on photograph of *A. saccharoides.*)

Low open ground; eastern Texas to Louisiana. (Houston.) Summer.

9. **A. BARBINODIS** Lag. (bär-bĭ-nō'dĭs) ; *Amphilophis barbinodis* (Lag.) Nash; this species has been confused with *A. saccharoides,* differing chiefly in the subflabellate panicle and larger spikelets; BEAR-GRASS.

Culms 1.5-4 feet tall, tufted, spreading to erect, slender, nodes bearded, simple or branched from the lower nodes, often glaucous; **Blades** 1-8' mostly 3-5' long, the upper short, 2-7 mm. wide, flat, margins and upper surface toward the tip rough; **Sheaths** shorter than the internodes, often sparsely villous at the throat; **Ligule** membranaceous, 2-3 mm. long; **Panicle** long-exserted, 3-5' long, at first 4-6 mm. thick, linear-oblong, greenish, finally becoming ovate, obovate or fan-shaped, and silvery-white, the axis mostly 1-1.5' long, with about 7-10 branches or racemes 2' long or less, the last usually subdivided into 2-3 or even more branches or racemes, usually less than 1.5' long, the rachis-joints and pedicels villous, the hairs about twice as long as the rachis-joints and pedicels, the hairs on the average longer than those of *A. saccharoides;* **Sessile Spikelets** 3-5 mm. (5-6) long, lanceolate, flattened; **Glumes,** the first with the keels hispidulous toward the apex, pubescent at the base, the inrolled margins ciliate, the second 3-nerved, hispidulous on the keels, at or near the apex; **Sterile Lemma** and **Lemma** about equal, the latter bearing a scabrous awn, geniculate and twisted, 10-16 mm. (20-25) long, glabrous or sparingly pubescent; **Pedicellate Spikelets** about 2 mm. long, a single narrow scale, with pedicel about 3 mm. long.

Mesas, rocky slopes and open ground, Texas, Oklahoma, Arizona and Mexico. Summer-fall.

10. **A. GLOMERATUS** (Walt.) B. S. P. (glŏm-ēr-ā'tŭs) ; BUSHY BEARD-GRASS.

Culms 2-5 feet tall, tufted, erect, rather stout, somewhat flattened below, simple below, freely branching above, the branches repeatedly and fastigiately branched, the lower somewhat elongated, forming a large compound oblong or sometimes glomerate inflorescence; **Blades,** the upper 6-10' or longer, the lower or basal often 24' long or even longer, 7 mm. wide or less, flat, often revolute when dry, sometimes pubescent above near the base, rough above; **Sheaths** mostly longer than the internodes, somewhat flattened, rough, often pubescent at the throat, ciliate on the margins, sometimes sparsely pubescent and papillose; **Ligule** membranaceous, truncate, about 1 mm. long, fimbriate; **Inflorescence** as much as two feet long, dense, silky, the branches elongated so as to form a compact oblong or sometimes glomerate inflorescence, the clusters being numerous and finally spreading, villous just below the upper nodes of branches, branchlets and common peduncle of the pair of racemes, the racemes in pairs, 20-30 mm. long, of about 6-12 joints, protruding from the side or exserted from the apex of the scabrous spathe, the spathe shorter, as long as or longer than the racemes; **Rachis-joint** about as long as the spikelet, flexuous, the rachis-joints and pedicels villous with long spreading silky hairs; **Sessile Spikelets** about 3.5 mm. long, narrow; **Glumes**, the first 2-keeled, scabrous on the keels toward the apex, two strong nerves near the margins, 2-toothed, the second keeled above; **Lemma** thin, shorter than the glumes, awn from bifid apex, 12-18 mm long; **Pedicellate Spikelet,** an awn-shaped rudimentary glume, or wanting

Damp soil, Texas to Florida, north to New York, southern California and Nevada. Summer-fall.

11. A. VIRGINICUS L. (vĕr-jĭn'ĭ-kŭs); BROOM SEDGE.

Culms 2-5 feet tall, often in large tufts, erect, slender, simple at the base, much branched above; **Blades** 6-16' long, 2-5 mm. wide, flat, hirsute near the base on the upper surface, slightly rough, especially on the margins; **Sheaths** shorter than the internodes, somewhat hirsute on the margins, with rather long hairs, especially the lower, sometimes somewhat papillose; **Ligule** membranaceous, rounded, short, ciliate; **Inflorescence** long-linear, terminal and from axillary branches, the racemes mostly in pairs, rarely 3-4, 20-30 mm. long, flexuous, loose, protruding from the sides of the spathes which usually extend beyond the racemes, the smooth spathes about 1.5-2' long, not enlarged, villous below the nodes of the upper spathes, about 8-12 joints to each raceme, the slender rachis-joints and pedicels as long as the spikelets, villous with long spreading hairs from less than two to three times as long as the rachis-joints and pedicels; **Sessile Spikelet** 3-4 mm. long, narrow; **Glumes** about equal, the first 2-keeled above; the **Sterile Lemma** and **Lemma** hyaline, the lemma with a scabrous straight awn 10-20 mm. long; **Stamen** one; **Pedicellate Spikelet** wanting, or rarely present as a minute scale, the pedicel exceeding the sessile spikelet.

In dry or moist fields and open woods, Texas to Florida, north to Massachusetts and Illinois. Summer-fall.

11a. A. VIRGINICUS var. **HIRSUTIOR** (Hack.) Hitchc. (hĕr-sū'tĭ-ĕr).

Flowering branches more numerous than in the species, the inflorescence often rather more dense, resembling that of *A. glomeratus,* but the spathes mostly larger and the peduncles usually shorter. Intergrades with *A. virginicus,* and appears to be intermediate between that species and *A. glomeratus.*

Moist meadows and old fields; Texas and Mexico to Florida.

12. A. ELLIOTTII Chapm. (ĕl-ĭ-ŭt'ĭ-ī); ELLIOTT'S BEARD-GRASS.

Culms 1-3 feet tall, tufted, simple or sparingly branched above, the nodes below the inflated sheaths villous, somewhat flattened; **Blades** 2-12' long, 1-5 mm. wide, those of the inflated sheaths short, slightly rough or smooth, hirsute above near the base; **Sheaths** shorter than the internodes, he lower narrow, the upper elongated and inflated, imbricate, glabrous or the lower and those of the innovations loosely appressed-hirsute, the flattened ferruginous upper sheath conspicuous in winter; **Ligule** a short almost truncate membrane; **Peduncle** usually not more than 10 mm. long, the inflorescence finally flabellate; **Racemes** in pairs rarely in 3's, 1-2' long, rarely longer, loose, some of them exserted; **Rachis** slender, flexuous, its joints and pedicels villous with long spreading hairs; **Sessile Spikelets** 4-5 mm. long, scabrous on the keel, usually exceeding the rachis-joint, awn 14-20 mm. long, geniculate, scabrous, the inclosed racemes in late season *cleistogamous;* **Pedicellate Spikelet** a minute scale, the pedicel slightly longer than the sessile spikelet.

In dry or moist soil, east Texas to Florida, north to New Jersey and Missouri. Summer-fall.

Note: Sometimes individuals occur with less aggregate upper sheaths, and others with scarcely dilated sheaths, aggregate or scarcely aggregate. This form is distinguished as *A. elliottii* var. *gracilior* Hack.

Open ground, fields and woods, mostly on coastal plain; Texas to Florida, north to New Jersey and Missouri.

13. A. TERNARIUS Michx. (tẽr-nā'rǐ'ŭs) ; *A. argyraeus* Schult.; SILVERY BEARD-GRASS.

Culms 2.5-4 feet tall, about twice as long as the basal leaves, tufted, erect, simple below, much branched above, in 1-3's, the upper nodes sometimes pubescent, otherwise smooth and glabrous; **Blades**, the first below the axillary racemes very short, the others 4-25' long, the basal very long, 2-3 mm. wide, flat, soon becoming revolute, smooth to slightly rough, sometimes sparsely hirsute below near the base; **Sheaths** mostly shorter than the internodes, smooth to slightly rough, sometimes sparsely hirsute and sometimes papillose; **Ligule** membranaceous, truncate, about 1 mm. long; **Racemes** in pairs, often in 3's, 1-2.5' long, silvery-gray, rather stout, more or less exserted on slender peduncles, without bracts, the rachis-joints about 3 mm. long, the pedicels about 4 mm. long, both densely villous, the hairs about one and a half to two times their length; **Sessile Spikelets** 5-6 mm. long, lanceolate, acuminate; **Glumes** membranaceous, lanceolate, acuminate, the first broad at the base, deeply depressed on the back, 2-toothed, nerveless between the keels except toward the apex, 2-keeled, hispid especially on the keels, glabrous between the keels, the second about as long as the first, keeled, 3-nerved, margins ciliate, the keel scabrous; **Sterile Lemma** and **Lemma** shorter than the glumes, hyaline; **Lemma** about 2-2.5 mm. long, with an awn from the bifid apex, 15-25 mm. long, more or less twisted, scabrous, straight or slightly bent or curved; **Pedicellate Spikelet** of a single lanceolate glume 1-3 mm. long, scabrous, the pedicel a little shorter than the sessile spikelet.

In dry sandy soil, east Texas to Florida, north to Delaware and Missouri. Late summer and fall.

14. A. FURCATUS Muhl. (fûr-kā'tŭs) ; has been referred to as *A. provincialis* Lam.; TURKEY-FOOT, BIG BLUESTEM.

Culms 3-6 feet tall, often in large bunches, often glaucous or purplish, stout, simple at the base, branched above, sometimes with short rootstocks; **Blades** 6-18' long, 4-14 mm. wide, flat, margins scabrous, smooth or rough, glabrous, or often hirsute above toward the base; **Sheaths** mostly shorter than the internodes, often glaucous, glabrous or sometimes

hairy towards the base; **Ligule** membranaceous, about 3 mm. long, some
times fringed; **Racemes** mostly 2-6 (sometimes as many as 12), in pair,
or threes, or approximate on peduncles at the summit of culm or latera
branches, 1-5′ long, rachis-joints about 5 mm. long, and pedicel o:
pedicellate spikelet about 4 mm. long, with hairs 2 mm. long or less
Sessile Spikelet about 7-10 mm. long, lanceolate; **Glumes** more or les:
hispidulous all over, acute, the first 2-keeled, the second scabrous on the
keel, glabrous to hispidulous; **Lemma** about as long as the glumes, 2-
toothed, with a spiral geniculate scabrous awn 7-18 mm. long; **Pedicellate
Spikelet** 7-10 mm. long, awnless, staminate, otherwise similar to the sessile
spikelet.

In dry or moist soil, over most of the United States east of the Rocky
Mountains and northern Mexico.   Summer-fall.

15. **A. HALLII** Hack. (häl′ĭ-ī) ; HALL'S BEARD-GRASS.

Culms 3-6 feet tall, from creeping rootstocks, erect, robust, simple at
the base, branched above, more or less glabrous; intergrades with
A. furcatus; **Blades,** upper as short as 1.5′, the middle as long as 16′, 5-8
mm. wide, flat, margins scabrous, otherwise smooth or slightly rough;
Sheaths shorter than the internodes, glaucous; **Ligule** membranaceous, 3-4
mm. long, villous, just back of ligule; **Racemes** 2-5, on peduncles, in pairs
or approximate, 2-4′ long, the lateral ones often included in the sheaths,
the rachis-joints 4.5 mm. long, pedicel of pedicellate spikelet about 5 mm.
long, both copiously villous with rather stiff hairs 2-4 mm. long; **Sessile
Spikelets** 8-10 mm. long, acuminate; **Glumes,** the first pubescent to
glabrous below, pubescent to villous toward the apex, somewhat pubescent
along the margins; **Sterile Lemma** empty, hyaline; **Lemma** shorter than
the glumes, awnless or with an awn usually less than length of the spikelet; **Pedicellate Spikelet** slightly larger than the sessile, awnless, subtending a staminate flower; **Stamens** 3.

Sandhills and sandy soil, Texas to Arizona, north to North Dakota
and Wyoming, Utah and Arizona.   Summer-fall.

Note: A form of this species with yellow-villous racemes and awns
5-10 mm. long has been segregated as *A. chrysocomus* Nash.

16. A. DIVERGENS (Hack.) Anderss. (dī-vẽr′jĕns).

Culms rather robust, 2.5-4 feet tall, sparingly branching toward the
summit; **Blades** elongated, 3-6 mm. wide, rather firm, flat or folded,
glabrous to villous; **Sheaths,** the lower crowded, compressed-keeled,
grayish-villous, especially the lower; **Racemes** mostly 30-40 mm. long,
mostly 6-8-jointed, rather stout, usually partly included, the rachis from
slightly to strongly flexuous, the joints and pedicels long-ciliate on the
upper half and with a short tuft of hairs at the base; **Sessile Spikelets**
6-8 mm. long, minutely roughened, the awn 5-10 mm. long; **Pedicellate
Spikelets** about as long as the sessile, the first glume awn-tipped.

Pine lands, eastern Texas.   (Kirbyville.)

17. A. ISCHAEMUM L. (ĭs′kē-mŭm).

Culms 1.5-2.5 feet tall, tufted, erect or ascending from a decumbent
base, freely branching, slender, the lower nodes pubescent, the upper
villous; **Blades** 1-6′ long, 1.5-3 mm. wide, the upper short, flat, soon becoming revolute on drying, papillose-pilose on the upper surface at the
base, sparsely so above, somewhat rough on the upper surface; **Sheaths**
shorter than the internodes; **Ligule** membranaceous, fimbriate, about

mm. long; **Racemes** mostly three, approximate, usually 4-5 mm. distant, -2′ long, commonly long-exserted on slender peduncles, as many as three lowering branches from the upper node, the axillary sometimes included .t the base, the rachis-joints and pedicels 2-2.5 mm. long, ciliate-villous, he upper hairs about as long as or shorter than the internodes and)edicels, the lower shorter; **Sessile Spikelets** 3.5-4 mm. long, oblong, anceolate; **Glumes** subequal, the second often slightly longer, the first :-keeled, 5-7-nerved, entire or 2-toothed, hirsute on the lower half and uispid on the margins, the second keeled, 3-nerved, acute, slightly)ubescent and scabrous toward the apex; **Sterile Lemma** slightly shorter han the glumes; **Lemma** shorter than the sterile lemma, with a scabrous \wn about 15 mm. long, geniculate near the middle, much twisted below :he bend; **Pedicellate Spikelet** about 4 mm. long, darker in color, awnless, glumes about equal, staminate or neuter, not hirsute below, otherwise similar to the sessile spikelet.

Native of Mediterranean Europe. Introduced by A. and M. College at Experiment Station, Angleton, R. H. Stanfield, Supt. Fall.

18. A. ANNULATUS Forsk. (ăn-ū-lā′tŭs).

Culms 2-3.5 feet tall, tufted, freely branching, flattened, nodes barbed; **Blades** 3-12′ long, 4-7 mm. wide, flat, soon revolute at the base on drying, margins and surface toward the apex rough, papillose-hirsute on the upper surface at the base, sparsely so above; **Sheaths** shorter than the internodes, flattened, often hirsute at the throat; **Ligule** membranaceous, about 1 mm. long, fimbriate; **Racemes** 2-5, pale-green, exserted or included at the base, approximate, 1-2′ long, terminal or axillary, rachis-joints and pedicels about 1.5 mm. long, villous at the base and along one side, the spikelets crowded; **Sessile Spikelets** 4-5 mm. long, obovate, flattened; **Glumes** about equal, the second sometimes slightly longer, margins inrolled, the first obovate, the broad apex somewhat winged, many-nerved, the two prominent nerves, one on each side, extending to the obtuse apex, flattened or rounded on the back, hispid-ciliate on the margins, especially toward the apex, the back covered with rather coarse appressed hairs, the second lanceolate, obtuse, comparatively narrow, keeled, finely pubescent; **Sterile Lemma** lanceolate, nearly as long as the glumes; **Lemma** shorter, with a scabrous awn, 15-18 mm. long, twice geniculate, twisted to the second bend, the first bend about 4 mm. from the base, the second about 5 mm. above the first; **Stamens** 3; **Pedicellate Spikelets** 4-5 mm. long, awnless, staminate, otherwise similar to the sessile ones.

Introduced by A. and M. College at Experiment Station. Fall.

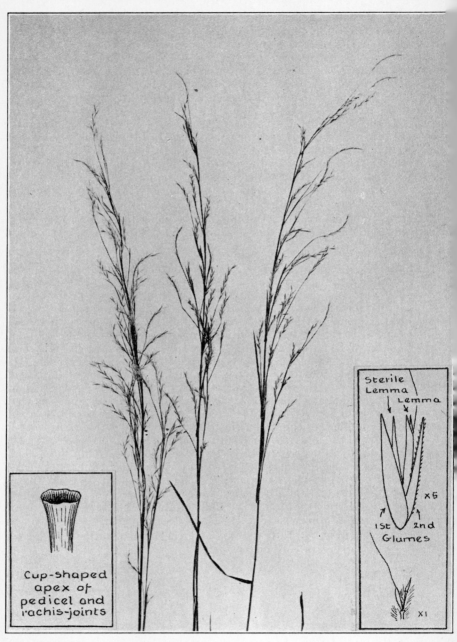

Sterile
Lemma
Lemma

×5

1st   2nd
Glumes

×1

Cup-shaped
apex of
pedicel and
rachis-joints

ANDROPOGON SCOPARIUS; Little Bluestem, Broom-sedge

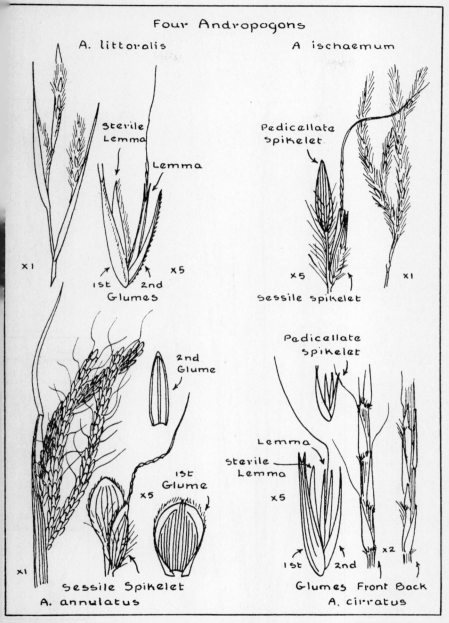

Four Andropogons

A. littoralis   A ischaemum

Sterile
Lemma

Lemma

x1

1st   2nd
Glumes   x5

Pedicellate
Spikelet

x5   x1

Sessile spikelet

2nd
Glume

1st
Glume   x5

x1

Sessile Spikelet

A. annulatus

Pedicellate
Spikelet

Lemma

Sterile
Lemma   x5

1st   2nd   x2
Glumes Front Back

A. cirratus

ANDROPOGON LITTORALIS, A. ISCHAEMUM, A. ANNULATUS, AND
A. CIRRATUS

Andropogon hirtifloris
var.
feensis

Sterile
Lemma

Lemma

1st   2nd
Glumes

X1

Sterile
Lemma

Lemma

1st   2nd
Glumes

X1

ANDROPOGON HIRTIFLORUS

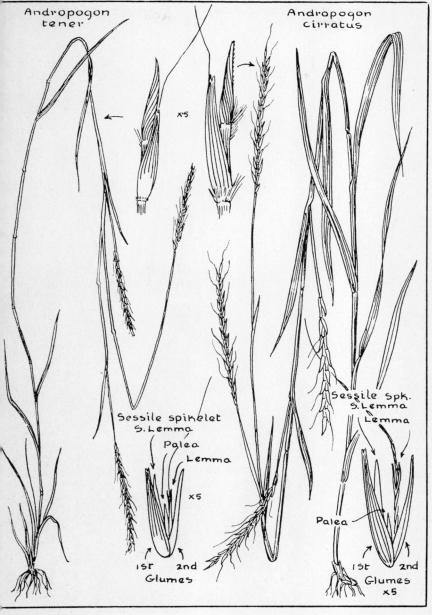

ANDROPOGON TENER AND ANDROPOGON CIRRATUS

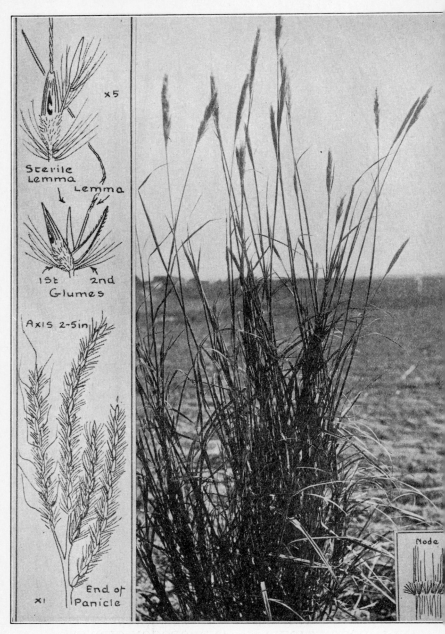

ANDROPOGON PERFORATUS

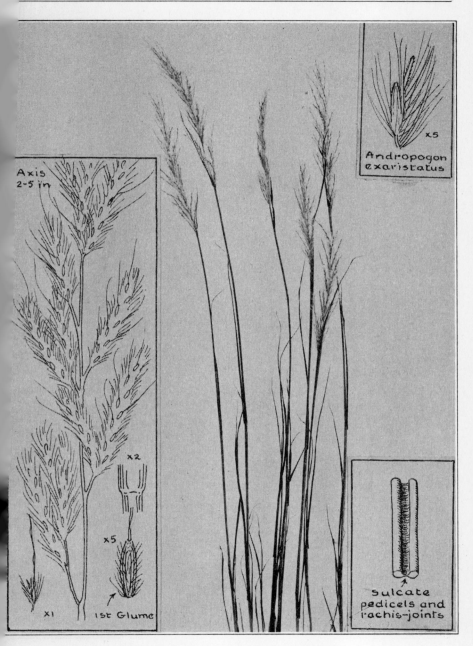

Axis
2-5 in

x2

x5

x1   1st Glume

Andropogon
exaristatus

x5

sulcate
pedicels and
rachis-joints

ANDROPOGON SACCHAROIDES

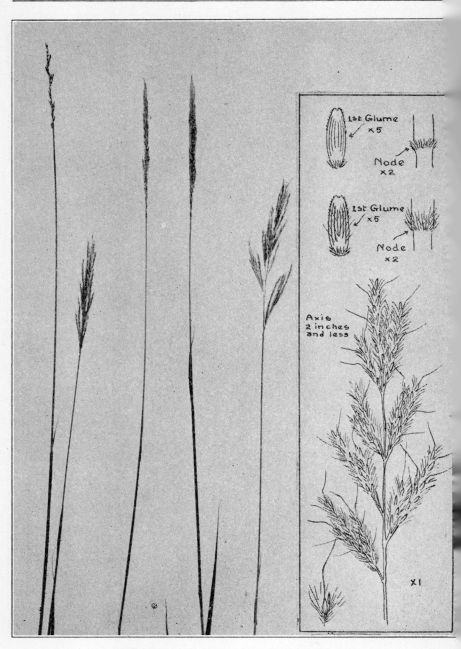

ANDROPOGON BARBINODIS; BEARD-GRASS

ANDROPOGON GLOMERATUS; Bushy Beard-grass

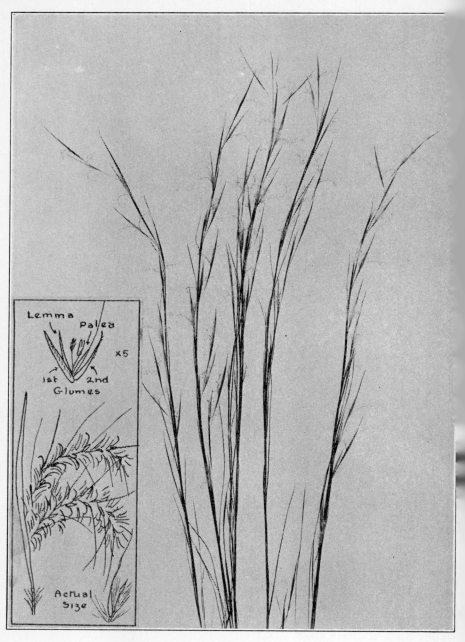

ANDROPOGON VIRGINICUS; Broom Sedge

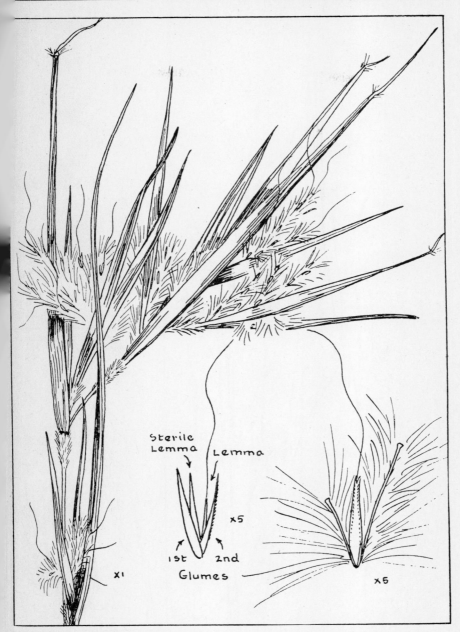

ANDROPOGON ELLIOTTII; Elliott's Beard-grass

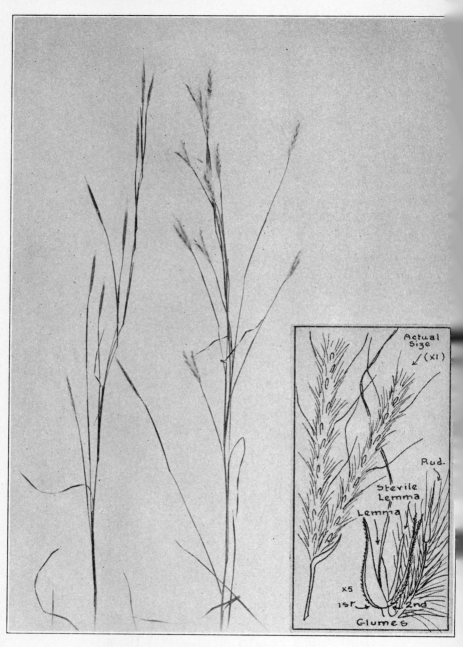

ANDROPOGON TERNARIUS; SILVERY BEARD-GRASS

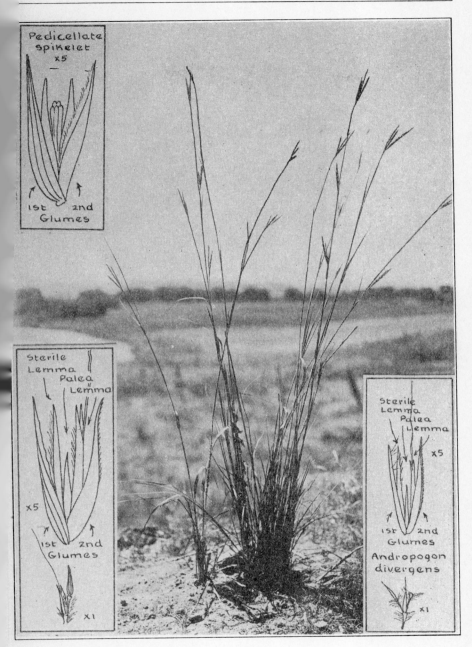

Pedicellate
spikelet
x5

1st   2nd
Glumes

Sterile
Lemma
Palea
Lemma

x5

1st   2nd
Glumes
x1

Sterile
Lemma
Palea
Lemma
x5

1st   2nd
Glumes
Andropogon
divergens
x1

ANDROPOGON FURCATUS; BIG BLUESTEM

ANDROPOGON HALLII; Turkey-foot

101. VETIVERIA Bory. (vĕt-ĭ-vē′rĭ-à)
(Anatherum Beauv. in part)

This genus is closely allied to *Andropogon*, and is represented by one ▪ecies in Texas.

It is a tall **perennial** with a large, nearly oblong, erect **panicle**, the ▪rimary branches of the panicle in dense whorls of 6-20, naked at the base, ▪sually less than 5′ long, readily disarticulating at the nodes, with many ▪airs of spikelets; the **sessile spikelet** perfect, somewhat laterally com-▪ressed, and the **pedicellate spikelet** staminate.

It is an Old World grass, frequently cultivated in the warmer parts ▪f America for hedges and for the aromatic roots which are used for ▪aking screens and mats to perfume the air in houses. These roots readily ▪npart perfume when wet. It is cultivated at Riviera Beach, Texas, and ▪erhaps in the Rio Grande Valley.

▪. ZIZANIOIDES (L.) Nash (zī-zăn-ĭ-oi′dēz); *Anatherum zizanioides*
(L.) Hitchc. & Chase; *Andropogon muricatus* Retz.; Vetiver, Khus-
khus and Khas-khas.

Culms 4-7 feet tall, robust, often 12 mm. thick, woody, rigid, erect, ▪n rather large tufts, the basal leaves numerous; **Blades** 15-42′ long, 5-12 ▪m. wide, conduplicate below and flat above, the junction with the sheath ▪bscure, slightly rough toward the tip, papillose-pubescent above towards ▪he base; **Sheaths** longer than the internodes, compressed-keeled; **Ligule** ▪ very minutely pubescent line; **Panicle** erect, light-green to purplish, ▪pen, rather dense, 8-16′ long, oblong or nearly so, the primary branches ▪commonly 6-20 to a whorl, the whorls 1-1.5′ distant, naked at the base, ▪usually less than 5′ long, sometimes with 1-3 short branchlets or racemes, ▪slender, erect, ascending or somewhat spreading, the rachis-joints 4-6 mm. long, flattened, slightly scabrous on the margins, the numerous spikelets in pairs; **Sessile Spikelet** 4-4.5 mm. long, about equal to the rachis-joints, narrow, acute; **Glumes** subequal, the first minutely scabrous or roughened, 2-keeled, the keels with a few curved, short, stout prickles (muricate), the second keeled, the keel muricate, the margins membranaceous, ciliate; **Sterile Lemma** and **Lemma** hyaline, about equal, the margins of the sterile lemma ciliate; **Lemma** nearly as long as the glumes, with a short awn from the bifid apex; **Palea** short and hyaline; **Stamens** 3, styles distinct, stigmas plumose, purple; **Pedicellate Spikelet** about 4 mm. long, with scabrous pedicels about 2.5 mm. long, the glumes sparingly muricate; **Stamens** 3. In cultivation, escaping in fields, Texas to Louisiana. (Riviera Beach.) Fall.

VETIVERIA ZIZANIOIDES; Vetiver, Khus-khus, Khas-khas

102. SORGHUM Moench. (sôr'gŭm)
(Holcus L.)

Spikelets in pairs, one **Sessile** and **Fertile**, the other **Pedicellate,** erile but well developed, usually **Staminate,** the terminal sessile spikelet ith two pedicellate spikelets.

Annual or *perennial,* tall or moderately tall grasses, with flat blades nd terminal panicles of 1-5 jointed tardily disarticulating racemes. Species bout six, one Mexican, the others in the Old World; two cultivated or in-roduced into America, both in Texas, *S. vulgare,* an annual, usually more obust than *S. halepense,* a perennial.

S. halepense, known as Johnson grass, is a stout plant, commonly 3-5 eet tall, from rather long stout creeping rootstocks, the blades usually arrower than those of plants of sorghum of the same height. It is a ative of the Mediterranean region, but is now common through the South. t is highly praised by some as an excellent forage grass, but its ability o spread rapidly, and the difficulty of eradicating it from cultivated fields, as given it the reputation of being a pernicious weed. The smaller plants f sudan grass may be mistaken for Johnson grass, but are differentiated by he absence of rootstocks. Sudan grass, in favorable soil, is a tall rigidly rect plant with rather rigid erect panicles.

S. vulgare has been cultivated from prehistoric times for the seed, which has been used for food, for the sweet juice, and for forage. In the United States it is cultivated under the general name of sorghum or sorgo. There are many races and varieties, the chief of which are sorgo, kafir, hegari, milo, broom-corn, shallu, kaoliang, and durra. Sorgo includes the varieties with sweet juice, these varieties often being known collectively as saccharine sorghums.

In this country sorgo is cultivated chiefly in the region from Kansas south to Texas and east to North Carolina, for the juice which is made into sirup and for foliage which is used for fodder. The other races of sorghum are often classed together as non-saccharine sorghums. The large panicles of one race, broom-corn, grown especially in Illinois, also in Texas, furnish the material for brooms. The other races are used for forage or for the seed which is used for food. Kafir, milo, and a recently introduced variety, feterita, are of especial value in the southern part of the Great Plains and other semiarid regions where dry-land farming is practiced. Kafir, or Kafir-corn, is a rather low form with compact cylindric heads and awnless spike-lets. Milo, or milo-maize, is a usually taller form, with ovate heads, a straight or recurved peduncle, awned spikelets and larger seeds. Durra differs from milo in having densely pubescent grayish or greenish glumes (instead of brown or black and slightly pubescent), and strongly flattened seeds. Some of these forms are called Egyptian corn, chicken corn and Jerusalem corn. The name chicken corn should be restricted to a variety spontaneous in Louisiana and Mississippi, *Sorghum vulgare* var. *drummondii* (Nees) Hitchc. (*Andropogon drummondii* Nees, *Holcus sor-ghum* var. *drummondii* (Nees) Hitchc.). A recently introduced variety, *Sorghum vulgare* var. *sudanense* (Piper) Hitchc. (*Andropogon sorghum* var. *sudanensis* Piper, *Holcus sorghum* var. *sudanensis*), is now extensively cultivated for hay in the semiarid regions under the name of Sudan grass. This is a rather slender annual, 6 to 9 feet tall, the panicle open and spreading. The absence of rhizomes shows its affinity to sorgo.

The sorghums and Johnson grass sometimes produce hydrocyanic acid in sufficient abundance, especially in the second growth, to poison grazing animals. The plants are often splotched with purple due to a bacteria disease. While the spikelets of sorghum and Johnson grass are similar the differ as to size and pubescence.

PLANTS perennial; from long creeping rootstocks.   1. S. halepens
PLANTS annual.   2. S. vulgar

1. S. HALEPENSE (L.) Pers. (hăl-ē-pěn′sē) ; *Holcus halepensis* L. JOHNSON GRASS.

Culms commonly 3-5 feet tall, simple or branched from stout root stocks, glabrous and smooth throughout except where noted; **Blades** 24 long more or less, commonly 8-15′ long, 5-30 mm. wide, flat, somewha narrowed toward the rounded base, the apex drooping, margins mostl rough, often villous on the upper surface, close to the ligule; **Sheath** usually shorter than the internodes; **Ligule** membranaceous, ciliate, 2-? mm. long; **Panicle** finally exserted, 6-12′ long, sometimes much longer ovate-oblong to pyramidal, erect or drooping, the axils pubescent to villous, its branches mostly in whorls of four, naked at the base, ascending or spreading, the lower and longer ones 3-6′ long, the short branchlets with short peduncled racemes, each with one-to-few racemes, of a few joints, the spikelets in pairs, or the end ones in threes, at each node, one sessile and perfect, awned, the other pedicellate, awnless, usually staminate; **Spikelets Sessile**, 4-5.5 mm. long, ovate-lanceolate, pale-green or yellowish to purplish; **Glumes** as long as the spikelet, sparsely or densely pubescent with appressed silky hairs, several-nerved, the first broad, flattened dorsally, 3-toothed at the obtuse apex, the margins inrolled, the second not so broad, somewhat keeled; **Sterile Lemma** slightly shorter than the glumes, hyaline; **Lemma** about half as long as the spikelet, broadly oval, two-lobed, hyaline, pubescent, bearing a readily deciduous awn 8-15 mm. long, spiral below, much exserted, more or less bent; **Pedicellate Spikelet** 5-6 mm. long, lanceolate, narrower than the sessile one, glabrous to sparsely pubescent, acuminate, usually *staminate*, its lemma and palea shorter and narrower, hyaline. In fields and waste places, southern states, rarely found in the North. Spring-fall.

2. S. VULGARE Pers. (vŭl-gā′rē) ; *Holcus sorghum* L.; *Andropogon sorghum* Brot.; SORGHUMS.

This species (and its many varieties) is distinguished from Johnson grass by its annual duration, absence of rootstocks and usually more robust habit.

It is beyond the scope of this work to describe the many races and varieties of this species. As they are fully described in bulletins issued by the U. S. Department of Agriculture, it seems sufficient to quote generously from Hitchcock (Bulletin No. 772), and present photographs of a few of the varieties.

The names of the seven varieties of *Sorghum vulgare* Pers. shown in photograph are from left to right: Dwarf Hegari, for forage or grain; sumac sorgo (sweet sorghum), for forage or sirup; honey sorgo (sweet sorghum), for forage or sirup; black Spanish broom-corn (standard); spur feterita, for grain or occasionally for forage; dwarf blackhall kafir, for grain or forage; dwarf yellow milo, for grain.

The photograph of these varieties was taken at the U. S. Dry Land Field Station at Dalhart, Texas. The plants were selected and classified by B. F. Barnes, Superinendent, and B. F. Martin, specialist on sorghums from Department of Agriculture at Washington.

Lemma
Palea
1st
2nd
Glumes ×3

SORGHUM HALEPENSE; Johnson Grass

SEVEN VARIETIES OF SORGHUM VULGARE.   See Sorghum vulgare
for names of varieties

SORGHUM VULGARE var. SUDANENSE; Sudan Grass

103. SORGHASTRUM Nash (sôr-găs'trŭm)

Spikelets in pairs, one nearly terete, sessile and fertile, **the oth**
wanting, only the hairy pedicel being present; **Glumes** coriaceous, brow
or yellowish, the first hirsute, the edges inflexed over the second; **Steri**
and **Fertile Lemmas** thin and hyaline, the latter extending into a usuall
well-developed bent and twisted awn.

Perennial, erect, rather tall grasses, with narrow flat blades an
narrow terminal panicles of one-to-few jointed racemes. Three species i
the United States, east of the Rocky Mountains.

The units of the inflorescence are racemes reduced to one or two joint:
or in *S. nutans* sometimes four or five. The slender villous rachis disart:
culates at the top of each joint, the spikelets falling with two villous stalk
attached, one the rachis-joint, the other the pedicel of the obsolete steril
spikelet. The articulation is more or less oblique, leaving a bearded blun
callus, or, in some South American species, a long sharp callus. In *S. nutan*
the racemes not infrequently occur in pairs with a sessile spikelet in th
fork, that is, the pedicel of the sterile spikelet of the lowest joint has bee
replaced by a short raceme of one or two joints.

The commonest species of the genus in the United States is *S. nutans*
sometimes called Indian reed or Indian grass. It is a tall, erect grass witl
handsome bronze-colored panicles as much as a foot long, the awns about ε
half inch long, the anthers a brilliant yellow, and is found in prairies anε
open woods throughout the eastern United States and southwest to Arizonε
and Mexico. It is a common constituent of prairie hay in the eastern par
of the Great Plains region.

Two other species are found in the southern states, both with awns
about an inch long, *S. elliottii,* with a chestnut-brown panicle, the ultimate
branchlet mainly villous at the very tip, and *S. secundum,* with a one-sided
golden panicle, the ultimate branchlets reflexed and villous along the upper
portion.

AWNS 10-18 mm. LONG, once bent, closely twisted to the first bend; panicle
    dense, bronze or golden.   1. S. nutans
AWNS ABOUT AN INCH LONG, twice bent, closely twisted to the second bend.
   PANICLE chestnut-brown, the ultimate branchlets straight, exceeding the
      internodes of the axis, with a few hairs at the tip only.   2. S. elliottii
   PANICLE usually golden, one-sided, the ultimate branchlets curved, shorter
      than the internodes of the axis, conspicuously long-villous toward the apex,
      spikelets reflexed.   3. S. secundum

1. S. NUTANS (L.) Nash (nŭ'tăns) ; *Sorghum nutans* A. Gray; INDIAN
REED, INDIAN GRASS.

    Culms 3-8 feet tall, erect, nodes pubescent or bearded; **Blades** 3-18'
long, 3-15 mm. wide, narrowed toward the base, flat above and conduplicate below, often glaucous, rough, the margins often hispid-ciliate;
Sheaths, the upper shorter than the internodes, glabrous, or the lower
sometimes pubescent; **Ligule** 2-4 mm. long, thick, stiff; **Panicle** exserted,
bronze-yellow, the anthers a brilliant yellow, 8-12' long, loose and open
but narrow, usually nodding at the apex, the branches exceeding the internodes, erect or ascending, the lower as much as 4' long, the ultimate subdivisions reduced to 4-5 joints or less, the rachis or ultimate branchlet
and pedicels villous; **Sessile Spikelet** 6-8 mm. long, slightly flattened;
Glumes lanceolate, about equal, golden-brown-tinged, the first 9-nerved,
flat or rounded, hirsute, the second 5-nerved, ciliate on the margins above

nd at the apex; **Sterile Lemma** about 5 mm. long, lance-oblong, hyaline, ubescent above; **Lemma** 4-5 mm. long, hyaline, the awn from the sinus of bifid apex, 10-18 mm. long, once bent, twisted to the bend, loosely so bove; **Pedicellate Spikelet** wanting, the pedicels one-half to two-thirds s long as the spikelet.

In dry or moist soil, eastern United States, west to New Mexico, Arizona, Texas and Florida. Found over most of Texas. Fall.

S. ELLIOTTII (C. Mohr) Nash (ĕl-ĭ-ŭt'ĭ-ī); *S. linnaeanum* Nash; LONG-BRISTLED INDIAN-GRASS.

Culms 2.5-5.5 feet tall, tufted or solitary, erect, nodes glabrous or puberulent; **Blades** 2.5-18' mostly 8-15' long, the upper short, 1.5-8 mm. wide, narrowed toward both ends, flat, folded or involute toward the base; **Sheaths** mostly longer than the internodes, striate; **Ligule** firm, truncate, 2-3 mm. long; **Panicle** chestnut-brown, exserted, 6-12' long, nodding, the axis slender and purplish, the capillary branches erect or nearly so, at least the lower, exceeding the internodes, commonly 1-3' long, mostly solitary, branching near the base, the ultimate subdivisions straight, the apex of the branchlets sparingly pilose, sometimes a few hairs below, the pedicel villous and slightly shorter than the sessile spikelet; **Sessile Spikelets** 6-8 mm. long; **Glumes** subequal, the second slightly longer, both chestnut-brown, the first broad, slightly rounded on the back, obtuse or truncate, hirsute, the hairs tawny and ascending, the second glabrous or sparingly hirsute, ciliate on the upper margins and apex; **Sterile Lemma** shorter than the glumes, ciliate; **Lemma** terminating in an awn 20-35 mm. long, twice bent, closely twisted to the second bend, thence loosely twisted, the column much exserted; **Pedicellate Spikelet** reduced to a hairy pedicel or to a very minute rudiment, the pedicel about two-thirds as long as the spikelet.

Open ground and open woods, usually sandy land, Texas to Florida and north to Virginia. (Pine woods, Liberty and Teague.) Fall.

3. S. SECUNDUM (Ell.) Nash (sē-kŭn'dŭm); *Sorghum secundum* (Ell.) Chapm.; WILD OATS.

Culms 2.5-4 feet tall, erect, rather stout, the nodes puberulent or glabrous; **Blades** 24' long more or less, 3-7 mm. wide more or less, narrowed at the base, flat or involute, rough above, pilose toward the base on the upper surface; **Sheaths,** the upper shorter than the internodes, ciliate, smooth or slightly rough; **Ligule** firm, 4-5 mm. long; **Panicles** golden-brown, one-sided, 4-6' long, linear-oblong, dense or open, the capillary branches erect or nearly so, rarely exceeding 40 mm. long, usually shorter than the internodes of the axis, the ultimate subdivisions curved, causing the spikelets to be reflexed, the pedicels half to two-thirds as long as the spikelets, the upper portion of the branchlets villous; **Sessile Spikelet** 6-8 mm. long, linear oblong, golden-brown and indurate at maturity; **Glumes** subequal, the first 7-9-nerved, truncate, sparsely pilose, the hairs long and erect, the second slightly longer than the first, 5-nerved, keeled above; **Lemma** shorter than the first glume, the awn twice bent, 25-30 mm. long, closely twisted to the second bend, thence loosely twisted, the column very much exserted; **Pedicellate Spikelet** wanting, the pedicel villous, one-half to two-thirds as long as the spikelet.

In dry sandy soil, often on pine lands, Texas to Georgia, South Carolina and Florida. Fall.

SORGHASTRUM NUTANS; Indian Reed or Indian Grass

SORGHASTRUM ELLIOTTII

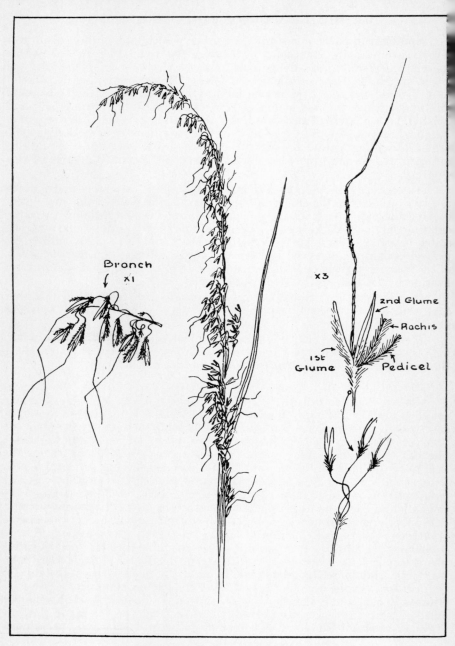

Branch
x1

x3

2nd Glume

Rachis

1st
Glume

Pedicel

SORGHASTRUM SECUNDUM

104. HETEROPOGON Pers. (hĕt-ēr-ō-pō'gŏn)

Spikelets in pairs, one sessile, the other pedicellate, both of the lower ew-to-several pairs staminate or neuter, the remainder of the sessile pikelets perfect, terete, long-awned, the pedicellate spikelets, like the ower, staminate, flat, conspicuous, awnless; **Glumes** of the fertile spikelet ·qual, coriaceous, the first brown-hirsute, infolding the second; **Lemmas** hin and hyaline, the fertile one narrow, extending into a strong bent and ·wisted brown awn; **Palea** wanting; **Glumes** of the staminate spikelet nembranaceous, the first green, faintly many-nerved, asymmetric, one ·ubmarginal keel rather broadly winged, the other wingless, the margins inflexed, the second glume narrower, symmetric; **Lemmas** hyaline; **Palea** wanting.

Annual or *perennial,* often robust grasses, with flat blades and solitary racemes terminal on the culms and branches; *Rachis* slender, the lower part, bearing the pairs of staminate spikelets, continuous, the remainder disarticulating obliquely at the base of each joint, the joint forming a sharp barbed callus below the fertile spikelet, the pedicellate spikelet readily falling, its pedicel remaining, obscured in the hairs of the callus. Species about seven, in the warmer regions of both hemispheres; two in the United States, from Florida to Arizona, one in Texas, a *perennial.*

H. contortus, a perennial 1-3 feet tall, usually in large tufts, with rather dark long-awned racemes, has the first glume of the staminate spikelets papillose-pilose.

H. melanocarpus (Ell.) Benth., an annual species usually much taller, with the first glume of the staminate spikelet bearing a row of glands along the back, is found in Arizona, Florida, Alabama and Georgia.

H. CONTORTUS (L.) Beauv. (kŏn-tôr'tŭs).

Culms 1-3 feet tall, tufted, erect or ascending, branching above, rough below the racemes; **Blades** 2-12′ mostly 4-8′ long, flat or conduplicate, rough or the lower surface smooth, sometimes ciliate toward the base, or sometimes sparsely villous on the upper surface near the base; **Sheaths** shorter than the internodes, compressed-keeled, smooth on the keel, often villous at the throat; **Ligule** membranaceous, about 1.5 mm. long, rounded at the apex, ciliate; **Racemes** included at the base or usually long-exserted on hispidulous peduncles, cylindric, erect or curved, the rachis-joints between the upper spikelets (the awned portion) with a dense tuft of long nearly appressed chestnut-brown hairs, the sessile spikelets on the upper portion of the raceme, fertile and awned; **Fertile Spikelets** (the upper awned sessile spikelets) including the villous callus about 6 mm. long, pubescent, with a strong bent and twisted hairy awn 2-4′ long; **Staminate Spikelets** (including all the pedicellate spikelets and the awnless sessile spikelets below) 8-10 mm. long, staminate or sterile; **Glumes** about equal, the first acute, flattened, twisted, keeled near the margins, thick, green, many-nerved, papillose-hispid on the upper portion, especially toward the apex and near and along the margins, the second narrower, thinner, 3-nerved, sometimes sparsely papillose-hispid, sparsely ciliate on the margins and at the apex.

In dry sandy or rocky soil, western Texas to Arizona and Mexico. Spring-fall.

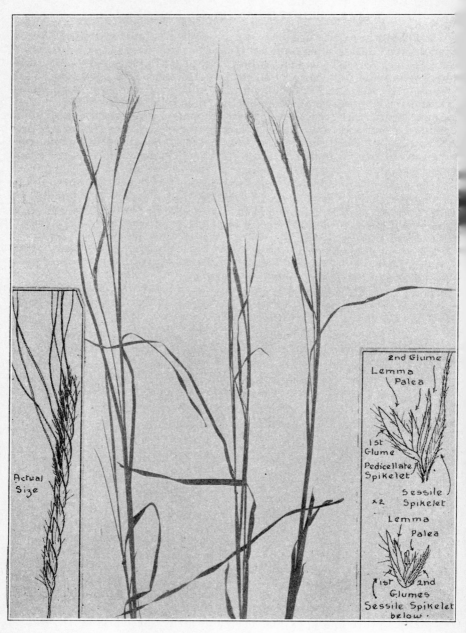

Actual
Size

2nd Glume
Lemma
Palea
1st
Glume
Pedicellate
Spikelet
Sessile
Spikelet
x2
Lemma
Palea
1st 2nd
Glumes
Sessile Spikelet
below.

HETEROPOGON CONTORTUS

105. TRACHYPOGON Nees (trăk-ĭ-pō'gŏn)

Spikelets in pairs, along a slender continuous rachis, one nearly sessile, staminate, awnless, the other pedicellate, perfect, long-awned, the pedicel of the perfect spikelet obliquely disarticulating near the base, forming a sharp barbed callus below the spikelet; **First Glume** firm-membranaceous, rounded on the back, several-nerved, obtuse; **Second Glume** firm, obscurely nerved; **Fertile Lemma** narrow, extending into a stout twisted and bent or flexuous awn; **Palea** obsolete; **Sessile Spikelet** persistent, as large as the fertile spikelet and similar but awnless.

Perennial, moderately tall grasses, with terminal spikelike racemes, these single or clustered. Species about seven, Mexico to South America, one extending into southern Arizona, New Mexico and Texas.

T. MONTUFARI (H. B. K.) Nees (mŏn-tū-fâr'ī) ; *T. polymorphus* var. *montufari* (H. B. K.) Hack.; *T. secundus* (Presl) Scribn.

Culms 2-3.5 feet tall, tufted, erect, rather slender, rarely branching, nodes bearded; **Blades** 6-17' long, those of the sterile shoots long, 2-6 mm. wide, flat or convolute toward the apex, especially the blades on the sterile shoots, attenuated into a long point, narrowed at the base, upper surface and margins rough and sometimes sparingly hirsute and papillose; **Sheaths** longer than the internodes, pubescent near the nodes, otherwise glabrous to pubescent; **Ligule** with erect sometimes sparsely hirsute auricles 8-25 mm. long at the summit, joined by a shorter membranaceous ligule; **Racemes** 4-7' long, exserted or slightly included at the base, solitary, terminal, somewhat unilateral, erect or slightly nodding, slender, rather loose, the rachis slightly hairy at the joints, otherwise glabrous, the lower spikelet of each pair with pedicel less than 1 mm. long, staminate, the upper with pedicel and villous callus about 4 mm. long, perfect; the **Perfect Spikelet** 6-8 mm. long; **Glumes,** the first as long as the spikelet, 7-11-nerved, cross-veined, very pubescent, the second equal or slightly shorter, mostly inclosed by the first glume, keeled, with margins inrolled appearing 3-keeled, ciliate on the margins and midnerve, otherwise glabrous except for a few scattered hairs; **Sterile Lemma** hyaline; **Lemma** membranaceous, with an awn commonly 1.5-2.5' long, twisted and geniculate about one-third the distance from the base, the hairs more numerous and longer below the bend; **Staminate Spikelet** similar, but the lemma awnless and 2-toothed.

In sandy soil, Texas to Arizona, south into Mexico. (Edna.) Late summer and fall.

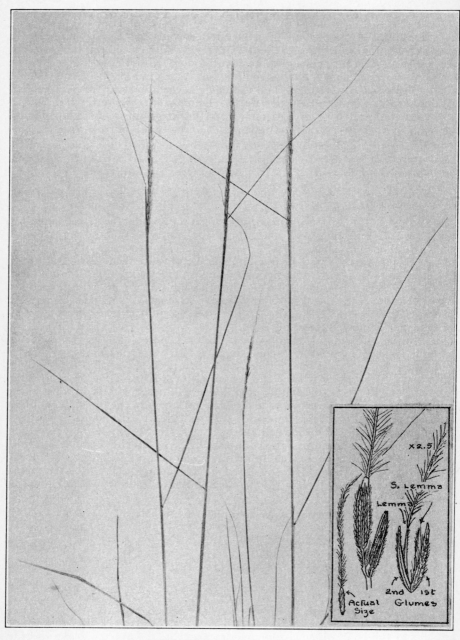

TRACHYPOGON MONTUFARI

106. ELYONURUS Humb. & Bonpl. (ĕl-ĭ-ō-nū'rŭs)

Spikelets in pairs along a somewhat tardily disarticulating rachis, the joints and pedicels thickened and parallel, the sessile spikelets appressed to the concave side, the pedicellate spikelet staminate, similar to the sessile one, both awnless, the pair falling with a joint of the rachis; **First Glume** firm, somewhat coriaceous, depressed on the back, the margins inflexed around the second glume, a line of balsam glands on the marginal nerves, the apex entire and acute or acuminate, or bifid with aristate teeth; **Second Glume** similar to the first; **Sterile** and **Fertile Lemmas** thin and hyaline; **Palea** obsolete.

Erect, moderately tall *perennials,* with solitary spikelike often woolly racemes. Species about 15, in the warmer regions of both hemispheres; two species extending into our southern states.

E. barbiculmis, a densely tufted plant, 2-3 feet tall, with conspicuously woolly racemes, is found in west Texas. *E. tripsacoides,* a loosely tufted plant, 3-4 feet tall, with inconspicuously hairy racemes, is found from Texas to Mexico and Florida.

RACEMES conspicuously woolly; culms villous below the nodes; rhizomes wanting. 1. E. barbiculmis
RACEMES inconspicuously hairy; culms glabrous; rhizomes present. 2. E. tripsacoides

1. E. BARBICULMIS Hack. (bär-bĭ-kŭl'mĭs).

Culms 1-3 feet tall, densely tufted, slender, rigid, villous below the nodes, a little lower scabrous, and lower yet glabrous, usually 3-4 nodes, the upper one or two bearing solitary branches with a single spike; **Blades** 1.5-8' long, 2 mm. or less wide, involute, those of the sterile shoots as much as a foot long, and flexuous at the tip, long-pilose on the margin and villous above near the base; **Sheaths** shorter than the internodes, loose, terete, ciliate on margins above; **Ligule** a dense row of stiff hairs; **Racemes** more or less pedunculate, 2-4' long, about 6 mm. thick, spikelets, pedicels and flat rachis densely villous; **Sessile Spikelets** 6-8 mm. long; **Glumes** lanceolate, flat on back, the first about 6-8 mm. long, 2-toothed, villous, obscurely 5-7-nerved, with a *balsam-bearing line along the lateral nerves,* the second about 5-6 mm. long, 3-nerved, sparsely hairy about the middle; **Sterile Lemma** and **Lemma** membranaceous, 3-4 mm. long, thin; **Palea** none; **Grain** light-brown, elliptical-lanceolate, flattened, acute; **Pedicellate Spikelet** staminate or neuter, smaller than the sessile ones.

Mesas and rocky hills, western Texas to Arizona and Mexico. Summer-fall.

2. E. TRIPSACOIDES Humb. & Bonpl. (trĭp-sȧ-koi'dēz).

Culms 2-4 feet tall, loosely tufted, erect, solid, branching above, from short rootstocks, smooth and glabrous or often pubescent near the nodes; **Blades** 1.5-20' long, the uppermost short, 1-5 mm. wide, flat below, narrowed into a long involute point, usually densely hirsute on the upper surface at the base, otherwise glabrous; **Sheaths,** the upper mostly shorter and the lower longer than the internodes, somewhat flattened, rather loose, narrowed gradually toward the summit into the blade, glabrous, or a few rather long hairs scattered over the surface, especially along the margins, or the lower from sparsely to densely papillose-hirsute; **Ligule** membranaceous, very short, densely short-ciliate; **Racemes** 2-5' long, narrow, 2-3 mm. thick, subcylindric, single, mostly long-exserted, **axillary**

sometimes included at the base, the rachis internodes about 2.5 mm. long, flattened, pubescent except on the side next to the spikelet, the spikelet overlapping; **Sessile Spikelet** 6-8 mm. long, on a flattened pubescent callus, widened above, about 1.5 mm. long; **Glumes,** the first about 6-7 mm. long, lanceolate, nearly flat, acute and entire, or deeply bifid at the apex, hispid-ciliate on the prominent (wing-like) nerves, also 5-7 less prominent nerves, with *balsam-bearing glands along the lateral nerves,* the second somewhat shorter, obscurely 3-nerved, minutely hispid on the keel; **Sterile Lemma** and **Lemma** lanceolate, acute, hyaline, shorter than the second glume; **Palea** wanting; **Pedicellate Spikelet** staminate, similar, but all parts smaller, the first glume being acute and less hispid on the margins, the hairy pedicels about 3 mm. long.

Sandy open ground and roads, Texas and Mexico to Florida. Summer-fall.

ELYONURUS BARBICULMIS

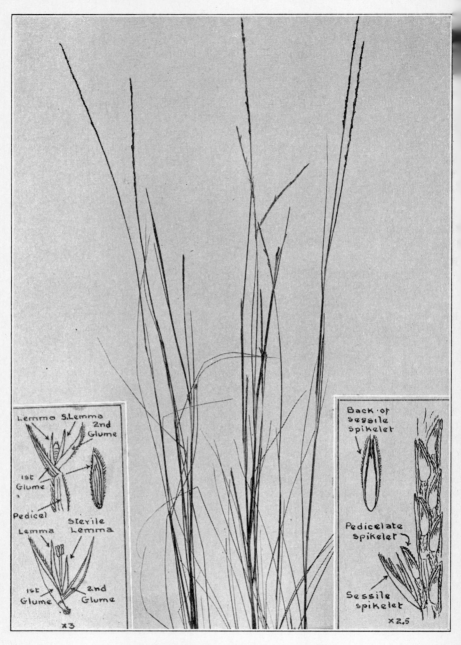

ELYONURUS TRIPSACOIDES

107. MANISURIS L. (măn-ĭ-sū′rĭs)

Spikelets awnless, in pairs at the nodes of a thickened articulate achis, one sessile and fertile, the other pedicellate and sterile, the pedicel hickened and appressed to the rachis, the sessile spikelet fitting closely gainst the rachis, forming a cylindric or subcylindric raceme; **Glumes** btuse, awnless, the first coriaceous, fitting over the hollow containing he spikelet, the second less coriaceous than the first; **Sterile Lemma,** **Fertile Lemma** and **Palea** thin and hyaline, inclosed within the glumes; **Pedicellate Spikelet** reduced, often rudimentary.

Perennial slender, moderately tall or tall grasses, with usually numerous smooth cylindric or flattened spikes, single on the culms and branches. Species about 30, in the warm regions of both hemispheres; 5 in southern United States, 3 in Texas.

M. fasciculata, with flattened racemes, is very rare, the other two species with cylindric racemes having the first glumes variously marked, those of *M. cylindrica* being somewhat pitted, and those of *M. rugosa* prominently transversely wrinkled or ridged.

RACEMES CYLINDRIC.
  FIRST glume of the sessile spikelet pitted; culms round, sheaths narrow, round; from horizontal rootstocks.   1. M. cylindrica
  FIRST glume of the sessile spikelet prominently transverse-rugose or ridged; culms flattened, sheaths broad, compressed-keeled.   2. M. rugosa
RACEMES FLATTENED.
  FIRST glume of the sessile spikelet neither pitted nor rugose; culms and sheaths flattened and compressed-keeled.   3. M. fasciculata

1. M. CYLINDRICA (Michx.) Kuntze (sĭ-lĭn′drĭ-kà) ; *Rottboellia cylindrica* (Michx.) Torr. not Willd.; *Coelorachis cylindrica* (Michx.) Nash; Pitted Joint-grass.

Culms 1-3.5 feet tall, tufted, slender, rounded, from a short rootstock; **Blades** 14′ long or less, the upper as short as 1.5′, 2-3 mm. wide, flat, soon becoming involute; **Sheaths** shorter than the internodes, round or slightly flattened; **Ligule** membranaceous, short; **Racemes** purple, solitary on the culm and branches, 3.5-7′ long, 2-3 mm. thick, exserted, cylindric, straight or curved, on a long slender peduncle, the rachis barely if at all contracted at the nodes, the rachis-joints readily disarticulating; **Sessile Spikelets,** 5-7 mm. long (with a callus about 1 mm. long) as long as or longer than the rachis-joint, fertile; **Glumes** subequal, the second slightly shorter, the first hardened, with seven obscure nerves, obtuse, bifid, longitudinally pitted, the second less hardened, 3-nerved, irregular in shape, acute, pale; **Sterile** and **Fertile Lemmas** hyaline, 3-4 mm. long, acute; **Palea** slightly shorter, acute; **Grains** slightly over 2 mm. long and 1 mm. thick, oblong, rugose; **Pedicellate Spikelet** sterile, rudimentary, consisting of two small glumes, the pedicel thickened, linear, slightly shorter than and curved around the margin of the sessile spikelet.

In sandy soil, often in pine woods, Texas to Florida, Georgia, Missouri and Oklahoma. Summer.

2. M. RUGOSA (Nutt.) Kuntze (rū-gō′sà) ; *Rottboellia rugosa* Nutt.; *R. corrugata* Baldw.; *Coelorachis rugosa* (Nutt.) Nash.

Culms 2-4.5 feet tall, tufted, stout, flattened, freely branching above, the branches spreading; **Blades** 18′ long or less, the upper very short, 2-7 mm. wide, flat, acuminate; **Sheaths,** the upper shorter than the internodes, broad, flattened, keeled, loose; **Ligule** about 1 mm. long, a ciliate membrane; **Racemes** numerous, included at the base or more or less exserted the lateral ones on short clustered branches in the axils of the blades 1.5-2.5′ long, 3-4 mm. in diameter, straight or somewhat curved, the rachis joints narrowed toward the base, puberulent; **Sessile Spikelet** 3.2-4 mm long, equaling or slightly exceeding the rachis-joint, a swollen spongy ring at the base; **Glumes** subequal, the second slightly shorter, the first oblong ovate, 3.2-4 mm. long, strongly transversely rugose, much elevated, often extending all the way across the width of the glume, the *longitudinal ridges often prominent;* **Sterile Lemma** slightly shorter than the glumes exceeding the obtuse **Lemma,** which is about equaled by the **Palea Pedicellate Spikelet** usually less than 2 mm. long, on a pedicel less than the length of the sessile spikelet.

Low, wet pine barrens, coastal plains, Texas and Florida, Maryland to New Jersey. (Jefferson.)   Summer and fall.

3. M. FASCICULATA (Lam.) Hitchc. (fă-sĭk-ū-lā′tà) ; *Rottboellia fascicu-
    lata* Lam.; *Hemarthria fasciculata* (Lam.) Kunth. Has been confused
    with *M. compressa* (L. f.) Kuntze.

Culms 2-4 feet tall, rather robust, angular or flattened, ascending from a long creeping base, freely branching; **Blades** 1.5-3.5′ long, 3-8 mm. wide, mostly flat; **Sheaths** short, shorter than the internodes, keeled, ciliate, loose; **Ligule** a very thin membrane about 1 mm. long, minutely fringed; **Racemes** numerous, fascicled from several of the upper sheaths of the culm and its branches, spreading, flattened, not rigid, 2-4′ long, the rachis-joints striate and tardily disarticulating; **Sessile Spikelet** flattened, 4.5-5.5 mm. long, slightly exceeding the rachis-joint; **Glumes** coriaceous, many-nerved, about equal; **Sterile Lemma** about 3 mm. long; **Lemma** about 3.5 mm. long; **Palea** about half as long as the lemma; **Pedicellate Spikelet** about 4 mm. long, or including the awn-tipped point about as long as the sessile spikelet, the pedicel appressed to the rachis, similar to the sessile spikelet.

Ponds and ditches and along bank of the Rio Grande at Laredo, September, 1884. Fall.

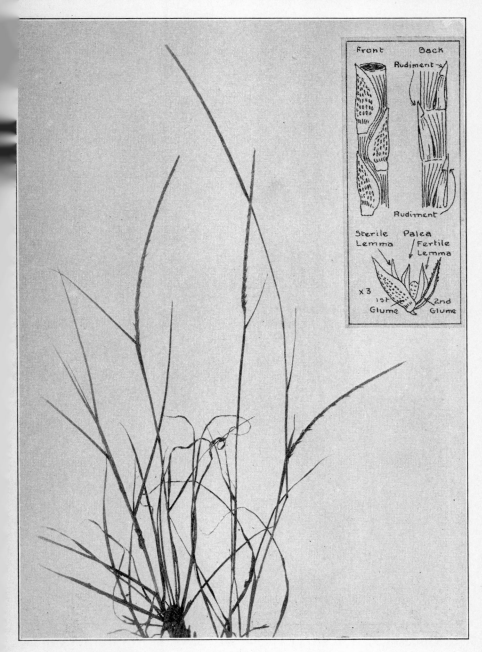

MANISURIS CYLINDRICA; Pitted Joint-grass

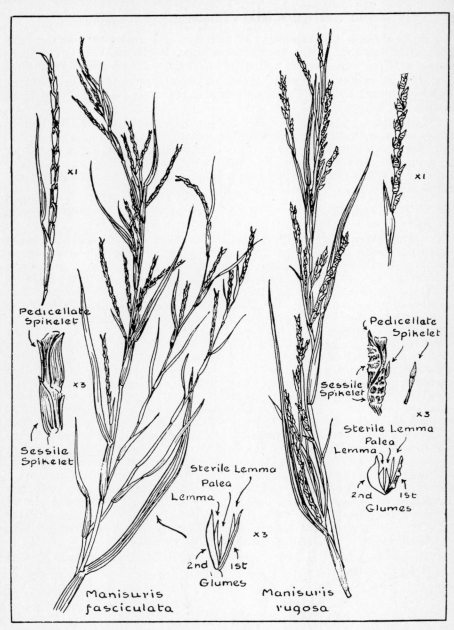

Pedicellate
Spikelet

×3

Sessile
Spikelet

Sterile Lemma
Palea
Lemma

×3

2nd   1st
Glumes

Manisuris
fasciculata

×1

Pedicellate
Spikelet

Sessile
Spikelet

×3

Sterile Lemma
Palea
Lemma

2nd   1st
Glumes

Manisuris
rugosa

×1

MANISURIS FASCICULATA to the left; **MANISURIS RUGOSA** to the
right

108. EREMOCHLOA Munro. (ĕr-ē-mŏk'lō-à)

In this genus the racemes are solitary and spikelets awnless, the pedicellate spikelets rudimentary or reduced to the pedicels. They are ornamental or lawn grasses, natives of southeastern Asia and East Indies.

Our one species, lazy man's grass, has been introduced by Agricultural and Mechanical College, at Angleton, R. H. Stanfield, Supt. of Substation No. 3.

Lazy man's grass is a *creeping perennial,* the stolons, culms, and short leaves and sheaths forming a dense mat, the flowering culms commonly 2-4' tall, bearing a solitary raceme. It is often used as a lawn grass, and as the upright culms are short it does not need mowing very often, hence lazy man's grass, and because of the resemblance of the stolons to a centipede, hence also the name centipede grass.

E. OPHIUROIDES (Munro) Hack. (ŏf-ĭ-ū-roi'dēz) ; CENTIPEDE GRASS, LAZY MAN'S GRASS.

Culms extensively creeping, slender, branching, rooting at the sometimes pubescent nodes, erect or ascending, the slender flowering culms mostly 2-4' tall, the stolons, leaves and short-crowded sheaths forming a dense tangled mat ; **Blades** 4-55 mm. commonly 15-30 mm. long, 2-4 mm. wide, flat, lanceolate, rounded at the base, sparsely ciliate and papillose on the margins, especially toward the base, numerous, crowded on the stolons and at the base of the flowering culms ; **Sheaths** much overlapping, pubescent at the throat ; **Ligule** a membranaceous line, short-ciliate ; **Racemes** solitary, spikelike, brownish or purplish, finally long-exserted, commonly 1-2' long, about 2 mm. thick, somewhat flattened, falcate, the spikelets in two rows, alternate, in pairs, at each joint of the articulate rachis (the rachis-joints about two-thirds at long as the spikelet), one sessile and perfect, the other pediceled with a very small rudimentary spikelet, pedicel and rudiment together about as long as the sessile spikelet ; **Sessile Spikelets** 3-3.5 mm. long, oblong, brownish to tawny ; **Glumes** about equal, the second often slightly shorter, indurate, the lower margins inrolled, glabrous and smooth, the first broad, flattened dorsally, winged, broadly so toward the erose apex, the inflexed margins sometimes toothed, the body of the glume about 7-nerved, the broad wings at the apex with several green nerves, the second lanceolate, acute, nerves obscure ; **Sterile Lemma** and its nearly equal palea, nearly as long as the second glume, both hyaline ; **Lemma** nearly as long as the glumes, with palea slightly shorter, both hyaline ; **Stamens** 3 ; **Grain** about 1.7 mm. long, 0.7 mm. thick, narrowly elliptic ; **Pedicellate Spikelet** rudimentary.

Introduced by A. and M. College at Angleton. (Experimental Station No. 3, R. H. Stanfield, Supt.) Fall.

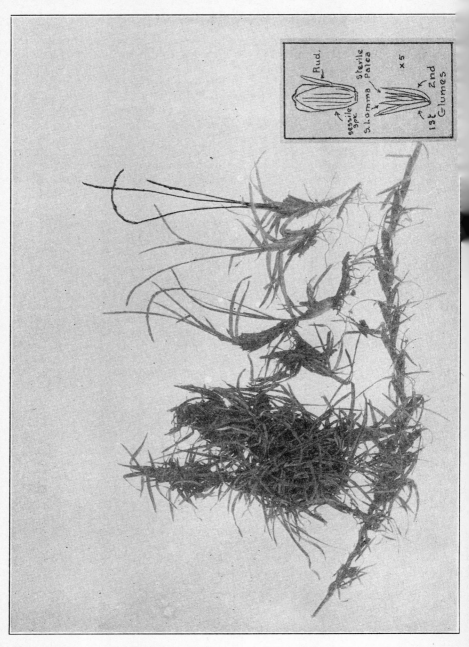

EREMOCHLOA OPHIUROIDES; Lazy Man's Grass, Centipede Grass

109. HACKELOCHLOA Kuntze (hăk-ē-lŏk′lō-à)
(Rytilix Raf.)

Spikelets awnless, in pairs, the rachis-joint and pedicel grown together, the two clasped between the edges of the globose alveolate first glume of the sessile spikelet; **Pedicellate Spikelet** conspicuous, staminate.

A much-branched *annual* with flat blades, the numerous spikes single and more or less inclosed in the sheathing bract, these somewhat clustered in the axils of the foliage leaves. Species one, in the tropical regions of the world, extending into the United States from Florida to Arizona. The little pitted globose spikelets are very characteristic.

H. GRANULARIS (L.) Kuntze (grăn-ū-lăr′ĭs) ; *Rytilix granularis* (L.) Skeels; *Manisuris granularis* (L.) Swartz; LIZARD-TAIL GRASS.

Although this species has not been collected in Texas it will probably be found.

It is a slender plant 1-3 feet tall, with blades 2.5-7′ long and 4-12 mm. wide, both blades and sheaths papillose-hirsute. The racemes are 15-25 mm. long and about 1.5 mm. in diameter, crowded with the small sessile and pedicellate spikelets.

In cultivated and waste places, Florida to Arizona. Summer and fall.

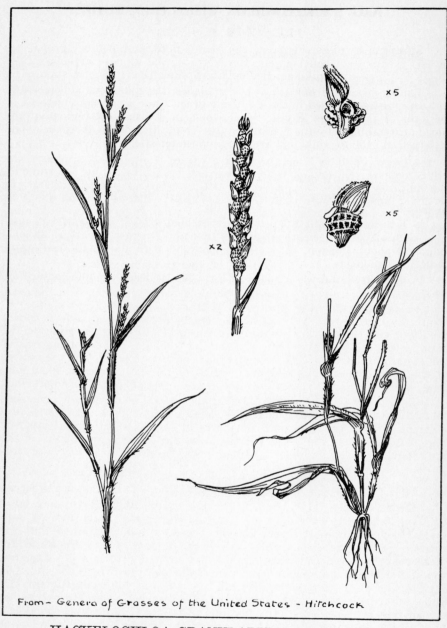

From— Genera of Grasses of the United States - Hitchcock

HACKELOCHLOA GRANULARIS; Lizard-tail Grass

XIII. TRIPSACEAE, THE CORN TRIBE

110. COIX L. (kō′ĭks)

Spikelets unisexual; **Staminate** spikelets 2-flowered, in twos or threes on the continuous rachis, the normal group consisting of a pair of sessile spikelets with a single pedicellate spikelet between, the latter sometimes reduced to a pedicel or wanting; **Glumes** membranaceous, obscurely nerved; **Lemma** hyaline, nearly as long as the glumes, awnless, 5-nerved; **Palea** hyaline, a little shorter than the lemma; **Stamens** 3; **Pistillate** spikelets 3 together, 1 fertile and 2 sterile at the base of the inflorescence; **Fertile** spikelet consisting of 2 glumes, 1 sterile lemma, a fertile lemma, and a palea; **Glumes** several-nerved, hyaline below, chartaceous in the upper narrow pointed part, the first very broad, infolding the spikelet, the margins infolded beyond the 2 lateral stronger pair of nerves, the second glume narrower than the first, keeled; **Sterile Lemma** about as long as the second glume, similar in shape but a little narrower, hyaline below, somewhat chartaceous above; **Fertile Lemma** hyaline, narrow, somewhat shorter than the sterile lemma; **Palea** hyaline, narrow, shorter than the lemma; **Sterile** spikelets consisting of a single narrow tubular glume as long as the fertile spikelet, somewhat chartaceous.

Tall branched grasses with broad flat blades, the monoecious inflorescence numerous on long stout peduncles, these clustered in the axils of the leaves, each inflorescence consisting of an ovate or oval, pearly-white or drab, beadlike, very hard, tardily deciduous involucre (much modified sheathing bract) containing the pistillate lower portion of the inflorescence, the points of the pistillate spikelets and the slender axis of the staminate portion of the inflorescence protruding through the orifice at the apex, the staminate upper portion of the inflorescence 20-40 mm. long, soon deciduous, consisting of several clusters of staminate spikelets.

Coix lachryma-jobi is cultivated in all tropical countries for ornament and has escaped into waste places, especially around dwellings. It is also cultivated in greenhouses and sometimes in the open in warm temperate regions. The name, Job's tears, comes from the fancied resemblance of the fruit to tears. The fruits, or so-called seeds, are used for a variety of purposes, such as beads, and for rosaries.

C. LACHRYMA-JOBI L. (lăk-rĭ-mȧ-jō′bī); Job's Tears, Christ's Tears.

Culms 1-3 feet tall, tufted, branching, erect; **Blades** 5-10′ long more or less, 15-28 mm. wide more or less, flat, lanceolate, narrowed at both ends, the apex pointed; **Upper Sheaths** shorter, the lower longer than the internodes; **Ligule** membranaceous, about 1 mm. long; **Pistillate Inflorescence** inclosed in a beadlike involucre about 8-10 mm. in diameter, ovoid, the beads white or bluish-white; **Spikelets,** the two sterile spikelets on one side of the fertile spikelet, all about 9 mm. long; **Fertile** spikelet fully described above; the **Staminate Inflorescence** protruding through the orifice at the apex of the involucre, the staminate upper portion a spikelike raceme, usually 20-40 mm. long, one or more of the spikelets at the base with one of the two flowers often fertile; **Spikelets** about 8 mm. long, oblong, green; **Glumes** subequal, about 8 mm. long, broad, obscurely many-nerved, the first subacute, the second acute (fully described above).

Waste places and gardens, south Texas and Mexico. Spring and summer.

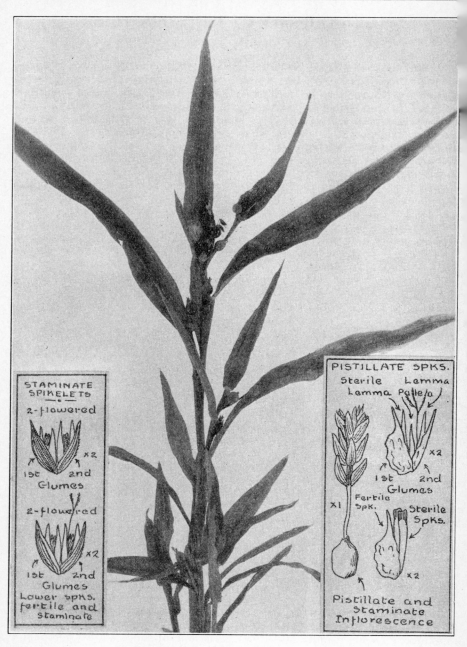

COIX LACHRYMA-JOBI; JOB'S TEARS

111. TRIPSACUM L. (trĭp′sȧ-kŭm)

Spikelets unisexual; **Staminate** spikelets 2-flowered, in pairs on one ide of a continuous rachis, one sessile, the other sessile or pedicellate, imilar to those of *Zea*, the glumes firmer; **Pistillate** spikelets single and n opposite sides at each joint of the thick hard articulate lower part of he same rachis, sunken in hollows in the joints, consisting of one perfect loret and a sterile lemma; **First Glume** coriaceous, nearly infolding the pikelet, fitting into and closing the hollow of the rachis; **Second Glume** imilar to the first but smaller, infolding the remainder of the spikelet; **Sterile Lemma, Fertile Lemma** and **Palea** very thin and hyaline, these progressively smaller.

Robust *perennial* grasses, with usually broad flat blades and monoecious terminal and axillary inflorescences of 1-3 spikes, the pistillate part below, breaking up into bony seedlike joints, the staminate above on the same rachis, deciduous as a whole. Species about seven, all American, extending from the middle United States to northern South America; three species in the United States, one in Texas.

Our only species, *T. dactyloides*, known as Gama grass, is a robust plant, 3-6 feet tall, with blades 10-30 mm. wide, the terminal spikes mostly in threes and the axillary mostly solitary. It is found here and there from Texas and Florida north to Kansas and Connecticut, mostly confined to swamps and banks of streams.

T. floridanum Porter, with blades usually less than 10 mm. wide, and a solitary terminal spike, is found in Florida and has been reported in Texas, but there are no specimens from Texas in the National Herbarium at Washington; *T. lanceolatum* Rupr. (*T. lemmoni* Vasey) with pilose lower sheaths, is found in Arizona.

1. T. DACTYLOIDES (L.) L. (dăk-tĭ-loi′dēz); EASTERN GAMA-GRASS.

Culms commonly 3-6 feet tall, robust, flattened, tufted, from stout rootstocks; **Blades** 5-16′ or the blades of the sterile shoots as much as 30′ long, 10-30 mm. wide, flat, long-acuminate, midrib large, both surfaces and margins scabrous, glabrous and sparsely hispid on the upper surface, especially below; **Sheaths** flattened, shorter than the internodes; **Ligule** a ring of short ciliate hairs; **Spikes,** the terminal mostly in threes, sometimes 1 or 2, the lateral usually solitary, the rigid lower one-fourth to one-third **Pistillate,** the upper part **Staminate; Pistillate Spikelets** 8-10 mm. long, narrowly ovate; **Glumes,** the first thick, hard, polished, ovate, many nerves visible from inside, acute, closing the ovate mouth of the excavation and fitting around the balance of the spikelet, the second glume similar, but thinner, and also folded around the sterile lemma and perfect floret; **Sterile Lemma** hyaline, nearly as long as the glumes; **Fertile Lemma** hyaline, with a hyaline palea about as long; **Stigmas** exserted as much as an inch; **Staminate Spikelets** 2-flowered, 6-11 mm. long, about 2 mm. wide, oblong, similar to the staminate spikelets on the tassels of corn, exceeding the internodes, often purple; **Glumes** about equal, the first 2-keeled, scabrous on the keel, about 9-nerved, rigid, acute, the second membranaceous, about 5-nerved, the two lemmas and the paleas about equal, each with three stamens.

In swamps and along banks of streams, Texas to Florida, north to Iowa, Nebraska and Connecticut. Spring-summer.

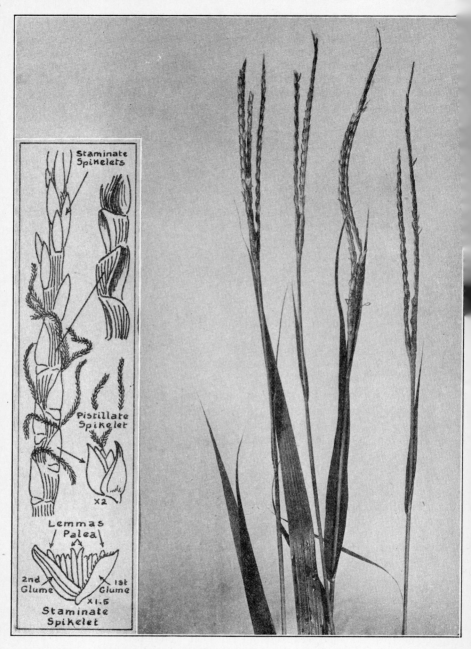

TRIPSACUM DACTYLOIDES; Gama Grass

112. EUCHLAENA Schrad. (ū-klē′nȧ)

Staminate Spikelets as in *Zea*; **Pistillate Spikelets** single, on opposite ides, sunk in cavities in the hardened joints of an obliquely articulate achis, the indurate **First Glume** covering the cavity; **Second Glume** mem-iranaceous, the **Lemmas** hyaline. **Spikes** infolded in foliaceous bracts or iusks, 2-to-several of these together inclosed in the leaf sheaths.

Two species, natives of Mexico, cultivated occasionally in the southern tates.

These species have the aspect of corn, and grow in large clumps. *E. mexicana,* known as teosinte, is cultivated chiefly for soiling. *E. perennis,* a freely branching perennial from creeping rootstocks, is being cultivated by R. H. Stanfield, Supt. of Substation of A. and M. College at Angleton, Texas. The author's knowledge of this grass is confined to one large clump. It may grow stouter and taller.

ANNUAL; tall plant, sometimes 15 feet tall, branching at the base.
1. E. mexicana
PERENNIAL; not so tall, freely branching, from creeping rootstocks.
2. E. perennis

1. E. MEXICANA Schrad. (mĕks-ĭ-kā′nȧ); *Reana luxurians* Durieu; TEOSINTE.

The writer being unable to collect teosinte, the artist copied the draw-ing of the plant and spikes as well as the spikelets from *the Genera of Grasses of the United States* by Hitchcock. It is not only a taller and stouter plant, but has longer and many more racemes in the staminate in-florescence than *E. perennis.*

2. E. PERENNIS Hitchc. (pĕr-ĕn′ĭs).

Culms 3-5 feet tall, erect, solid, as much as 1′ thick at the base, from creeping rhizomes, rooting at the lower nodes, freely branching; **Blades** 1-2 feet long more or less, 1′ wide more or less, flat, lanceolate, cordate at the base, smooth or rough on both surfaces, rough on the margin, the upper surface sparsely papillose, with rather stiff hairs from the papillae; **Sheaths** mostly shorter than the internodes, more or less papillose, cross-veined; **Ligule** membranaceous, about 1 mm. long; **Pistillate Inflorescence** usually of two axillary spikes, mostly inclosed in the sheaths, the spikes 30-35 mm. long, with about six joints, on peduncles 1-2′ long, each inclosed in thin bracts, the rachis-joints 6-8 mm. long; **Spikelets** 6-8 mm. long, usually slightly shorter than the rachis-joints; **Glumes** about equal, the first broad, hardened, thick, abruptly acute, inclosing the balance of the spikelet, the second much thinner, narrower and acuminate, rather abruptly pointed; **Sterile Lemma** about two-thirds as long as the glumes, hyaline; **Lemma** and **Palea** about equal, hyaline; **Grain** about 4 mm. long, 2.5 mm. thick, ovate, mucronate; **Staminate Inflorescence,** aggregate terminal racemes much like those of corn, purplish, 1-4′ commonly 2-4′ long, the angled rachis hispid-ciliate; **Spikelets** 6-9 mm. long, the pedicel of one of the pair about 2.5 mm. long; **Glumes,** the first slightly longer, subobtuse, hispid-ciliate toward the apex, flattened on the back, many-nerved, the second acute, the lemmas and paleas about equal to the second glume, all hyaline.

In cultivation at Experimental Station at Angleton. (Jalisco, Mexico.) Fall.

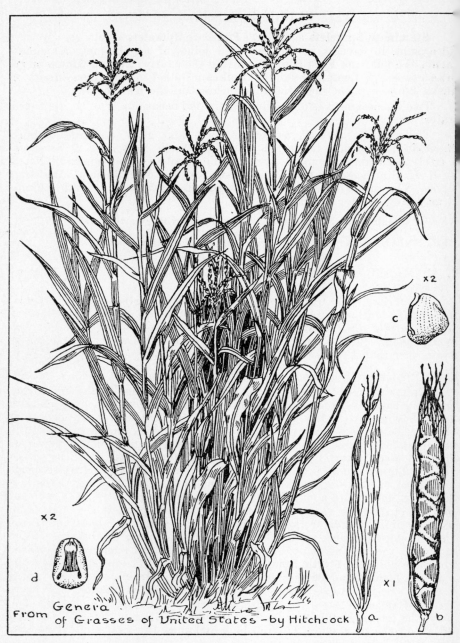

EUCHLAENA MEXICANA; Teosinte. Sketch of plant much reduced;
PISTILLATE INFLORESCENCE inclosed in bract (a) and with portion
of bract removed (b); lateral view of joint of rachis and the fertile spikelet
(c); dorsal view of same, showing first glume (d).

EUCHLAENA PERENNIS; STAMINATE spikelets on the left,
PISTILLATE racemes and spikelet on the right

113. ZEA L. (zē'ȧ)
(Maize, Indian Corn)

Spikelets unisexual; **Staminate** spikelets 2-flowered, in pairs, on one side of a continuous rachis, one nearly sessile, the other pedicellate; **Glumes** membranaceous, acute; **Lemma** and **Palea** hyaline; **Pistillate** spikelets sessile, in pairs, consisting of one fertile floret and one sterile floret, the latter sometimes developed as a second fertile floret; **Glumes** broad, rounded or emarginate at apex; **Sterile Lemma** similar to the fertile, the palea present; **Style** very long and slender, stigmatic along both sides well toward the base.

A tall *annual* grass, with broad, conspicuously distichous blades, *monoecious inflorescence*, the *staminate flowers* in spikelike racemes, these numerous, forming large spreading panicles (tassels) terminating the stems, the *pistillate inflorescence* in the axils of the leaves, the spikelets in 8 to 16 or even as many as 30 rows on a thickened almost woody axis (cob), the whole inclosed in numerous large foliaceous bracts (husks), the long styles (silk) protruding from the top of a silky mass of threads. In the common varieties of corn the floral bracts are much shorter than the kernel and remain on the cob when the kernels are shelled. Species one.

Z. MAYS L. (māz).

In the United States Z. *mays* is usually called corn; in Europe and sometimes in America, especially in literature, it is called maize. Corn is one of the important economic plants of the world, being cultivated for food for man and domestic animals and for forage. It originated in America, probably on the Mexican Plateau, and was cultivated from prehistoric times by the early races of American aborigines, from Peru to middle North America. Several races of corn are grown in the United States, the most important being dent, the common commercial field sort, flint, sweet, and pop. Pod corn (Z. *mays* var. *tunicata* Larr.), occasionally cultivated as a curiosity, is a variety in which each kernel is developed in the elongated floral bracts. A variety with variegated leaves (Z. *mays* var. *japonica* Körn.) is cultivated for ornament.

The culms of field corn are robust, erect, tufted, usually 3-8 feet tall, the flat blades from 12-40' long, and 1.5-5' wide, the racemes of the tassel numerous, mostly 6-10' long, the central one of the main axis sometimes 18' long. It bears an ear of corn in one or more axils of the leaves, commonly in one or two of the axils, the ear usually 6-12' long and 1.5-2' thick. There are many varieties of corn, differing in size of culms, blades, tassels and ears. As Indian corn is a common plant, and Mr. Hitchcock has fully described the inflorescences and spikelets, further description is unnecessary.

Cultivated throughout the United States and many other countries. Summer.

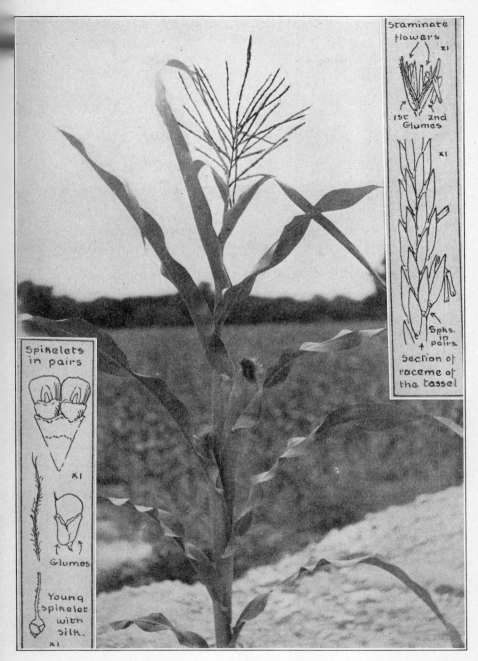

ZEA MAYS; Indian Corn, Maize

BIBLIOGRAPHY

BEAL, Grasses of North America. Vol. I, 1887. Vol. II, 1896 (systematic portion). Descriptions.

BAILEY, Cyclopedia of American Agriculture, Vol. II, 365-376. 1907. Grasses, by Hitchcock.

BAILEY, Cyclopedia of American Horticulture. Grasses, by Hitchcock, the genera alphabetically arranged.

BRITTON & BROWN, Illustrated Flora of the Northern United States, Canada and the British Possessions, 2d edition. Vol. I, 1913. Descriptions.

CHASE, North American Species of Paspalum. Contr. U. S. Natl. Herb. v. 28, pt. 1. 1929.

CHASE, First Book of Grasses, the structure of grasses explained for beginners. Macmillan 1922.

CLEMENTS AND CLEMENTS, Flower Families and Ancestors. The H. W. Wilson Co. 1928.

CLEMENTS AND CLEMENTS, Rocky Mountain Flowers. The H. W. Wilson Co. 1928.

COULTER & NELSON, New Manual of Botany of the Central Rocky Mountains. 1909. Descriptions.

COULTER, Botany of Western Texas (Contr. U. S. Natl. Herb. V. 2:347-568; grasses in part 3. 1894). Descriptions.

FRANCIS, Book of Grasses, an illustrated guide to the common grasses and the most common of the rushes and sedges. Doubleday, Page & Co. 1912.

GRAY, New Manual of Botany, 7th edition. A handbook of the flowering plants and ferns of the central and northeastern United States and adjacent Canada, by Robinson & Fernald. Descriptions. American Book Co. 1908.

GRIFFITHS, Grama Grasses Contr. U. S. Natl. Herb. V. 14, pt. 3. 1912.

HITCHCOCK, North American Species of Panicum. Contr. U. S. Natl. Herb. v. 15. 1910.

HITCHCOCK, Revisions of North American Grasses. (Contains Brachiaria and Cenchrus.) Contr. U. S. Natl. Herb. v. 22, pt. 1. 1920.

HITCHCOCK, Revisions of North American Grasses (containing Echinochloa and Chaetochloa). Contr. U. S. Natl. Herb. v. 22, pt. 3. 1920.

HITCHCOCK, North American Species of Aristida. Contr. U. S. Natl. Herb. v. 22, pt. 7. 1924.

HITCHCOCK, North American species of Stipa. Contr. U. S. Natl. Herb. v. 24, pt. 7. 1925.

HITCHCOCK, Genera of Grasses of the United States, with special reference to the economic species. U. S. Dept. Agr. Bull. 772. 1920 (Washington Superintendent of Documents).

HITCHCOCK, Text Book of Grasses, with special reference to the economic species of the U. S. N. Y., Macmillan, 1914.

RYDBERG, Flora of the Rocky Mountains and Adjacent Plains, 1922. Descriptions.

SMALL, Flora of the Southeastern United States, 1913. Descriptions.

WOOTON & STANDLEY, The Grasses and Grass-like Plants of New Mexico (N. Mex. Agr. Exp. Sta. Bull. 81. 1911). Annotated list.

INDEX

Italic words signify synonyms. Boldface figures indicate tribes, genera, species and other groups. Italic figures indicate photographs and drawings. Ordinary figures are used for all other purposes.

Abbreviations and Symbols XII
Achyrodes 116
Aegopogon rigidisetus 431
Agave lechuguilla 425
Agropyron 157-62 167
  arizonicum **158** *160* 157
  divergens 157
  occidentale 158
  pauciflorum **158** *160* 157
  pseudorepens 158
  repens **158** *161*
  smithii **158** *162* 167
  spicatum 157 *160* 158
  tenerum 158
Agrostideae 206-356
  XXXV XL
Agrostis 210-18 234 278
  XXXI XXXVII XL
  alba **211** *214* 210
  arachnoides 213
  asperifolia 212
  bromoides 333
  elliottiana **213** *218* 210
  exarata **212** *218* 210
  grandis 212
  hiemalis **212** *217* 210 211
  lutosa 225
  maritima 212
  palustris **212** 210 211
  perennans **212** *215*
  retrofracta **211** *215* 210
  scabra 212
  verticillata **211** *216* 210
Agrostoidia 575
Agrostology IX
  Descriptive Systematic IX
  Economic IX XI
  Systematic IX X
Aira 201-2 XL
  capillaris **201** *202*
Alfalfa IX
Alkali saccaton *302* 285
Alopecurus 223-4 XLI
  carolinianus **223** *224*
  geniculatus 223
  ramosus 223
Amphilophis 712
  barbinodis 717
Anastrophus 509
  compressus 509
  furcatus 510
Anatherum 735
  zizanioides 735
Andropogon 712-34 735
  XXXI
  annulatus **721** *723*
  argyraeus 719
  barbinodis **717** *728* 712

chrysocomus **720**
cirratus **715** *723 725* 712
divergens **720** *733*
drummondii 737
elliottii **718** *731*
elliottii var. gracilior **719**
exaristatus **717** *727* 712
furcatus **719** *733* 712
glomeratus **717** *729* 718
hallii **720** *734* 712
hirtiflorus **715** *724* 712
hirtiflorus var. feensis **715** *724*
ischaemum **720** *723*
littoralis **714** *723* 712
muricatus 735
perforatus **716** *726* 712
provincialis 719
saccharoides **716** *727* 712 717
scoparius **714** *722* 712
scoparius var. neomexicanus **714**
scoparius var. villosissimus **714**
sorghum 738
sorghum var. *sudanensis* 737
tener **716** *725* 712
ternarius **719** *732*
torreyanus 716
virginicus **718** *730*
virginicus var. hirsutior **718**
Andropogoneae 697-762
  XXXI XXXVI XLV XLVI
Angustifolia 615 553
Anthaenantia 476-8 486
  rufa **476** *478* 477
  villosa **476** *478*
Anthoxanthus 452-3
  aristatum **452** *453*
  odoratum **452** *453*
Aparejo-grass *270* 245
Aquatic Tribe **471-5**
Aristida 327-56 XLI
  adscensionis **333** *348* 327
  affinis **340** *347* 328
  arizonica **339** *354* 328
  barbata **334** *350* 327-8 335
  bromoides 333
  chapmaniana 340
  desmantha **330** *341* 327
  dichotoma **331** *345* 327
  dispersa 333
  divaricata **334** *351* 327 335
  divergens 331
  fasciculata 333

fendleriana **337** *342* 328
glauca **336** *352* 328
gracilis 333
havardii 334
intermedia **334** *349* 327
lanata 338
lanosa **338** *354* 328
longespica **333** *348* 327 340
longiseta **338** *356* 328
longiseta var. rariflora **338** 328
longiseta var. robusta **338** 328
oligantha **332** *346* 327
palustris 340
pansa **335** *350* 328
purpurea **336** *353* 328
purpurea var. *fendleri* 337
purpurea var. laxiflora **337** 338
purpurea var. micrantha **336** *353*
purpurascens **339** *355* 328 340
ramosissima **332** *347* 327
reverchoni 336
schiedeana **330** *343* 327
schiedeana var. *minor* 331
spiciformis **335** *345* 328
ternipes divergens 331
ternipes var. minor **331** *344* 327
tuberculosa **330** *342* 327
vaseyi 336
virgata **340** *354* 328
wrightii **337** *348* 328
Arrow-grass 339
Arundinaria 1-4 XXXVII
  gigantea **1** *2*
  japonica 1 XXXVII
  macrosperma 1
  tecta **1**
Arundo 108-10 XXXVIII
  donax **108** *110* 471
  donax var. versicolor **108**
Aspris 201
  capillaris 201
Atheropogon curtipendulus 430
Avena 199-200
  fatua 199
  sativa **199** *200*
Aveneae 191-205 XXXV XL
Axonopus 509-12 553
  compressus **509** *511*
  furcatus **510** *512*

Bahia Grass 521
Bamboo Tribe 1-4 XXXIV
Bamboos XXXVII
Bambos bambos XXXVII
Bambusa 1 *3 4*
  nana 1 *3*
  vulgaris XXXVII
Bambuseae 1-4 XXXIII
  XXXIV XXXVII
Barley X
  beardless *182* 180
  cultivated *182* 179
  foxtail 180-1
  little *183* 180
  meadow *184* 180
  mouse 181
  sea *185* 181
  squirrel-tail *186* 180
  wall 181
Barley-grass 181
Barley Tribe 157-90 XXXV
Barnyard Grass *665*
Beach-grass 104
Beans IX
Beard-grass *728* 706
  annual *227* 225
  broad-leaved 403
  bushy *729* 717
  Elliott's *731* 718
  Hall's 720
  seacoast *723* 714
  short-leaved 403
  silver 716
  silvery *732* 719
  woolly 706
Bear-grass 717
Bent-grasses 210-18
Bermuda-grass *388* 387
  X XXXII
Bifidum 515
Black Oat-grass 319
Blepharidachne 145-6
  XXXIV XXXVII
  XXXVIII
  bigelovii 145 *146*
  kingii 145 *146*
Blepharoneuron 310-11
  tricholepis 310 *311*
Blow-out grass *254* 238
Blue-grass 33-48
  annual *39* 33-34
  Canada *42* 33-35
  inland 37
  Kentucky *44* 33 36 X
  Texas *43* 33 35
Bluestem *162* 157 158
  big *733* 719
  little *722* 714
Botanical Terms Illus-
  trated XVI XVII
Bouteloua 425-44 XLII
  aristidoides *432* *444* 426
  barbata 428 *437* 426
  breviseta 428 *436* 425
  bromoides 431
  burkii 425 429

chondrosioides 431 *441*
  445
curtipendula 430 *440*
eriopoda 429 *439*
filiformis 431 *443*
gracilis 428 *435*
havardii 431
hirsuta 427 *434*
humboltiana 431
microstachys 428
oligostachya 428
procumbens 427
prostrata 427
racemosa 430
rigidiseta 431 *442* 445
  426
simplex 427 *433* 426
texana 426 431 445
trifida 429 *438* 425
trinii 425 429
uniflora 430 *440* 425 426
Brachiaria 505-8 553 XLIV
  ciliatissima 505 *507* 505
  extensa 506 *508* 505
  platyphylla 506
Broad-leaved spike-grass
  106 103
Brome-grass 5-20
  awnless 8
  fringed 7
  Hungarian 8
  spreading 10
  wild *14* 7
Bromus 5-20 XXXI
  XXXIII XXXVII
  anomalus 8 *16* 5
  anomalus var. *lanatipes* 9
  arvensis 5
  carinatus 5
  catharticus 6 *12* XXXII
    XXXIII
  ciliatus 7 *14* 5
  commutatus 11 *18* 5
  hordeaceous 9
  incanus 9
  inermis 8 *16* 6
  japonicus 10 *19* 5 11
  marginatus 7 *13* 5
  mollis 9 *17* 5
  . patulus 10
  polyanthus 7 *13* 5
  porteri 8
  porteri lanatipes 9
  purgans 9 *15* 5
  purgans var. incanus 9
    15 5
  purgans var. *texensis* 8
  rigidus 11 *20* 5
  secalinus 10 *18* 5 11
  texensis 8 *15* 5
  unioloides 6
Broom-corn 737 738 X
Broom-sedge *722* *730* 339
  714 718
Buchloe 449-51
  dactyloides 449 *451*
. Buffalo-grass 449 451 X

Bulbilis 449
  dactyloides 449
Bunch-grass *303* 36 157
  285
Burbank, Luther X
Burro-grass *149* 147

Calamovilfa 206-9
  gigantea 206 *208*
  longifolia 206 *209*
Campulosus XXXIV
  aromaticus 401
Canary-grass *459* 455
  reed 454
  southern *458* 454 455
Canary Grass Tribe 452-
  460 XXXIV
Capillaria 565
Capriola 387
  dactylon 387
Carpet-grass *511* 509
Catch-fly-grass 463
Cathestecum 445-6 XLII
  erectum 445 *446*
Cenchropsis myosuroides
  691
Cenchrus 691-6 682
  XLIV
  carolinianus 693
  echinatus 692 *695* 691
  incertus 692 *696* 691
  myosuroides 691 *694*
  pauciflorus 693 *696* 691
  tribuloides 693
Centipede Grass *760* 759
Chaetochloa 670
  composita 674
  geniculata 671
  glauca 671
  grisebachii 672
  italica 674
  lutescens 671
  macrostachya 674
  magna 673
  polystachya 675
  scheelei 675
  verticillata 672
  villosissima 675
  viridis 673
Chase, Agnes XI XXXII
Cheat or Chess *18* 5 10
Chino *436* 425 428
Chlorideae 367-451 XXXVI
  XLII
Chloris 405-21 XLII
  alba 410
  andropogonoides 407 *414*
    405 409
  brevispica 409
  chloridea 407 *413* 405
  ciliata 410 *420* 405
  clandestina 407
  cucullata 409 *417* 405
  distichophylla 406 *412*
    405
  elegans 410
  gayana 411 *421* 405

latisquamea **409** *418*
nashii 410
nealleyi 408
petraea **406** *412* 405
subdolichostachya **409**
  414 405
swartziana 406
tenuispica 407
texana 410
texensis **408** *415* 405
verticillata **408** *416* 405
virgata **410** *419* 405
Chondrosium eriopodum
  429
trinii 429
Christ's Tears 763
Cinna 219-20 XLI
  arundinacea **219**, *220*
Clover IX
Coelorachis cylindrica 755
  rugosa 755
Coix 763-4
  lachryma-jobi **763** *764*
Colorado Grass *586* 563
Comb's Paspalum *539* 521
Commutata **636**
Congho Grass *586* 563
Conjugata **514**
Corn 770 X
  chicken 737
  Egyptian 737
  Indian *771*
  Jerusalem 737
Corn Tribe 763-71 XXXVI
Cortaderia **108-9** XXXVIII
  argentea 109
  selloana **109** *111* 108
Cottea **150-1**
  pappophoroides **150** *151*
Couch-grass *161* 157 158
Couch-quitch 158
Crab Grass 486-93
Creeping-bent 212
Creeping Meadow-grass *67*
  52
Creeping Mesquite 361
Crow-foot Grass *386* 385
Ctenium **401-2** XLII
  aromaticum **401** *402*
Curly Mesquite *364* 361 X
Curly Mesquite Tribe **357-**
  66 XXXV
Cynodon **387-8**
  dactylon **387** *388*
Cyperaceae IX

Dactylis 114-5
  glomerata **114** *115*
Dactyloctenium 385-6
  aegyptium **385** *386*
Dallis Grass *546* 527
Danthonia 204-5 XXXI
  spicata **204** *205*
Darnel *190* 188
Dasyochloa pulchella 124
Decumbentes **514**
Deer-grass *275* 249

Deer-tongue Grass 637
Depauperata **613** 554
Diarina 95
  diandra 95
  festucoides 95
Diarrhena **95-6**
  americana **95** *96*
Dichanthelium, Subgenus
  609-55 553 554 633
Dichotoma **618** 554
Dichotomiflora **564**
Diffusa **567** 554
Diffuse Crab-grass *495* 494
Digitaria **486-93** 479 494
  553
  filiformis **488** *492* 486
  runyoni **487** *491* 486 488
  sanguinalis **486** *489*
  texana **488** 486
  villosa **488** *493* 486
  violascens **487** *490* 486
Dilatata **514**
Diplachne 367
  chloridiformis 368
  dubia 368
  fascicularis 370
  imbricata 370
  rigida 62
  spicata 381
  viscida 371
Dissecta **513**
Disticha **513**
Distichlis **99-102** XXXVIII
  multinervosa 141
  spicata **99** *102*
  stricta 99
  texana **100** *101* 99
Dog-town Grass **338** *356*
Drawings of Botanical
  Equipment XIV
Drop-seed-grass
  pointed **300** 284
  purple *301* 285
  rock 243
  rough-leaved 239
  Texas *308* 287
  Vasey's 284
  woodland 245
Durra **737**
Dwarf Meadow-grass 34

Eatonia 195
  dudleyi 196
  filiformis 196
  nitida 196
  pennsylvanica var.
    filiformis 196
Echinochloa **659-67** XLIV
  colonum **660** *663* 659
  crusgalli **660** *665* 659 662
  crusgalli var. *crus-*
    pavonis 664 660
  crusgalli var. edulis **661**
    664
  crusgalli frumentacea
    661
  crusgalli var. mitis **661**
    664 666

crusgalli var. zelayensis
  661 *664*
crus-pavonis **660**
frumentacea 661
longearistata 661
walteri **661** *667* 659
Egyptian-grass 385
Elephant-grass 682 684
Eleusine 383-4 XXXI XLII
  indica **383** *384*
Elymus **167-176** 157 177
  arkansanus 170
  canadensis **169** *174*
  canadensis var.
    brachystachys **170** *175*
  canadensis var. robustus
    169 *175* 167
  diversiglumis 170
  elymoides 177
  hirsutiglumis 168
  interruptus **170** *174*
  striatus 170
  triticoides **168** *171* 167
  villosus **170** *176*
  villosus forma
    arkansanus **170** *176*
  virginicus **168** *172* 167
  virginicus var. australis
    168 *172*
  virginicus var.
    glabriflorus **169** *173*
    168
  virginicus var.
    hirsutiglumis 168
  virginicus var.
    intermedius **168** *173*
Elyonurus **751-4**
  barbiculmis **751** *753*
  tripsacoides **751** *754*
Epicampes 235
  berlandieri 250
  emersleyi 250
  rigens 249
  subpatens 250
Equipment XI
  Drawings of XIV
Eragrostis **49-94** XXXVII
  XXXVIII
  amabilis **54** *70* 49
  arida **56** *77* 50
  barrelieri **56** *76* 50 57
  beyrichii **59** *83* 50
  campestris 62
  capillaris **55** *73* 49
  caroliniana *78* 57
  cilianensis **54** *72* 49
  ciliaris **53** *69* 49
  conferta 54
  curtipedicellata **62** *89*
  diffusa **57** *79* 49
  elliottii **65** *94* 50
  eragrostis 55
  erosa **65** *93* 50
  frankii **55** *74* 49
  glomerata **54** *71* 49
  grandiflora *90* 63
  hirsuta **61** *87* 50

hypnoides **53** *68* 49
intermedia **60** *85* 50 61
interrupta 59
lugens **61** *86* **50**
major 54 49
megastachya 54
mexicana 58 49
minor 55
neomexicana 58 *80* 49
nitida 65
oxylepis 59
palmeri 64 *93* 50
pectinacea 57 *78* *91* 49
   50 64
pilifera 63 *90* 50
pilosa 56 *75* 49 50
plumosa 54
poaeoides 55 *71* 49
purshii 57
refracta 62 *84*
reptans 52 *67* 49
rigida 62
secundiflora 59 *82* 50
sessilispica 62 *88* 50
silveana 64 *92* 50
spectabilis 64 *91* 50
spicata 59 *81* 50
swalleni 60 *84* 50
tephrosanthos 58 *70* 50
trichodes 63 50
weigeltiana 52
Eremochloa 759-62
   ophiuroides **759** *760*
Eremochloë 145
Erianthus 705-11
   alopecuroides **706** *710*
      705
   contortus **706** *710* 705
   divaricatus 706
   ravennae 705 *709* 705
   saccharoides **707** *711* 705
   strictus **707** *711* 705
Eriochloa 498-504 553
   XLIV
   acuminata 500
   contracta **499** 498 *503*
   gracilis 500 *504* 498
   gracilis var. minor **500**
   polystachya 500
   punctata **499** *502* 498
   sericea 498 *501*
Eriocoma cuspidata 312
Erioneuron pilosum 125
Euchlaena 767-69
   mexicana 767 *768*
   perennis 767 *769*
Eulalia 699
Eupanicum, Subgenus 553
Eustachys distichophylla
   406
   petraea 406
Everlasting-grass *502* 499
Explanations XI

False Buffalo-grass *448* 447
False Needle-grass *149* 147
Fasciculata **561**

Feather Finger-grass 410
Fescue Grasses **21-8**
Fescue-grass
   nodding 2 3
   slender *25* 21 22
   southern *26* 21 22
Fescue Tribe **5-156** XXXV
Festuca 21-8 XXXI
   ligulata 23 *26* 21
   megalura 21 *25* 21 22
   myuros 22 *25* 21
   nutans 23
   obtusa 23 *27* 21
   octoflora 22 *25*
   octoflora var. hirtella 22
   parviflora 22
   sciurea 22 *26*
   shortii 23 *27* 21
   texana 24
   versuta 24 *28* 21
Festuceae **5-156** 367
   XXXIII XXXV
   XXXVII XLII
Feterita 738
Few-flowered Aristida 332
Finger-grass, Southern
   Slender *493* **488**
Flat Crab-grass *512* 509
   510
Flat Joint-grass 509
Floating Manna-grass *32* 29
Floridana **514**
Fly-away-grass *217* 212
Fountain-grass *683* *687*
Fowl meadow-grass *31* 29
Foxtail-grass 672
   branching 408
   giant *678* 673
   green *679* 673
Galleta-grass *365* 362
Gama Grass *766* 765
   eastern 765
Gardener's Garters *457* 455
Gastridium **232-3** XLI
   australe 232
   lendigerum 232
   ventricosum **232** *233*
Geminata **559** 553 554
Giant Cane *2* 1
Glabrous and Smooth XI
Glyceria **29-32** XXXI
   nervata 29
   septentrionalis 29 *32*
   striata 29 *31*
Goldentop-grass *117* 116
Golden-wonder 670
Goose-grass *384* 383
Grama, black *439* 429 425
   427
   blue 428 435
   hairy *434* 425 427
   needle 432
   side-oat 430
   six-weeks 432
   tall 430
   woolly-spiked 426 431
Grama Grasses **425-44**

Grama Tribe **367-451**
   XXXV
Gramineae IX
Grapevine Mesquite *605*
   603
Grasses, How to Identify
   XXXII
Guinea-grass *596* 570
Gymnopogon **403-4**
   ambiguus **403** *404*
   brevifolius **403**
Gynerium 108 XXXVIII
   sagittatum 108
Gyp Grass *436* 425 428

Hackelochloa 761-2
   granularis **761** *762*
Hairy Cheat 9
Hairy Wood Chess 9
Hedge-hog Grass *695* 692
Hegari 737 738
Hemarthria fasciculata 756
Heteropogon **747-8**
   contortus **747** *748*
   melanocarpus 747
Hilaria **361-6**
   belangeri **361** *364*
   cenchroides var. *texana*
      361
   jamesii 362 *365* 361
   mutica 362 *366* 361
   rigida 361
   texana 361
Hitchcock, Dr. A. S. XI
   XIII XXXII XXXIII
Holcus **203** 737
   halepensis 738
   lanatus **203** *205*
   sorghum 738
   sorghum var.
      drummondii 737
   sorghum var.
      sudanensis 737
Homalocenchrus 463
   hexandrus 464
   lenticularis 463
   monandrus 463
   oryzoides 465
   virginicus 464
Hordeae **157-90** XXXV
   XXXIX
Hordeum **179-86** XXXIX
   jubatum 180 *186* 179
   murinum 181 *185* 179
   nodosum 180 *184* 179
   pratense 180
   pusillum 180 *183* 179
   pusillum var. pubens **180**
      179
   sativum 179
   vulgare **179** *182* 180
   vulgare var. trifurcatum
      180 *182*

Imperata 697-8
   hookeri **697** *698*
Indian Grass *744* 742
   long-bristled 743

Indian Reed 744 742
Indian Rice Tribe 471-5
  XXXIV

Job's Tears 764 763
Johnson Grass 739 387 737
  738 X
Joint-grass 519
  pitted 757 755
Juncaceae IX
June-grass 36

Kafir Corn 737 738 X
Kaoling 737
Keys and Distinctive
  Words XIII
Khas-Khas 736 735
Khus-Khus 736 735
Knot-grass 519
Koeleria 191-2 XL
  cristata 191 192
  gracilis 191
Koeler's Grass 192 191
Korycarpus arundinaceus
  95
  diandrus 95

Lace-grass 73
Laevia 514
Lamarckia 116-7
  aurea 116 117
Lancearia 629
Lanuginosa 623 554
Large Crab-grass 489 486
Large Giant Cane 2
Large Mesquite 443 426
  431
Latifolia 637
Laxiflora 615
Lazy Man's Grass 760 759
Leersia 463-70
  hexandra 464 469 463
  lenticularis 463 467 463
  monandra 463 466
  oryzoides 465 470 463
  virginica 464 468
Leptochloa 367-78 379
  XLII
  chloridiformis 368 373
    367
  dubia 368 372 367
  fascicularis 370 378 367
  filiformis 369 375 367
  floribunda 370 376 367
  imbricata 370
  mucronata 369
  nealleyi 369 374 367
  rigida 62
  spicata 381
  uninervia 370 377 367
  virgata 369 374 367
  viscida 371 376 367
Leptoloma 494-5
  cognatum 494 495
Limnodea 221-2 XLI
  arkansana 221 222
  arkansana var. pilosa
    221

Livida 513
Lizard-tail Grass 762 761
Lolium 187-90 XXXIX
  italicum 187
  multiflorum 187 189
  perenne 187 189
  temulentum 188 190 187
  temulentum var.
    leptochaeton 188 190
    187
Long-awned Aristida 338
Long-awned Hair-grass 264
  242
Long-leaved Reed-grass 209
  206
Long-leaved Rush-grass
  281
Long Tom 520
Love-grass 73 55 64
  Frank's 74 55
  low 55
  meadow 68 62
  purple 91 64
  Pursh's 57
  short-stalked 62
  stout 61
  strong-scented 72 54
  tiny 73 55
Lycurus 228-9 XLI
  phleoides 228 229

Magnifier XIV
Maiden Cane 606 604
Maize 771
Manila Grass 359
Manisuris 755-8
  compressa 756
  cylindrica 755 757
  fasciculata 756 758 755
  granularis 761
  rugosa 755 758 755
Marsh-grass 396 394
  salt 400 395
  tall 396 394
Mascarene-grass 360 359
Maxima 570
Maydeae XLVI
Meadow Creeping-grass 68
Melica 118-22 XXXI
  XXXVIII
  bella 119
  bulbosa 119 122
  diffusa 118
  multinervosa 141
  mutica 118 120
  nitens 118 121
  porteri 119 120
Mesquite-grass 253 442 237
  431
  large 253 431
Microscope XIV
Millet, Broom Corn 567
  German 670
  Hungarian 670
  Italian 680 674
  Japanese barnyard 661
  marsh 471

pearl 688 683
proso 589
Texas 586 563
water 472 471
Millet Tribe 476-655
  XXXVI
Milo 737 738
Milo-maize X
Miscanthus 699-701
  sinensis 699
  sinensis var. gracillimus
    700 699
  sinensis var. variegatus
    700 699
  sinensis var. zebrinus
    699 701
Miscellaneous Species
  603-8 553 554
Monanthochloë 97-8
  XXXVIII
  littoralis 97 98
Muhlenbergia 234-77 235
  278
  acuminata 248 272
  arenacea 239 257 234
  arenicola 240 259 234
  asperifolia 239 258 234
  berlandieri 241
  brachyphylla 244 269
  buckleyana 237
  capillaris 242 264 235
  diffusa 243
  emersleyi 250 277 235
  expansa 241 262 235
  fournieriana 250 276 235
  glabriflora 246 272
  glomerata 246
  gracilis 242
  gracillima 238
  involuta 240 260 234 241
  lemmoni 246 271
  metcalfei 249 263 235
  mexicana 245 271 245
    246
  montana 242 265 235
  monticola 247 274 235
  parviglumis 247 252 235
  pauciflora 248 252 235
  polycaulis 247 274
  porteri 237 253 234 235
  pungens 238 254 234
  racemosa 246 273
  repens 244 270 235
  reverchoni 240 261 234
  rigens 249 275 235
  rigida 241 263 234
  schreberi 243 267 235
    657
  setifolia 242 266 235
  sobolifera 243 268 244
  sobolifera var. setigera
    244 268
  sylvatica 245
  texana 237 252 234
  torreyi 238 255 256 234
  trichopodes 241
  trifida 242

umbrosa **245** *269* 244
utilis **245** *270* 235
vaseyana 250
wrightii **248** *263*
Munroa **447-8**
squarrosa 447 *448* 124
Munro-grass 575
Munro's Grass *448* 447
Mutton-grass 38

Napier Grass 6 84
Narrow Melic-grass 118
Natal Grass *669* 668
Nazia 357
aliena 357
racemosa 357
Nazieae XLII
Needle-and-thread-grass
318
Needle, Dissecting XIV
Needle-grasses **327-356**
Nerved Manna-grass *31* 29
Nimble Will *267* 243
Nit-grass *233* 232
Nomenclature XII
Notata **514**
Notholcus 203
lanatus 203

Oat Tribe **191-205** XXXV
Oat, cultivated *200* 199 X
wild 743
Oligosanthia **630**
Onion-grass 119
Oplismenus **657-8** XLIV
setarius **657** *658*
Orchard-grass *115* 114
Oryza **461-2**
sativa **461** *462*
Oryzeae **461-70** XXXV
XLIII
Oryzopsis **312-3** 316
fimbriata 314
hymenoides **312** *313*
membranacea 312
Osterdamia 359
tenuifolia 359

Painted-grass *457* 455
Pampas-grass *111* 109
hardy *709* 705
Panicatae IX XXXII
XXXVI
Paniceae **476-696** XXXI
XXXVI
Panic-grass, barbed 619
beaked 577
bog 621
bulbous 571 *595*
early branching 626
Eaton's 622
flat-stemmed 577
forked 620
gibbous 656
hairy 624
Lindheimer's 622
long-leaved 577
long-stalked 613

low white-haired *640* 614
narrow-leaved 617
red-top 575
round-fruited 628
soft-leaved 630
starved 613
tall flat 576
tall swamp 635
variable 636
velvety 634
Werner's 614
white-haired 626
woolly 625
Panicoideae XXXII
Panicularia 29
nervata 29
septentrionalis 29
Panicum **553-655** 479 486
505 513 515 659 670
XIII
aciculare **616** *641* 618
agrostoides **575** *601* 576
577
amarulum **574**
amarum **573** *598* 574
anceps **577** *600* 578
angustifolium **617** *641*
553 618
arenicoloides **618** *641*
arizonicum **563** *585*
autumnale 494
barbinode 561
barbipulvinatum 567
barbulatum **620** *641*
boscii **638** *655*
brachyanthum **579** *590*
bulbosum **571** *595*
bulbosum var. minus **571**
bulbosum sciaphilum 571
capillare **566** *588* 565
capillare var. occidentale
567 *590*
capillarioides **568** *591*
chrysopsidifolium **616**
ciliatissimum 505
clandestinum **637** *645*
commutatum **636** *654*
condensum **576** *602*
consanguineum **617** *641*
cryptanthum **635** *653*
curtivaginum 621
depauperatum **613** *639*
614
dichotomiflorum **564**
587
dichotomum **620** *641* 621
divergens 494
eatoni 622
fasciculatum **562** *584*
fasciculatum var.
reticulatum **562** *584*
filipes **568** *594*
firmulum **555** *558*
flexile **565** *590*
fuscum 562
fuscum var. *fasciculatum*
562

geminatum **560** *580* 553
554 559
gibbum 656
gymnocarpon **603** *607*
553
hallii **569** *593* 568
havardii **573**
helleri **631** *649*
hemitomon **604** *606* 553
hians **604** *608*
hirsutum **569** *592* 562
hirticaule **567** *590* 565
huachucae **624** *645* 565
huachucae var.
fasciculatum **624** *645*
625
huachucae silvicola 624
joorii **637** *654*
lachnanthum 480
lanatum 480
lancearium **630** *649*
lanuginosum **625** *645*
leucophaeum 480
lindheimeri **622** *643* *644*
linearifolium **614** *640*
longifolium **577** *590*
lucidum **621** *641*
malacophyllum **630** *648*
maximum **570** *596*
microcarpon **619** 641
miliaceum **567** *589* 565
670
molle 561
neuranthum 616
nitidum **619** *642*
nodatum **633** *651*
obtusum **603** *605* 553
oligosanthes **632** 648
ovale **627** *645*
ovinum **618** *641*
paludivagum **560** *581* 553
554 559
pauciciliatum 629
paucipilum 622
pedicellatum **633** *651* 634
perlongum **613** *639*
philadelphicum **566** *590*
565
plenum **571** *597*
polyanthes **628** 647
portoricense **629** *645*
praecocius **626** *645*
pubescens 623
purpurascens **561** *582*
554 559
ramisetum **554** *557* 556
ravenelii **632** *645*
repens **572** *599*
reptans **561** *583*
reverchoni **555** *557*
rhizomatum **578** *590*
roanokense **621** *641* 618
rostratum 577
saccharatum 480
scabriusculum **635** *653*
636

scoparium **634** *652 653*
625
scribnerianum **631** *650*
silvicola 624
sparsiflorum 579
sphaerocarpon **628** *647*
628
sphaerocarpon var.
 inflatum **628** *647*
spretum **622** *643*
stenodes 575
stipitatum **576** *590*
subspicatum 554
tenerum **575** *590*
texanum **563** *583* 586
thurowii **625** *646*
unciphyllum 624
verrucosum **578** *590*
villosissimum **626** *645*
virgatum **573** *599*
virgatum var.
 macranthum 573
werneri **614** *639*
wrightianum **623** *643*
xalapense **615** *639*
Pappophorum **152-6** 150
 XXXVII
bicolor **152** *155*
mucronulatum **153** *156*
vaginatum 153
wrightii **152** *154*
Para-grass *582* 561
Paspalum **513-52** 486 515
 527 553 XLIV
acuminatum **517** *534* 513
almum **521** *539* 514
angustifolium 528
australe 528 529
bifidum **532** *549* 515
buckleyanum 520
bushii 523
ciliatifolium **524** *542* 513
 514
circulare **529** *550* 514
conjugatum **526** *545* 514
debile **522** *540* 513 514
dilatatum **527** *546* 514
dissectum **517** *534* 513
distichum **519** *536* 513
eggertii 524
epile 524
floridanum **530** *551* 514
floridanum var.
 glabratum **531** *551* 514
fluitans 518
geminum 520
glabratum 531
hartwegianum **520** *538*
 513
kearneyi 530
laeve **528** *548* 514 529
laeve var. *pilosum* 529
laeviglume 520
langei **526** *544* 514
larranagae 527
lentiferum **530** *550* 514
lividum **520** *537* 513

longipilum **529** *549* 514
membranaceum 517
minus **521** 514
monostachyum **525** *543*
 514
mucronatum 518
muhlenbergii 523
notatum **521** *539* 514
plenipilum 529
plicatulum **532** *552* 514
praecox **529** *548* 514 530
pubescens **523** *542* 514
pubiflorum **519** *537* 513
pubiflorum var. glabrum
 520 *537* 514
racemosum 532
repens **518** *534* 513
rigidifolium **524** *540* 514
scrobiculatum **532** 513
 514
setaceum **522** *540* 513 514
solitarium 525
stramineum **523** *541* 514
tardum 530
unispicatum **525** *543* 514
urvillei **527** *547* 514
vaginatum **518** *535* 513
vaseyanum 527
villosissimum 522
virgatum **531** *549* 514
virgatum var.
 pubiflorum 527
walterianum 517
Paspalum Grass 527
Paurochaetium, Subgenus
 554-58 553
Peas IX
Pedicellata **633**
Penicillaria spicata 683
Pennisetum **682-90** XLIV
glaucum **683** *688* 682
longistylum 682
nervosum **684** *690* 682
purpureum **684** *689* 682
ruppelii **683** *687* 682
typhoideum 683
villosum **682** *686* 682
Peterson, Samuel XII
Phalarideae **452-60** XXXIV
 XLIII
Phalaris **454-60** XLIII
angusta **455** *457* 454
arundinacea 454
arundinacea var. picta
 455 *457* 454
brachystachys **456** *460*
 454
canariensis **455** *459* 454
 456
caroliniana **455** *458* 454
intermedia 455
minor **456** *459* 454
Phanopyrum gymnocarpon
 603
Phleum **230-31**
 pratense **230** *231*

Photographs and Drawings
 XIII
Phragmites **112-3** XXXVIII
communis **112** 113 471
 XXXVIII
phragmites 112
Phyllostachys **1** *4* XXXVII
Pigeon-grass 671
Piptochaetium **314-5**
fimbriatum **314** *315*
Plains Aristida 334
Pleuraphis 361
jamesii 362
mutica 362
Plicatula 514
Plume-grass 705
Poa **33-48** XXXVIII
andina 36
annua **34** *39* 33
arachnifera **35** *43*
arida **36** *45*
autumnalis **37** *47* 33
bigelovii **35** *41* 33
californica 38
chapmaniana **34** *40* 33
compressa **35** *42*
fendleriana **38** *48*
flava 128
flexuosa 37
interior **37** *46*
involuta **37** *46*
nemoralis 37
pratensis **36** *44*
pratericola 36
sylvestris **37** *40* 33
Poaceae, The Grass Family
 IX XXXI
Poacoideae XXXII
Poales IX
Poatae IX XXXII XLII
 XXXIV
Poison Darnell *190* 188
Polyodon texanus 431
Polypogon **225-7** XL
littoralis 225
lutosus **225** *227*
monspeliensis **225** *227*
Poaeoideae XXXII
Poverty-grass 331
Prairie-grass 36
Prickle-grass 357
Pronunciation of Latin
 Names XII
"Pull-and-be-damned" 520
Purple Hair-grass 238
Purple Needle-grass 336

Quack-grass *161* 157 158
Quick-grass 158
Quitch-grass 158

Ravenna Grass *709* 705
Ray-grass 187
Reana luxurians 767
Red Sprangle-top 369
Reed Canary-grass 454

Reed-grass
  giant *110 208* 108 206
  long-leaved *209* 206
Reed 112
Rescue Grass *12* 5 6
  XXXII
  Spikelets and Parts of
    XV
Rhodes' Grass *421* 367 411
Ribbon Cane *703*
Ribbon-grass *457* 455
Rice, cultivated *462* 461 X
  Indian Mountain *313* 312
  jungle 660
Rice Cut-grass *470* 465
Rice Tribe 461-70 XXXV
Ring-grass *255 256* 238
Ripgut *20* 5 11
Rock Muhlenbergia 243
Rottboellia corrugata 755
  cylindrica 755
  fasciculata 756
  rugosa 755
Rough Hair-grass 212
Rushes IX
Rush Salt-grass *398* 394
Rye, cultivated *166* 165 X
Rye-grass, English *189* 187
  Italian *189* 187
  perennial *189* 187
Rytilix 761
  granularis 761

Saccaton 285
Saccharum 702-4
  narenga 702 *704*
  officinarum 702 *703*
Sacciolepis 656
  gibba 656
  striata 656 *669*
Salt Cedar *98* 97
Salt-grass *102* 99
Salt Marsh Cockspur-grass
  667 661
Salt Marsh-grass *400* 395
Salt Meadow-grass *378* 370
Salt Reed-grass *397* 394
Sand-bur *696* 691 693
Sand-grass *144* 143
Sand Knot-grass *696* 693
Satin-grass *273* 243 246
  slender 244
Scale XIV
Schedonnardus 391-2
  paniculatus 391 *392*
Schizachyrium 712
  littorale 714
  neomexicanum 714
  scoparium 714
  tenerum 716
  villosissimum 714
Schrader's Grass 5 6
Scleropogon 147-9
  XXXVIII
  brevifolius 147 *149*
  karwinskyanus 147
Scoparia 634

Sea-beach Aristida 330
Sea-shore Rush-grass *298*
  283
Seaside Oats *105* 103 104
Secale 165-6
  cereale 165 *166*
Sedges IX
Selaginella riddelii 381
Setacea 514
Setaria 670-81 553 670 682
  XLIV
  geniculata 671 *676* 670
  grisebachii 672 *677* 670
  italica 674 *680* 670
  lutescens 671 *676*
  macrostachya 674 *681*
    670
  magna 673 *678* 670
  polystachya 675
  scheelei 675 *681* 670 674
  verticillata 672 *677* 670
  villosissima 675 *677*
  viridïs 673 *679*
Shallu 737
Shore-grass 496
Sieglingia albescens 124
  acuminata 125
  ambigua 128
  congesta 125
  eragrostoides 128
  pilosa 125
  pulchella 124
  texana 129
Silky-grass *313* 312
Simpson's Grass 604
Sitanion 177-8 XXXIX
  hystrix 177 *178*
Sleepy-grass *326* 321
Slender-grass 369
Slender Finger-grass 488
Slender Sphenopholis 196
Slender Spike-grass 104
Slough-grass *396* 394
Small Rush-grass *290* 280
Smooth Creeping-grass 53
Smut-grass *296* 283
Soft Chess *17* 9
Sorghastrum 742-6 XLV
  ellïottii 743 *745* 742
  linnaeanum 743
  nutans 742 *744*
  secundum 743 *746* 742
Sorghum Tribe 697-762
  XXXVI
Sorghum 737-41 XLV
  halepense 738 *739* 737
  nutans 742
  secundum 743
  sweet X
  vulgare 738 *740* 737
  vulgare var. *drummondii*
    737
  vulgare var. sudanense
    737 *741*
Sorghums 737 738
Sorgo 737 738
Sour-grass *483 545* 480 526

Southern Canary-grass *458*
  454 455
Southern Poverty-grass *289*
  280
Southern Slender Finger-
  grass *493* 488
Spartina 393-400
  alterniflora var. glabra
    395 *400* 393
  cynosuroides 394 *397* 393
  juncea 394
  junciformis 395
  michauxiana 394
  patens var. juncea 394
    398 393
  pectinata 394 *396* 393
  spartinae 395 *399* 393
Spear-grass *323* 319
  Chapman's 34
  flexuous 37
  low 34
  sylvan 37
  wiry 318
Spear-grasses 316-26
Sphaerocarpa 627
Sphenopholis 195-8 193 XL
  filiformïs 196 *198* 195
  glabra 196
  intermedia 195 *198*
  longiflora 196 *198* 195
  nitida 196 *198* 195
  obtusata 195 *197*
  obtusata var. *lobata* 195
  pallens 195
  pallens var. *longiflora*
    196
  pubescens 195
Spikelet of Rescue-grass
  XV
Sporobolus 278-309 234
  XXXI
  airoides 285 *302* 278
  angustus 283
  arenaceus 239
  argutus 284 *300* 278
  asper 281 *294* 278
  asper var. *drummondii*
    282
  asper var. hookeri
    282 *295* 278
  asper var. pilosus 282
  asperifolius 239
  attenuatus 282 278
  auriculatus 239
  berteroanus 283
  buckleyi 287 *307* 278
  canovirens 283
  clandestinus 283 *297*
  confusus 284
  contractus 281 *292* 278
  cryptandrus 286 *306* 278
  cryptandrus var.
    flexuosus 286
  cryptandrus var.
    giganteus 280
  cryptandrus strictus 281
  drummondii 278 282

flexuosus **286** *305* 278
giganteus **280** *291* 278
gracilis **285** *301*
heterolepis **284** *297*
indicus 283
junceus 285
longifolius 278 281
microspermus **284** *299* 278
minutissimus 284
nealleyi **286** *304* 278
neglectus **280** *290* 278
pilosus 282
poiretii **283** *296* 278
purpurascens **281** *293* 278
strictus 281
texanus **287** *308* 279
tharpii **288** *309* 278
tricholepis 310
utilis 245
vaginaeflorus **280** *289* 278
virginicus **283** *278* 298
wrightii **285** *303* 278
Sprangle-top *372* 368
Spreta **622**
Squirreltail-grass *186* 180
St. Augustine Grass *497* 496
Steinchisma hians 604
Stenotaphrum **496-7**
americanum 496
secundatum **496** *497*
Stipa **316-26** 234 327 XLI
avenacea **319** *322*
columbiana **321** *322* 316
comata **318** *324* 316
eminens **320** *325*
fimbriata 314
flexuosa 320
leucotricha **318** *323* 316
lobata **320** *325* 316
minor 321
neomexicana **317** *322* 316
pennata var.
neomexicana 317
pringlei **319** *325* 316
robusta **321** *326* 316
scribneri 320
spartea XLI
tenuissima **318** *322* 316
vaseyi 321
viridula **321** *326*
viridula var. *minor* 321
Sudan-grass *741* 737 X
Sugar-cane *703* 702 X
Swamp-chess 7
Switch-grass **599** 573
Syntherisma filiforme 488
sanguinalis 486
villosum 488

Tall Melic-grass *121* 118
Tall Red-top or Purple-top 128
Tall Reed-grass *113* 112

Tenera **574**
Teosinte *768* 767
Terrell-grass *172* 168
Texas Crow-foot *372* 368
Tharp, B. C. XIII
Thin-grass 212
Thurberia arkansana 221
Tickle-grass 212
Timothy Tribe **206** 356 X XXXV
Timothy-grass *231* 230
Texas *229* 228
Tobosa-grass *366* 362
Toothache-grass *402* 401
Trachypogon **749-50** XLV
montufari **749** *750*
polymorphus var.
montufari 749
secundus 749
Tragus **357-8**
berteronianus **357** *358*
racemosus **357** *358*
Triathera aristidoides 432
Trichachne **479-85** 486
californica **480** *484* 479
hitchcockii **479** *482*
insularis **480** *483* 479
patens **481** *485*
saccharata **480** 481
Trichloris **422-424**
fasciculata 422
mendocina **422** *424*
pluriflora **422** *424*
Tricholaena **668-9** XLIV
rosea **668** *669*
Trichoneura **379-80**
elegans **379** *380*
Tricuspis mutica 126
Tridens albescens 124
elongatus 127
eragrostoides 128
flavus 128
muticus 126
strictus 125
texanus 129
Triodia **123-40** 379 XXXVII
acuminata 125
albescens **124** *130*
ambigua 128
avenacea 126
buckleyana **127** *132*
congesta **125** *134*
elongata **127** *137*
eragrostoides **128** *139* 123
flava **128** *138* 123
grandiflora **126** *135* 123
langloisii **128** *139* 123
multinervosa 141
mutica **126** *136* 123
nealleyi 126
pilosa **125** *132* 123
pulchella **124** *131* 123 145
stricta **125** *133*
texana **129** *140* 123
trinerviglumis 127

Triplasis **143-4** XXXVII
purpurea **143** *144*
Tripogon **381-2**
spicatus **381** *382*
Tripsaceae **763-71** XXXI XXXVI XLVI
Tripsacum **765-6**
dactyloides **765** *766*
floridanum 765
lanceolatum 765
lemmoni 765
Trisetum **193-4** XL
hallii 193
interruptum **193** *194*
Triticum **163-4** XXXIX
aestivum **163** *164*
sativum 163
vulgare 163
Turkey-foot *734* 719
Tweezers XIV

Uniola **103-7** XXXIV XXXVIII
gracilis 104
latifolia **103** *106*
laxa **104** *107* 103
longifolia 104
paniculata **104** *105*
sessiliflora **104** *107* 103

Valota 479
hitchcockii 479
insularis 480
saccharata 480
Vasey Grass *547* 527
Vaseyochloa **141-2**
multinervosa **141** *142*
Velvet-grass *205* 203 359
Vernal-grass
sweet *453* 452
sweet annual 452
Verrucosa **578**
Vetches IX
Vetiver *736* 735
Vetiveria **735-6**
zizanioides **735** *736*
Vilfa utilis 245
Virgata **572** 554 572
Virginia Cut-grass *468* 464

Water-grass 560
Water Paspalum 518
Western Triple-awned-grass 330
Western Wheat-grass *162* 158
Wheat **163** *164* X
White-grass 464
Wild-rye, beardless 168
long-bristled *178* 177
nodding *174* 169
slender 170
smooth southern 169
Willkommia **389-90**
texana **389** *390*

Windmill-grass *416* 408
Wire-grass 387
Witch-grass, barbed 567
    fall *495* 494
    old *588* 566
    spreading 564
    wiry 565
    wood 566
Wolf-tail *229* 228
Wood-grass 219 *220*
Woolly-foot *439* 429

Woolly Triple-awned-grass
    338
Wright's Triple-awned-
    grass 337

Yard-grass *384* 383

Zea **770-1** XLVI
    mays **770** *771*
    mays var. *japonica* 770
    mays var. *tunicata* 770
Zizania **473-5** XLIII
    aquatica 473

    palustris 473
    texana **473** *474* *475*
Zizanieae **471-5** XXXIV
    XLIII
Zizaniopsis **471-2**
    miliacea **471** *472*
Zoysia **359-60** XLII
    japonica 359
    matrella 359
    tenuifolia **359** *360*
Zoysieae **357-66** XXXV
    XLII

Date Due			
Due	Returned	Due	Returned